The Modern
Coral Reef Aquarium

Svein A. Fosså · Alf Jacob Nilsen
—————— Volume 2 ——————

Cnidarians are the dominating animals in natural coral reefs and in the modern coral reef aquarium.
The picture shows the stony coral *Heliofungia actiniformis* in an Indonesian reef.

Credits:
All the photos, drawings, diagrams and tables are by the autors, except where otherwise stated in the captions.

Agents:

* Australia - ABS Technologies
             P. O. Box 697
             Stirling
             South Australia 5152
             Tel.: (61-8) 83 70 10 66
             Fax: (61-8) 83 70 10 68

* Norway - NorZoo A/S
             Marken 4
             5017 Bergen
             Tel.: 55 31 11 21
             Fax: 55 96 07 28

* UK - Tropical Marine Centre Ltd.
        Solesbridge Lane
        Chorleywood
        Herforshire
        WD3 5SX England
        Tel.: 0 19 23 - 28 41 51
        Fax: 0 19 23 - 28 58 40

The Modern Coral Reef Aquarium, Volume 2
First edition, 1998

Original title: "Korallrevsakvariet", © Svein A. Fosså/Alf Jacob Nilsen

Translations: Gerhard Brünner, Hamburg, Germany; Georg Zurlo, Bergkamen-Rünthe, Germany;
             Kari Jackson-Klönther, Wesseling, Germany

Editors and layout: Dr. Dieter Brockmann, Mülheim, Germany, and
                  Werner Schmettkamp, Bornheim, Germany

Editorial Consultant for the English Edition: John Dawes, Sabinillas, Manilva, Spain

Printed and bound by J.C.C. Bruns GmbH, Minden, Germany

ISBN 3-9288 19-23-2

Peter Wilkens

Our first real progress towards successful coral reef aquarium keeping came in the late seventies after reading Peter Wilkens' book "Niedere Tiere im tropischen Seewasser-Aquarium" (volume 1). Since then, and up to this very day, Peter Wilkens has contributed to the reef aquatics in many ways, in his lectures, articles and books. He is - in the true meaning of the word - a pioneer of the reef aquarium. Without his work and efforts, reef aquarium keeping would never have attained its present status!
(Photo: D. Ramirez)

Table of Contents

Preface

Watching nature programs on TV, or reading popular books on natural history, one can easily get the impression that the animal world consists, predominantly, of large species. Sharks, lions, crocodiles and venomous snakes are popular subjects for films and adventure stories. Generally speaking, we tend to focus on large or dangerous species, or those, like cats and dogs, that mean a lot to us personally. However, vertebrate animals comprise only about 4% of the animal world. The rest is made up of invertebrates, or animals without backbones, most of them tiny organisms which are easily overlooked or ignored. There are more than 1 million known species of invertebrates and probably an equal number of unknown ones, with insects forming, by far, the most dominant group, accounting for as much as 85% of the total.

For many years now, reef enthusiasts have enjoyed the diversity and beauty of one particular, large group of invertebrates: those inhabiting marine environments. During the past decade, more and more invertebrates have been kept successfully in modern reef aquaria, to the extent that while the fishes, which were dominant 20 years ago, are still kept today, they now usually form part of a combined collection that includes invertebrates. „Corals" - or, more precisely, members of one order in the Phylum Cnidaria - are the builders of the coral reefs. This group first showed up in the trade in Europe in the late seventies. Since then, the skill of reef aquarists, backed up by the quality of the available technical equipment, have made it possible to grow and keep this group of invertebrates very successfully in captivity. This level of success is such these days that, in contrast to the early days of reef aquaria when we struggled to keep corals alive for more than a few weeks or months, we must now, in the modern coral reef aquarium, prune them to prevent them from overgrowing the aquarium decorations. The first reports of mass spawning in reef aquaria are also beginning to be published and are yet another sign of the progress that has been made in the hobby during recent years. The reef aquarium has therefore become an important tool that allows us to study the biology of corals at close quarters. We devote this second volume of The Modern Coral Reef Aquarium exclusively to the Cnidaria. It is our hope that this work will contribute to further success in keeping corals in captivity and to a better understanding of how the group functions biologically.

It would, however, not have been possible to publish this volume without the kind and enthusiastic help and devotion from a number of people. First of all, many thanks to our friends Birgit and Werner Schmettkamp, of Birgit Schmettkamp Verlag (BSV), Bornheim, Germany, for their sustained efforts in making the book series „Korallenriff Aquarium" and „The Modern Coral Reef Aquarium" an eventual success. Without their enthusiasm, this series would never have become a reality. Dr. Dieter Brockmann, Mülheim a. d. Ruhr, Germany has done a great job with the layout of this volume and we thank him most sincerely. Many thanks to the translators Gerhard Brünner, Hamburg, Georg Zurlo, Bergkamen-Rünthe, Germany and Kari Klönther-Jackson, Wesseling. Germany. Also, very special thanks to John and Vivian Dawes, Sabinillas, Manilva, Spain, who have done a great job overseeing the English-language translation of this volume.

A number of scientists have proofread the manuscript and contributed with corrections and suggestions. A most special thanks to Dr. Phil Alderslade, Northern Territory Museums for Arts and Science, Darwin, Australia, who has contributed with an introductory chapter to the Octocorals and has also updated the chapters in this section to contain the very latest scientific information on the groups concerned. Many other scientists have helped in various ways with the manuscript and deserve a big thank you. We mention, in alphabetical order: Professor Fredrik Bayer, Smithsonian Institution, Washington D.C., USA; Robert Brons, Red Sea Fish pHarm, Eilat, Israel; Dr. Bruce Carlson, Waikiki Aquarium, Honolulu, Hawaii, USA; Chaolun Allen Chen, formerly working at James Cook University, Townsville, Australia, (but now based in Taiwan); Professor Daphne Fautin, University of Kansas, Kansas, USA; Dr. J. C. Den Hartog and Dr. Bert Hoeksema, both of the National Natural Museum, Leiden, Holland; Dr. Peter Harrison, Southern Cross University, Australia;

Professor Dr. Thomas Heeger, the Philippines; Dr. G. Jarms, Germany; Professor John Ryland, University of Wales; Dr. Wolfgang Sterrer, Bermuda Aquarium, Bermuda; Professor J. E. N. Veron, Australia Institute of Marine Science, Townsville, Australia, and Dr. Carden Wallace, Museum of Tropical Queensland, Townsville, Australia. Without their help, the content of this volume would not have been the same.

During the preparation of this volume, we have - as occurred with the previous volumes in German and English - received a great deal of assistance from numerous reef enthusiasts. Many thanks to Jan Olsen, Aqua Design, Oldenburg, who arranged and financed an expedition to North Sulawesi, Indonesia, and to our travel mate and aquarist, Kjell Nagy, Flekkefjord, Norway, who also allowed us to use his magnificent reef tank for our personal studies. Also, many thanks to Hans Beul, LTFI, Aw Oss, Holland; to Julian Sprung, Miami, Florida, USA; Steve Tyree, Reef Breeder, Los Angeles, USA, and to Flemming Jørgensen, Larvik, Norway. Thanks to the goodwill of Aqua Design, Oldenburg; Biotop Aquaristik, St. Augustin-Hangelar; Kölle Zoo, Stuttgart, and Welke Zoo, Lünen (all German companies), we were afforded the opportunity of collecting samples of soft corals for scientific identification.

Many of the more than 800 high-quality photographs in this volume have been made available to us thanks to the skills and goodwill of many photographers worldwide. A very special thanks to Janine Cairns-Michael and Scott W. Michael, Lincoln, Nebraska, USA, and Erling Svensen, Egersund, Norway, who shot photographs according to our wishes on their many expeditions around the world. Also, a special thanks to Professor J. N. Veron, Australian Institute of Marine Science, Townsville, Australia, who allowed us to use illustrations from his publications.

In this context, we would also like to thank Great Barrier Reef Marine Park Authority (G.B.R.M.P.A.), Townsville, Australia; Deep Sky Exploration, Vestfold, Norway; Dr. Terry Done, Australian Institute of Marine Science, Townsville, Australia; Enrico Enzmann, Geretsried, Germany; Dr. Mike Gawel, Guam; Dr. Peter Harrison, Southern Cross University, Lismore, NSW, Australia; Dr. J. C. den Hartog and Dr. Bert Hoeksema, Natural History Museum, Leiden, Holland; Professor David Hopley, James Cook University, Townsville, Australia; Het Zee-Aquarium, Holland; Ed Lovell, Lami, Fiji; A. Jensen and Dr. Hans A. Narkim, Paleontologisk Museum, Oslo, Norway; Dr. Leslie Newman and Dr. Adrew Flowers, Washington DC, USA; Dr. Bette Willis, James Cook University, Townsville, Australia; Professor Peter Wirtz, Universidade da Madeira, Funchal, Madeira, Portugal, and Joseph Yaiullo and Frank Greco, New York, USA.

Many people have contributed with their suggestions or services, both major and minor. Thanks to: Johannes Birkholz, Linz, Germany; J. Charles Delbeek, Waikiki Aquarium, Honolulu, Hawaii, USA; Ingvald Erga, Orre, Norway; Rolf F. Hansen, Bergen, Norway; Carl-Eric Helén, Sweden; Professor Andrew Heyward, SARDI, Adelaide, Australia; Dr. Maizan Hassan Maniku, Marine Research Station, Male, Maldives; Uwe Richter, Hagenbecks Tierpark Aquarium, Hamburg; Dietrich Stüber, Berlin; Professor South, Johnson Seeto and Sunia Lavaki, The University of South Pacific, Suva, Fiji; Professor Endre Willassen, Zoologisk Museum, Bergen, Norway, and Angelika Wolfrum, Thiersheim, Germany.

Lastly, a very special thanks to our beloved wives, Kristin Fosså and Lise Nilsen, who, despite our endless hours behind the computer, in front of our aquarium, or away on some remote location, still strongly supported us throughout the project!

Grimstad and Hidra, Norway, February 1998

Svein A. Fosså and Alf Jacob Nilsen

The Cnidarians
in their
Natural Habitat
and in the
Modern Coral Reef Aquarium

Chapter 1:

The Evolution and Biology of the Cnidarians

For more than twenty years a great variety of cnidarians has been available from aquarium shops. During this time developments and new trends in aquarium technology have made it possible not only to keep these invertebrates alive, but also to offer them an ecologically "balanced" system in which they can grow and thrive. Thus it has become possible to watch and study the life history and biology of cnidarians in detail in our aquaria.

Many kinds of cnidarians will grow rapidly and reproduce asexually in an aquarium. In our modern coral reef aquaria even stony corals grow and thrive. Stony corals were merely a decade ago regarded as very difficult to keep and impossible to grow. Although the situation has changed since then, and great progress have been made in the understanding of how to grow corals, they still must be regarded as delicate animals that should be treated with great care and respect.

In order to be able to give the cnidarians the best possible conditions in captivity, the aquarists should have a thorough knowledge of the general biology, the ecology and the taxonomy of these animals. This is a prerequisite to the further improvement of marine aquaristics and a reason why the introductory chapters of this volume deal at length with the life history of cnidarians.

Today intensive research into the biology of coral reefs is carried out. Every year a considerable number of papers published on this subject in scientific or popular journals are of special importance for aquarists. The careful study of these publications provides the aquarist with valuable information. This is why we advise our readers to make use of the references which are given in each chapter and listed in the reference chapter.

Our improved knowledge about the ecology of the coral reefs and the biology of stony corals, together with the development of aquarium technology have made it possible in recent years to keep stony corals successfully in an aquarium and even to make them reproduce. The picture shows *Acropora* colonies in E. Enzmann's aquarium with stony corals in Germany.

Photo: K. Kindermann

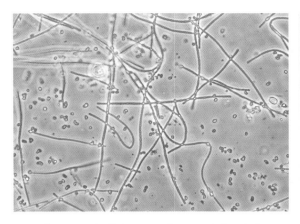

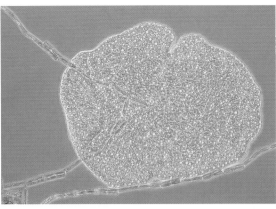

Bacteria are unicellular organisms and live independently of each other. They developed on earth much earlier than the cnidarians did (magnification: 900x).

Trichoplax adhaerens is the only known species in the phylum Placozoa and the closest we can get to the ancient planuloids. Photo: R. Brons

The evolution of the cnidarians

Unicellular animals of the Kingdom Protista are very common all over the world, especially in wet habitats such as in the ocean, in lakes and ponds, in wet mud and in the body-fluid of other organisms. A lot of them are parasites and known for example as the causes of certain fish diseases.

As we can see from their popular name they consist of **one** cell only. This implies that they are, with some exceptions, very small: they can only be observed under the microscope.

Besides the unicellular animals (and the phylum Placozoa), only the sponges (phylum Porifera) are more primitive than the cnidarians. We shall return to both groups in one of the next volumes of this book-series and then deal with them more closely. In this context they are nevertheless important as the single celled animals gave rise to **multicelled** or-

ganisms some 750 million years ago. Although scientists agree that multicellular animals (metazoans) evolved from unicelled animals, there are, according to BARNES (1980), at least three different viewpoints on the subject: (1) The ancestral metazoans (planuloids) either arose from a multinucleated protozoan that became compartmented or cellularized, (2) arose by way of a colonial flagellate through increasing cellular specialization and interdependence or (3) have had a polyphyletic origin and have evolved from different unicellular

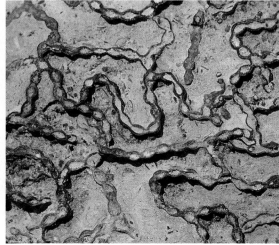

Rugose coral, *Streptelasma* sp., from upper Ordovician found in the Oslo region (to the left) and Tabulate coral, *Halysites* sp., from the Silurian (to the right). Photos: Prof. D. Bruton, Paleontological Museum, Oslo

groups. In any case both the Cnidarians and the Sponges probably developed independantly from protozoan ancestors. It is assumed that the first cnidarians were free-swimming medusae. These medusae, which swam in the primeval ocean of the Cambrian 600 million years ago, probably developed from multicelled free swimming organisms (planuloids), resembling recent Hydrozoan planula larvae. The closest we can get to seeing planuloids today is by looking at the strange *Trichoplax adhaerens*, the only known species of the phylum Placozoa. This animal was discovered in a seawater aquarium in Europe in 1883. It has a flattened body composed of two outer layers of flagellated epitheloid cells, which house between them an inner layer of mesenchyma like cells. *Trichoplax adhaerens* is relativly common in reef aquaria, a fact that we shall return to in volume 3 of this series.

Probably the free-swimming larvae of the early cnidarians gradually began to inhabit the bottom of the sea, where they could find and exploit new sources of food. Later asexual reproduction by budding developed and with that the first sessile coral animals arose.

Animals without skeletons, like jellyfish, can only become fossilized if they are preserved in the mud immediately after they have died. This is why such fossils are rare, though a few have really been found. Jellyfish were the first fossil soft bodied cnidarians to be found at all. Best known are the Ediacara fauna, named after the "Ediacara Hills" in South Australia where they were found by the geolist R. C. Sprigg in the 1940s. The fauna dated to be 580-560 million years old, contain fossils of jellyfish-like and seapen-like animals, but their true identity is still much debated.

More diverse and perhaps the most important invertebrate fossil site at all is that of the "Burgess Shale" in British Columbia, Canada, discovered in 1909 by the palaeontologist Charles Do-

The drawing to the right represents the arrangement on the photo.

Legend:
1 - Coral colony, *Stauria* sp., from the order Rugosa.
2 - Coral, *Halysites* sp., from the order Tabulata.
2 - Coral, *Catenipora* sp., from the order Tabulata.
4 - Sponge, *Stromatopora* sp., from the order Stromatoporida.
5 - Solitary coral, *Tryplasma* sp., from the order Rugosa.
6 - Sea-Lily, *Crotalocrinetes* sp., from the order Inadunata.
7 - Brachiopod, *Pentamerus oblongus*, from the order Articulata.

Fossil coral of the genus *Favoistes*. It dates from the Silurian and was found near Oslo, Norway. The picture above shows a side view, the one below a top view.   Photos: A. Jensen, Paleontologisk Museum, Oslo

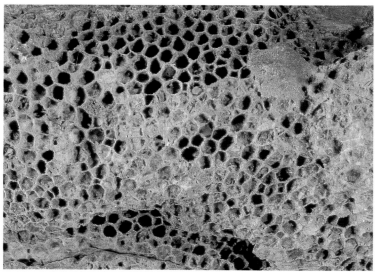

little Walcott (1850-1927). The fossils were found in a layer of clay and slate and can be dated back to the Cambrian period (570-500 million years old). Unlike most other findings from this period, even soft bodied animals are well preserved giving us a fantastic glimpse into an ancient time. 500 million years ago this area was the bottom of the primeval ocean. Today it is situated 2000 m above sea-level. In the same layer of clay and slate a great number of other fossils were discovered too. They give a general idea of what the fauna of the primeval ocean was like. Unfortunately no fossil sites like these exist elsewhere in the world as far as we know today. Do see BRIGGS et al. (1994) for an overview about this subject.

Sponges, lampshells (brachiopods), worms, trilobites and echinoderms lived alongside the early cnidarians in this era. They have all become extinct long ago, but some recent invertebrates have descended from them (READER, 1988).

Because fossils of that era are rare, our knowledge of the cnidarians of the Cambrian is limited. In the Ordovician (510-439 million years ago) the coral fauna was still quite scanty. There were communities consisting of calcareous algae, sponges, calcareous bryozoans and primitive corals of the order Rugosa (Tetracoralla), which probably are the predecessors of today's corals with skeletons, although the matter is still debated. They became extinct 200 million years ago. Contrary to the majority of the recent corals the Rugosa presumably lacked symbiotic algae (ACHITUV & DUBINSKY, 1990). 225 million years ago the subclass Tabulata disappeared, a group of corals growing in a slablike form with polyps living in tubes.

During the Silurian, 439-408 million years ago, a tremendous development of the skeleton-forming Rugose and Tabulate coral species occurred. According to ACHITUV & DUBINSKY (1990) there is indirect evidence that zooxanthellae were present in Tabulate corals from this period. In the late Devonian 408-362 million years ago, coral reefs developed rapidly and grew on a scale which was unique in the history of coral reefs. At the end of the Devonian this development stopped, however. The reason why this happened is not known. It is a fact, however, that the development of coral reefs was interrupted for nearly 120 million years, i.e. from the end of the Devonian up to the beginning of the Triassic about 245 million years ago.

Calcareous organisms can easily be fossilized. More than 500 species of fossilized "stony corals" have been described. These fossils are so well preserved that it is even possible to study details of the skeletal structure. Like the corals that exist today the corals of that era are assumed to have been animals that needed warm water of at least 18-

20 °C. Fossil coral reefs were distributed much more widely geographically than coral reefs are today. Their distribution is generally taken as evidence of the type of climate during geological eras.

Today corals are in the retreat. We know 7000 species altogether, of which 5000 are extinct. Climatic changes, the development of new barriers and the disappearance of old ones were probably the main reasons why many corals became extinct during the Miocene 23 million years ago. From a geological point of view the corals (like most other organisms) existing today are rather young. The genus *Favia*, however, came into existence during the Jurassic about 150 million years ago. Its numerous descendants still thrive in our coral reefs today. The genera *Acropora*, *Fungia*, *Galaxea*, *Pocillopora* and *Seriatopora* only developed during the Tertiary 65-23 million years ago, but most of the corals that we find today only developed during the last 15 million years. The species of the best known family of stony corals, the Acroporidae, are actually not older than 1.8 million years.

Scientists assume today that there were two centres of development of corals: one in the Atlantic (Caribbean) and one in the Indo-Pacific with a concentration in the Indo-Australian region (Indonesia to the Philippines). The corals of the Atlantic date from 100 million years ago and are geologically older, whereas those of the Indo-Pacific are 54-40 million years old and thus younger. Nevertheless the number of species in the Indo-Pacific is higher. This suggests that the evolution of the Indo-Pacific species developed much faster than that of the Atlantic species (ACHITUV & DUBINSKY, 1990). The general question to be dealt with in this volume is: what explains the relative succes of cnidarians in shallow tropical sea areas and why do they occur here in such high diversity? For an in-depth study of this subject we recommend the book by ROSEN (1981).

Peninsula Huon, Papua New Guinea: probably the best-known exposed fossil coral reef in the world. It developed about 125,000 years ago.

Guam: The front reef in the middle ground is about 125,000 years old, the one further back between 2 and 5 million years.

Guam: A rather young reef which is about 5,000 to 10,000 years old. It is situated only a few metres above the present sea level.

Anatomy and physiology of the cnidarians

During the last 600 million years the cnidarians basically have not developed much physiologically. They are still primitive animals with two cell layers (epithelia) and have no specialised inner organs. Most animals have one axis of symmetry, i.e. the left half of their body is symmetrical to the right half. This is called bilateral symmetry. The structure of the body of cnidarians is different. They are radially symmetrical and have several axes of symmetry, like the radii of a circle. Apart from in Cnidaria this type of symmetrical form is also found in the Cteno-phores (phylum: Ctenophora) and the echinoderms (phylum: Echinodermata).

There are two main forms of cnidarians:

❶ sessile polyps and

❷ free-swimming medusae.

The sea anemones, soft and stony corals are examples of cnidarians that only exist as polyps. In the life cycle of both Hydrozoa and Scyphozoa we find both a polyp and a medusa stage. In the Scyphozoa the medusa stage is relatively large and the polyps are usually small. In the Hydrozoa the polyp stage is relatively large, since often branched colonies are formed and the free swimming medusa stage is small. Many Hydrozoans have a reduced medusa stage that remains attached to the polyp colony.

Body structure of the cnidarians

As we mentioned before, the cnidarians have two layers of cells: the Epidermis (Ectoderm) on the outside, and the Gastrodermis (Endoderm), on the inside. Between the Epidermis and the

The mouth and the tentacles of this solitary stony coral of the genus *Fungia* show very well in this picture.

Sweeper tentacles, as in this stony coral of the family Faviidae, are used to defend a territory in the reef as well as in the aquarium. They contain a large number of nematocysts with which they damage other corals that encroach them.

Gastrodermis lies the Mesogloea. The mesogloea consists of a special amorphous substance formed by both the Epi- and Gastrodermis, and may contain motile (amoeboid) cells, which are capable of transporting substances within the animal. The functions of the mesogloea is different in the various groups of cnidarians. It may serve as the antagonist of the muscle fibers in the medusa stages of Scyphozoa and Hydrozoa, and mantain the body form of soft bodied Cnidarians. In some cnidarians that contain a lot of water, e.g. jellyfish, the mesogloea accounts for more than 90% of the body volume, whereas it comes to only a few percent in some hydroids. For further reading we recommend the text by CHAPMAN (1966).

While the epidermis (Ectoderm) of the cnidarians serves as a layer separating the animal from its surroundings, the Gastrodermis (Endoderm) lines the internal cavity called gastro-vascular cavity or coelenteron. The gastro-vascular cavity is connected with the environment via the mouth opening and therefore filled with water. Ingested food is here de-

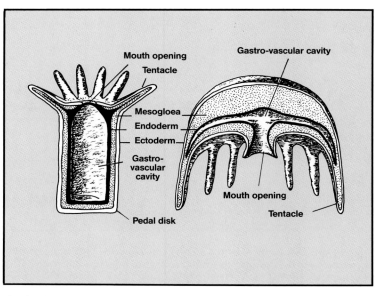

The fundamental principles of the body structure of cnidarians: a polyp to the left, a medusa to the right. After BARNES, 1980

composed by enzymes and broken up into small particles. These particles are absorbed by the gastrodermis cells, by means of phagocytosis (captured by cells possessing pseudopodia) and the rest of the digestion takes place inside these cells. In Scy-

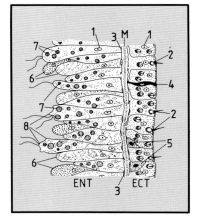

A longitudinal section of the cell structures in the tissue of a cnidarian. (After BARNES, 1980):

ENT = Gastrodermis (Endoderm); ECT = Epidermis (Ectoderm); M = Mesogloea; 1 = nucleus of the cell; 2 = nematocysts; 3 = nervous system; 4 = nerve cells connected with the sensory cells; 5 = interstitial cells, from which sexual cells or other cell types may develop; 6 = glandular cells that produce enzymes; 7 = food vacuoles which ingest food particles in endodermal cells for intracellular digestion; 8 = pseudopods, structures which serve to collect food particles.

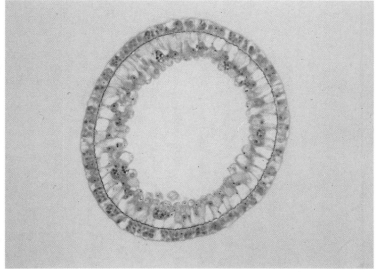

Cross-section (slide preparation) of *Hydra* sp., which very clearly shows the types of cells which are represented in the drawing to the right. Epidermis (Ectoderm) and Gastrodermis (Endoderm) can be made out quite clearly, as well as the thin layer between them, the mesogloea. Photo: R. Brons

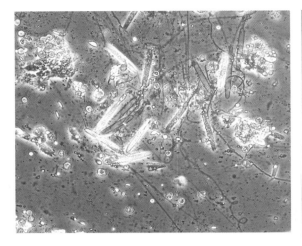

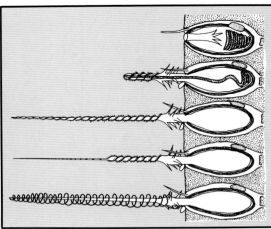

Stinging capsules (cnidae) of the stony coral *Euphyllia ancora*. Some of the capsules are unfired, others half-way or completely everted (magnification: 400x).

Stinging capsules (cnidae) top: unfired; below: the tubule is everted half-way; the three bottom drawings show different types of fully everted cnidae.

phozoa and Anthozoa the gastro-vascular cavity is divided by radial mesenteries or septa. These are wall-like structures which extend inward and divide the coelenteron into compartments. The type, number and position of these mesenteries are important taxonomic features in many Cnidarians.

The mouth is usually surrounded by tentacles, which extend from the polyp and are of crucial importance for the capturing of food. The size, shape and structure of the tentacles varies in the different species.

Generally we can say that the tentacles of ahermatypic (non reef-building) corals are larger and more effective than those of the hermatypic (reef-building) corals. The most primitive evolutionary types of cnidarians are species in which the tentacles are only used for the ingestion of food and the cilia between the tentacles only clean the surface. This arrangement is most common among the solitary ahermatypic species. In the evolutionarily more advanced cnidarians the movement of food items, regardless whether these are microscopically small or larger particles, is effected by tiny cilia, which all wave and move the food particle in the right direction towards (or away from) the mouth. As these movements can be controlled by the coral animal, they can select their food by respective changes of the direction in which the food items are propelled.

In some cnidarians, especially in the stony corals of the family Faviidae, sweeper tentacles (fighting tentacles) occur. These are supposed to protect the cnidarian against potential predators and thus play an important role in the fight for space and survival in the reef. In the aquarium they may constitute a limiting factor to the number of animals that we can keep there.

The diagram on page 19 illustrates the fundamental principles of the body structure of cnidarians.

The fight for survival and space in the aquarium: The yellow encrusting colonial anemone (probably an as yet undescribed species and erroneously called *Parazoanthus gracilis*) has badly hurt and damaged the stony coral *Turbinaria peltata* with its stinging toxin.

Structure and function of the Epidermis (Ectoderm)

The Epidermis (Ectoderm) consists of epthelial cells combined with muscle fibers forming epitheliomuscular cells. These cells close the animal from the outside world and also give the animal the ability to change its shape. When the muscular part of the epitheliomuscular cells of Hydrozoa and many Scyphozoans contract the animal shortens, and when the fibers of only one side contract the animal bends. In Anthozoa we only have muscle fibers like these in the tentacles, but bundled longitudal muscle fibers run through the mesenteries. In the Gastrodermis (see page 22) we find muscle fibers arranged in circles in all groups of Cnidaria and these fibers are antagonists to those of the epidermis.

Between the epitheliomuscular cells there are nematocysts (cnidae) (see the drawing on page 20), which are especially numerous on the tentacles. There are many different types of nematocysts. The type of nematocyst **may** be an important taxonomic criterion in some groups, e.g. in the disk anemones of the order Corallimorpharia. The classification keys by WERNER (1965) and MARISCAL (1971) contain distinctive marks of different types of nematocysts. In the reef the poison of the cnidae is the most important defensive weapon against other cnidarians. Corals compete for the space they need by trying to kill intruders with the toxin of their nematocysts. If we place certain corals too close together in an aquarium, the same competition will take place. Many nematocysts eject their toxin when they come into contact with something, but some hold their prey like a lasso without secreting any toxin. The toxic effect of these substances differs from species to species. The poison itself has a protein structure (MEBS, 1992) and takes effect mainly in two ways. On the one hand it can disturb the function of the cell membrane and make it permea-

The fight for survival and space in a coral reef in the Fiji-Islands: a *Sarcophyton* soft coral overgrows a *Galaxea* stony coral.

Photo: Scott W. Michael

The fight for survival and space in the aquarium: a disc anemone stings a *Turbinaria* stony coral.　　　　Photo: Scott W. Michael

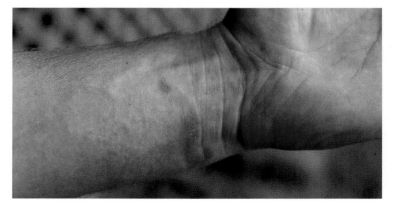

The toxins from the cnidae may hurt humans: here the hand of the photographer was stung by a Hydrozoan.　　　　Photo: Scott W. Michael

All corals excrete mucus: on the one hand to clean their surface, like this *Sarcophyton* sp., on the other hand to protect themselves against direct sunlight, for example at ebbtide.

may produce extreme pain and serious poisoning. Some stony corals may also cause burns, especially species from the genus *Euphyllia*. Some box jellyfishes of the class Cubozoa, the Sea Wasp *Chironex fleckeri* and the closely related *Chiropsalmus quadrigatus* have the strongest poison. Both come from Australian waters and may cause serious burns of the skin or even human fatalities (see chapter 5 and ANON., 1985.)

In addition to epitheliomuscular cells and cnidae there are also interstitial cells in the Epidermis (Ectoderm). From this group other types of cells develop (e.g egg cells and sperm cells during the period of sexual reproduction). Furthermore there are sensory cells (receptors), a few nerve cells and mucus producing cells. This last type of cell is of great importance for the animals for cleaning the surface of their body. In some groups we find these mucus cells in large numbers. This becomes especially obvious in the aquarium in soft corals of the order Alcyonacea. At certain intervals they contract and the colony secretes a layer of mucus. Organic substances produced by the coral and dirt particles that have settled on the surface of the coral are thus discarded.

ble for chemical compounds. This process neutralizes the osmotic pressure in the cell and changes the flow in both directions, out from the cell as well as into it. On the other hand the poison may have a neurotoxic effect and cause states of paralysis. This type of toxin is often found in anemones of the order Actinaria.

Even though the poison has a stunning effect on plankton and other tiny animals, humans normally do not have a strong reaction to it, even though some persons can be more sensitive to the

toxin than others. There is no danger that we could "burn" our skin on a soft coral (octocorallia). But there are some very toxic cnidarian species which may cause severe irritation or even damage of the skin in humans. Among these are for example the hydroids of the genera *Millepora* and the *Lytocarpus*-species (see chapter 4). The Portuguese Man-O-War, *Physalia physalis*, and *P. utricularia* are free swimming colonial Hydrozoans, consisting of modified polyps and medusae with an exceptionally powerful toxin that

Structure and function of the Gastrodermis (Endoderm)

The Gastrodermis (Endoderm) differs from the Epidermis (Ectoderm) in the function of its epitheliomuscular cells, which ingest food from the gastrovascular cavity and are therefore called nutritive muscular cells. They have flagellae which mix the digesting food in the gastro-vascular cavity. The pre-digested food particles are encapsulated in vacuoles inside the nutritive muscular cells after which they are further digested intracellularly. In between the nutritive muscular cells there are glandular cells which secrete enzymes that decompose the predigested food into particles which can then be taken up by phagocytosis. In addition to this the

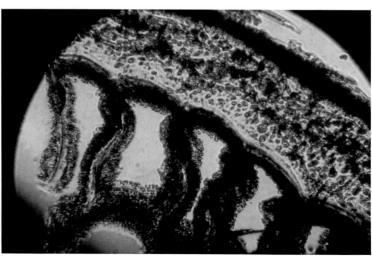

The position of the zooxanthellae in the cell tissue around the gastric cavity of a *Zoanthus* sp.
Photo R. Latka

Young corals of the family Fungiidae settle on the substrate. They consist of one individual only.
Photo: Scott W. Michael

Stony corals of the genus *Goniopora* have long and delicate polyps. A colony consists of a large number of individuals.

Stony corals of the genus *Montipora* have numerous polyps which often have a diameter of a few millimetres only.

The polyps of encrusting anemones, this one is probably a *Protopalythoa* sp., are of extraordinarily beautiful colour and structure.

The tissue between the polyps is called coenenchyme. It has a lot of important functions; here we see the coenenchyme of a *Sarcophyton* sp. soft coral in the Coral Sea.

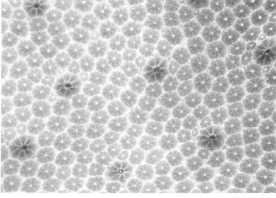

Two different types of polyps can be seen in this Leather coral *Sarcophyton* sp. when greatly magnified. The darker ones capture food, while the lighter ones, which cannot be expanded, have, among other things, a hydrostatic function.
Photo: J. Yaiullo and F. Greco

Gastrodermis of most tropical cnidarians contains millions of zooxanthellae, with which we deal in more detail on page 30, and also in volume 1.

Other anatomical and physiological characteristics

Cnidarians have no specialised organs for the exchange of gases. They obtain their oxygen and emit their carbon dioxide by diffusion through the cell membrane. Thus the animals are dependent on water currents that flow around them and into the individual polyps and out again. At the end of the body that is opposite to the mouth some groups of cnidarians have a pedal disk with which they can attach themselves to the substrate. This pedal disk is most conspicuous in the anemones. These and some other cnidarians, like the stony coral *Heliofungia actiniformis* consist of only one individual polyp. The majority of tropical cnidarians, however, lives in large colonies consisting of a great number of polyps or individuals. The soft coral *Sarcophyton trocheliophorum* is a typical example of this kind of colony. The polyps are connected with each other by a tissue, the coenenchyme, and the food captured by one polyp is distributed to the others.

Every sessile animal needs some sort of support mechanism or skeleton. The soft corals have calcareous needles (sclerites, spicules) to support them. These confer stiffness to the colony and enable the animals to rise high from the substrate. But the animals may also slump and eject the water from the colony.

With gorgonians, which are also called sea fans, the development has still gone one step further. Here the branched skeleton consists of gorgonin. This gives the skeleton a considerable degree of stiffness and keeps it from slumping. At the same time it is still quite elastic and thus well adapted to a life in strong currents.

The development of the skeleton is highest in the stony corals

In shallow water, like here off Heron Island in the Southern part of the Great Barrier Reef, a great variety of cnidarians can be found. The water only contains small amounts of nutrients and ....

of the order Scleractinia. They are really master builders whose small polyps bind minerals from the sea water and build a calcareous skeleton in the crystalline form of aragonite. The calcareous skeletons may grow into very different, also quite delicate forms. This depends on genetics, but differences in current and exposure to light can also alter the shape of a coral colony.

Food, feeding and metabolism of the cnidarians

The different processes taking place in all living organisms from the activity of feeding to the excretion of waste substances are described as metabolism. Green plants hold a very special position with regard to this phenomenon. They are able to make use of the energy of light for photosynthesis (see vol. 1, p. 198). In this process light energy is used to synthesize sugars from carbon dioxide, which can be stored as starch or cellulose. All organisms (including green plants) have to carry out respiration, during which oxygen is used to oxidize food, forming carbon dioxide as a waste product. Part of the energy released by this oxidation is used by the organisms' cells for their vital functions, the rest is lost into the environment as heat and waste.

... the enormous light intensity provides excellent conditions under which hermatypic corals can thrive.

Photo: G.B.R.M.P.A., L. Zell

It is essential, that the milieu created in a coral reef aquarium enables the organisms to respire. Cnidarians are adapted to a milieu in warm seas under intense light, and if we want to keep them in an aquarium under optimal living conditions, we must have a basic knowledge of their feeding and their metabolism.

Coral reefs are among the most complex and most productive ecological systems. The gross primary production (Pt) (of fixed carbon, C) may amount to up to 20 gC/m² per day under extreme circumstances, the average value for a shallow reef flat is about 8 gC/m² per day. The net primary production (Pn) of all the coral reefs in the world together amounts to 4 gC/m² per day (see vol. 1, pp.

25; and also EREZ, 1990; KINSEY, 1983; SOROKIN, 1995; STEPANOV, 1994). The productivity of coral reefs is thus 50 to 100 times higher than in the sorounding oceanic waters where productivity ranges between 0,05 and 0,3 gC/m² (SOROKIN, 1990).

Altogether the coral reefs cover about 15 % of the continental shelf. Every year they bind about half of the calcium that is introduced into the sea by rivers and streams (SMITH, 1978), i.e. more than 900 million tons of calcium carbonate! In spite of this high productivity and the enormous amount of calcium carbonate produced, the water of the coral reefs is not rich in nutrients. To elucidate these seemingly contradictory facts, a lot of intensive research is carried

out today about the metabolic processes in the coral reef.

Heterotrophic feeding

❶ Plankton

When we see a fully opened colony of corals in the sea with its thousands of fanning tentacles it might give us the idea that plankton is the most important source of food for them and that they are totally dependent on the plankton they catch. This is only true in the cases of ahermatypic stony corals, soft corals without zooxanthellae, certain hydroids and certain gorgonians. These cnidarians mostly live in the deeper zones of the reef, where currents are strong and carry along large amounts of plankton. With hermatypic stony corals and other cnidarians with zooxanthellae the nutritional situation is much more complex.

Cnidarians are in principle animals that depend on planktonic food that is carried to them by the water currents. They paralyze their prey with stinging toxins and then transport it to the mouth which is usually in the centre of a polyp. In relation to the surface it covers, a fully opened colony has an enormously large area which is effective in the capture of food. This is one of the reasons why they so successfully survived through all the epochs of the history of the earth (YONGE, 1930a, b, and 1968).

The coenenchyme between the polyps of a colony produces mucus and thus functions as a trap for those organisms which are too small to be captured with the tentacles, e.g. unicellular organisms and nanoplankton. The surface is covered with cilia which are able to sort the food particles by alternating movements according to their size. Dissolved food substances are at once detected by chemical re-

The polyps of this ahermatypic stony coral from the genus *Tubastraea*, found off the U.S Virgin Island in the Caribbean, are large and appropriately equipped to capture plankton.
Photo: Scott W. Michael

A typical underwater scenery off the Fiji-Islands: soft corals of the genus *Dendronephthya* are hanging upside down in the current to capture plankton.
Photo: Scott W. Michael

ceptors, which induces a reaction of the colony that may easily be observed in the aquarium. Even the smallest amount of food added to the water usually causes the corals to expand and to start capturing food.

The majority of the hermatypic stony corals and many other cnidarians that live in symbiosis with zooxanthellae are found on the reef flat and in zones of the reef down to 30 metres. The percentage of their energy requirements fulfilled by capturing plankton is very different in these cnidarians and not sufficiently studied. In the reef zones mentioned the water column does not usually contain enough plankton to meet the energy requirements of the cnidarians that live here in great numbers. Today we know for sure that hermatypic corals only meet a rather small part of their food requirements by capturing plankton.

MUSCATINE & PORTER (1977) examined 470 specimens of the stony coral *Montastrea cavernosa* from the Carribbean with regard to this question. They found that 20% at best of the energy demands are met by capturing plankton, which is most effectively done during the night. The majority of the plankton caught were copepods, unicellular organisms and larvae of crustaceans. JOHANNES & TEPLEY (1974) proved in the laboratory that the stony coral *Porites lobata* only meets 10% of its food requirements by capturing plankton. The way the plankton is caught differs from one species to the next. In general we can say, however, that species with large polyps and big tentacles capture more plankton than species with small polyps.

FRANZISKET (1969) was able to prove that corals with zooxanthellae that were kept for two months in an aquarium without any plankton kept growing nevertheless. It is also evident, however, that planktonic food provides the corals with vital elements and compounds like phosphate, vitamins and amino acids (JOHANNES et al., 1979).

Gorgonians which do not photosynthesize, like these off the Fiji-Islands, usually have rather small, yet very numerous polyps. For food the colony is totally dependent on capturing plankton.   Photo: Scott W. Michael

❷ Exploitation of bacteria and unicellular organisms

Corals may also feed on bacteria (DISALVO, 1971). The mucus excreted by corals contains considerable amounts of carbohydrates which are produced by the zooxanthellae (CROSSLAND & BOROWITZKA, 1980). Carbohydrates are the most important food source for bacteria. The micromilieu surrounding the stony corals contains a high concentration of bacteria and unicellular zooplankton, the latter of which in turn feed on bacteria. These organisms are also present in the polyps (PAUL et al., 1986). The corals not only feed on these bacteria directly; it is possible that the high concentration of bacteria attracts an increasing amount of zooplankton, which the corals feed on (SCHILLER & HERNDL, 1989). The corals are then not only supplied with bacteria, but also with organic phosphate. At the same time the zooxanthellae are given vital elements like nitrogen, iron and vitamine B_{12} (SOROKIN, 1973).

❸ Absorption of organic and inorganic compounds dissolved in the water

The symbiotic relationship between coral polyp and zooxanthellae results in a demand for nutrients like nitrogen, phosphorus and carbon for the algae. Readings taken on coral reefs show, however, a rather low average concentration (0.2-0.5 mg/l) of carbon (SOROKIN, 1973). In lagoons and litoral reefs (close to the coast) the nutrient concentration may be slightly higher, a fact that is also reflected in the composition of the fauna there. In neritic reefs (away from the coast) the nutrient concentration is extremely low.

Scientists have racked their brains for a long time to find out how it is possible that the demand for nutrients can be met for the immense amount of zooxanthellae that live in all the coral animals of only one reef. Some nutrients come from the plankton, of

Table 1

Experimental estimations of rates of heterotrophic feeding in some stony corals from Heron Island, GBR by the use of the radiocarbon method. Concentration of food in experimental aquaria = DOM (Dissolved Organic Material): 0.3 mgC/l, Bacterioplankton: 0.2 mgC/l, Naupli: 0.35 mgC/l. A = assimilated food and M_t = respiration, both as μgC/g/day. A/M_t in %.

Modified from SOROKIN, 1995.

| Stony coral species | FEEDING ON . . . | | | | | |
| | Predatory | | Bacteria | | DOM | |
	A	A/M_t	A	A/M_t	A	A/M_t
Acropora pulchra	161.3	105	33.8	22	44.7	52
Acropora palifera	38.7	35	10.8	10	33.5	30
Pocillopora damicornis	176.4	110	31.8	20	44.7	28
Stylophora pistillata	170.3	106	39.7	25	45.2	28
Seriatopora hystrix	163.6	93	37.9	22	50.9	29
Montipora erythraca	52.4	21	28.9	12	52.6	21
Porites annae	37.8	46	23.1	27	32.9	40
Psammocora contigua	32.2	29	7.5	7	23.3	21
Goniopora tenuidens	33.1	30	11.8	13	21.1	23
Galaxea fascicularis	54.6	59	17.4	19	42.9	47
Turbinaria danae	53.9	64	11.3	13	17.6	21
Favites abdita	37.3	72	26	50	16	31
Lobophyllia sp.	38.3	31	9.2	15	28	22
Fungia scutaria	70.5	64	21.5	19	26	24
Tubastraea sp.	176.3	280	84.3	133	44.4	70

course, but these are by far not enough. For more than thirty years continuous experiments have shown that corals are able to absorb dissolved organic compounds directly from the water. In experiments with different cnidarians (hydroids, anemones, stony corals and soft corals) the concentration of amino acids dissolved in the water decreased by 19-57% within 21 hours (SOROKIN, 1973; MUSCATINE, 1972). STEPHENS (1960 and 1962) proved that the solitary stony coral Fungia scutaria was able to absorb 1-2 mg glucose per hour per individual from a glucose solution. The absorption takes place continually by day and by night through the surface cells and not through the mouth. LEWIS & SMITH (1971) examined the effect of the glucose concentration on the absorption

rate. They found that it was inversely proportional, i.e. with high concentrations the absorption rate was low, with low concentrations it was high. The readings taken showed that per gram live tissue 30 mg glucose were absorbed in 4 hours, which is equal to 3% of the live tissue weight.

The ciliated surface tissue of a coral polyp, together with its enzyme contents makes the absorption of dissolved organic compounds possible. We do not know yet exactly how many of these compounds are used directly in the metabolism of the coral and how many are made available to the algae.

Dissolved inorganic compounds are also absorbed directly from the water. Substances like inorganic phosphate and nitrate are essential algae nutrients, which are used directly by the zooxanthellae. A considerable amount of these substances comes from the organic compounds in the food captured by the polyp and broken down in the metabolic processes in the cells.

As mentioned earlier especially phosphorus, but also nitrogen are present only in minor concentrations in the waters of the coral reefs. There are signs that amino acids produced by the zooxanthellae from inorganic nitrogen compounds are used by the host animal. In this way these compounds are recycled as well. There is also evidence that inorganic phosphorus is not only absorbed but also emitted at a much lower rate by corals with zooxanthellae as compared to those without symbiotic algae. This was regarded as a proof of the process in which these compounds are recycled between the coral cells and the zooxanthellae (YONG & NICHOLS, 1931; POMERCY & KUNZLER, 1969; YAMZOTO, 1966).

The inorganic compounds calcium (Ca^{2+}), magnesium (Mg^{2+}), strontium (Sr^{2+}) and some trace elements have an exceptional position. Seawater contains calcium ions in a concentration of about 420 mg/l. It is fixed by the hermatypic corals and has a function in the building of the calcareous skeleton form aragonite (see vol. 1., pp. 227-235). Also magnesium, which is more abundant in seawater, is incorporated into the skeleton. In the sea the normal concentration of strontium is 8 mg/l, but it may vary, however, according to the salinity. Often its relation to the calcium concentration is quoted as Sr/Ca (with concentrations in moles per litre). According to KINSMAN & HOLLAND (1969) this relation is 0.0086. Yet in the skeletons of many stony corals it seems to be higher. This indicates that under certain circumstances stony corals prefer strontium to calcium as a basic substance to build aragonite from (WEBER, 1973).

In fact considerable amounts of strontium are found in the ske-

In the Coral Sea the water is crystal clear and lacks nutrients, the light intensity is very high. When ebbtides are extremely low, which happens twice a month, the reef flat falls dry and is exposed to the full intensity of the sunlight without any protection. The living conditions for the corals here verge on the limits of what is possible for them to stand. They have developed different strategies to survive, to meet their energy demands. The complex details of their feeding strategies have not yet been fully revealed.

letons of many stony corals. Examinations of *Acropora cuneata*, *A. pulchra*, *Goniastrea benhami* and *Porites murrayensis* have shown concentrations of 550 mg Sr/1000 cm^3 on average (WEBER, 1973). The four species show considerable differences though. It is also interesting to notice that the ahermatypic stony corals have roughly the same concentration of strontium as the hermatypic ones. The opinions of the scientific experts on this diverge, however. The skeleton of the hermatypic blue octocoral *Heliopora coerulea* contains a smaller amount of strontium in comparison to hermatypic scleractinia.

There is an obvious connection between the strontium concentration of a coral skeleton and the water temperature. If the temperature rises, the strontium concentration decreases and vice versa. At water depths of up to 20 m the interrelation is just the other way round. Corals in shallow reef zones contain less strontium than those in deeper zones. These facts support our ideas about the skeleton growth of corals. In her-

matypic corals it increases when the temperature rises and decreases at greater depths and vice versa. If the fixation of calcium goes too slowly, part of the calcium is replaced by strontium. There are indications that the fixation of strontium is genetically determined - it may differ not only from one species to the next, but also from one colony of the same species to the next. Two colonies of the same species living side by side in a reef may show considerable differences as to their strontium concentration. More details about strontium and its application in the coral reef aquarium may be found in vol. 1, pp. 235-236

In addition to calcium and strontium, barium, copper, boron, lithium and zinc may be found in the skeletons of the stony corals. These element are probably deposited together with calcium during growth (LIVINGSTON & THOMPSON, 1971). The coral skeletons also contain organic compounds that are deposit in layers in between the inorganic molecules.

Table 2

A: Gross photosynthesis (P_t) and respiration (M_t) of corals expressed per cm^2 of their surface at optimal illumination. B: Gross photosynthesis (P_t) and respiration (M_t) in corals calculated per gram of weight at optimal illumination. A and B are not from the same samples.

Modified from SOROKIN, 1995.

| CORAL | A Values per colony cm^2 | | | | | B Values per gram dry weight | | | | |
| | µg C/day | | P_t/M_t day^{-1} | µg O_2/h | | µg C/day | | P_t/M_t day^{-1} | µg O_2/h | |
	P_t	M_t		P_t	M_t	P_t	M_t		P_t	M_t
Pocillopora damicornis	52	63	0.8	9-23	7-10	180	188	1.0	53	26
Pocillopora damicornis	-	-	-	-	-	400	113	3.5	117	16
Pocillopora damicornis	-	-	-	-	-	223	160	1.4	44-87*	8-36
Pocillopora eydouxi	165	79	1.6	53	11	-	-	-	-	-
Stylophora pistillata	137	118	1.2	40	17	248	115	2.2	-	-
Stylophora pistillata	105	94	1.1	32	13	138	180	0.8	-	-
Stylophora pistillata	137	180	0.8	26-62	15-33	203	226	0.9	-	-
Acropora cervicornis	119	72	1.6	37	10	136	72	1.9	40	10
Porites porites	375	103	3.6	15-35	11-18	-	-	-	-	-
Turbinaria reniformis	112	163	0.7	18-52	15-29	-	-	-	-	-
Millepora tenera	81	113	0.7	25	16	-	-	-	-	-
Montastrea cavernosa	58	73	0.8	7-29	7-13	-	-	-	-	-
Montipora tuberculosa	-	-	-	-	-	500	427	1.2	147*	59
Fungia fungites	-	-	-	-	-	269	236	1.1	79*	33
Psammocora contigua	-	-	-	-	-	136	216	0.6	104	30
Goniopora stokesi	-	-	-	-	-	92	113	0.8	27	16
Merulina laxa	-	-	-	-	-	565	322	1.8	166*	46

Autotrophic feeding

Scientists generally agree today that hermatypic corals would be able to survive on planktonic food only, provided a sufficient amount of plankton would be available to them. As these corals live in reef zones, however, where this is normally not the case, they have to meet their energy requirements in other ways.

If we want to keep hermatypic corals successfully in our coral reef aquaria, we as aquarists have to ask the same questions that have been asked by reef scientists for years: How do hermatypic corals meet their energy requirement if, on average, they can only cover a portion of it by capturing plankton? The answer is by autotrophic nutrition, which means that the organic products produced through photosynthesis by the zooxanthellae are partly translocated into the tissue of the polyps. To what extent autotrophic nutrition fills the energy budget varies from location to location, with depth and with species. The photosynthetic production in corals is usually expressed in units of gross photosynthesis (P_t), usually given in µgC/day. The total respiration of the coral and its symbionts is termed M_t, (as µgC/day). Net production (P_n) is the difference between the two values, consequently $P_n = P_t - M_t$. The metabolic rates of corals in their natural enviroment is given by the ratio P_t/M_t per day. The higher the ratio the higher the degree of autotrophy, see table above. This outline is, however, very simplified. See SOROKIN (1995) for details and further references. To understand a bit more of the autotrophic nutrition in corals, let us again look closer at

On oceanic reefs, like Boomerang Reef in the Coral Sea, the water is clear and lacks nutrients. Nevertheless the coral fauna is very complex immediately below the point that marks the lowest water level at ebbtide. It mostly consists of stony corals of the families Pocilloporidae and Acroporidae. Many of these corals probably make use of dissolved organic and inorganic compounds as nutrients.

their symbiotic relationship with algae.

Zooxanthellae are unicellular algae that live in a symbiotic relationship in the Gastrodermis (Endoderm) of a coral polyp. The symbiotic algae are primary producers that produce oxygen and energy rich organic compounds from carbon dioxide and water by photosynthesis. The energy source for this process is light.

The intensity of the light is of crucial importance for the corals. Coral animals living on a reef flat are exposed to an extremely high light intensity. They have zooxanthellae which are morphologically different from the symbiotic algae in corals which are exposed to less light (LATKA, 1993 a, b, and c). If the intensity of the light is very high the zooxanthellae together with a number of different types of proteins serve as a protective filter against ultraviolet radiation (DUNLAP & CHALKER, 1986; MOHAN, 1990; SHIBATA, 1969).

The intensity of the light is the limiting factor for the amount of CO_2 absorbed during photosynthesis. The amount of oxygen that is produced shows directly how effectively photosynthesis is taking place. When the intensity of the light increases, the rate of photosynthesis and the absorption of carbon dioxide increase accordingly. The increase, however, is not linear. As an example, the O_2-production in the stony coral *Acropora divaricata* reached a maximum of about 1.0 µmole O_2/h at light intensities of about 200 µEinsteins/m²/s. Even when the light intensity increased to 400 µEinsteins/m²/s, the O_2-production remained the same (BARNES & CHALKER, 1990). When the intensity of the light decreases, the rate of photosynthesis also decreases accordingly. The adaptation to the reduction of the light intensity results in changes of the shape of the colony, a reduction in the number of polyps and an increase in pigmentation (MUSCATINE, 1990).

The energy rich compounds which are produced by the zooxanthellae during photosynthesis are glucose, glycerol, a number of organic acids and organic phosphates. These are transferred into the cells of the host animals, a process also called translocation. The amount of carbon bound by photosynthesis and transferred into the cells of a coral during the course of a day was very high in corals that live at a depth of 3 to 10 metres: 96,6% in *Stylophora pistillata* and 78% in *Porites porites*. Much to our surprise there was only a minimal change of the translocation rate in *Stylophora pistillata* down to a depth of 35 m (MCCLOSKY & MUSCATINE, 1984).

Like all plants zooxanthellae need nutrients, most of all nitrogen and phosphate. The concentrations of inorganic nutrients in the oceanic waters surrounding the reefs most often drop to levels that limit the growth of phytoplankton (0.5 µmole/l NO_3 and 0.2 µmole/l PO_4; SOROKIN, 1995). The concentration of phosphate (PO_4-P) in waters over the reefs is usually just a little higher and thus phosphate seems to be a limiting factor for production. The concentration of inorganic nitrogen (NO_3^-, NO_2^- and NH_4^+) in reef waters varies between 0,6-1,5 μ mole/l and is usually higher than in the surrounding waters, but occurs primarily as ammonium in reef waters and as nitrate in oceanic waters (SOROKIN, 1995). The benthic communities of the reefs moreover lose these nutrients as salts and as organic compounds to the surrounding oceanic water that flush over the reefs.

So again the question arises: how do the zooxanthellae, that are responsible for the autotrophic nutrition of corals, cope with the lack of nutrients? On the one hand they take their nutrients directly from the water (see page 28) and on the other hand nutrients are recycled. From an ecological point of view recycling may be defined as the "multiple exploitation of food capacities that are in short supply".

Recycling applies to all nutrients, including carbon, and it takes place at several levels in the ecosystem of a coral reef. The best known example is again the translocation of substances between symbiotic algae and the cells of the host animal, while the algae benifit from the hosts' metabolically produced CO_2. This type of recycling is very effective. Even though not all substances are recycled, only small amounts of them are lost.

The recycling processes on higher levels are less effective by far. All organisms on the reef excrete nutrients as their metabolic waste (ammonium and phosphate), which could be used by the corals. Moreover other usable substances are released from the sediment (DISALVO, 1974). It is evident that nutrients that are released outside the coral polyp are much more difficult to absorb than those that are produced inside the polyp. On the outside the nutrients are carried off easily by currents or waves and lost. Es-

Table 3

Concentrations of nutrients (phosphat, ammonium, nitrit and nitrat) in μM, Chlorophyll in μg/l and the rate of primary production in μgC/l/h in reef lagoons and inter-reef waters. W: April - October, S: November - March.

After FURNAS et al., 1990.

Nutrients		Reef lagoons	Inter-reef water column
Phosphat PO_4^{3-}	W	0.15	0.18
	S	0.20	0.16
Ammonium NH_4^+	W	0.14	0.10
	S	0.17	0.16
Nitrit NO_2^-	W	0.04	0.01
	S	0.05	0.06
Nitrat NO_3^-	W	0.25	0.03
	S	0.60	0.03
Silicat $Si(OH)_4$	W	1.31	1.11
	S	0.10	1.03
Chlorophyll	W	0.18	0.24
	S	0.71	0.37
Primary production	W	1.25	0.86
	S	6.42	2.05

sential nutrients are lost as well, when organic material precipitates and when inorganic material is bound during skeletogenesis. To replace these losses, nutrients have to be carried into the ecosystem from outside. So far it was taken for granted that the only "new" nutrients for a coral reef were supplied by the binding of nitrogen by the algae and by the direct absorption of nutrients dissolved in the water.

Recently there have also been signs that corals and zooxanthellae are able to make use of nutrients that diffuse upwards from water reservoirs several hundred metres down under the reef, but this theory is controversial and much debated (see ROUGERIE & WAUTHY, 1993 and TRIBBLE et al., 1994).

It has been noticed that corals with zooxanthellae build their skeleton much faster than those without (skeletogenesis). SIMKISS (1964a and b) found that phosphate disturbs the skeletogenesis. Zooxanthellae consume phosphate and thus assist the

skeletogenesis of the corals. We will look at this again in more detail in the chapter on stony corals.

The life history of the symbiotic algae is very complex even though major progress in understanding their complex biology have been made. Perhaps the most controversial paper in this connection was that published in "Science" by MARSHALL (1996) where data indicated that the calcification rates in the ahermatypic coral Tubastraea faulkneri were the same as in the hermatypic coral Galaxea fascicularis. The author puts forward the theory that instead of being light-enhanced, calcification in corals might be dark-depressed, and the zooxanthellae might actually control and even limit the calcification processes in their hosts.

Although this latest theory and other aspects of the biology of the zooxanthellae will be much debated in the years to come, we are nowhere near the end of the topic. Obviously a lot still remains to be resolved on the biology of the zooxanthellae.

A detail measuring about 40 x 60 cm from an experimental aquarium for stony corals of the authors (taken in September 1993): The *Acropora hyacinthus* in the background to the right has grown to three times its original size in 18 months and shows the typical laminarian form. In the middle we can see *Acropora selago* growing pink buds. In the foreground to the left there is a beautiful *Montastrea* cf. *curta* from the family Faviidae. It keeps extremely well in aquaria. The *Platygyra* sp., to the right of the blue *Tridacna crocea*, was collected legally off the Maldives. The coral behind it is quite probably *Porites* cf. *rus* from the family Poritidae from the Maldives as well. The development of these corals is described in more detail in the chapter 16 "stony corals".

Conclusions for the Modern Coral Reef Aquarium

It is a crucial aspect that cnidarians with zooxanthellae are naturally adapted to a life in oligotrophic waters. As we have shown, corals developed various methods to meet their energy demands. In the aquarium we have to keep corals under conditions in which nutrients are not abundant. We think that this can only be achieved by effective protein skimming, careful application of activated carbon, and by feeding only sparingly. As mentioned in volume one (page 229-232) the addition of "kalkwasser" raises the pH to levels around 8.2-8.5 which again inhibits the availability of the phosphate-pool that exists in every aquarium. Moreover it is necessary to plan very carefully which organisms are to be kept together. Animals that need ample and frequent feeding are difficult to associate with animals that primarily make use of the energy of light through their symbiosis with zooxanthellae.

Some cnidarians, particularly anemones and some soft corals may, however, also thrive under conditions in which nutrients are available in large amounts. In the sea these animals often dominate the fauna on reefs along the shore where the water has a higher nutrient content, considerable variation of salinity, and a great deal of suspended particles. This type of reef is sometimes called "eutrophic reef". Compared to oligotrophic reefs they often present a richer algal flora.

We think that the best indicator of the nutrient concentration in an aquarium is the growth of algae. In aquaria rich in nutrients we often find that the growth of the algae is uninhibited and out of control. There are many different species, among them a lot of blue-green algae. If the concentration of nutrients in an aquarium is low, we will find that mainly red calcareous algae will grow. If the nutrient concentration increases, the algal flora will change. This often means that red and green turf algae will appear (see vol. 1, chapter 13).

Even if some cnidarians will thrive together with algae in a eutrophic aquarium this should not mislead us to think that protein skimming could be neglected or that there is no need to check the aquarium regularly and carefully. Under no circumstances may phosphate or nitrate be allowed to accumulate in a healthy coral reef aquarium!

Sexual reproduction on the reef: A *Caulastrea furcata* sets free a single egg (above), while an *Acropora* sp. ejects innumerable packages of eggs and sperm.

Photos: G.B.R.M.P.A., R. Babcok

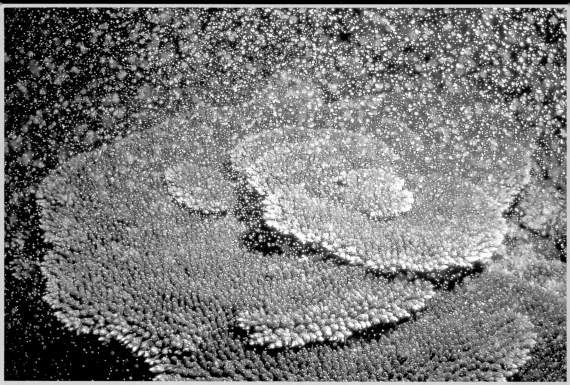

Chapter 2:

Reproduction in the Cnidarians

From humble beginnings, coral reef aquatics have developed since the 1970's to present standards that hardly anyone would have believed possible 25 years ago. In a coral reef aquarium that is run according to the principles described in this series of books, keeping stony corals successfully and getting them to reproduce through fragmentation is no longer a problem (see pages 59 - 63).

Hardly anyone, however, is willing to believe that it is possible to stimulate corals to adopt their natural life cycle in an aquarium and produce new colonies through sexual reproduction. Our experiences and those of some other aquarists working with hermatypic corals - put a different perspective on these problems. Against the background of the progress that has been made and the great things that have been achieved, we are convinced that one of the next steps to take will be the rearing of corals that have reproduced sexually in an aquarium! As soon as we can reproduce corals in bulk in aquaria, collecting them from reefs will become the exception, rather than the rule.

But, what are the problems that need to be to tackled? Firstly, we think that aquarists still need more basic knowledge about the reproduction of cnidarians to be able to keep a coral reef aquarium running successfully. Secondly, we believe that groups of aquarists, e.g. in aquarium societies, should work on projects to

Sexual reproduction in the coral reef aquarium: a *Fungia* sp., probably *F. fungites* releases sperm cells. No aquarist will ever forget such a moment, when one gets the chance to witness it.

understand the problems behind these subjects better - practically, as well as theoretically. Moreover, international cooperation between aquarists, public aquaria and scientific institutes should be intensified. Finally, we think that work in this field can only be successful if experts seeking information analyse and evaluate international publications, not only scientific ones, but also those written at the popular-science level.

As we believe that the sexual reproduction of corals, particu-

larly of stony corals, is the most important objective of coral reef aquatics to be attained during the next ten years, we would like to deal with the essential scientific knowledge required. In this, we follow HARRISON & WALLACE (1990) to a large extent, but others as well. Last, but not least, we also include our own experiences and those of other aquarists.

Our following treatment of the subject is based on what is known about sexual reproduction in stony corals. Much less is known about the sexual reproduction of other groups of cnidarians, i.e. hydroids, jellyfishes, box jellyfishes, soft corals, gorgonians, disc and encrusting anemones, and other anemones. We will deal with the sexual reproduction in these groups respectively when we come to them.

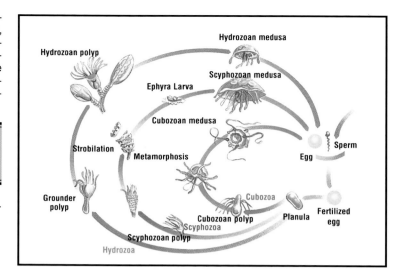

Types of reproduction

There are two main types of reproduction in cnidarians:

- **sexual** and
- **asexual.**

Sexual reproduction takes place when an egg cell is fertilized by a sperm cell. This results in a zygote, which usually develops into a larva that grows until it becomes an adult individual. The male and the female genotype are therefore mixed, which results in a greater genetic variety.

In **asexual** reproduction, no fertilization takes place. The offspring produced in this way are genetically identical to their parent. This kind of reproduction is quite common in cnidarians and can be effected in several ways.

There are organisms which have an alternating life-cycle of sexual and asexual reproduction. This phenomenon is called "alternation of generations" and is found e.g. in hydroids.

Sexual reproduction in stony corals

The sexual reproduction of stony corals is a varied and complex phenomenon. We will deal with this subject under the following seven aspects:

❶ **forms of reproduction,**
(Continued on page 38)

Reproduction in hydroids (Hydrozoa), jellyfishes (Scyphozoa) and box jellyfishes (Cubozoa). Drawing from Göthel (1993)

In jellyfishes and hydroids, polyps represent the asexual stage. In one of the polyps of the jellyfish *Aurelia aurita* (left) we can see how medusae are produced by strobilation. The two larger polyps of the hydroid *Campanularia johnstoni* (right) are feeding polyps, while the smaller one is a reproductive polyp.

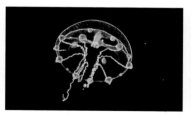

Medusae represent the sexual stage in jellyfishes and hydroids; they are either male or female. In the jellyfish *Aurelia aurita* (left) the gonads can be seen as transparent rings in the centre, which open towards the middle of the bell, while they appear as brownish spots in the hydroid *Campanularia johnstoni* (right).

In cnidarians, we find many different types of reproduction. The life cycle in which sexual and asexual generations alternate, also described as "alternation of generations" is particularly fascinating. This alternation is found in hydroids (Hydrozoa) and jellyfish (Scyphozoa), but not in corals and anemones (Anthozoa). These cycles are not uniform and vary from species to species.

All photos: R. Brons

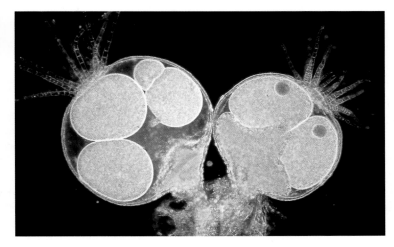

Sometimes, there are medusae which settle on polyps, as in this hydroid *Gonothyraea loveni*. The two medusae are females which contain oocytes (egg cells in the process of development). Cell division after fertilization has already taken place in the left medusa, while the right one has not yet been fertilized (magnification: 90x).

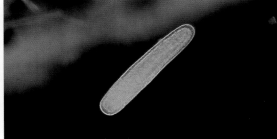

A male medusa of the hydroid *Eudendrium* sp. releases sperm cells (left). A fertilized egg develops into a free-swimming planula larva, as in the hydroid *Gonothyraea* sp. (on the right, magnification: 250X).

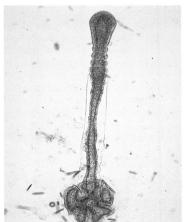

A planula larva (the one shown here is that of the hydroid *Gonothyraea loveni*) finally settles and develops into a new polyp (magnification: 60x).

❷ sexual development,

❸ sexual maturity and reproductive cycle,

❹ gametes,

❺ spawning (shedding of the sexual products),

❻ fertilization and larval development,

❼ dissemination (dispersal) of the larvae and development of primary polyps.

As a matter of principle, it may be assumed that much of what is described in the following paragraphs also holds true for other cnidarians.

❶ **Forms of reproduction**

Stony corals do not have a uniform type of sexual reproduction, but show great variety instead. Either they are hermaphroditic (bisexual), or the sexes are separate. In hermaphrodites, one individual may produce egg cells as well as sperm cells, while in corals with separate sexes, each individual can either produce male or female gametes.

Hermaphrodites may develop ovaries in which egg cells grow or testes in which sperm cells grow, and these may develop in the same mesentery, or in different mesenteries within one polyp (see the picture below on page 39). This is the most common situation in corals. Alternatively, they can simultaneously have male and female polyps in one colony. On the other hand, they may equally well develop male and female polyps in one colony at different points in time. Hermaphrodites that produce egg cells and sperm cells at the same time are called "simultaneous or synchronous hermaphrodites", while those that produce them alternately are "sequential or protandric/protogynous hermaphrodites". Little is known about the latter type in stony corals, but research has been done on "simul-

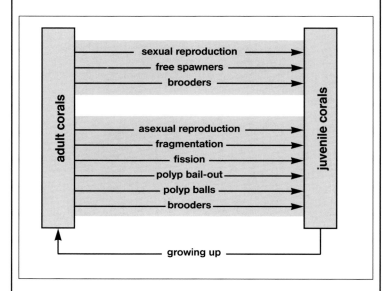

Reproduction in stony corals

Sexual reproduction

Sexual reproduction takes place in two different ways:
① Fertilization and development outside the polyps or the colony (free spawners).
② Fertilization and development of the larvae inside the polyps (brooders).

Asexual reproduction

Today, we are familiar with about five different types of asexual reproduction. In all types, the offspring are genetically identical with the parent polyp or the parent colony. Most of the offspring are unable to spread out very far and therefore remain close to the parent colony.

① Fragmentation: this type of asexual reproduction is quite common among branching corals or those that grow in the shape of a table, like e.g. *Acropora* spp. When pieces are broken off, e.g. by a storm, they develop into new colonies.
② Fission: A number of corals, among them the mushroom corals of the family *Fungiidae*, are able to split into two or more colonies during the early stages of their development.
③ Polyp bail-out: In certain situations, some stony corals, e.g. *Seriatopora hystrix* and *Pocillopora damicornis* may release single polyps. These polyps will then drift to new locations, where they settle.
④ Polyp balls: In *Goniopora* spp. e.g. parts of the colony which contain coral tissue and coral skeleton are separated from the main colony by budding. These polyp balls are cut off from the parent colony, settle on the reef and develop into new colonies.
⑤ Asexually brooded planula larvae: Planula larvae may not only be produced by sexual reproduction, but also asexually by a kind budding.

Description after SAMMARCO (1986)

taneous hermaphroditism" in some other cnidarians (FAUTIN, 1990).

In addition to this, stony corals may either be "free spawners" or "brooders". Free spawners shed their sexual products into the water surrounding them, where eggs are subsequently fertilized. With brooders, fertilization and the development of the larvae take place inside a polyp.

Most stony corals are free spawners and simultaneous hermaphrodites. They develop egg and sperm cells in one colony at the same time and release these into the open water during spawning.

Of 157 species of stony corals, with this type of reproduction that were examined, 56 belonged to the family Acroporidae and 45 to the family Faviidae (HARRISON & WALLACE, 1990). It was observed that, in *Porites astreoides*, one and the same colony contained polyps that were either male or female, and others that were bisexual (CHORNESKY & PETERS, 1987).

The case of *Galaxea fascicularis* from the family Oculinidae, a species which is quite common in marine aquatics, proves that the reproduction of stony corals is a very complex phenomenon. Here, we find female colonies which shed red eggs. At the same time, there are also hermaphroditic colonies which shed red eggs. In addition, there are hermaphroditic colonies which produce sperm cells and white eggs containing large lipid droplets. These white eggs, however, are not fertile, so these hermaphroditic colonies only function as males, and their reproduction pattern is not hermaphroditic at all. The same reproduction pattern was observed in *Galaxea astreata* as well. Combinations of different types of sexual reproduction have also been found in *Porites asteroides*. Colonies off Jamaica were either hermaphroditic or female (CHORNESKY & PETERS, 1987), while all the colonies of populations off Puerto Rico were hermaphrodites (SZMANT, 1986). There may also be geographic variations. These facts go to show just what com-

plex subjects sex and the reproductive patterns in stony corals are.

Among the stony corals which possess separate sexes are several species of the genus *Porites* from the family Poritidae, *Pavona cactus* from the family Agarici-

idae, *Turbinaria mesenteria* from the family Dendrophylliidae and *Montastrea cavernosa* from the family Faviidae. For *Acropora humilis* from the family Acroporidae, *Agaricia agaricites* from the family Agariciidae and *Caryophyllia ambrosia* from the family Caryophyl-

Most stony corals are free-spawning simultaneous hermaphrodites. They are therefore males and females at the same time and eject eggs and sperm cells together into the surrounding water. *Acropora tenuis* is a good example of this spawning pattern. The picture shows the simultaneous release of egg and sperm cells; white sperm bundles can be seen, together with red eggs.

Photo: P. Harrison, Southern Cross University

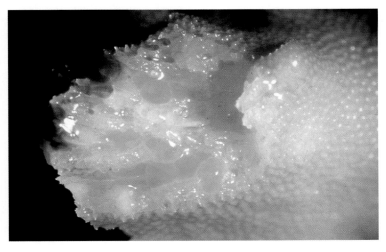

The stony coral *Acropora latistella* is also a simultaneous hermaphrodite. A piece of a colony was broken off just before spawning. Strings of red eggs can be seen along the mesenteries and white sperm bundles are visible in neighbouring mesenteries. **Photo: P. Harrison, Southern Cross University**

Table 4
Sex and types of reproduction in stony corals

After HARRISON & WALLACE (1990)

	Sex			Types of reproduction		
	H	H a. G	G	F	F a. B	B
Pocilloporidae	6	–	–	–	1	5*
Acroporidae	67	–	–	56	3	5
Agariciidae	–	2	6	3	–	6
Siderastreidae	–	–	5	1	–	1
Fungiidae	–	–	13	6	1	–
Poritidae	5	1	17	12	1	9
Faviidae	49	–	3	45	1	4
Oculinidae	–	2	–	1	1	1
Meandrinidae	–	–	1	1	–	–
Merulinidae	5	–	–	5	–	–
Mussidae	8	–	–	6	–	2
Pectiniidae	8	–	–	8	–	–
Caryophylliidae	–	1	7	6	1	3
Flabellidae	–	–	4	1	–	–
Dendrophylliidae	2	-	13	4	1	13*

Legend: H = hermaphrodite; G = separate sexes; F = free spawner; B = brooder; the numbers indicate the species on which reports are available; * = contains species in which planula larvae are produced sexually as well as asexually.

liidae, there have been reports of cases within one reef population of colonies being either male, female or hermaphroditic (see tables 4 and 5 for more details).

There are a lot of stony corals which are borderline in this respect, e.g. *Acropora humilis*, *A. palifera* and *Pocillopora damicornis* from the family Pocilloporidae, which is quite well known among aquarists. The last of these three may, however, also develop larvae by asexual budding (see page 61). Thus, it is not exactly a perfect example of a brooder. Better examples of this type of reproduction are *Seriatopora hystrix* and *Stylophora pistillata* from the family Pocilloporidae and *Porites porites* from the family Poritidae, which may release as many as 200 larvae from a section of the colony not larger than 2 cm^2 (FADLALLAH, 1983).

Pocillopora verrucosa from the family Pocilloporidae and *Heliofungia actiniformis* from the family Fungiidae have been reported to brood larvae and spawn gametes for external fertilization; the same holds true for *Tubastraea coccinea* from the family Dendrophylli-

idae. This is particularly interesting, because there are reports about *Tubastraea* sp. producing larvae in aquaria, as well as new colonies developing (see table 5, page 41).

There has been a lot of speculation about why there are so many different patterns of reproduction in stony corals. Among the various influences that have been suggested as influencing reproductive and sexual patterns are the size of the polyps and the colonies, the habitats and the water depth, and the water quality.

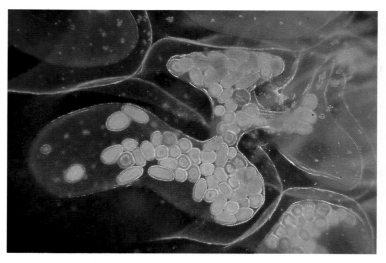

Some cnidirians are brooders in which the planula larvae develop inside the body cavity. Here we see planula larvae in different stages of development in the brooding pouches of the jellyfish *Chrysaora* sp. (magnification: 90x).
Photo: R. Brons

Some corals have separate sexes, like this *Fungia fungites*. In the picture on the left, a male can be seen releasing a sperm cloud. Sperm clouds are released at intervals of five minutes for about one hour. On the right, a cloud of eggs can be seen being released. The egg clouds are emitted at intervals as well.

Photos: P. Harrison, Southern Cross University

Table 5			
Stony corals that may be free spawners (F) or brooders (B), depending on their geographical distribution.			
After HARRISON & WALLACE (1990)			
Family	**Species**		**Geographical distribution**
Pocilloporidae	*Pocillopora verrucosa*	B F	Enewetak Red Sea
Acroporidae	*Acropora digitifera* *A. palmata* *Montipora digitata*	B F F B B? F	Enewetak GBR Puerto Rico Virgin Islands Belau GBR
Fungiidae	*Heliofungia actiniformis*	B F	Belau GBR
Poritidae	*Porites lutea*	B F	GBR GBR
Faviidae	*Diploria strigosa* *Favia Fragum* *Goniastrea* *Manicina areolata*	B F B+F B F B+F B	Puerto Rico, Virgin Islands Puerto Rico, Bermudas Jamaica Belau GBR, Okinawa Bahamas Jamaica, Tortugas
Oculinidae	*Galaxea fascicularis*	B F	Belau Okinawa, GBR, Red Sea
Dendrophylliidae	*Tubastraea*	B B+F	Hawaii, GBR GBR

These female colonies of the Crystal Coral *Galaxea fascicularis* are just begining to spawn, ejecting bundles of red eggs. Other colonies of this Crystal Coral may be hermaphrodites which produce eggs and sperm cells.

Photo: P. Harrison, Southern Cross University

❷ Sexual development

Cnidarians lack any external (secondary) sexual characteristics. Thus, it is not easy to find out which sex a colony possesses or whether it is hermaphroditic. The only way to determine the sex of a colony is to look for the gonads, i.e. the ovaries and testes. Usually, the gonads develop within the mesenteries, sometimes also within the mesogloea (see pages 18-20). The gonads can only be identified under the microscope, when a live polyp is dissected and checked for eggs and sperm. For perfect viewing, histological samples must be carefully prepared, a procedure which is difficult and time-consuming. To do this with stony corals, the skeleton must first be removed by placing chosen samples in a mixture of mild acid and formaldehyde and rinsing them carefully in this mixture. The samples are next embedded in paraffin and those which we want to examine under the microscope must then be prepared using a special piece of apparatus, called a microtome (which slices them very thinly); they must also be dyed afterwards.

❸ Sexual maturity and reproductive cycle

If we want to encourage stony corals to reproduce in an aquarium, we must first wait until they reach sexual maturity and are sufficiently stimulated to develop gonads. This development of the gonads may turn out to be the crucial problem, as reproductive processes in corals are influenced by the environment to a greater extent than by all the other biological functions.

Sexual maturity depends, largely, on the growth, as well as the age, of a colony. This was proved in an experiment by KOJIS & QUINN (1985). Table 6 on page 44 provides some details in this respect for a number of different corals. In the sea, the rate of growth of a colony can sometimes slow down as it gets older and this reduction may be a stimulus that induces sexual maturity. On average, brooders reach sexual maturity a few years earlier than free spawners. Ahermatypic stony corals also seem to reach sexual maturity earlier than hermatypic ones. In some species with larger polyps, it is the size of the polyps, rather than the size of the colony, that seems to determine how long it will take for sexual maturity to be reached (HARRIOT, 1983).

In stony corals, fecundity may

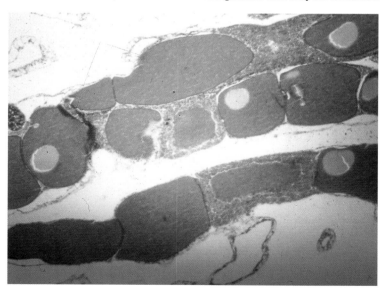

Tissue section of the ovary of a female colony of *Turbinaria mesenterina* (family Dendrophylliidae) from Magnetic Island, Great Barrier Reef. Mature oocytes (egg cells) stand out as red square shapes. The channel (duct) by which the eggs will eventually be ejected shows up in light red. In addition, immature and degenerated oocytes can be seen.

Photo: B. Willis

increase with age, since an older colony will usually emit more sexual cells than a younger one. In this connection, it is very interesting to note that polyps which are located near to active growth zones in branching colonies, e.g. as in *Acropora* spp., are young and therefore still sterile. Polyps that are able to reproduce can only be found in older sections of the branches. This is different in colonies that do not branch, but grow massively, e.g. most of the species in the family Faviidae. Here, all the polyps, even the youngest ones, have gonads at the same stage of maturity.

Stress may also exert a marked influence on sexual maturity. The increase of particles suspended in the water led to a heavy reduction in the fecundity of *Acropora palifera* in the coastal waters of Papua-New Guinea. Corals in deeper water also proved to be less fecund. This is an indication that a reduction in the light intensity has an adverse influence on sexual maturity (KOJIS & QUINN, 1984). When there is less light, less energy is available to the zooxanthellae, and this probably - in turn - has a negative influence on the development of the gametes.

In our aquaria, we have to control the amount of UV-light, as it may harm our corals (see vol. 1, pages 196-198). JOKIEL & YORK (1982) and JOKIEL (1984) have shown in experiments that the production of larvae in *Pocillopora damicornis* is reduced considerably when UV radiation decreases. We have to keep in mind that UV radiation may have a positive influence on the sexual maturity of corals.

For reproduction in aquaria, higher temperatures (up to a maximum of 30 °C) may, perhaps, stimulate sexual maturity. Temperatures should not be too high, however, because this might result in bleaching of the corals (see vol 1, page 214). A deviation from normal salinity may also have an adverse effect on sexual maturity (see vol 1, pages 218-219). In the sea, nutrition of stony corals is very closely adapted to their surroundings which do not

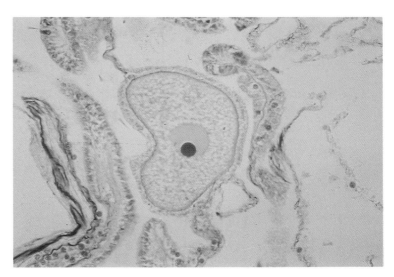

Tissue section of the ovary of a *Montipora digitata* (family Acroporidae).
Photo: B. Stobart

provide large amounts of nutrients (see pages 24-32). This is probably of great importance for their sexual maturity, too. In the aquarium, a wrong or unbalanced diet, or an inadequate supply of energy for the zooxanthellae, may also exert an equally negative effect. As yet, we do not know very much about these factors, so we need to observe the situation in our aquaria very precisely in order to discover what conditions apply immediately before spawning occurs. As this usually hap-

pens very suddenly, it is worthwhile keeping a regular aquarium diary, this being the only way of obtaining full information and determining facts that may be reproduced in experiments.

As in vertebrates and many other invertebrates, the maturation of egg cells and the ejection of eggs is controlled by sexual hormones. Among the hormones, the anabolic steroid, Estradiol-17β, which is produced by the ovaries, is most important. Some very interesting observations and

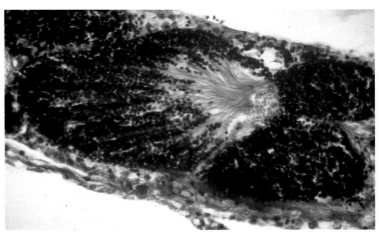

Tissue section from the testes of a male *Turbinaria mesenterina*. The tails of the spermatozoa reach into a central cavity, through which they lead to the mouth.
Photo: B. Willis

Table 6

Fecundity of sexually mature stony corals in the Caribbean

After Soong & Lang (1992)

Species	Magnitude (surface in cm^2)						
	0-4	4-15	15-60	60-250	250-1000	1000-4000	over 4000
Favia fragum							
%	63	93	94	–	–	–	–
n	38	74	17				
Siderea radians							
%	50	86	97	100	–	–	–
n	64	206	208	23			
Porites asteroides							
%	0	9	19	79	94	100	–
n	4	12	26	47	55	11	
Diplora cliviso							
%	0	0	40	57	93	100	100
n	1	5	5	14	29	23	3
Diplora strigosa							
%	–	–	20	42	100	100	100
n	–	–	5	12	9	6	9
Montastraea cavernosa							
%	–	0	100	92	100	94	100
n	–	1	6	13	20	18	5
Siderastrea siderea							
%	0	0	0	47	96	100	96
n	3	4	7	19	27	13	23
Acropora palmata							
%	–	0	0	7	31	43	88
n	–	4	9	14	16	7	33
	Magnitude (lenght of branches in cm)						
	under 1	1-2	2-7	5-9	9-13	13-17	over 17
Porites furcuta							
%	0	77	94	–	–	–	–
n	5	39	252	–	–	–	–
Acropora cervicornis							
%	–	–	–	0	38	59	89
n	–	–	–	4	13	17	18

Legend: % = percentage of sexually mature polyps in relation to the size of the colony
n = number of colonies

measurements were made by AT-KINSON & ATKINSON (1992) in connection with a mass spawning of corals in the Great Barrier Reef (see pages 51-52). There had been no reports about the excretion of Estradiol-17β by stony corals until then. During this mass spawning, the concentration of this hormone in the water increased to become eight times higher than normal. The following readings were taken: the concentration of the hormone increased from ist normal reading of 550 pg/l to 4200 pg/l (1 picogram = 10^{-12} grammes). Even in the contents of the eggs themselves, as much as 368 pg Estradiol-17β per gram dry weight was found. According to ATKINSON & ATKINSON (1992), this hormone probably has the function of completing the maturation of egg cells. It is also possible, however, that it plays a crucial role in the coordination of the ejection of eggs with the moon phases, the temperature and the tides.

❹ Gametes

Gonads are tissues which produce gametes (egg cells and sperm cells). The gonads of corals probably develop from the endoderm, but experts are not yet in complete agreement about this. Before and during the act of spawning, gametes in hermaphrodites are formed into egg-sperm bundles which consist of many eggs and millions of sperm cells.

The egg cells often contain fat and are, mostly, purple or red in

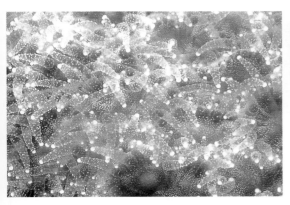 

This brain coral *Platygyra sinensis* is ready to spawn: egg-sperm bundles gather at the mouths of the polyps (left) and are finally ejected (right).   Photos: P. Harrison, Southern Cross University

colour; sometimes, they are also blue (see the pictures on page 47, below). The colours, which come from pigments, may be necessary as protection against too much UV radiation during development in the surface layers of the sea.

The eggs of stony corals of the genera *Montipora* and *Porites* also contain zooxanthellae. Some weeks or hours before spawning, they are transferred there from the host colony. Other stony corals lack zooxanthellae in their eggs.

The largest eggs observed so far were found in *Flabellum rubrum*, an ahermatypic, solitary stony coral. These eggs were 1.5 x 1.00 mm. Eggs of other corals are usually much smaller, however, but they are of different size in the different families. Species from the families Acroporidae and Mussidae, for example, have rather large eggs with a diameter of 0.4 to 0.8 mm, while, in the families Faviidae and Pectiniidae, they are medium-sized: 0.3 to 0.5 mm in diameter. The smallest eggs, with diameters of 0.05 to 0.25 mm, are produced by the families Poritidae, Agariciidae, Fungiidae and Pocilloporidae.

Sperm cells are far smaller than eggs; usually, the total length (including the flagellum) is not more than 0.005 mm. Thus, they are so tiny that it takes a high-quality microscope to examine a single specimen. Sperm can be

Egg-sperm bundles gather at the mouths of the polyps of an *Acropora* and wait to be released. This picture was taken in March off Houtman Abrohols Island, West Australia.   Photo: B. Willis

seen when they are ejected as a white cloud in the water (see pictures on page 35 and on page 41).

There are two main forms of sperm cells (HARRISON, 1985). One type is pear-shaped and is only produced by hermaphroditic corals. The structure of the other type is totally different in that it has a conical shape and a long pointed tip in front of the cell head. This type of sperm is usually found in corals which possess separate sexes, i.e. in many species of the families Faviidae, Fungiidae and Caryophylliidae. There has been a great deal of conjecture as to whether these two types of sperm are determined by the type of reproductive strategy, i.e. by whether a coral is hermaphroditic or bisexual (HARRISON, 1985). However, more definite information on this subject is required before a firm conclusion can be arrived at.

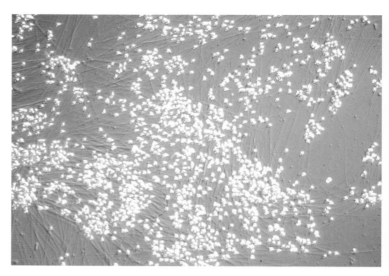

Photograph of sperm cells taken through a microscope: the diameter of the sperm heads is 3 μm.
Photo: B. Willis

❺ Spawning

One way or the other, the development of gametes (gametogenesis) and the act of spawning always occur in cycles. Although the eggs usually take a longer time to develop than the sperm cells, both generally mature in a particular population or colony in time to be ejected at about the same time. There are, however, exceptions and deviations to this pattern. For instance, in the well-known hermaphroditic coral *Stylophora pistillata* from the family Pocilloporidae, the gametes in one colony mature all at the same time, but the time is different in different colonies (RINKEVICH & LOYA, 1979). In populations of *Acropora palifera* off Papua-New Guinea, the gametes developed simultaneously in the populations that were examined. Yet, spawning took place in several stages, which were influenced by the moon phases (KOJIS, 1986b).

The most common spawning cycles are either yearly or determined by the seasons and/or the moon cycles. Free spawners usually have a yearly cycle or even a longer one. Here, the ma-

Macro-picture of egg-sperm bundles of *Acropora tenuis*. Soon after spawning (see picture on page 39, above), the bundles drift on the water surface. The white zones contain millions of sperm cells.
Photo: P. Harrison, Southern Cross University

turation of the gametes takes 12 months or longer. The act of spawning, however, does not take a long time. Brooders, on the other hand, have several cycles per year. This has been shown to be true, among others, for several *Acropora* spp.

Acropora cuneata from Heron Island in the Great Barrier Reef has two reproductive cycles per year, whereas only one has been

observed in *A. palifera* from the same biotope. Yet, populations of *A. palifera* from Lae, near Papua-New Guinea, turned out to have six reproductive cycles per year (KOJIS, 1986a and b). This example illustrates very clearly that the type of reproduction does not necessarily have to be the same throughout one species and that there may be variations due to the geographical distribution. Repro-

Drawings to the right: Stony corals may have two different types of sperm: one has a long pointed tip (see also photo below) and is quite common in species with separate sexes of the families Acroporidae, Caryophylliidae, Dendrophylliidae, Faviidae, Fungiidae, Rhizangiidae and Poritidae. The second type has no pointed tip and is found in hermaphroditic corals of the families Acroporidae, Faviidae, Mussidae and Pectiniidae. This type is perhaps characteristic of all hermaphroditic stony corals.   Drawings after HARRISON (1988a)

Photo below: Cross section of the head of a conical sperm cell of the stony coral *Turbinaria mesenterina*. The head is about 4 μm long (magnification: 17500x, electron microscope) and has a long pointed tip.
Photo: P. Harrison, Southern Cross University

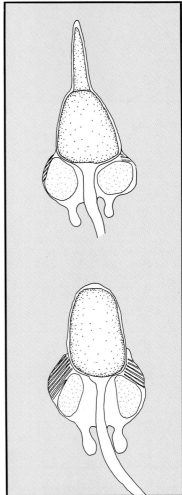

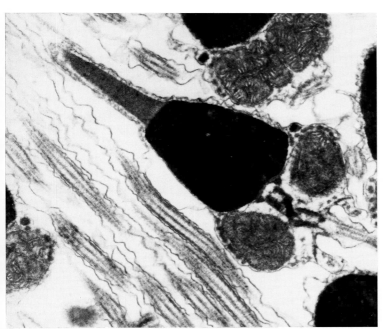

Usually, coral eggs are bright red, like those of the *Favites* sp. in the picture on the left, but, occasionally, they may also be blue, like those of the *Favites* sp. on the right.

Photos: P. Harrison, Southern Cross University

Table 7

Spawning of 7 species of stony corals off Hawaii and Eniwetok in relation to the moon phases.

After STIMSON (1978) in TYREE (1993)

Species	new moon (1.–7. day)	waxing moon (8.–14. day)	full moon (15.–21. day)	waning moon (22.–28. day)
Pocilloporo verrucosa				
June - July	55	29	1	0
January	16	53	0	0
Pocillopora damicornis				
June - July	65	12	0	38
January	57	100	0	8
Pocillopoora elegans				
June - July	60	5	0	0
January	0	40	0	0
Seriatopora hystrix				
June - July	54	43	27	0
January	0	0	0	13
Acropora humilis				
June - July	40	0	0	0
January	0	0	0	0
Acropora striata				
June - July	0	8	0	0
January	29	33	0	0
Acropora corymbosa				
June - July	12	20	0	0
January	0	0	0	0

All data expressed as percentages in relation to the total number of colonies

ductive cycles that are determined by the moon phases have been observed, among others, in *Pocillopora damicornis* in the Indo-Pacific and *Favia fragum* and *Agaricia* spp. in the Caribbean.

Stony corals generally have a reproductive season, but its exact timing and length vary. In some areas, variations e.g. of the temperature and the salinity of the sea water, are relatively large throughout the year, whereas in other regions, conditions are rather stable all year long. This is yet another influence on reproductive patterns. Again, *Acropora palifera* is a good example in that, while this species reproduces only once a year off Heron Island,

which lies 23° south, reproduction takes place all year through off Lizard Island, which, at 14° south, is much closer to the equator.

In hermaphroditic free spawners, the reproductive phase is short and the season is often limited to late spring, when the water temperature rises from a lower winter temperature to a maximum. This may induce intensive mass spawnings, which can take place for one or several nights. Free spawners with separate sexes often have a longer reproductive phase, which usually shows less synchronization, whereas most brooders release their larvae throughout the whole year. Their production of larvae is therefore

not restricted to a special season.

Again and again, experts have asked themselves what really triggers off spawning. How can stony corals, which do not even have a well-developed nervous system, synchronize their spawning so perfectly? In time, it was shown that the position of the moon is of crucial importance in this, with spawning usually beginning on the 15th to the 24th night of the lunar cycle, after the water temperature has started to increase rapidly in late spring. As the moon phases vary from year to year, the spawning season begins at a slightly different time each year. Spawning itself starts at dusk and continues until midnight.

The light of the moon is a key factor which stimulates spawning in stony corals on the reef. The light intensity of the full moon (photo of the moon: Deep Sky Exploration, Norway; photo of the reef: A.J. Nilsen) is only a fraction of the light intensity at noon, yet, many corals react to the cold bluish-white light of the moon and spawn in synchronisation with the moon phases (small photos: Bette Willis).

The moon phases control the maturation of the gametes, especially in free spawners, but also the releasing of the planula larvae in brooders. Among the brooders, there are also species, however, whose reproduction does not seem to be influenced by the moon phases.

JOKIEL et al. (1985) have measured the light intensity of the full moon, which is only a fractional amount of that of the light at midday in tropical areas. Around noon, the readings taken were 2000 $\mu E/m^2/sec$ ($\approx$ 100000 lux), while they were only 0.01 $\mu E/m^2/sec$ at full moon ($E/m^2/sec$ = Einstein per square metre per second, or, to put it another way, the light energy of a certain wavelength which hits an area of one square metre in one second). Measurements of the light energy taken in $E/m^2/sec$ are much more exact than those in lux or lumen,

but they are also much more difficult to accomplish, because a quantameter is needed. The relation between lux and $E/m^2/sec$ is not a linear one.

It may very difficult to carry out such measurements for an "aquarium moon". Nevertheless, we may take 50% of the intensity of the twilight in an aquarium room which receives scattered light from other light sources (street light, light from other

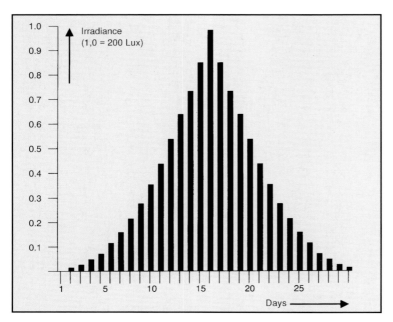

Artificial moonlight in the aquarium: the increase and decrease in the light intensity shows a logarithmic function and should have its peak at 200 lux on the 16th day measured next to the corals, according to the data provided by TYREE (1993 and 1994).

A holaxonian, probably *Swiftia exserta*, spawning in an aquarium at the time of the artificial full moon.   Photo: S. Tyree

rooms, etc.) as a suitable imitation of the light of the full moon. In this case, only a fractional amount of the twilight reaches the corals. If the aquarium is set up in a room which is totally dark during the night, a very weak light bulb may be used as artificial moonlight. TYREE (1993, 1994) informs us that the amount of "moonlight" which reaches the corals should be about 200 lux.

We have measured the light intensity at the surface in the middle of an aquarium. This tank had two fluorescent 40 W Philips TL 03 bulbs installed at the front at an angle of 45° in relation to the surface; the result: ca. 1850 lux (one fluorescent bulb produces 1200 lux). At the top of the coral colonies, about 20 cm below the surface, the light intensity was reduced to 650 and 400 lux, respectively. A 40 W blue light bulb produces about 200 lux at the surface, if installed about 10 cm above it. At the top of the coral colonies, about 20 cm below the surface, the light intensity that was left from such a source was only 20 lux.

Today it is possible to simulate natural moon cycles with highly developed, programmable devices like the "Simatic S5-95U", produced by Siemens, or with an electronic dimmer. Both systems are, however, very expensive, but in connection with e.g. a Philips 18 W TL 03, moonlight and its natural cycles may be simulated. Nowadays, we can even find the first computerized "moonlights" on the market. Do note, though, that the "aquarium moon" should be simulated, both with respect to nightly sequence, which increases by about 50 minutes each night, as well as increasing intensity. If aquarists want the stony corals in their aquaria to reproduce, they should try set-ups like those described here.

In an experiment, TYREE (1993) initially tried to reduce the normal lunar cycle from 29.5 days to 15 days to achieve a synchronized mass spawning of stony corals in a test period of three months. Even though the experiment did not work, important information was gained (see page 58). In a second experiment, he changed the system to the natural cycle of 29.5 days (the results of the experiment are summarized in the diagram on page 50, see also vol. 1, page 201). This caused a holaxonian, probably *Swiftia exserta*, spawn. Before the gametes are emitted into the free water, they are detached from the gonads and enter the stomach cavity of the polyp. Here, the eggs are clearly visible. The sperm cells, however, are far too small to be seen. The eggs are often ejected in lumps, yet, in certain species, they can also be released one by one. We could observe in *Fungia* spp. that polyps were heavily inflated while they ejected the sperm cells. A similar behaviour was observed in *Heliofungia actiniformis* in the sea while it released fully developed planula larvae.

In connection with spawning, one of the most fascinating natural phenomena has to be mentioned. It is a great natural spectacle which could not be explained in its entirety until 1982. Every year, a gigantic mass spawning of stony corals takes place in the Great Barrier Reef. This event includes 134 of the 356 coral species, which belong to 11 different families. During a few nights in

The mass spawning of stony corals in the Great Barrier Reef (GBR) is a fantastic natural event. Myriads of sexual cells are released at the same time. After spawning, eggs and sperm gather at the surface, where they look like large pink ribbons. The aerial photo at the top (photo: M. Cuthill) shows a ribbon of eggs, sperm and embryos which is about 50 m long about 12 hours after a mass spawning in a lagoon of Bowden Reef, GBR, in November. In the lower photo (photo: B. Willis), the embryos and larvae of the corals stand out, owing to their pink colour, against the brownish-grey cyanobacteria (blue-green algae) which can develop into floating mats in shallow waters.

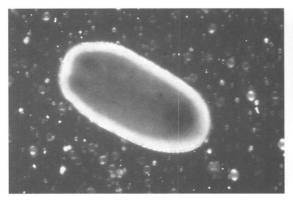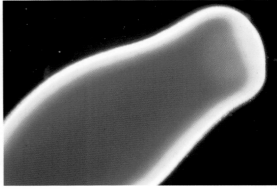

Three-day-old planula larvae of *Acropora tenuis* (to the left; photo: P. Harrison) and *Tubastraea faulkneri* (to the right; photo: J. Wolstenholme). Planula larvae lead a planktonic existence and it usually takes four to seven days' development before they can settle and grow into primary polyps.

spring or early summer, myriads of eggs and sperm cells are released into the water, which turns red as a result. This phenomenon was well-known in Japan in former times and gave rise of the myth of the "princess in the dragon palace under the sea, who had her menstruation once a year".

Today, some Japanese reefs are no longer what they used to be, and mass spawning has become quite rare here. It is only in the last ten years, that the real reasons for the "red water" and details of mass spawning have been discovered.

As described earlier, reproduction in stony corals is determined by several factors. When the water temperature in the Great Barrier Reef starts rising again after its minimum during the colder season, gametes in the coral polyps start maturing. Spawning is then induced by the moon phases and the tides. Three to six nights after the first full moon, when the water has reached the optimum temperature, many different species begin spawning. The egg-sperm bundles drift to the surface of the sea, where they lose their cohesiveness. At this stage, the sperm cells begin "seeking" out the eggs. Spawning tends to occur during neap tids, as a consequence of which, the concentration of eggs and sperm cells is always high in the upper

layers of the water, thus increasing the probability of fertilization.

Mass spawning has also been observed in parts of the Indian Ocean and in West Australia (SIMPSON, 1985). Here, however, spawning takes place at a different time of the year. While mass spawning in the Great Barrier Reef begins just before the maximum temperature is reached, it only occurs long after this has been achieved in West Australia (SIMPSON, 1985; BABCOCK et al., 1986). In the Great Barrier Reef, the combination of water temperature, moon phases, length of day, water quality and food supply is probably responsible for triggering off mass spawning. It is possible that, once reproduction has been initiated, the hormones (see page 43) which are released stimulate the fulminant mass spawning which then takes place.

Why does mass spawning take place at all? Some experts hold the opinion that natural variations in sea conditions, like changes of temperature and tides, cause these events. When compared to the Red Sea and the Caribbean, these variations are more extreme in the Great Barrier Reef.

Simultaneous spawning increases the probability of successful fertilization. At the same time, it offers a better chance of survival in an area where natural selection by predators is a potential threat (HARRISON et al., 1984).

Of course, mass spawning also increases the risk of total disaster if the gametes are destroyed by heavy rain. Science cannot yet fully explain the extraordinary phenomenon of mass spawning. WALLACE et al. (1986a) deal with this subject in a way that is generally intelligible, while BABCOCK et al. (1986) and HARRISON & WALLACE (1990) treat it at length.

❺ Fertilization and development of the larvae

After spawning, the gametes usually gather in great numbers at the surface, thus increasing the fertilization rate. The higher the concentration of gametes, the higher, of course, are the chances of a successful fertilization. In *Goniastrea favulus* from the family Faviidae, eggs are held in masses of mucus around the parent colonies until the ejection of the sperm cells (KOJIS & QUINN, 1981; BABCOCK, 1984; BABCOCK et al., 1986).

Immediately after they are ejected, the eggs undergo chemical changes, and it is only after they have released their polar bodies, that they can be fertilized. Usually, this stage is reached about 30 minutes after spawning. When egg and sperm cells come into direct contact, chemotaxis (orientation or movement of organisms in relation to chemical agents) may be very important for successful fertilization. It is chemotaxis which shows the sperm cells of the cnidarians the right way when they are still several millimeters away from their destination, the egg. We do not yet know if it is also chemotaxis that is responsible for sperm cells and eggs of one species finding each other in the milling mass of gametes of so many species after mass spawning events.

As we have shown above, most stony corals are hermaphroditic free spawners that produce egg and sperm cells at the same time. Yet, this fact also increases the probability of self fertilization. Generally, this is not desirable, because it may reduce genetic variety. It has been shown, however, that the degree of self fertilization may differ considerably. In *Montipora* spp., for instance, no self fertilization takes place and in *Acropora* spp., it is not very common. In two *Goniastrea* spp., though, it was found to be just the opposite (HEYWARD & BABCOCK, 1986).

The development of an embryo (embryogenesis) begins with the first cell division, which usually takes place one to two hours after fertilization of the egg cell, and it ends with the development of the planula larva developing cilia. In free spawners, the time that this development takes varies from six to eight hours in e.g. *Astrangia danae* from the family Rhizangiidae (SZMANT-FROELICH et al. , 1980), up to 24 hours in others (KOJIS & QUINN, 1982; HEYWARD & BABCOCK, 1986; BULL, 1986; HEYWARD, 1986). In brooders, embryogenesis takes considerably longer, lasting e.g. four days in *Favia fragum* SZMANT-FROELICH et al., 1985).

When the cnidarian larva is completely developed and covered with cilia, it is called "planula larva". Planula larvae are able to move around with the help of their cilia. First, they move to the surface of the water, where they drift along. At this stage, they still have the form of a ball. Planula larvae of brooders are larger when they are "released" than those of free spawners, but their

The ahermatypic stony coral *Tubastraea coccinea* from the family Dendrophyllidae, has spawned in aquaria very often. The photographers of the planula larvae in the picture above, J. Yaiullo and F. Greco from the "Aquarium for Wildlife conservation", have seen the event take place several times. At the end of 1993, they were able to count more than 200 primary polyps in their aquarium.

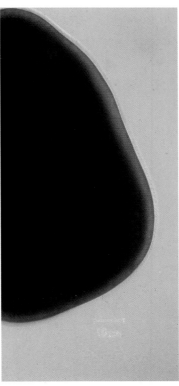

Through the microscope, the cilia on the outer skin, which are used by the planula larvae to move about, can be seen.   Photo: J. Yaiullo

development in the parent animal takes longer.

The typical shape of a planula larva, which resembles a barrel or a pear, only develops after three to seven days. At the posterior end, the larva has an opening which leads to a cavity. At this stage, larvae are 1.5 mm long on average and have fully developed and differentiated cells; the mesenteries are developed as well. This is the time when the planula larvae move into deeper water and closer to the bottom of the sea.

Planula larvae have energy reserves which were probably transferred into the egg cell from the metabolism of the zooxanthellae of the parent colony. At the moment, not a great deal is known about this. There are also examples of planula larvae feeding actively, like e.g. in the North Atlantic coral, *Caryophyllia smithi*.

Planula larvae of brooders nearly always contain zooxanthellae and pigments, and this is a reason why they can exist longer than those of free spawners, which lack zooxanthellae. The species of the genera *Montipora* and *Porites*, however, are exceptions to this, as their eggs contain zooxanthellae.

❼ Dissemination (dispersal) of the larvae and development of primary polyps

Possessing a larval stage generally improves the ability of a species to spread geographically. This might therefore suggest that a planktonic larval stage like that of the planula larvae enables a species of stony coral to settle far from its place of origin. In some brooding corals this may not be true, however, as their planula larvae tend to settle close to where they originate, i.e. hardly more than 1 km away. Only planula larvae with a longer planktonic stage may settle at greater distances. There is no generally accepted idea among experts as to how far the larvae of stony corals may spread. See the review by HARRI-

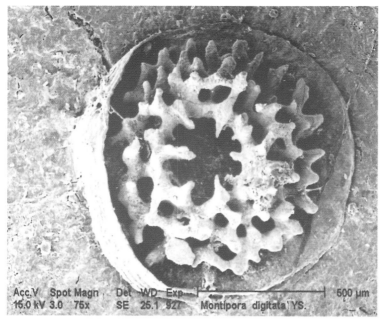

Picture of a four-month-old foot disc of *Montipora digitata* taken with a scanning electron microscope (SEM). Photo: B. Stobart

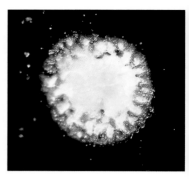

Primary polyp of an *Acropora* immediately after it has settled. The first signs of a skeleton can be seen on the periphery.

Photo: P. Harrison

SON & WALLACE (1990) for a detailed discussion of this subject.

On the reef, planula larvae try to occupy an empty space, where they can settle and develop primary polyps, from which new colonies may grow if living conditions are good. The chance of survival is not very good for primary polyps, though, only a small number growing into new colonies.

Further the chances of survival are not the same in different places. Thus, it is important where the planula larvae settle down on the reef. The water in lagoons or close to the shore contains large amounts of organic substances and particles and here, the death rate of planula larvae and primary polyps may be very high. There are some species of corals, however, which tolerate such conditions. The chances of survival are not higher close to the reef edge either, as the breakers there may destroy the primary polyps. Indeed, their best chance of development is on the reef flat. The water currents are strong there, but they do not harm the primary polyps.

In the first stage of its development, the primary polyp is no larger than 2 mm in diameter and is barely visible. A new colony hardly ever reaches more than 10 mm size in the first year. This, however, depends on several factors: what family the coral be-

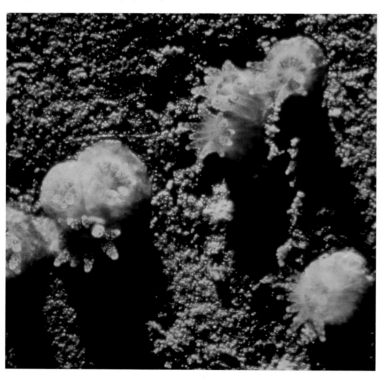

Young corals (about one week old) of *Tubastraea faulkneri* off Magnetic Island, GBR. The polyps have a diameter of about 5 mm.

Photo: J. Wolstenholme

longs to, by which type of reproduction (free spawning or brooding) the colony has been started and which conditions the micromilieu in the immediate neighboorhood offers (BABCOCK, 1985; SATO, 1985). New colonies of brooders grow faster than those of free spawners - see HARRISON & WALLACE (1990), who relate a number of details on the speed with which colonies grow during their first year.

Sexual reproduction in the aquarium

As we have pointed out above, the reproduction of stony corals is a very complicated and variable process and is still a rare event in a coral reef aquarium. It is anything but easy to manage to get stony corals to go through their complete life cycle in an aquarium. However, taking into consideration the rapid development of coral reef aquatics during the last ten years, we dare say that more and more reports about the sexual reproduction of stony corals in aquaria will soon be published.

We would like to suggest here that aquarists give this task their undivided attention and report on their observations, either in articles, or notes in aquatic magazines, or by writing to us directly. Aquarium societies should also apply themselves to this subject. Teams of aquarists could work on the various aspects of this challenge, dealing with questions like temperature cycles, moon phases, sexual maturity, food and feeding and water conditioners. We, ourselves, have also been able to gather some practical knowledge about the sexual reproduction of stony corals in aquaria from our experiences. Moreover, information has been passed on to us about the sexual reproduction of stony corals in the aquaria of other marine aquarists.

On November 2nd, 1992, we observed the ejaculation of a small amount of sperm from an *Euphyllia divisa* from the family

The following series of pictures (this page and page 56) shows a planula larva of the stony coral *Pocillopora verrucosa* in an aquarium settling and growing into a new colony.   All photos: S. Tyree

The parent colony

 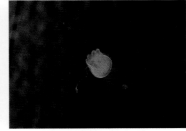

The planula larva (to the left) swims free five days before it settles down. A few hours after it has settled (on the right) the primary polyp starts growing (magnification: ca. 6x).

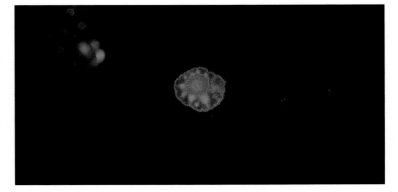

Two or three days later, a foot disc has developed, tentacles can be distinguished and the polyp is starting to grow (magnification: ca. 6x).

The polyp when it is six or seven days old: the brownish spots that can be seen are zooxanthellae (magnification: ca. 20x).

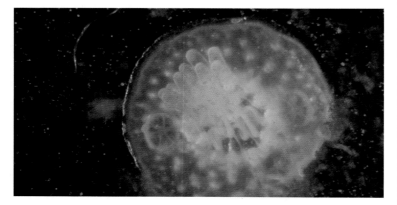

Two weeks later, two more polyps have developed (magnification: ca. 20x).

After one hundred days, several polyps have grown and are developing into a new colony (magnification: ca. 30x).

Caryophylliidae in our experimental aquarium setup. The sperm could be identified microscopically. The coral, which had been in the aquarium for about a year, had nine large polyps (currently, the number of polyps has risen to 18, and the coral is still thriving). The quantity of sperm was very small and could only be observed because the power heads in the aquarium had been removed for some reason. If the pumps had been in full operation, this event would most certainly not have been noticed at all. These were the results of the water analysis:

- temperature: 26.8 °C,
- pH: 8.45,
- salinity: 50.1 mS = 33.5 ‰,
- redox potential: 404 mV,
- nitrate: 1 mg/l.

On April, 8th, 1993, between 10.30 and 11.15 AM, we also observed the release of sperm from a *Fungia fungites*, which had been imported from Indonesia in December 1992. As this happened not more than five months after it had been imported, we assume that this specimen had already reached sexual maturity, or was close to it, when we obtained it. Many species from the family Fungiidae have separate sexes and this coral was a male. The sperm were ejected spasmodically, which took about 45 minutes altogether. The intervals between the release of the sperm portions varied from one to three minutes (see the series of pictures on page 57) and the largest cloud of sperm rose nearly 40 cm above the coral. The polyp swelled to such an extent that the tentacles could hardly be distinguished. Water quality and light light intensity on this occasion were as follows:

- temperature 26.0 °C,
- pH: 8.35,
- salinity: 50.6 mS = 34 ‰,
- redox potential: 392 mV,
- nitrate: 1 mg/l,
- light intensity: 8000 - 10000 lux during 12 - 14 h/day.

Four days before the release of these sperm, about 6 % of the total volume of the aquarium water had been changed. Intentionally, this had been the first water change for one and a half years. At the same time, we had installed a "moonlight" unit. There is, however, no clear evidence that the spawning was triggered by these changes.

In an aquarium owned by Kjell Nagy, of Flekkefjord, Norway, a *Polyphyllia talpina* from the family Fungiidae released sperm on November 21st, 1993, at 11.00 PM. At that time, the aquarium was only illuminated by an actinic-blue fluorescent lamp (Philips TL 03). The coral had been imported together with the Fungia sp. mentioned before and, thus, had been in the aquarium for under a year. It is therefore not very probable that the colony had already contained mature sperm when it arrived. These sperm must have matured under aquarium conditions, instead. Water quality and light intensity were as follows:

- temperature: 28 °C for a few days prior to the event, but usually 26 °C,
- pH: 8.2 in the morning and 8.5 in the evening,
- nitrate: 1mg/l,
- light intensity close to the colony about 10,000 lux: HQI-T 1000 W/D (Osram) for 12 h/day.

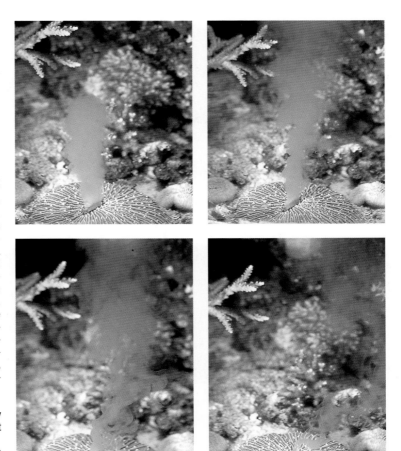

A male polyp of a *Fungia fungites* (?) spawned in our aquarium between 10.30 and 11.15 AM: the release of a sperm cloud took about one minute and was repeated at intervals of about three minutes.

The intervals between the release of the sperm "portions" were about one and a half minutes. Three days later, spawning took place again in the same manner and at the same time of day.

After we had read about the results published by TYREE (1993) and contacted him, we altered our "moonlight" to the cycle described by him (see the diagram on page 50 and vol. 1, page 201). We started the phase with about 17% of the light intensity of the full moon on January 17th, 1994, to keep to the natural cyclic development of the moonlight. Surprisingly, spawning started on January 25th, 8 days later, when 54% of the full moonlight was re-

ached (see diagram on page 50). There is no way of proving, however, that there is a direct causal relation. Unfortunately, we were not in the aquarium room when spawning took place, but we came in a few minutes later while the water was still cloudy. As a result, we could not determine exactly which coral, or which corals, had spawned. Spawning must have taken place between 9.10 and 9.30 AM, that is, about 15 to 35 minutes after the blue fluorescent lamps are switched on in the morning, and about 45 to 25 minutes before the first HQI lamp is added. The "moonlight" is on between 11.00 PM and 6.00 AM. We filtered water from the

aquarium through a sieve with 15 μm mesh and found that sperm cells could easily be recognized under the microscope. The analysis of the water showed the following results:

- temperature: 25.7 °C,
- salinity: 50.3 mS = ca. 33 ‰,
- redox potential: 440 mV,
- nitrate: 1mg/l.

The special importance of this spawning event lies in the fact that no new corals had been added to the aquarium. Thus, the sperm cells must have matured under aquarium conditions. This is proof that corals can reach sexual maturity in aquaria!

Customers admire this magnificent 7500-litre aquarium on display at "Aquariumgarten" in Unterföhring, near Munich/Germany.
Photo: G. Fainer

With stony corals, we have, so far, only been able to observe the release of sperm cells, but never of egg cells. There are, however, reports from the USA on the emission of eggs by an *Euphyllia* sp. and a gorgonian (J. C. Delbeek, pers. comm.), and we once watched a soft coral from the genus *Sarcophyton* producing eggs. Egg production by a *Sandalolitha robusta* from the family Fungiidae and a *Pocillopora* sp. is also reported from the Waikiki Aquarium in Hawaii (see vol. 1, page 268). The aquaria of this institution are directly connected to the sea itself, so there is continuous exchange of water between the two. Such aquaria cannot therefore be regarded as representing a closed system (see also vol. 1, pages 238 and 268).

Steve Tyree from California is an aquarist from whom we have learned a lot about the sexual reproduction of stony corals in the aquarium. The analysis of the water in his 680-litre aquarium yields the following results:

- pH: 8.2 - 8.5 (morning through evening),
- carbonate hardness: 7 -10,
- temperature: 26 °C on average, but 27 to 27.5 °C when the reported spawning took place,
- salinity: about 36 ‰,
- calcium: 380 - 450 mg/l.

The aquarium water is produced from osmosis water by adding an artificial sea salt mixture. There is no filtering equipment, except for a protein skimmer. Once a month, about forty litres of water are changed and the water is filtered through activated carbon for a while every two or three months. The aquarium is decorated with 30 kg of porous material as basic structure, and with 75 kg of live rocks.

During the past three years, Steve Tyree has been able to observe the spawning of a number of different cnidarians, not only stony corals, but also gorgonians and disc anemones. He has discovered (pers. comm.) that brooders which produce planula larvae every month, are not able to adapt their spawning cycle to a doubling of the moon cycle to 15 days. Annual free spawners, however, once their gonads have matured, are able to adapt their spawning rhythm to the cycle of the artificial moonlight, even if this is twice as fast, i.e. 15 days instead of 29.5 days. These results show clearly that artificial moonlight with a light intensity corresponding to that of the natural rhythm of the moon cycle, is crucial for the emulation of a natural life cycle of stony corals in aquaria (for further data see the diagram on page 50).

There have been several reports relating to the larval development of the stony coral *Pocillopora damicornis*, among others, from aquarists from the USA and from Germany. In some of these cases, it is certainly correct to refer to the observations as the development of larvae. In many other cases, though, what has actually been observed has been asexual reproduction, which works on the principle we have described as polyp bail-out earlier on (see pages 38 and 61).

Marine aquarists in many different places of the world have noted the existence of small colonies of the ahermatypic stony coral *Tubastraea coccinea*. Most probably, these have resulted from larval development as well. However, planula larvae may also be produced asexually by brooders (asexually brooded planulae, see page 62).

Cyclones are one of the main reasons for the devastation of reefs. Shown here, is the Bougainville Reef in the Coral Sea, which was hit by a cyclone in 1991. New colonies develop soon after such a catastrophe because corals are capable of reproducing by branch breakage (fragmentation).

Asexual reproduction in stony corals

Asexual reproduction has been defined as "reproduction without fertilization". In every case of asexual reproduction, the offspring are genetic copies (clones) of the parent individual. Thus, this type of reproduction is not important for the genetic development of a species, but it is a very effective way of accelerating its distribution by the rapid production of many new individuals. For a genotype that has successfully adapted to a certain environment, it is the most successful form of reproduction, as it guarantees the continued existence and the distribution of a well-adapted genotype. That is the reason why asexual reproduction prevails in a stable environment and usually only gives way to sexual reproduction when enviromental changes take place.

Electrophoretic examinations carried out on a reef showed that some coral populations consisted almost exclusively of individuals that resulted from asexual reproduction. In such populations, all the individuals belonged to the same genotype, i.e. their genetic material was identical. These results were found especially for the hermatypic corals *Pocillopora damicornis*, *Pavona cactus*, *Porites compressa* and the ahermatypic *Tubastraea coccinea* (HUNTER, 1985; WILLIS & AYRE, 1985; AYRE & RESING, 1986). Just the opposite holds true for *Acropora palifera*, *Seriatopora hystrix* and *Stylophora pistillata* (RESING & AYRE 1985; AYRE & RESING, 1986).

So far, five types of asexual reproduction are known (see the diagram on page 38). We must assume, however, that more types may be discovered in future.

The ability of stony corals to reproduce by fragmentation is also of great advantage to aquarists. A fragment which is fixed to a suitable substrate will soon take root and grow into a new colony. This type of asexual reproduction is especially successful with *Acropora* spp. The fragment shown here is about 1.5 cm high.

In the sea, many soft corals split their tissues by fission, thus forming new colonies. This picture shows a *Cespitularia* sp. in the process of fission.

Mushroom corals of the family Fungiidae may produce many single polyps.
Photo: D. Stüber

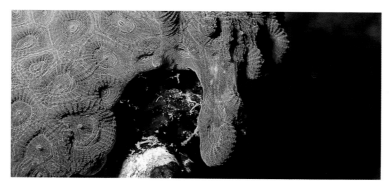

Many species of stony corals from the family Faviidae have been reported as being able to reproduce asexually by releasing fragments like this one in the aquarium owned by Mr. Kenneth Olsen, Oslo. Such fragments settle easily and grow into new colonies in the aquarium. This is also an excellent way of spreading corals to fellow aquarists.

❶ Fragmentation

Many corals are damaged by other organisms or by external (physical) forces, e.g. the breaking of the waves. This can break a colony into pieces which may then be scattered and fall to the bottom somewhere away from the original colony. Often, the tissues do not die, but continue to grow on the new substrate and, if conditions are favourable, new colonies will gradually develop from these fragments.

Branch breakage, as this fragmentation is called, is the most important form of asexual reproduction on the reef and it is a crucial factor in the fight for survival. It is the way in which a reef regenerates itself from bits and pieces after the devastating cyclones that sometimes hit it, literally wiping it out (see the picture on page 59). The tendency to reproduce by branch breakage is quite high in many stony corals, especially *Acropora* spp. This is why these are among the stony corals that are most easily kept in aquaria, since they may be propagated by breaking off pieces from the parent colony and placing them somewhere else. In the chapter on "stony corals" (chapter 16) we will deal with this method of reproducing such corals in the aquarium in greater detail.

❷ Fission

In the process of division or fission, either the parent individual splits in two halves lengthways or crossways, or new individuals appear at its foot. This form of reproduction is well known to aquarists and is most often observed in disc anemones, although anemones, stony corals or soft corals may also split into two colonies in this way. In principle, even the normal growth of a colony is a process of asexual division of single individuals, which are, however, not released by the parent colony to form new colonies. Soft corals may be divided by aquarists themselves because it is safe to cut the colony in two or more pieces with a scalpel. We will come back to this question in the chapter on soft corals.

❸ Polyp bail-out

Polyp bail-out has been observed in the stony corals *Seriatopora hystrix* and *Pocillopora damicornis* and was first described by Sammarco (1982). In this process, single polyps detach themselves from the skeleton of the colony and are carried to new substrates by water currents. This phenomenon was first observed with *Seriatopora hystrix* in the laboratory, when the coral was put under stress by keeping it under unfavourable conditions. Just over 5 % of the polyps set free in this way settled down again and grew a new skeleton under laboratory conditions. Later on, polyp bail-out was observed in *Seriatopora hystrix* in Britomart Reef and in Davis Reef (both in the GBR, Sammarco, 1982). Other cases of polyp bail-out were then reported in *Pocillopora damicornis*, when fully developed colonies suffered from pressure and stress caused by predators feeding on them (Richmond, 1985).

Pocillopora damicornis is among the stony corals most commonly kept in aquaria. On several occasions, we have found small, newly established colonies of this species in our aquaria. At the same time, the parent colony has exhibited a white branch where tissue has been missing, so we believe that these have also been examples of reproduction by polyp bail-out.

So far, the reproduction of *Pocillopora damicornis* has been the subject of the highest number and most detailed reports on the reproduction of corals. Sometimes, we can find a white branch (above) on a colony of this species, followed, a little later, by the discovery of tiny new colonies in different places in the aquarium. This type of reproduction is called polyp bail-out. Asexual reproduction of this type is a guarantee of survival when living conditions deteriorate. The small colony to the left (below), consists of about 15 polyps and has settled on a PVC tube, while the slightly older colony to the right (below), already has several hundred polyps.

❹ Polyp balls

Now and then, there are reports about reproduction by secondary colonies. In these cases, new polyp balls with polyps, tissue, skeleton and zooxanthellae grow on the parent colony. Eventually, these polyp balls detach themselves from the parent colony and settle somewhere else as secondary colonies.

In aquaria this type of asexual reproduction has most often been observed in stony corals from the family Faviidae, *Goniopora spp.*, *Fungia* spp., *Heliofungia actiniformis* and *Euphyllia ancora*.

Some corals may grow very small polyp balls, e.g. *Porites* spp., as in the aquarium owned by Fleming Jørgensen from Stavern, Norway, where about twenty secondary colonies with a maximum diameter of 3 mm were discovered. The parent colony had

developed from a piece of live rock and had grown from a size of 2 x 2 cm to about 10 x 7 cm within one and a half years when the first polyp balls were found at the beginning of 1994. Two months later, after the first daughter colonies had detached themselves from the parent colony, new polyp balls grew. We have examined the secondary colonies and have found that they consist of one, two

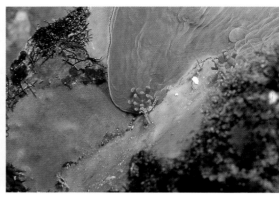

Polyp balls developing on a coral of the family Faviidae. Photo: J. Yaiullo and F. Greco

These miniature colonies, with a diameter of only about 5 mm, have grown at the foot of a *Euphyllia ancora*.

Some new colonies developed from this *Cynarina lacrymalis* in the aquarium owned by Kjell Nagy about a month after it had been stung by another cnidarian.

Goniopora spp. may also develop secondary (daughter) colonies which detach themselves from the parent colony and settle somewhere else. Photo: J. Sprung

or three polyps. The parent colony grew directly under blue fluorescent lamps (one Philips TL 03 and one TL 05).

❺ Asexually brooded planula larvae

Planula larvae normally develop from sexual reproduction, i.e. after fertilization has taken place. However, there are some brooding corals that release asexually developed planula larvae (see page 38). Even though fertilization had never been observed in a coral polyp, biologists generally assumed that these planula larvae could only result from sexual reproduction. Later, it was discovered that self fertilization occurs in some corals, such as *Acropora palifera* and *Seriatopora hystrix* (AYRE & RESING, 1986) and a number of others (see pages 40-42).

Electrophoretic technology has made it possible to examine planula larvae more closely with regard to their genetic qualities, and research on the planula larvae of *Pocillopora damicornis* has shown that they are genetically identical, proving that they cannot result from fertilization.

Asexually brooded planula larvae do not possess the genetic variety of the species, yet they can be produced in enormous quantities and are released into surroundings which have already proved to be favourable (STODDARD, 1986).

MUIR (1984) put forward the theory that the asexually brooded planula larvae of *Pocillopora damicornis* develop from lipid bodies and detach themselves from the polyps. Up to the present, planula larvae of this type have only been found in *P. damicornis*. This stony coral has therefore recently been examined very closely as far as its reproduction is concerned. Further, it is the species which presents the greatest and, so far, most confusing variations in this respect.

These two aquaria contain a lot of hermatypic corals, among them many *Acropora* species. Most of these have been grown from fragments collected in other aquarist's aquaria. In this way it is possible to "grow a reef without harvesting the natural environment". The aquarium above belongs to Mr. Leif Lindström, Stavanger, Norway and the one below to Mr. Kenneth Olson, Oslo, Norway.

Chapter 3:

Taxonomy and Nomenclature of the Cnidarians

Taxonomy is the science of classifying all living creatures. All organisms are divided into hierarchically ordered groups: for example, into species, genera, families, orders, and classes. In each of these groups, a name identifies the creature as a formal taxon, and distinguishes it from other taxa at the same level in the system.

The principles of taxonomy and scientific nomenclature are the same for all animal groups. See, for instance, MAYR & ASHLOCK (1991), SIMPSON (1990) or WILEY (1981). It is clear, though, that the identification and classification of some animal groups is considerably more difficult than that of others. For example, while many fish can be identified immediately on the basis of their external characteristics, the identification of some organisms can present difficulties even for taxonomists.

The majority of cnidarians do not have any special external and easily recognized species or genus characters. An untrained person could therefore search in vain for years for distinct characteristics necessary for identification and never find them. The few visible characters, like the shape and colour of a colony, are often so influenced by environmental conditions, such as light intensity or water movement, that they cannot be used to identify a species with any degree of certainty. Neverthe-

Left: The reef flat at Bunaken, North Sulawesi, dries out during extreme low tides, exposing the corals to the burning sun.

Kjell Nagy (left) and Alf J. Nilsen search for symbiotically living animals in a colony of the stony coral *Seriatopora hystrix* on a reef in North Sulawesi, Indonesia. Photo: J. Olsen

less, the phenotype of living cnidarians - the growth forms of colonies, their appearance and their colour - can be very helpful in the species classification of a particular reef. In many groups, these characters can be sufficiently distinct to allow us to make a "probable" or "preliminary" identification. For an exact identification of cnidarians, however, it is necessary to have more detailed information, the amount depending on what hierarchical level we are looking at: species, genus, or family.

For species identification, the following main information is required: the corallite structure for stony corals, the sclerite structure

for soft corals, the size and division of the nematocysts for anemones. It is of particular importance to recognize to what extent these characters vary with geographical distribution and environmental conditions.* To put it another way: how do the structures change from area to area and from environmental condition to another? Often, especially with soft corals, but also with stony corals, even the structure within a colony varies. For example, in soft corals the spicules at the base of a colony differs from those in the thin branches. The well known stony coral *Pocillopora damicornis* shows, for instance, a dramatic difference in branch- and co-

Through the study of materials gathered in the Fall of 1991 from Suva Reef, Fiji, we learned a great deal about stony corals, especially about their growth in aquaria.   Photo: E. Svensen

lony-structure depending on which habitat of the reef it occupies.

To verify whether we are dealing with a separate species, or with an ecotype of a species, is, in most cases, a task for those few taxonomists who possess an expert knowledge of the corresponding animal group. In many cases, in addition to studying the living creature, it is also necessary to carry out an examination of the skeleton or body tissue. The goal of the taxonomist is to find objective criteria for a classification to be made, but, even so, a certain amount of subjective opinion cannot be excluded.

At the genus and family level, the priorities are different. While

In April 1992, we obtained a permit to collect stony corals legally off the Maldives. Through this our knowledge was significantly expanded (photo to the left: K. Nagy).

In the Spring of 1994 the company Aqua Design, Oldenburg, organized an expedition to the reefs of North Sulawesi, Indonesia. During this expedition we were able to study the variety of organisms on a reef flat near Bunaken in detail.

species can be understood as natural units, all the higher taxa can be seen as artificial, manmade concepts. It is the taxonomists' task to classify the individual species into the nomenclature hierarchy based on the degree of relationship between the species. For the majority of cnidarians, it is much easier to identify the genus and family than the species.

To classify stony corals at generic (genus) level, we often need to use the form of the skeleton, while, with anemones, the design of the tentacles and the presence or absence of wart-like growths, are examples of generic characters. It is therefore normally easier to say which family and genus a cnidarian belongs to than identify the species. VERON (1995) offers interesting perspectives on these topics.

Taxonomy of Cnidarians

The cnidarians constitute a phylum, which is, in turn, divided into four classes and several orders (see table to the right). Although we follow this classification in the book, individual chapters do not correspond with individual grouping levels of the nomenclature system. For example, one chapter deals with only one particular order, while, in another, several orders and a suborder are discussed. In yet others, complete classes are dealt with. We feel that this division will create a more practical book for aquarists. Additionally, more space and attention has been dedicated to the animal groups which are most interesting to aquarists.

Phylum **Cnidaria** Cnidarians
    Class **Hydrozoa** Hydroids
    Class **Scyphozoa** Jellyfish
    Class **Cubozoa**
    Class **Anthozoa**
        Subclass **Ceriantipatharia**
            Order **Antipatharia** Black corals
            Order **Ceriantharia** Tube anemones
        Subclass **Octocorallia**
            Order **Alcyonacea**
                Suborder **Protoalcyonaria** Deepwater octocorals
                Suborder **Stolonifera** Star polyps
                Suborder **Alcyoniina** Soft corals
                Suborder **Scleraxonia**
                Suborder **Holaxonia** Horned corals
            Order **Helioporacea** Blue corals
            Order **Pennatulacea** Sea feathers
        Subclass **Zoantharia**
            Order **Actiniaria** Sea anemones
            Order **Zoanthiniaria** Colonial anemones
            Order **Corallimorpharia** Mushroom anemones
            Order **Scleractinia** Stony corals

Identification explanatory notes

As we were writing this book, it was of utmost importance to us to determine the identity of the animals as accurately as possible. We photographed the majority of individual species or colonies available in pet stores, and, at the same time, took tissue and skeleton samples for examination. In many cases, the photos and spe-

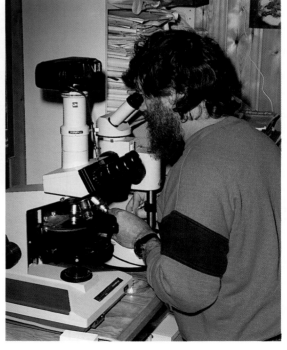

We have attempted to identify the majority of cnidarians that are obtainable in aquarium stores. Samples from soft corals or mushroom anemones, for example, were sent to many experts for identification. In this picture we are taking samples from aquaria in Kölle Zoo, Stuttgart, which, along with Aqua Design, Oldenburg, and Zoo Welke, Lünen, helped us carry out this project (photo above: J. Elmer). Dr. Phil Alderslade (photo to the right) has helped us with the identification of soft corals. Here he is using a binocular microscope to identify an "unknown" species.

These tropical corals are very similar to *Alcyonium* species, which appear in the Mediterranean and North Atlantic. This does not necessarily mean, though, that the tropical "twin" also belongs to the genus *Alcyonium*. There are numerous tropical soft corals with similar appearances. If the polyps are monomorphic, the corals can belong to the genera *Bellonella*, *Nidalia*, or *Eleutherobia*. If the polyps are dimorphic, however, the corals can belong to the genus *Minabea*.

In 1994 we encountered these unknown soft corals in the Maldives at a depth of 10 m. The coral looked so weird that we were almost certain that we had found something very strange and new. The coral was legally collected by Mr. Leif Lindstrøm a year later, and when shipped to Dr. Alderslade for classification it turned out that it was "only" a *Stereonephthya* sp. This is a good example illustrating why hasty conclusions should not be drawn in coral identifications.

cimens were sent for classification to taxonomists specialized in the animal group in question. At this point we would like to express our thanks and acknowledgment for their cooperation on:

Antipatharia and Ceriantharia
- Dr. J. C. den Hartog, National Naturhistorisch Museum, Leiden, Netherlands

Alcyonacea and Stolonifera
- Dr. P. Alderslade, Museum and Art Gallery of the Northern Territory, Darwin, Australia
- M. Gawel, Guam, USA

Holaxonia and Scleraxonia
- Dr. P. Alderslade, Museum and Art Gallery of the Northern, Darwin, Australia
- Dr. F. Bayer, Smithsonian Institution, Washington D.C., USA

Actiniaria
- Dr. J. C. den Hartog, National Naturhistorisch Museum, Leiden, Netherlands
- Prof. D. G. Fautin, University of Kansas, USA

Corallimorpharia
- Dr. J. C. den Hartog, National Naturhistorisch Museum, Leiden, Netherlands
- A. Chen, James Cook University, Townsville, Australia

Zoanthiniaria
- Prof. J. S. Ryland, University of Wales, Swansea, Great Britian

Scleractinia
- Prof. J. E. N. Veron, Institute of Marine Science, Townsville, Australia
- Prof. C. Wallace, Museum of Tropical Queensland, Townsville, Australia
- Dr. B. Carlson, Waikiki Aquarium, Honolulu, Hawaii, USA

We are especially grateful for the help received from several of the above in proof-reading certain chapters (see acknowledgements in the foreword). Nevertheless, the evaluation of scientific information, as well as of identificati-

ons provided, has been totally in the hands of the authors. Complete responsibility for any mistakes is therefore ours.

Classification in Aquarium Literature

In aquarium literature there is a tendency to show the scientific name of every pictured animal. We would like to assert (with a certain amount of disapproval) that some authors have simply picked out a scientific name at random, rather than having the courage to admit that they do not know which species is being shown. These false "fabricated" names are often promptly taken up and used by successive authors. Consequently, the aquarium literature is overflowing with scientific names that do not have any basis in science at all. By meticulously "digging" through the scientific literature, it is clear and easy to see the large number of false identifications in the aquarium literature.

The reader will see that in this book the exact species classification is frequently left completely open. This is always the case when it is felt that it is too complicated to make an exact classification and the risk of a false identification is too high. For some animal groups, we have therefore only provided information for the family or genus.

In order to give the aquarist the possibility of communication with our book as reference, we have given several easily recognized but not yet identified species a code number. For example, *Sarcophyton* sp. **KA4-ALC-18** refers to the original German edition of the book series called "**K**orallenriff **A**quarium", volume **4**, Order **Alc**yonacea, species number **18**. If, at some stage in the future, any of these species can be identified with certainty, the identification will be published in the monthly German magazine "das Aquarium" and in subsequent editions of this book. We have no doubt that this approach makes much more sense than running the risk bringing incorrect scientific names into use.

Summaries

We have inserted "summaries" for important cnidarians in the systematic sections of this book. However, because of the above mentioned difficulties in identification, these summaries (in certain cases) refer, not only to species, but also to species group, genus, or even family. This is only done when we want to minimize confusion regarding an exact identification. If authors before us have given more detailed information about the classification of an organism, and we have decided, in spite of that, not to follow them, we detail our opinion in the summaries or in the text.

In every case in which we have found other identifications from earlier authors, we list the previously used names in the synonym list in the summary. Our synonym list is **not**, however, a reference relating to correct nomenclature and scientific rules. It is simply a list of other names that have been previously used in popular literature.

In addition to the scientific name, the summaries include details regarding the popular name (if available), the habitat, a description, growth forms, diet, aquarium husbandry techniques, and a conclusion using the following abbreviations:

GA: General aquarium suitability
-    = less than good
+/- = relatively good
+   = good
0   = unknown

TO: Toxicity
-    = strong
+/- = relatively strong
+   = negligible
0   = unknown

SE: Sensitivity
-    = very sensitive
+/- = relatively sensitive
+   = not sensitive
0   = unknown.

Mushroom anemones - blue *Actinodiscus*, red *Actinodiscus*: Are they only colour variations of one and the same species or are they different species? Do they really belong to the genus *Actinodiscus*? It is more likely that they constitute several undescribed species of *Discosoma*.

We discovered this "black gorgonian" in a deep cave off the Maldives. So far no one can tell us what it might be. It would be easy to jump to the conclusion that this is a new species. Such assertions are, however, dangerous, especially when dealing with corals. In this case it appears that a black sponge has overgrown a gorgonian, to such an extent that the tissue appears black. Only a very detailed examination can give us a "safe" answer.

Chapter 4

Hydroids

The class Hydrozoa (hydroids) is the first of four classes in the phylum cnidaria. In addition to the hydroids of the order Hydroidea, which are of great interest within the aquatic hobby, the class also includes the orders Siphonophora and Trachylina, which are not dealt with here.

Among the hydroids, there are cnidarians which go through one stage as a sessile (fixed) polyp and a second stage as a free-swimming medusa. There are quite a few species that have occasionally been imported on live rock and have developed - if they were sessile polyps - into beautiful colonies. These colonies consist of a large number of small polyps that grow from a common tissue called a stolon or hydrorhiza. The polyps of one colony can often be highly specialized; some take in food, while others have the tasks of defending the colony or helping it to reproduce. A special feature of the hydroids is the perisarc, a dead, protective

Hydroids are a very variable group of cnidarians. Many of them are very small and therefore not noticed at all. Their structure, however, is very interesting, and the colony of *Gonothyraea loveni* in the photo on the left reveals both feeding, as well as, reproductive polyps (photo: R. Brons). Others do not look like hydroids at all, but much more like corals. Thus, the popular name for *Millepora* spp. is fire corals, just as lace corals is the popular name for *Stylaster* spp. The picture on the right shows a *Stylaster* sp. on a reef off Bequia (photo: Dr. D. Brockmann).

Systematics of the order Hydroidea

(Only the taxa mentioned in this chapter are included in this table.)

Suborder **Athecata**
    Family **Solanderiidae**
    Family **Corynidae**
    Family **Milleporidae** - Fire corals
    Family **Cladonemidae**
    Family **Eudendriidae**
    Family **Hydractiniidae**
    Family **Clavidae**
    Family **Stylasteridae** - Lace corals

Suborder **Thecata**
    Family **Campanulariidae**
    Family **Sertulariidae**
    Family **Plumulariidae**

Solanderia spp. resemble gorgonians, yet they are undoubtedly hydroids. This picture of a *Solanderia* was taken on the Great Barrier Reef.

In the suborder Athecata, we find hydroids with unprotected, i.e. naked, polyps (this is in contrast to the order Thecata, under which this is explained in more detail) and very variable tentacles. Most of the species are very small and their life history is extremely interesting. In some families, however, like the Milleporidae and the Stylasteridae, there are also large, calcareous species, which are among the most conspicuous and beautiful hydroids on coral reefs.

Family Solanderiidae

The skeleton of the species of this family has a tissue layer on the outside that makes them look similar to gorgonians. In other respects they show the typical characteristics of hydroids. The family includes species that grow in branching, creeping, crustlike or in upright forms. The most important species *Solanderia*, which is found in the Caribbean and in the Indo-Pacific, grows in branching colonies which may be up to 30 cm high. Some species are said to be found mainly in shallow waters, while COLIN & ARNESON (1995) report that some species have been found as deep as 100 metres. The same authors mention *S. misakinensis* from Japan and Hawaii, *S. minima* from Zanzibar and, possibly, from Hawaii and *S. secunda* from the central Indo-Pacific.

Family Corynidae

The species of Corynidae have scattered capitate tentacles (i.e. tentacles with swollen tips) and can reproduce either by means of free-living medusa (as in *Sarsia* sp.) or by sporosacs (as in *Coryne*). *Coryne* spp. are often found on shallow, inshore reefs and have also been found in reef aquaria where, at least, one spe-

proteinous cylinder enclosing the live tissue.

One of the most interesting biological aspects among the hydroids is their cycle of reproduction which alternates between two generations: a sessile, asexual polyp stage and (in principle) a free-living, sexual medusa stage. Although the medusa stage is reduced in many species, and is sometimes even found only as a stage attached to the polyp, it is nevertheless the class Hydrozoa that best demonstrates alternating generations among the Cnidaria. We also find similar alternation of generations among the jellyfish (class Scyphozoa), but never in Anthozoa (see figure page 36). The polyps which specialize in reproduction produce medusae by asexual division or budding. The medusae have separate sexes and produce eggs or sperm which unite and develop into free-swimming planula larvae. Planula larvae are able to move freely with the help of their numerous cilia and can settle on a suitable substrate to grow into a new hydroid colony. We sometimes find small medusae in an aquarium, but they either end up in the filter before long, or are eaten by other animals before egg or

sperm cells can be produced and sexual reproduction take place.

The Portuguese Man of War, *Physalia physalis*, which is common and notorious in all tropical and subtropical seas, is a hydroid. It is often looked upon as a jellyfish, yet, it is not a medusa, but a colony of polyps floating on a gas bubble. The Portuguese Man of War is among the most poisonous cnidarians. Even humans who come into close contact with it are in danger. Medical care is absolutely necessary (MEBS 1992).

In this chapter, we would like to deal with a small selection of families and genera that we regard as interesting for marine aquarists. It is, of course, impossible to present all hydroids comprehensively, as only little is known about their systematics as yet. Expert opinion differs considerably on many issues, e.g. many of the genera that are found in coral reefs are placed in different families. The systematic survey we give is based on a critical appreciation and summary of the works of various authors, particularly DEVANEY & ELDREDGE (1977), GEORGE & GEORGE (1979), KAESTNER (1984), LEWIS (1989) and MERGNER & WEDLER (1977).

Fire corals of the family Milleporidae

 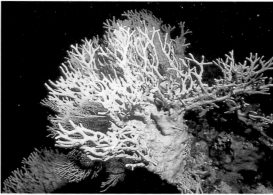

Millepora dichotoma and a parrotfish, *Scarus* sp. on a shallow reef off Kurumba, Maldives.

A *Millepora* sp. on the seaward side of the Flinders Reef in the Coral Sea.

Millepora platyphylla growing on a shallow reef in Indonesia.

Table 8
Summary of the fire corals of the genus Millepora
(adapted after Lewis 1989)

Species	Shape	Depth, reef zone	water circulation
Caribbean species			
M. complanata	sheets, leaves	0.5 - 10 m, reef edge, reef flat	strong to powerful
M. squarrosa	thick slabs that are joined in the shapes of boxes or honeycombs	0 - 20 m, all reef zones	medium to turbulent; at greater depths, strong currents
M. alcicornis	crustlike in sheets on gorgonians	0 - 50 m, all reef zones	moderate to strong
Brazilian species			
M. braziliensis	robust branches	1 - 5 m, fore reef	medium to strong
M. nitida	rounded lobes in short branches	0 - 5 m, inner reef	medium
Indo-Pacific species			
M. dichotoma	fans, branches, vertical sheets and walls	0 - 5 m, reef edge	turbulent, area of the surf
M. exaesa	robust branches or solid and round	0 - 10 m, reef edge, outer reef slope	moderate to turbulent
M. platyphylla	sheets, leaves, fans, branches	0 - 10 m, reef edge, reef flat	strong to powerful, turbulent
M. tenella	fans, branches, sheets	0 - 10 m, reef edge, outer reef slope	medium to strong

cies projects like hair-thin threads which make whip-like movements. Other members of the genus grow along the inside of the burrows made in massive corals by Alpheid shrimps. The polyps are small, less than 0.5 cm, with 12 scattered tentacles (Dewany & Eldredge, 1977). Colin & Arneson (1995) report another species (*Rhizogeton* sp.?, family Clavidae) lining Alpheid burrows. We have observed the burrows lined with hydroids several times ourselves, but have never seen them in reef aquaria.

Family Milleporidae
Fire corals

The hydroids on coral reefs are most typically represented by the monotypic family Milleporidae with the species of the genus *Millepora*. *Millepora* species are very common in the areas from the Red Sea down to South Africa and eastwards to Hawaii and to the Marquesas Islands. Some species, like the fire coral, *Millepora alcicornis*, which does very well in aquaria, are also found in the Caribbean Sea. *Millepora* spp. contain symbiotic algae and are hermaphroditic organisms. The most robust and most conspicuous species grow in the upper zone of the reef slope or at the reef edge, where they are exposed to strong waves and powerful currents.

The skeleton of *Millepora* spp.

is often very brittle and porous, and there may be enormous differences in its shape in the various species. The total number of species is unknown, but Lewis (1989) refers to nine certain species, gives an excellent description of the life history of the genus and quotes many important sources in the literature. Veron (1986) lists at least 48 described *Millepora* spp., but the validity of many of these is dubious. Table 8 (see above) gives a survey of the typical biotopes and of the structure of the most important species.

In all fire corals, the skeleton is perforated with innumerable microscopically small holes through which the specialized polyps protrude. Five to seven of

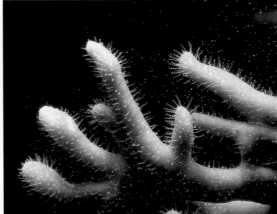

Millepora alcicornis

Distribution: Very common in the Caribbean, especially in reefs close to the shore (see also page 37, volume 1).

Size and growth form: This species usually covers the substrate like a crust, thus adopting the shape of the substrate, e.g. dead gorgonians.

Food: This species subsists mainly on the products of its zooxanthellae, but is probably also able to take in very small plankton and dissolved nutrients from the water.

Description: Yellow to tan-coloured antler-like sheets with a smooth surface cover the substrate on which the coral settles; the end of the sheets appear notched and are whitish.

Aquarium maintenance:

— **General conditions:** The fact that this coral has a very strong stinging poison may cause some problems. Like other fire corals, *M. alcicornis* should not be placed too close to other cnidarians. They are hardy in the aquarium, but are only rarely on sale in shops.

— **Lighting:** This species needs a great deal of light.

— **Water circulation:** Medium to strong.

— **Reproduction:** May easily be spread by fragmentation. Even the tiniest fragment can grow into a beautiful colony.

GA: + ; TO: - ; SE: +

Photos

Top left: Aquarium photo of a *Millepora alcicornis*.

Top right: Close-up of the polyps.

Bottom: *Millepora alcicornis* overgrows a gorgonian in a coral reef aquarium.

Millepora dichotoma

Distribution: Very common in the Indo-Pacific.

Size and growth form: Antler-like branches with the end branches always divided into two (dichotomos, Greek = divided into two parts); many colonies grow to a height of more than 1 metre.

Food: This species subsists mainly on the products of its zooxanthellae, but is probably also able to take in very small plankton and dissolved nutrients from the water.

Description: Brownish to yellow, with white branch tips; smooth surface.

Aquarium maintenance:

– **General conditions:** The fact that this coral has a very strong stinging poison may cause some problems. Like other species in the genus, *M. dichotoma* should not be placed too close to other cnidarians. Hardly anything is known about its maintenance in aquaria.

– **Lighting:** This species needs a great deal of light.

– **Water circulation:** Medium to strong.

– **Reproduction:** Unknown, probably just as easy as *M. alcicornis*.

GA: 0 ; TO: - ; SE: 0

Photos

Top left: A large piece of rock off Bunaken, North Sulawesi which has been colonized by *M. dichotoma*.

Top right: Close-up of the polyps. The photo also shows a brittle star and a crab of the genus *Macropodia* covered with other hydroids. A small goby clings to one of the branches and, if you look very closely, you will be able to see that barnacles occupy small spots on the branches.

Photo: E. Svensen

Bottom: A large colony in the Red Sea.

Photo: E. Svensen

In the family Cladonemidae, we find tall polyps with four tentacles. These are polyps which produce bell-shaped medusae. The picture on the left shows a polyp of *Cladonema radiatum* with a budding medusa (magnification 30x), while the one on the right shows a free-swimming medusa (magnification 20x). Photo: R. Brons

these defence polyps, which are heavily equipped with stinging cells (nematocysts), surround each polyp that is specialized for feeding. Such an arrangement of polyps is called a "cyclosystem". In addition to these, special reproductive polyps may be recognized, and these produce free-swimming medusa larvae. An inner system of channels connects the individual polyps to each other.

All *Millepora* species secrete a strong stinging poison from their nematocysts, and this has led to their popular name "fire corals". Touching the polyp of a fire coral proves, at once, to be an extremely painful experience, very much like touching nettles. The skin turns red and there may even be slight swellings. In some cases, even blisters may result, so that the upper layer of the skin comes off. People with a sensitive skin, or with allergies, may show very intense reaction to this. According to MEBS (1992), however, no medical assistance is needed in most cases. We recommend treating the skin with a mild ointment or a lotion.

In spite of their strong stinging poison, there are a number of parasites or predators that feed on or off fire corals. The best known one is the cirriped *Pyrgoma* sp. which, under extreme conditions, may cover and destroy a complete colony. The polychaete worm *Polychaetopterus* sp. may be just as destructive. Moreover, fire corals are eaten by molluscs and some fish species, but there have also been reports of cases of commensalism that have been observed, as, for example, with shrimps like *Thor* sp. and *Alpheus* sp., and the brittle star *Ophiotrix* sp.

Fire corals are only occasionally imported for aquarium purposes, but they may grow from live rock. It is important to note that they may harm other cnidarians because of their strong stinging poison, especially when two colonies grow close together and touch. Other animals can also come to considerable harm if fire corals are placed close to circulation pumps. We have observed that their stinging cells may drift into other animals and hurt them.

Family Cladonemidae

In the family Cladonemidae, the medusae are larger and much more conspicuous than the polyps. *Cladonema radiatum* is a rather common, cosmopolitan species which shows great variation between the specimens coming from different places of origin. The medusa has the typical shape of a bell with a thin wall and a diameter of about 3 mm. The

The colonies of the genus *Eudendrium* have separate sexes. The picture on page 37 shows a male colony releasing sperm, while the picture above shows a female colony with oocytes. Photo: R. Brons

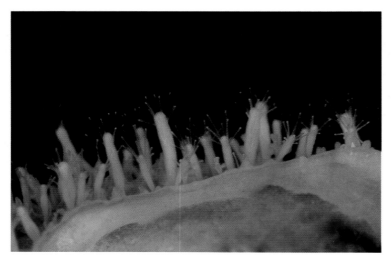

Hydractinia echinata is very common in tropical and subtropical seas. Colonies are often found on clam shells.

Photo: R. Brons

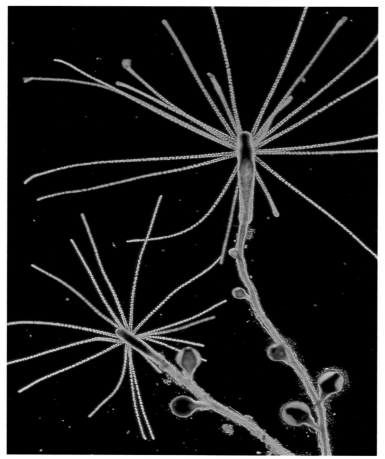

Species of the family Clavidae have a delicate structure with long, filigree tentacles.

Photo: R. Brons

polyps are only 1 m in height, have four tentacles and grow from a prostrate (creeping) stolon. *Cladonema radiatum* is often found on green algae of the genus *Ulva* in calm and shallow water.

Family Eudendriidae

This monotypic family, with *Eudendrium* as the only genus, is common all over the world. *Eudendrium* spp. may be distinguished from other hydroids by possessing a trumpet-like structure directly beneath the mouth. These colonies develop sessile medusae and have separate sexes. The picture on the left handside in the middle row on page 37 shows a male colony giving off sperm cells.

Family Hydractiniidae

In this family, the colonies consist of a large number of small polyps which spring from a conical stolon and have a ring of ten tentacles. The medusae are free-swimming and rather small, with a diameter of about 2 to 3 mm.

The genus *Hydractinia* is commonly found in shallow tropical waters, often on the topside of rocks. The most frequently encountered species is *Hydractinia echinata*, which often settles on clam shells.

Family Clavidae

The filamentous tentacles of the polyps are the most obvious characteristic trait of this family. The colonies have either a creeping, or branching hydrorhiza. The colonies release either planula larvae that were brooded internally, or free-swimming medusae.

Cordylophora caspia is a species which grows to a height of about 15 mm and a diameter of 0.25 mm. It is found worldwide, and even in brackish water (DEVANEY & ELDREDGE, 1977).

Turritopsis nutricula has a circumtropical distribution and its polyps often grow from a matlike stolon. However, upright-growing stolons are also found.

Lace corals of the family Stylasteridae

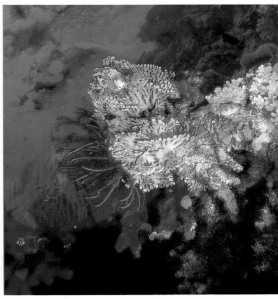

Stylaster sp. photographed in the Fiji islands.
Photo: Scott W. Michael

Distichopora sp. in the Coral Sea.

Photo: E. Svensen

Distichopora violacea is perhaps the most common species in the genus in the Indo-Pacific. It is occasionally introduced into aquaria on the base of corals. Photo from the Maldives.

Family Stylasteridae
Lace corals

In the family Stylasteridae, we find hydroids that have a calcareous skeleton like the fire corals of the family Milleporidae. They are very common in tropical waters and prefer places under overhanging rocks or in caves. The genera *Stylaster* and *Distichopora* can be distinguished by their beautiful colours and their branching shapes, which have led to their popular name "lace corals" (a popular name also used for some calcium-fixing species of Bryozoans).

Stylaster species have thin and pointed branches. The polyps are arranged in a circle (cyclosystem), just as in fire corals of the family Milleporidae. *Distichopora* species have a sturdier and blunter structure in comparison, with the polyps arranged in rows and not in a cyclosystem. The feeding polyps sit on the sides of the branches and are each equipped with a row of defence tentacles on each side. *Distichopora violacea*, with its strong violet colour, is common in large areas of the Indo-Pacific and grows in profusion under rocks and in shady places. SCHEER & OBRIST (1986) provide further details about this genus.

There is only very little information available about the maintenance of lace corals in the aquarium. It is rather unlikely that someone will be able to obtain, keep and reproduce these corals on purpose, as they have no zooxanthellae and must be fed on very small plankton. Indeed, unless fed regulary, they will die. They should also be provided with strong water movement. A cave aquarium (see volume 1, page 149), might, however, be the best type of tank for them, but they must be regarded as very difficult organisms reserved only for well experienced aquarists.

Obelia geniculata **from the family Campanariidae can be found worldwide. The species belongs to the suborder Thecata. In this suborder the polyps live in a protective cup (theca). Note the medusa that just has been released.**

Photo: R. Brons

Suborder Thecata

In this suborder, the individual polyps live in a cup into which they can withdraw. This coating, built from a horny material, is called the perisarc and protects the polyps which always have a ring of similar, strong tentacles. The free-swimming medusae are hemispherical to saucer-shaped and, usually, have many tentacles around the edge of the bell.

Family Campanulariidae

The structure of the hydroids of this family is well-known. They have a characteristic saucer-shaped case, into which the polyp may be retracted. Many species are widely distributed, some are even cosmopolitans, like e.g. *Obelia geniculata*, which is probably the most widespread sea animal of all. The species develops colonies of up to 5 cm length, which are frequently found on seaweeds along the shore. *Obelia dichotomata* is another species of this genus that is found all over the world.

The species of the genus *Campanularia* are very beautiful, but rather tiny. They are also widespread and are found e.g. in the North Sea and the Red Sea. In *Obelia geniculata* and *Campanularia johnstoni*, we can observe an alternation of generations between the sessile polyp and the free-swimming medusa stage. Other species of the family, e.g. *Gonothyraea loveni* have no free-swimming medusa stage. Their medusae settle on the polyps, as shown in the picture at the top of page 37.

Between the two extremes of free-swimming medusae and completely reduced medusae which produce their gametes directly close to the polyp (and in which rudiments of the medusae can no longer be detected), there are a number of intermediate stages, which exhibit a gradual structural simplification of the medusa stage. *Gonothyraea* spp. are examples of this (BRONS, 1989).

Family Sertulariidae

On live rock, we often find small hydroids from the family Sertula-

Most species from the family Sertulariidae form tiny, encrusting colonies. However, this *Sertularella* sp. off the Maldives, grows as a bush of about 20 cm height.

riidae, among which the genera *Dynamena*, *Sertularella* and *Sertularia* are quite well-known. The size of such colonies often does not exceed a few centimetres, with individuals measuring not more than 0.5 - 1 mm. *Sertularella speciosa*, however, grows in upright colonies which reach a height of 20 cm or more. This species is found on reefs in the Indo-Pacific. Its polyps are 0.5 mm in height and between 0.2 and 2.4 mm in diameter. They may, in fact, be identical with, and a synonym of, *Sertularella diaphana* from Australia. DEVANEY & ELDRIDGE (1977) provide a good survey about the geographical distribution of this family and others off Hawaii.

Family Plumulariidae

This family includes a large number of species from the genera *Aglaophenia*, *Antennella*, *Gymnangium*, *Halopteris*, *Cnidoscyphus*, *Lytocarpus* and *Plumularia*, which all grow in a feather-like shape and reach heights of 5 to 50 cm. Most of the species are

difficult to keep in the aquarium, as they have to be fed on very small plankton. There is no intentional or planned import of these species; they usually grow from live rock. The beautiful *Antennellopsis* spp. grows like thin branches that project into the open water, often attached to dead black coral branches (see p. 84).

On coral reefs, the fern- or moss-like-growing *Lytocarpus* and *Aglaophenia* species are very common and catch the eye. Some authors place the genus *Aglaophenia* in the family Aglaophenidae. The species in both genera have a strong stinging poison which causes heavy skin rashes on contact. The reaction may actually be worse than with the fire corals of the genus *Millepora*. MEBS (1992), nevertheless, says that their stings do not normally require medical attention.

The small, bright yellow *Myronema* sp. (see photo in volume 1, page 175) can sometimes grow profusely in reef aquaria and can even overgrow other sessile animals like corals. In nature, the genus is common in very shallow

Plumularia species from the family Plumulariidae grow as feather-like colonies, resembling ferns or mosses. This picture shows a species off Bunaken, North Sulawesi.

Detail of the "fern leaves" of an *Aglaophenia* sp. from the family Plumulariidae from the Red Sea.

Photo: E. Svensen

Aglaophenia cupressina

Distribution: Central Indo-Pacific.

Size and growth form: Fern-like; height up to 20 cm. Can cover large areas of the reef in some locations.

Food: This species subsists mainly on the products of its zooxanthellae, but is probably also able to take in very small plankton and dissolved nutrients from the water.

Description: The sting from this species is extremely sharp and painful and can leave a rash that may last for several days. This species should never be touched! Colonies of *A. cupressina* prefer to settle in groups on a rock or coral substrate. The species has brownish to yellow colours and its polyps are extremely small.

Aquarium maintenance:

— **General conditions:** There are no reports about how to keep this species in aquaria. We do expect problems, however, because of its strong stinging power.

— **Lighting:** A high light intensity will undoubtedly be necessary.

— **Water circulation:** Strong, as the species lives in exposed places on the reef.

— **Reproduction:** Unknown.

GA: + ; TO: - ; SE: +

Photos

Above: Close-up of the "fern leaves" of the coral shown below.

Below: A colony settleing on a stony coral in the Coral Sea.

Lytocarpus philippinus

Distribution: Indo-Pacific.
Size and growth form: Fern-like; height up to 25 cm.
Food: This species has no zooxanthellae. The main food most probably consists of very small plankton. Accordingly, substitute food has to be provided in the aquarium.
Description: Numerous fern-like grey and white branches grow on a dark brown stem. The polyps are extremely small and can only be seen with a strong magnifying glass or other means of magnification. Like other members of the genus, *L. philippinus* has a painful sting.
Aquarium maintenance:
— **General conditions:** Very little is known. We do expect problems, however, because of the strong and painful sting and the species' requirement for minute planktonic food.
— **Lighting:** This species probably does best if the light is not too strong.
— **Water circulation:** Strong, as this species lives in exposed places on the reef.
— **Reproduction:** Unknown.
GA: + ; TO: - ; SE: +

Photos
Above: A colony in the Great Barrier Reef.
Photo: E. Svensen
Below: A colony in the Great Barrier Reef near Cairns.
Photo: Dr. D. Brockmann

Thin and very slender colonies of *Antennellopsis* on an Indonesian reef.

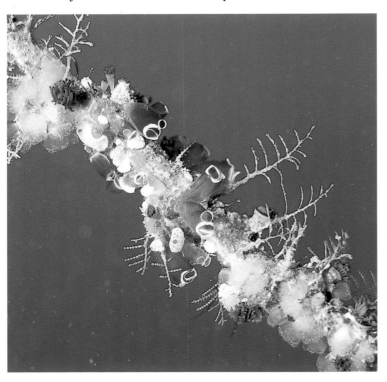

Tunicates, sponges, and other small animals live side by side close to a reef wall near Indonesia. The fern-like hydroids probably belong to the genus *Cnidoscyphus*.

water, where it overgrows rocks and dead branches and can reach a height of 2.5 cm (COLIN and ARNESON, 1995). In the aquarium, it is usually smaller.

Keeping hydroids in the Coral Reef Aquarium

Even though hydroids are present in most coral reef aquaria, they are usually not recognized because they are so small. Thus, they are not normally purposely kept in aquaria, but often arise from live rock. *Myronema* sp. may grow very well under strong light and may spread over large parts of the aquarium, so that it needs culling from time to time (BROCK-MANN, 1990). This species probably feeds only on the products of its zooxanthellae and disappears at once if the light intensity is reduced. In the Maldives, we found colonies in masses in shallow lagoons experiencing extremely high light intensity.

If we use natural (temperate) seawater for our coral reef aquarium, we may observe hydroid polyps or medusae of indigenous species in late summer or autumn, but because of the higher temperature in a coral reef aquarium, they will disappear of their own accord in due course. BIRK-HOLZ (pers. com.) told us about a mass reproduction of hydromedusae in his aquarium. This is, however, probably a rare event.

Angelfishes eat small hydroids. For example, Kleins butterflyfish, *Chaetodon kleinii*, and the copperband butterflyfish, *Chelmon rostratus*, which are very good at keeping down *Aiptasia* sp., also destroy every single hydroid they can find. To keep small hydroids in an aquarium, 10 to 30 litre tanks are sufficient. Many cosmopolitan species of hydroids can also be found on our shores and a microscope will help us explore the wonderful world of these organisms.

Numerous small hydroids have settled on this spider crab of the genus *Macropodia* (?). The spider crab, in turn, lives between the branches of a soft coral of the genus *Dendronephthya* in the Red Sea.   Photo: E. Svensen

This organism puzzled our minds when we first found it in a reef tank in Stavanger, Norway. It formed whip-like movements and projected as thin "threads" up to 5 cm long, from the bottom and from the side walls of the aquarium. It is a hydroid from the genus *Coryne*, commonly found in tropical habitats.

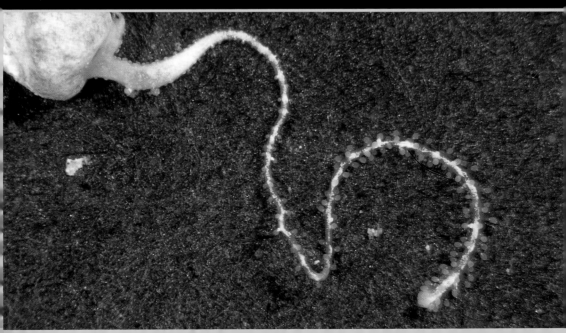

Chapter 5:

Sea Jellyfish (scyphozoans) and Box Jellyfish (cubozoans)

The popular term "jellyfish" covers a very varied mixture of animals, which very often are not really closely related to each other. There is no scientific concept on which the collection of species referred to by this word is based. The subject of this chapter, the Sea jellies and Box jellies, for example, are not closely related, making up two separate classes - the Scyphozoa and Cubozoa - of the Subphylum Medusozoa (the hydroids, class Hydrozoa, also belong to this Subphylum) but, nevertheless, they have enough characters in common to justify joint treatment (for systematics see page 88).

The Portuguese man-of-war, *Physalia physalis* and its relatives are often regarded as jellyfish by non-experts, but they are actually hydroids (class Hydrozoa) instead and have a completely different internal structure.

The animals called comb jellyfish (or jellies) are sufficiently different, even, to be placed in a separate phylum, the Ctenophora. The comb jellies were formerly united with the cnidarians to make up a larger phylum called the Coelenterata. Though comb jellies have some characteristics in common with the cnidarians (some comb jellies, for instance, possess nematocysts), this is not sufficient reason for most scientists to incorporate them in a single phylum. Thus, comb jellies are not considered in this volume.

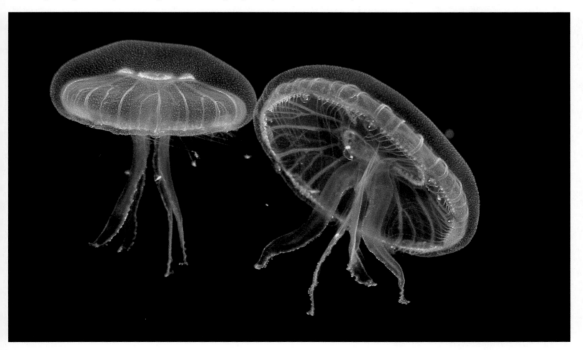

Among the jellyfish, we find some of the most beautiful and most fascinating creatures of the sea. Their unique structure offers an unforgettable sight. The picture to the left (photo: T. Kelly) shows the Papua Rootmouth jelly, *Mastigias papua* from the Indo-Pacific, the picture above shows two young specimens of the Moon or Common jellyfish, *Aurelia aurita*.

Reproduction

While the hydroids have a two-generation life with, in general, a dominant polyp stage and only a short-lived, small medusa stage, the reverse applies to the Scyphozoans which have a dominant medusa stage and a modest polyp stage.

The scyphopolyps may reproduce asexually by budding. Of greater importance, however, is the development of a number of ephyrae (juvenile medusae) by strobilation (see the drawing on page 36). The next step in the development, the medusae or more correctly the scyphomedusae, which normally have separate sexes, reproduce sexually to produce ciliated planula larvae which in most species settle down on rocks to pass through the short polypoid stage. In a few pelagic open-sea species, the larva develops directly into a small medusa, without any intermediate polypoid stage. One species is also known to be a brooder.

The box jellyfish omit the common polypoid stage altogether and produce a very small, specialized cubopolyp instead, which metamorphoses directly into a medusa. The cubopolyp is also capable of reproducing asexually

Adult and sexually mature medusae of the Moon jelly or Common jellyfish, *Aurelia aurita*. Photo: G. Spies

by budding, but then, it only produces additional cubopolyps.

Anatomy

The difference in the life cycles of scyphozoans and cubozoans may, on its own, be enough evidence to prove that they are not very closely related. In addition, there are also some important anatomical differences.

In principle scyphozoans and cubozoans have very much the same structure as most other cnidarians: they have an ectoderm and an endoderm, separated by the mesogloea. The mesogloea is especially thick and firm in the medusae, giving the animal shape and stability. The gastrovascular cavity (the coelenteron), which is responsible for digestion and circulation, is enclosed by the endoderm (see the drawing on page 19). Its purpose is to digest food and to provide the rest of the body with nutrients. This is achieved with the help of a series of channels which run off in different directions from the centre of the coelenteron. The coelenteron opens to the outside via the mouth aperture, which is directed downwards.

Differences between scyphozoans and cubozoans include the possession, by the Cubozoa, of a velum, an annular curtain-like shelf projecting inwards from the margin of the umbrella. The velum is considered to be a (phylogenetically) primitive feature, which is also present in most of the hydromedusae, but missing in the scy-phozoans. Moreover, most of the scyphozoans have the typical umbrella-like shaped bell, while the cubozoans have a distinct cubelike shape with four flattened sides. In the Scyphozoa, the margin of the bell is usually structured into a number of lobes carrying several tentacles, while, in the Cubozoa, one tentacle (or a group of tentacles) is situated at each of the four corners of the bell.

Scyphozoans move by rhythmic movements of their umbrella, which contracts and expands alternately, forcing water out from under the umbrella in weak, but highly effective, jets. The movements are coordinated by rhopalia. Rhopalia (singular: rhopalium) are structures at the border of the umbrella that are sensitive to light and help to keep the animal balanced. Scyphozoans, which are sometimes described as the largest planktonic organisms, may grow to rather substantial sizes (some species are known to grow as large as 1 m in diameter). They are able to swim, but their propulsion is so weak that they cannot move against sea currents. This is why, at certain times, thousands, even millions, are washed ashore by the wind. The way cubozoans swim is, basically, the same, but they are stronger swimmers and are able to hunt actively for prey.

Both groups of jellyfish feed mainly on small fish, but almost any animal of an appropriate size may be included in their diet. Most species catch their prey with their tentacles, which are covered with nematocysts (stinging cells). There are also a few species of scyphozoans, however, which feed on tiny planktonic organisms, which they trap in the mucus that they secrete on the upper side of the their body.

On the following pages we give a survey of the families mentioned in the systematic overview on page 88.

Stauromedusae
Sessile sea jellyfish

The members of the order Stauromedusae are a highly specialized group of sea jellies and quite atypical of the scyphozoans. They are mainly found in colder seas and are therefore generally of no interest for the coral reef aquarium. They are only mentioned here to demonstrate the enormous variety of the Scyphozoa.

The medusae of the Stauromedusae lead a sessile existence, attached to seaweeds and rocks by a stalk; they "take root" with a stem that is found on their trumpet-shaped body on the side opposite to their mouth opening. Moreover, they often have adhesive, cushionlike structures, called anchors, between their tentacles. Some of the Stauromedusae are able to detach themselves from the substrate, to move some distance by grasping with their tentacles and their anchors, and settle down and reattach themselves elsewhere. Most of the Stauromedusae only have a diameter of a few centimetres.

Coronatae
Crown jellyfish

The Coronatae consists of species with normal, free-swimming medusae with diameters ranging from 2 to 25 cm. The name of the order refers to a groove or wreath which makes the bell (umbrella) look like a crown. Immediately below this coronal groove or wreath, the bell is fashioned into a circlet of thick pedalia (feet), some or all of which bear a single, solid tentacle. The brim of the bell is normally scalloped into lappets (lobelike structures), which alternate with the pedalia.

Most of the species of the Coronatae only live in deeper, colder water. They are extremely beautiful and have magnificent colours; some of them even luminesce. Only a few species are found in the shallower waters of tropical seas.

There is one species of Coronatae, in particular, which is not uncommon in coral reef aquaria, although few aquarists would recognize it as being a sea jelly at all. It is an Indo-Pacific species of the genus *Nausithoe* from the Indo-Pacific, which is frequently imported as polyps on live rock. In general appearance, the polyp stage is very similar to a hydroid and, at first, we actually identified it as such. The correct identification was brought to our attention by Robert Brons, Eilat, Israel. There are no other reports about Coronatae as aquarium animals.

Semaeostomae
Banner jellyfish

Among the Semaeostomae, we find the majority of the common and best known jellyfish which are recognized by practically all people. These include the harmless Moon or Common jellyfish, *Aurelia aurita*, which is well-known on the shores of the northern seas, and the beautiful, yet painfully stinging, species of the genus *Cyanea*. Species of this order are found in all seas.

The Semaeostomae all have bowl- or saucer-shaped bells with scalloped margins. The tentacles may either be distributed evenly around the margin, or arranged in tufts. In the gastrovascular cavity (coelenteron) radial canals or channels run from the

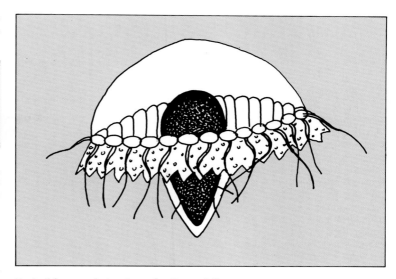

Typical form and structure of a Crown jelly.

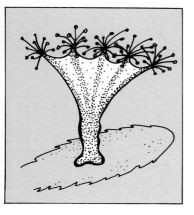

Typical form and structure of a Sessile sea jelly.

Nausithoe sp.

Range: Shallow water areas of the tropical Indo-Pacific; related species also occur in other areas.

Shape and height: The polyps reach a height of 1 to 2 cm, and live individually, but in colonies. Newly strobilated larvae (ephyrae) have a diameter of about 2 mm. The size of adult medusae is unknown, but will probably not exceed 2-3 cm in diameter.

Food: The polyps contain zooxanthellae, which probably provide most of the nutrients needed; in addition, plankton is taken; in the aquarium *Artemia* are eagerly accepted. The medusae probably feed on small planktonic organisms.

Description: The polyps, which live in a horny tube, have a uniform brown colour, which is due to the zooxanthellae. The beautifully marked ephyrae larvae also contain zooxanthellae; they swim rather quickly and with a pulsating movement.

Aquarium maintenance

– **General conditions:** The polyps are commonly imported on live rock, but are mostly mistaken for hydroids. In some aquaria, the polyps survive for quite a long time, yet they seem to be quite delicate.

– **Lighting:** Polyps and ephyrae larvae need high light intensity.

– **Water circulation:** Moderate.

– **Reproduction:** The polyps may produce new polyps asexually. Strobilation may also take place in aquaria - often following water changes. The ephyrae larvae, however, seem to die within a few days. Therefore, fully grown medusae are unknown in aquaria. If no special precautions are taken, most ephyrae are rapidly sucked into the filters.

GA: +/- ; TO : 0; SE: -

Photos
Above: Small polyp colony in an aquarium.
Below: Polyp during the strobilation.
Left: Newly strobilated ephyra.

Photos: R. Brons

centre to the bell margin. The edges of the mouth are drawn out into four long, frill-like arms or lobes.

Most of the Semaeostomae are about 5 to 50 cm in diameter, yet the record specimens spotted were more than 1 m in diameter and had tentacles of more than 30 m in length. Many species feed on fish and other animals that they seize with their tentacles. Some also eat small planktonic organisms that are trapped in mucus on the upper part of the bell and are transported to the mouth with the help of tiny cilia.

The practically transparent Moon jelly, *Aurelia aurita*, is an extremely widespread species and is found in oceans all over the world, including coral reefs. The Moon jellies have separate sexes. Their gonads, which have the shape of a four-leaved clover, can be seen inside the body. The eggs are brooded by the female in clefts on the corners of its four mouth lobes, until planula larvae can be released.

From the planula larva, a polyp develops, as can be seen on page 37. This scyphopolyp, which may be up to 1 cm long, feeds mainly on small crustaceans. During strobilation (also sometimes referred to as strobilization), every polyp produces a number of tiny ephyrae larvae with a diameter of about 3 mm. Within two to three months, the ephyrae have grown into medusae, measuring some 5 cm in diameter.

Having been commonly kept as a laboratory animal, the Moon jelly is one of the jellyfish about which we have the most knowledge regarding captive care (more about this subject can be found in Brons, 1992). Most of the experiments described were performed with the coldwater variant, however, which needs lower temperatures (15 °C or less). Although it is probable that tropical forms may also be kept in captivity, they would need special aquaria, like all animals that lead a pelagic life.

A number of Semaeostomae, e.g. from the genera *Aurelia*,

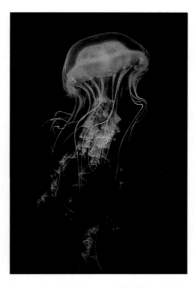

A wonderful Banner jellyfish of the genus *Chrysaora* in an aquarium.
Photo: R. Brons

***Pelagia noctiluca* is a Banner jelly which is widely distributed in subtropical and tropical seas. This picture was taken near the Canary Islands. Photo: E. Svensen**

Chrysaora, *Cyanea*, *Pelagia* and *Sanderia* may be seen by diving aquarists in tropical seas. There is, however, little or no information at all about how they fare in aquaria. It would also be difficult to import them as aquarium animals, unless this is done while they are at the polypoid stage. The medusae of most jellyfish are practically impossible to transport and/or acclimatize. All successful introductions to aquaria have been made via polyps, even today

(Lange & Kaiser, 1994; Zahn, 1980).

Rhizostomae
Rootmouth jellyfish

Most of the Rhizostomae have medusae with very solid bells and an especially dense mesogloea. The average size is some 20-30 cm in diameter, but a few species may approach 1 metre across. There are no tentacles on the margin. However, the four mouth lobes around the mouth divide to form eight fleshy, branched, root-like appendages. These appendages usually function like tentacles, as they have nematocysts and are used for food capture. Most of the Rhizostomae do not have a central mouth opening. The food, primarily plankton, is sucked in through many small openings into the deep folds of the mouth arms. From these "secondary mouths" the food passes through a complicated system of canals and is finally transported into the coelenteron.

The Rhizostomae are most commonly found in the shallow waters of tropical seas. A few species, however, also live in the temperate zones. Many are among the most beautiful jellyfish, and several are occasionally kept in captivity, but mainly by public aquaria.

The more robust build of the Rootmouth jellies may be the reason why they are kept more successfully in aquaria than other jellyfish. Nevertheless, one should realize that no jellyfish leading a pelagic life is easy to keep in aquaria. They all require a special aquarium with a continuous, weak water circulation. Brons (1982) recommends an undergravel filtration system with a reversed flow of water to support the floating movement of the medusae. At the same time, a normal bottom layer (gravel) may best be omitted, in order to avoid damage to the medusae upon contact with the bottom. Most jellyfish need frequent and ample feedings with *Artemia* and/or other planktonic organisms or substitutes.

Cassiopea spp. Upside-down jellies or Mangrove jellies (called *Cassiopeia* spp. by several authors).

Range: The genus is widely distributed in the Caribbean and the Indo-Pacific. Large numbers of medusae are often observed in mangrove areas or in other soft-bottom habitats.

Shape and height: The polyps grow to about 1 cm and are, thus, rather small. They live individually, but in colonies. The maximum size of medusae has been reported to be 10-15 cm in diameter for *C. andromeda*, and up to 30 cm for most other species.

Food: The polyps need small plankton. In the aquarium, they accept *Brachionus* (rotifers) and, at larger size, nauplii of *Artemia*. The polyps, at least of some species, also contain zooxanthellae, but rarely in sufficient quantities to survive on their translocated products alone. The medusae obtain most of the necessary nutrients from the products of their zooxanthellae.

Description: The polyps are all identical: cup-like, whitish with very long tentacles and attached to a long stalk. They live in shadow on the underside of rocks and mangrove roots. The medusae, which lie upside down on the sea floor, often exhibit very beautiful colours. Several species have been described, the most frequent reports being about *C. andromeda* from the Indo-Pacific and *C. frondosa* and *C. xamachana* from the Caribbean. The distinguishing features of the various species are very uncertain, however, so identification is difficult, especially when dealing with juvenile specimens.

Aquarium maintenance

– **General conditions:** Polyps are occasionally imported on live rock. Young medusae, especially from the Caribbean, can often be found in the aquarium trade. They are probably the most robust jellyfish. Even relatively large medusae stand a chance of surviving transport and acclimatization. Wide sandy areas in the aquarium are of vital importance for these species (see also vol. 1, pages 138-144).

– **Lighting:** Medusae demand high light intensity in order to obtain sufficient energy from the zooxanthellae.

– **Water circulation:** Moderate.

Photos

Top: Young medusa in an aquarium.

Middle: Medusae dorsally attached to the glass of an aquarium at the Berlin Zoo Aquarium, Germany.

Bottom: A group of medusae, possibly *C. xamachana*, in Florida.   Photo: Julian Sprung

– Reproduction: Asexual budding of the polyps; discharge of ephyrae and sexual reproduction by medusae have been observed several times in aquaria and under laboratory conditions, both in *C. andromeda* and *C. xamachana* (Dr. J. Gerhard, pers. com.). The polyps also propagate asexually by producing planula larvae and this accounts for most of the reproductive success achieved in aquaria. If the polyps are well fed and have sufficient zooxanthellae, they will produce young medusae by monodisc strobilation (where one polyp produces a single medusa). Nevertheless, successful reproduction, where the medusae spawn sexually, will, most likely, only be possible in a special aquarium.

From Sweden, we know a case of long-term cultivation and reproduction of *C. andromeda* (identification courtesy of Dr. T. Heeger and Dr. G. Jarms) in a hobbyist aquarium owned by Sven Eriksson, Stockholm: The aquarium is high and narrow (L:200 cm, H:70 cm, W:35 cm) containing 490 litres of water. It is illuminated with 4 x 18 W light tubes and 2 x 36 W light tubes, a mixture of Sylvania Grolux and Philips TLD84 daylight tubes. The light period is about 12 h/day. The decoration consists of 40 kg of lava rocks and a small amount (about 2 kg) of live rock. Each second month, a 60litre water change is carried out. Average temperature is 23.5 °C, pH = 8.2 and density = 1.0215. The aquarium contains a lot of *Caulerpa sertularoides* and a variety of small fish, such as clownfishes, damsels and *Pseudochromis paccagnellae*. *Cassiopea andromeda* was introduced as polyps, most probably with live rock that was obtained from another aquarium 2 years ago. A few polyps appeared from the rocks after a while and spread (by producing asexual planula larvae) to settle all over the decorations. It seems that a heavy feeding with *Artemia* (originally intended for the fishes) led to the polyps starting to propagate. The first medusae were produced after 10 months. The medusae grew from 2.5 mm in diameter to 30 mm in three months. The medusae typically place themselves upside-down against the bottom or against the front and sides of the aquarium. The maximum number of polyps counted has been, at least, a thousand specimens (Sven Eriksson, Carl-Eric Helén and Christian Krog-Jensen, pers. com.).

GA: +/- ; TO: + ; SE: +/-

Photos

Top: Partial overview of the "*Cassiopea*-aquarium" belonging to Mr. Sven Eriksson, Stockholm.
Photo from March 1997: C. Helén.
Middle: A swimming 2cm diameter medusa of *C. andromeda* raised in an aquarium by Mr. Eriksson.
Bottom: Close up of a fully expanded (about 5 mm long) polyp of *C. andromeda* that has settled on a piece of lava rock.

Phyllorhita punctata from the Indo-Pacific is a typical representative of the pelagic Rootmouth jellyfish. Photo: T. Kelly

Among those pelagic Rhizostomae known to have been successfully kept in aquaria are the Indo-Pacific species *Mastigias papua* and *Phyllorhiza punctata*, as well as the Mediterranean *Cotylorhiza tuberculata*, *Mastigias roseus* and *Rhizostoma pulmo*.

In addition to the pelagic jellyfish, the order Rhizostomae also includes a genus of most fascinating sessile species that have been imported for aquarium purposes. They are the Upside-down or Mangrove jellies of the genus *Cassiopea*, which have really spectacular medusae. Their anatomy is, basically, the same as in the other Rootmouth jellies, yet the mouth arms branch into thousands of lacy lappets containing zooxanthellae. Upside-down jellies are able to swim in the normal way (i.e. with their mouth downwards), but they prefer to rest upside down on the sea floor. While they are in this position, they expose their zooxanthellae most effectively to the sunlight to enhance the process of photosynthesis. In areas with soft sediment, hundreds of individuals of these species may cover the bottom.

This sedentary way of life also makes *Cassiopea* spp. more suitable than pelagic species for keeping in aquaria. Thus, it is not surprising that a number of reports exist on their maintenance in captivity. These species have been bred in public aquaria, e.g. the Löbbecke Museum and Aquazoo, Düsseldorf, and the Berlin Zoo-Aquarium, for several generations (LANGE & KAISER, 1992; ZAHN, 1990). If special places are provided for them when an aquarium is decorated, *Cassiopea* spp. will, under certain conditions, also be suitable for a coral reef aquarium.

Box jellyfish
Class Cubozoa

Among the cubozoans, which are all more or less cube-shaped, we find the marine animals which are most dangerous to human beings. There are 72 certifiable reports of fatal injuries since 1884 caused by the Indo-Pacific sea wasp, *Chironex fleckeri*. The real number is probably even higher. Two deaths per year are reported, on average, in Australia alone. A closer analysis of the accidents shows that, in one third of the cases, the injured persons died within the first three minutes of having been stung (ANON., 1985).

Adult sea wasps reach a diameter of up to 20 cm and have up to 60 ribbon-like tentacles. The tentacles may be retracted until they are less than 10 cm long. They may attain lengths of about 3 m, however, when they are completely extended. There are estimates that the tentacles of an adult specimen may contain up to 5 billion (5,000,000,000) nematocysts. Their venom is a mixture of proteins with a high molecular weight and has the same effects as a neurotoxin, paralyzing the respiration of the victim. Thus, immediate expired air resuscitation (artificial respiration) following an accident, could prove life-saving. In addition, the toxin may cause skin lesions and destroy the erythrocytes (red blood cells), which may, in turn, cause acute inflammation.

Most other box jellies are less venomous, but direct contact with them may still result in acute pain or, even, critical injuries. Cubozoans can swim quite rapidly, some at a rate of about 6 m per minute, and may take a careless swimmer by surprise. As many species swim together in groups, it is possible for one person to be stung by several of these jellyfish at the same time.

There are several species known in tropical and subtropical oceans, some of which have been kept by public aquaria. For the amateur aquarist, these animals are, clearly, not a choice!

Pictures to the right: In the Jellyfish Lake, Palau, jellyfish (most probably *Mastigas* sp.) can be found in large numbers. The lake is crowded with millions of jellyfish which live in symbiosis with zooxanthellae. During the day they stay near the surface to provide the zooxanthellae with light energy for photosynthesis. At night they sink to the bottom, where they absorb nitrate and phosphate to "feed" the algae.

Photos: Dr. D. Brockmann

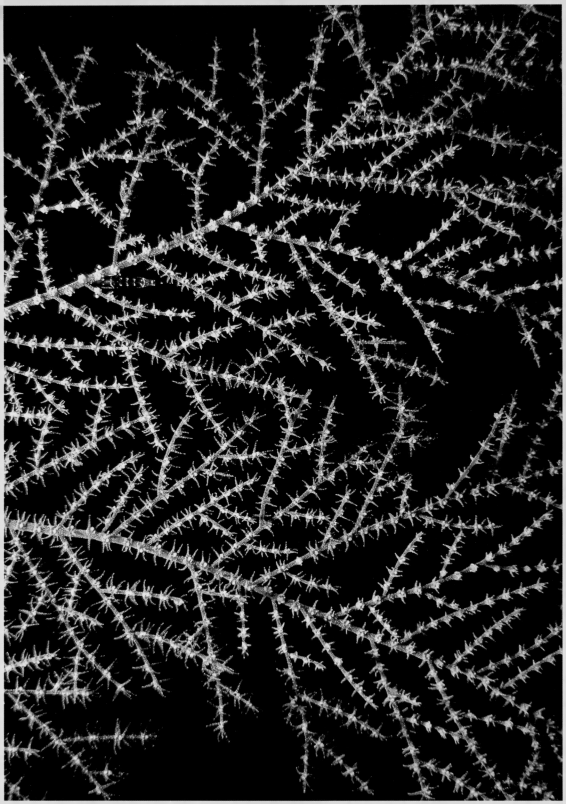

Chapter 6

Black Corals and Tube Anemones

The black corals of the order Antipatharia and the tube anemones of the order Ceriantharia constitute the subclass Cerianthipatharia. VAN BENEDEN (1898) united the two orders without, however, mentioning the status of the taxon. Today this view is by no means generally accepted. Recent research by SCHMIDT (1972, 1974) based on morphology and cnidom/nematocyst structure, and by SCHMIDT & ZISSLER (1979), based on the structure of spermatozoa, suggest that the two

Above: Tube anemones are not really suited for a coral reef aquarium. It is better to keep them in their own aquarium with a thick layer of sand on the bottom. Tube anemones usually catch planktonic food, but sometimes they also ingest small fish, as can be seen in this picture. We are not sure if the tube anemones are able to catch small fish in the nature though.   Photo: J. Carlén

To the left: Black corals, here *Antipathes* sp. from the Caribbean with a small shrimp with which it lives in a symbiotic relationship.   Photo: J. Cairns-Michael

groups are perhaps the least related among all non-octocoralloid Anthozoa (DEN HARTOG, pers. com.). The taxonomy of Cerianthipatharia might therefore very well be subject to change in the future.

There are relatively few species in this subclass of sessile cnidarians. They live in colonies or solitary. For aquarists the tube anemones are the best known animals among the Ceriantipatharia. The rare and much sought-after black corals of the genus *Antipathes* also belong to this subclass.

Black corals
Order Antipatharia

Members of the order Antipatharia are found in all seas from immediately below the low tide mark down to several thousand metres. The majority of these some 150 species live in tropical seas at depths of more than 100 m, only a few species are found in more shallow waters of less than 20 m depth. These species usually grow in places where the intensity of light is low, e.g. in caves or under rock overhangs.

The skeletons of some of the largest and most robust of the species of black corals - colonies of *Antipathes grandis* - often grow to a height of more than 2 m. These were much sought after for a long time because of their magnificent ebony colour and were used in the creation of jewelry. The earliest utilisation of black corals for these purposes, which dates back several thousand years, is reported from the area of the Red Sea (PAX, 1940). The exploitation of these populations was so extreme in many places that they were in danger of becoming (locally) extinct. That is the reason why black corals are under protection in many countries today.

At first glance black corals and gorgonians seem to have much in

The wire coral *Cirrhipathes spiralis*, here in a reef off the Maldives grows in a whiplike shape. The end of the whip is wound up in spirals. It is not suited for a coral reef aquarium, as it can grow to a length of several metres.

common. If we have a closer look at the colonies, however, considerable morphological differences are evident. In black corals there is a brown or black skeleton around the coenenchyme. It consists of a very hard substance that contains proteins, and nearly always bears small spines. Unlike the gorgonians (and most other Octocorallia) the Antipatharia always lack sklerites. The polyps, which have six simple tentacles, cannot be pulled back completely into the coenenchyme. They have a remarkable shape with the mouth somewhat elevated, similar to the shape that we also find in anemones. As with other colony-forming cnidarians the polyps are connected internally. The indivi-

dual polyps have weak muscles and react only slowly when they are touched. Some colonies grow in bushlike shapes, others in straight or spiral branches of a considerable length.

Research on the systematics of the order Antipatharia is incomplete. The two rather common genera *Cirrhipathes* and *Antipathes* belong to the family Anthipathidae.

The species of the genus *Cirrhipathes* are usually referred to as wire corals. Among them is *Cirrhipathes spiralis*, a species with a most peculiar shape (see photo above). *C. spiralis* develops spirally from a single straight branch which may be several metres long. Off the Maldives we found *C.*

Cirrhipathes anguina

Range: Indo-Pacific.
Height: 1 m and more.
Food: Plankton; also accepts planktonic substitute food in the aquarium.
Description: Usually brownish. Mostly grows as a single, spiralling branch on outer reef slopes at depths of more than 5 m. Difficult to identify because several species in the genus look very similar, and species of *Cirrhipathes* are in general difficult to identify even for specialists.
Aquarium maintenance:
– **General conditions:** Little is known about the maintenance of this species in aquaria. According to BROCKMANN (1985c) *Cirrhipathes anguina* is not difficult to keep, if the right type of food, *Artemia* and other small live or frozen plankton, is available.
– **Lighting:** According to BROCKMANN (1985c) not important, as specimens in full light showed the same growth as those in the shadow.
– **Water circulation:** Medium to strong.
– **Reproduction:** Unknown.
GA: +/-; TO: 0; SE: +/-

Photos
Above: Aquarium picture: Dr. D. Brockmann
Below: Close-up of a branch: Underwaterphoto taken off the Maldives.

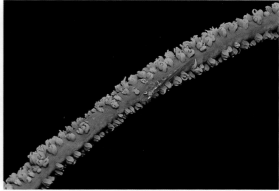

These are macrophotos of the branches of two *Antipathes* spp. The special form of the polyps shows very clearly. Often small fish, like the little goby of the genus *Bryaninops* on the picture to the right, live in association with black corals.
Photos: Scott W. Michael

spiralis only at depths greater than 20 m. This wire coral does not grow in groups, but single individuals are found on the reef everywhere where there are strong currents.

Cirrhipathes spp. generally prefer strong currents and their polyps do not open if the current is too weak. The light intensity, however, does not influence the activity of the polyps. We found *Cirrhipathes* spp. quite regularly on most reefs of the Maldives, but as a rule at depths of more than 7 m.

The species in the genus *Antipathes* grow in rather large, bush-shaped colonies. They include the genuine black corals. We usually find them at depths of more than 20 m (OAKLEY, 1988). They grow very slowly as a rule. *A. dichotoma* is a very common species both in the Red Sea and the Indian Ocean.

Not very much is known about Antipatharia kept in aquaria: BROCKMANN (1985c) describes his experiences with *Cirrhipathes anguina* from the Maldives. One of his observations was that they must be fed small food particles as the polyps are small and the food is caught particularly in the area of the coenenchyme.

Tube anemones
Order Cerantharia

Tube anemones are well known among marine aquarists. In the natural environment tube anemones do not live among reef-building corals, however. They occur most often at depths of 1 to 50 m on the muddy or sandy bottoms of lagoons or between coral structures, but there are also species present in the abyssal seas. According to DEN HARTOG (1977) the group is known by only a few dozen species, belonging to 3 families and 8 genera (see systematic overview, page 101). However, as about twice as many larvae forms than adults are known, but discovery of many more adult species is likely to happen in the future. In general a systematic revision of Ceriantharia is badly needed.

Tube anemones build a tube in the muddy ground, which they line with the slime they secrete. The tube consists mainly of a network of discharged ptychocysts, a special type of atrichous nematocysts (MARISCAL et al., 1977). Other organisms, particularly horsehoe worms, phylum Phoronida (especially the cosmopolitan *Phoronis australis*), are frequently

The black corals of the genus *Antipathes* are not black at all when alive. It is their skeleton that is black. The photo shows a colony off the Maldives at a depth of 15 m.
Photo: E. Svensen

found embedded in the tube walls, while bristleworms may live on the surface of the tube. In these natural surroundings such a tube may be as long as one metre, although the animal itself is shorter. The tubes which are imported for aquaristic purposes do not grow longer than 20 or 30 cm, however. The colours of tube anemones differ considerably, from white through yellow to orange. Now and then specimens with incredibly green or violet colours are imported.

There are two types of tentacles; long marginal tentacles which may be as long as 30 cm, yet not any thicker than a few millimetres, and short mouth tentacles (labial tentacles). The marginal tentacles are used to catch small plankton and not larger food particles, as is often supposed.

The ectoderm of the tentacles contains large numbers of nematocysts which contain a strong nettling poison. This is the reason why most tube anemones should not be kept together with other cnidarians, but should be given a special aquarium. Tube anemones frequently lose their beautiful marginal tentacles in aquaria. Although it is known that tentacles can be naturally reduced in Cnidaria, as we have seen in true anemones, we think that in aquaria the reason is most often because they are fed too much coarse food or because the food is placed in the middle of the mouth opening. Tube anemones should be fed live food such as *Artemia*, which should be suspended in the water. This method is an imita-

Tube anemones are well known to marine aquarists. They live in tubes that they build themselves. Various "lodgers" may reside in these tubes as well, like Phoronids and Polychaets.   Photo: T. Luther

tion of their natural way of feeding add it offers them good living conditions. We should also take care not to overfeed them.

As an alternative to reef tanks containing a variety of corals we could imagine a special aquarium for tube anemones with a thicker layer of gravel and an almost continuous, drop by drop feeding with live plankton. Such a tank housing a few tube anemones, their associated animals and a few fishes would certainly be a very nice scenic aquarium.

Cerianthus orientalis is often imported from the region of the Indo-Pacific. During our nightdives off the Maldives we saw several specimens of the species *Pachycerianthus* spp. on sandy ground. During the day these animals were completely hidden in their tubes dug in the bottom. *Pachycerianthus* is also well known from the Red Sea and is widespread in the rest of the Indo-Pacific.

Systematic overview of Ceriantharia
(after DEN HARTOG, 1977)

Order **Ceriantharia**
    Family **Cerianthidae**
        Cerianthus, Pachycerianthus,
        Ceriantheopsis, Ceriantheomorphe
    Family **Arachnactidae**
        Arachnanthus, Isarachnanthus
    Family **Botrucnidiferidae**
        Boutrucnidifer, Botruanthus

Cerianthidae species
Tube anemones

Range: Common in all seas.
Height: In most species the animal itself reaches 20 to 40 cm, but the tubes can be as long as up to one metre.
Food: Plankton; also accepts planktonic substitute food in the aquarium.
Description: The Tube anemones dig into the bottom and live in tubes that are secreted from the animals themselves. The tubes are constructed mainly from the long filaments of special atrichous nematocysts (called ptychocysts) which are massively secreted by the body ectoderm, forming dense and very tough mats. The tubes are also incrusted with foreign particles and mud (MARISCAL et al., 1977; DEN HARTOG, 1977). The tentacles are extremely long and sticky. Various species and genera are imported: e.g. *Anthoactis* spp., *Arachnanthus* spp., *Cerianthus* spp., *Ceriantheopsis* spp., *Isarachnanthus* spp. and *Pachycerianthus* spp. These taxa are difficult to identify, and identification is in general a matter for specialists.
Aquarium maintenance:
– **General conditions:** They need a thick layer of bottom ground or PVC tubes that are accepted as a substitute. Tube anemones are best kept in a large aquarium on their own. If kept with other Cnidaria, like soft and stony corals, they will normally burn these with their long, sweeping tentacles.
– **Lighting:** Medium to weak.
– **Water circulation:** Medium.
– **Reproduction:** Unknown under aquarium conditions.
GA: +/-; TO: -; SE: +/-

Photos
All pictures were taken in an aquarium.

This nocturnal tube anemone, possibly *Pachycerianthus mana*, is found in the tropical areas of the Indo-Pacific. Divers can see them along the coast and in fields of seagrass, as in the picture above (photo: E. Svensen) on a reef flat in the Red Sea. We found the *Arachnanthus* sp. or possibly *Isarachnanthus* sp., in the picture below at the bottom of a cave at the outward side of a reef off the Maldives.

Chapter 7

Introduction to the Octocorals

By Dr. P. Alderslade

Museum and Art Gallery of the Northern Territory, Darwin, Australia

A visitor to a tropical coral reef who ventures underwater to examine the natural history will, in all probability, not need to swim very far before coming across some octocorals. These animals form a major portion of the warm water reef and shoal-bottom fauna in many parts of the world, occasionally dominating the underwater scene to the virtual exclusion of most other large sedentary organisms. Yet, most casual observers who recognise coral and may be familiar with such varietal terminology as "brain coral" and "staghorn coral" will, in the majority of cases, have no idea as to the identity of the green and brown fleshy masses, or the colourful sea fans, over which they swim. This may appear somewhat startling when you consider that octocorals are found throughout the seas of the world from pole to pole, with some species growing as large as small trees, and others thickly encrust several square metres of substrate and weighing tens of kilograms.

They occur from the intertidal zone to the depths of the abyss. Their common occurrence is perhaps highlighted by a photograph taken inside the wreck of the Titanic. It shows a sea fan attached to a light fitting above the grand staircase, over 4 kilometres down. Unfortunately, the abundance and diversity of the fauna is in stark contrast to the

The octocorals are a highly varied group. They all have an 8-fold symmetry in common. Their anatomy and systematics is very complicated. The picture on this page shows a Clove polyp. The pictures on the left page show a representative of the soft-corals genus *Sarcophyton* (above left), a gorgonian *Nicella* (above right), a large fan-shaped colony from the family Melithaeidae (below left), and (this time with symbiotic algae), *Briareum asbestinum* (below right). Photos: J. Cairns-Michael (the picture above right, left page) and S. W. Michael

relatively small amount of information available on its constituents. Even now with the increased attention that this group is being given as a source of naturally occurring biologically active compounds with potentials in medicine and industry, there are only a handful of taxonomists scattered throughout the globe; and even less is known about the habits of the octocorals than about their identities.

Octocorals are marine cnidarians. They are sedentary in habit, preferring a hard substrate but also occurring on soft bottoms (one order exclusively). Virtually all octocorals are colonial animals made up of modular units called polyps, which, by iterative vegetative clonal growth, form structures of numerous organically united individuals. They fall into three major groups. The first combines the overlapping Stolonifera, Telestacea and Alcyonacea with the Gorgonacea, the soft corals with the gorgonians, (whose taxonomic boundaries have historically been controversial) under the one order Alcyonacea. Major discontinuity's within the octocorals can no longer be justified as more and more taxa are re-evaluated or discovered. For more than a decade now there has been general acceptance that the currently recognised genera and families form a more or less uninterrupted series from the most primitive of soft corals through to the most complex of the gorgonians. The other major categories are the Helioporacea and the Pennatulacea.

The acceptance of the inclusion of the old order Gorgonacea under the Alcyonacea has had an effect on casual terminology. Reference to the members of the order Pennatulacea as "sea pens", and of the order Helioporacea as "blue coral", is unaffected (even though the latter has become dibasic of recent times, with only the original species, *Heliopora coerulea*, being blue). In the past, members of the order Alcyonacea have been known as the soft corals, those of the order Gorgo-

nacea as the gorgonians (also as sea fans and sea whips), and those of the orders Stolonifera and Telestacea have either been referred to using scientific names or loosely labelled as soft corals. Acknowledging the unification of the four groups under one order, is to concede that present knowledge does not permit the drawing of a line between soft corals and gorgonians, ie. they cannot be exclusively defined. A somewhat similar argument holds as to the scientific terminology for axial form. On structural grounds, the octocorals without an axis overlap those with a scleraxonian axis (separable skeletal elements) which overlap those with a holaxonian axis (proteinaceous, sometimes with calcification). All of these terms are firmly entrenched in both the taxonomic history of the group and, particularly soft coral and gorgonian, in casual descriptive terminology. As taxonomic techniques become refined and new animals discovered, this system of classification will in all probability become modified. However, even if the single order status of these animals remains unchanged, it seems likely that these labels will stay as irreplaceable terms of convenience. A "typical" soft coral, such as *Sarcophyton*, and a "typical" gorgonian, such as *Rumphella*, cannot be confused. Nor can a "typical" scleraxonian octocoral and a "typical" holaxonian octocoral. But intermediates exist and more will be found. Perhaps, also, as scleractinians have become known as hard corals, alcyonaceans may become known as scleritic corals.

In September, 1981, the First International Workshop on Octocorals was held at the Australian Institute of Marine Sciences in Townsville. One task addressed by the workshop was a critical revision of the confused terminology used in the descriptive literature. The final outcome was a published trilingual glossary of suggested terms (BAYER et al., 1983). The document is a must for students requiring further reading,

despite the inevitability that some definitions will be modified with time, and others will be added.

Members of the subclass Octocorallia can be clearly differentiated from the remainder of the Anthozoa by the structure of their polyps. It is the ability of these polyps to undergo vegetative reproduction that has allowed them to develop a considerable variety of complex structures. The basic octocoral anatomy was briefly documented as far back as the middle of the 18th century. A great controversy arose at that time over the nature of the so called "zoophytes" which LINNEAUS argued were part plant and part animal. Descriptions and figures of the polyps of the cold water soft coral, *Alcyonium digitatum,* were made by JUSSIEU in 1742. A thorough account of this animal's anatomy, however, did not eventuate until the work of HICKSON in 1895. Morphological and anatomical descriptions of taxa are scattered throughout the literature. Some treat isolated taxa while others concern related groups. In recent decades the advent of the electron-microscope has seen publications covering a number of ultrastructure studies of several species of octocoral. However, in this authors opinion, by far the best general accounts of octocoral structure, and its relationships to colonial development and organisation, are those of BAYER (1956, 1961, 1973) and GRASSHOFF (1981).

Although much of the following information can generally be applied to all three octocoral groups, the material primarily concerns the alcyonaceans. The Pennatulacea and the Helioporacea are referred to for purposes of comparison.

Morphology and anatomy

Octocorals are exclusively polypoid radiobilateral animals. The main structural modular unit is an

autozooid polyp, commonly just termed **polyp** if no modified polyps are also present. An autozooid has a mouth invaginated to form a tubular **pharynx** which is lined with glandular epithelium and extends down into the **gastrovascular cavity**. The gastrovascular cavity is partitioned by eight radially arranged, thin, non-calcareous **septa** (or mesenteries), and extends upwards between the septa into eight hollow and pinnately branched tentacles arranged in a circle around the mouth. It is this invariable presence of eight tentacles that give the group their name "octocorals".

All orders have modular polyp units as described above. The Pennatulacea and the Alcyonacea have taxa where a modified form of this polyp occurs together with the autozooids. These units, called **siphonozooids**, are smaller than autozooids, the tentacles are absent or very rudimentary (one small tentacle may remain in the Pennatulacea) and the septa are markedly reduced. In the Pennatulacea a specially modified primary or axial polyp called an **oozooid** is also present. As well as autozooids and siphonozooids, some sea pens also possess **mesozooids** which are specialised as exhalant polyps in contrast to the inhalant siphonozooids.

The upper portion of an expanded autozooid is called the **anthocodia** (pl. anthocodiae). In most groups this portion of the polyp is capable of being retracted within the general colonial mass, called the **coenenchyme**, or into a stiffened, elevated coenenchymal rim called the **calyx** which remains hillock-like on the surface. In contraction, polyp anthocodiae shorten and the tentacles fold over the oral disc and often into the mouth. In retraction this is accompanied by introversion of the contracted anthocodia into the gastric cavity. The canal-like extension of the gastric cavity below the surface of the coenenchyme is called the **anthostele**. The coenenchyme is a thick gelatinous **mesogloea**

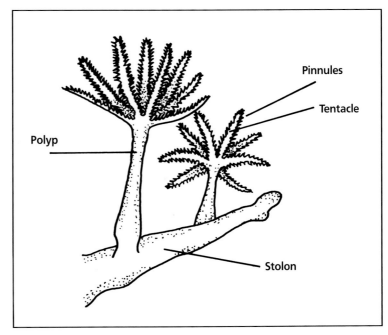

Typical octocoral polyp.

Modified from sketches by M. GAWEL

which may contain skeletal elements.

In their most simple form octocorals of the genus *Taiaroa* are solitary autozooids. The simplest colonial forms consist of basal ribbon-like stolons from which isolated polyps arise erect and unbranched, as in some species of *Clavularia*, or branched, as in *Telestula*. The walls of the polyps are commonly stiffened by minute skeletal elements. More commonly, the lower portions of the polyps are united in thick coenenchyme, permitting considerable architectural diversity.

The skeletal elements of octocorals are called **sclerites**. They are polycrystalline aggregates of calcite in an organic matrix. In soft corals and gorgonians they can be about 0.02-10 mm in length, and their shape varies enormously. Although first figured by ELLIS (1755) their real value in systematics was only recognised and firmly established in the literature by KALLIKER (1864). But decades latter taxonomists were still describing new taxa with little or no reference to the sclerites, and occasionally it still occurs today.

A number of octocorals, besides having free sclerites in the coenenchyme, have axial structures which are produced basically in either of two ways. In species previously referred to the suborder Scleraxonia, sclerites are consolidated to various degrees by **gorgonin** and/or calcareous deposits forming a **medulla**. Gorgonin is a proteinaceous material similar to horn and black coral. In other taxa, previously grouped in the suborder Holaxonia, the axis consists of a horny central rod (gorgonin) which is often calcified and sometimes alternates with calcareous sections. The first process produces an essentially internal structure (it is a product of the coenenchymal cells) often penetrated extensively by thin canals called **solenia**. The second method produces an analogous but not homologous structure which is layed down external to the coenenchyme and is never penetrated by solenia. One family, the Keroiididae, contains species with an axis showing characteristics of both of the above forms. They have a proteinaceous holaxonian medulla in the centre sur-

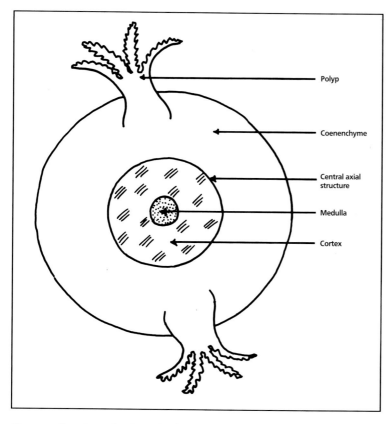

Cross-section through a branch of an octocorallia.

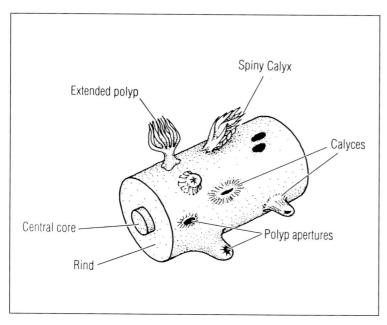

Details of the anatomy of a Holaxonian branch. After HUMANN (1993)

rounded by a layer of sclerites in a gorgonin matrix of scleraxonian style.

All octocorals, other than the solitary forms and the sea pens, increase in size asexually by budding from the system of solenial canals. The sea pens bud directly from the oozooid wall. Vegetative reproduction in stolonate or membranous forms produces isolated polyps of similar height. Colonies so produced are of a somewhat similar architecture although they have different arrangements and forms of sclerites. Most taxa previously referred to the order Stolonifera, such as *Clavularia* are of this form. Increasing complexity is seen in other species of *Clavularia* where stolonic structures also grow outwardly from the body wall of the polyps, linking some polyps and allowing other polyps to originate at different heights within the colony. In *Tubipora*, the organ pipe coral, a similar arrangement occurs, but the secondary stolons are platform-like and the sclerites within both polyp walls and stolons fuse together producing large, hard colonial masses.

In the subfamily Telestinae we see another level of complexity in which the body walls of the polyps are thicker and daughter polyps arise from the primary polyps which themselves arise from branching basal stolons. Quite bushy colonies can result from repeated branching, in a pinnate or sympodial manner, which are sometimes given extra rigidity by the occasional fusing of clumps of sclerites, for example *Carijoa*.

In the Alcyoniidae, Nephtheidae, and related families the coenenchyme of the polyp walls has become confluent. New polyps bud off the superficial portion of the network of solenial canals between older polyps and become embedded as the colony grows. Many genera of the Alcyoniidae, such as *Sinularia* and *Lobophytum*, have species that have large, lobed colonial forms with considerable amounts of scleritic coenenchyme. In the Nephtheidae the coenenchyme between

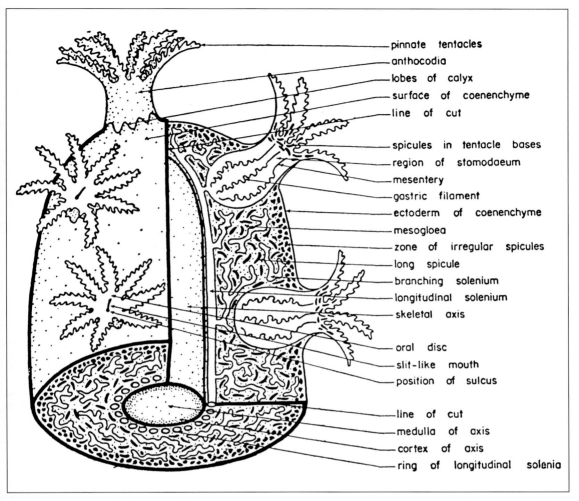

pinnate tentacles
anthocodia
lobes of calyx
surface of coenenchyme
line of cut

spicules in tentacle bases
region of stomodaeum
mesentery
gastric filament
ectoderm of coenenchyme
mesogloea
zone of irregular spicules
long spicule
branching solenium
longitudinal solenium
skeletal axis

oral disc
slit-like mouth
position of sulcus

line of cut
medulla of axis
cortex of axis
ring of longitudinal solenia

A detailed structure of a horny coral.   After BULLOUGH (1981)

polyps is extremely thin however, and the gastric canals are closely adjoined. These colonies are arborescent, often tall, and the anthocodiae are grouped at the ends of branches. The Paralcyoniidae also has taxa with lobed to arborescent upper portions, but the colonies are able to completely retract this region into the lower stalk which has become modified as a firm cup, often rigidly reinforced with large sclerites.

In the Xeniidae, most genera have species that are extremely fleshy with relatively little sclerite mass. The tentacles commonly have more than one row of pinnules each side and the sclerites, when present, are minute flatte-

ned ovate rods and disks.

In the Nidaliid genus *Siphonogorgia*, the ratio of the volume of sclerites to that of mesogloea is extremely high in contrast to the xeniids, and rigid, brittle arborescent colonies with narrow stems and branches are produced. In *Siphonogorgia* we see the beginnings of differentiation of zones within the coenenchyme. The gastric canals of the longer zooids are grouped closely together in the very centre of the stem and branches with extremely little mesogloeal separation. In this mesogloea is found a sclerite of a different style, and often a different colour, from those occupying the bulk of the surrounding coenen-

chyme. There is, however, no consolidation, partial or otherwise, calcareous or horny, forming an axis.

Differentiation towards a central axial structure becomes more evident in the Briareidae and the Anthothelidae, and increasingly so in the Subergorgiidae. The coenenchyme becomes divided into an inner medulla zone and an outer cortex, with the gastric canals in some genera chiefly confined to the cortex and in others permeating the medulla. Sometimes the sclerites of the two zones are very similar whilst in other genera the regions are easily distinguished. Some sclerites of the medulla have demonstrable horny sheaths, but they remain quite separable. In some taxa, the medulla is separated from the cortex by a ring of boundary canals. This is an extensive network formed from the narrow extensions of the short gastrovascular cavities of the polyps. In the Subergorgiidae the medulla becomes quite consolidated with considerable amounts of gorgonin forming a matrix in which are embedded branched sclerites that commonly anastomose.

The precious coral *Corallium* has an extremely rigid axis. No gorgonin is present, however, and the sclerites are immovably fused by interstitial calcareous material. A similar axial structure is seen in the Melithaeidae and Parisididae where solid scleritic internodes alternate with soft nodes of a compact mixture of sclerites and gorgonin.

In other major families, such as the Plexauridae and the Gorgoniidae, the axis consists of a cylinder of either gorgonin alone, gorgonin permeated with non-scleritic calcareous deposits or, in the Isididae, gorgonin alternating with solid non-scleritic calcareous joints. This type of axis has a narrow medullary region, preferably referred to as the central chord, and an outer secondary thickening, the axial cortex. The central chord maybe solid and calcified or hollow and cross-chambered. The secondary axial cortex may be impregnated with calcareous deposits to variable degrees. The axial structure found in Pennatulids is also constructed of sclero-proteinaceous material; however, it is a product of the primary polyp within which it is situated.

In the families where an axial structure can be demonstrated, the polyps are only laterally united basally in a relatively shallow coenenchyme supported on the erect axis. The gastrovascular cavities are short but the polyps are interconnected by an extensive solenial network and commonly, a set of longitudinal canals that parallel the axis.

The strength afforded to colonies possessing an axis has allowed them to concurrently evolve tall and exceptionally branched growth patterns. Some species are whip-like or flagellate but most are branched. Overall branching patterns are usually consistent for a species. Many of the ramification strategies found amongst plants are present, such as dichotomous, pinnate, sympodial, irregular, planar and bushy branching. In some genera, such as the spiral *Iridogorgia*, branching is exceptionally regular. The distribution of the polyps commonly follows a pattern specific to a taxa but, along with the mode of branching, this likely to be subject to environmental influences.

Many octocorals, particularly those of shallow habitats, have abundant symbiotic zooxanthellae within their tissues. Commonly, they are quite concentrated in the tentacles and oral discs.

Other than in the Pennatulacea, polyp dimorphism is not a common trait amongst octocorallian genera, although there are many specific examples. All octocoral species have autozooids which, in monomorphic species, are able to perform the functions of food intake and water movement, and bear the gonads. In dimorphic species the siphonozooids, which are generally in larger numbers than the autozooids and scattered amongst them, commonly take over the function of water movement; they have exceptionally developed siphonoglyphs, and occasionally bear the gonads. Dimorphism is most common amongst the Alcyoniidae and the fact that *Sarcophyton* and *Lobophytum* are amongst the most massive octocorals may indicate that siphonozooids arose in a response to a need for a more efficient water transport system within large colonies. Greater water flow would also fit them better for sexual reproductive functions, and in *Heteroxenia* siphonozooids only develop during the breeding season where they are involved with the

female gonads. *Bathyalcyon robustum* deserves a mention for its remarkable development as a single giant autozooid whose body wall houses numerous fertile siphonozooids.

The Helioporacea, represented by only two known living species, is the only order within the octocorallia where horny sclero-proteinaceous structures are not reported. The group is distinct from the other two orders because its members construct hard, perforated calcareous (aragonite) skeletons. Sclerites are present only in the soft tissues of the genus *Epiphaxum*, which has a stolonate colonial form. *Heliopora*, the blue coral, produces massive colonies and does not possess sclerites.

Some aspects of systematics

Throughout the taxonomic history of the octocorals the main characters employed for systematic study have been those which are easily observable in both dried and wet-preserved material. These are both macroscopic characters, ie. the features of colonial morphology, and microscopic characters, ie. traits of the skeletal system. Histological features, such as septal arrangement and musculature, are of little general use.

With respect to the colony as a whole, the size and shape of the animal is of important taxonomic value. Ascertaining whether a colony is stoloniferous, membranous, massive or arborescent, is an insight to its possible major grouping and, on a more detailed level, sometimes also to a minor grouping. The leaf-like branches of *Hicksonella expansa*, for example, are known in only one other octocoral species.

As the structure of the branches in arborescent octocorals is significant, so is the shape, size and arrangement of the lobes in fleshier taxa. *Sinularia*, for example, includes more variety of gross colonial form than any other octocoral genus.

The distributions of the polyps is also of systematic importance. In the lobed or arborescent forms, it tends to parallel the divarication of the colony. In the Xeniidae, however, branched species of *Xenia* can be distinguished from *Cespitularia* because the former has polyps confined only to the capitula of the branches. In *Dendronephthya* the grouping of the polyps has led some taxonomists to divide the genus into three subgenera. In practice the three forms intergrade completely, but the divisions are convenient for labelling the typical forms of each group. In the arborescent octocorals that have an axis, the arrangement of the polyps usually relates to the system of longitudinal canals. Where two canals are present, as in some of the family Ellisellidae, the polyps are arranged biserially. Where several canals occur, the polyps are more commonly scattered all around the branches, but such an arrangement is often modified by local environmental conditions. In many of the genera of the family Primnoidae, the polyps are characteristically arranged in whorls around the stem and branches.

The arrangement and number of pinnules on polyp tentacles are used as the major taxonomic characters for members of the family Xeniidae, as there is little variation in sclerites and gross colonial form among the species in each genera. Although the possible number of pinnules in a row and the number of rows on a tentacle may have an upper limit for a particular species, it has been shown that the arrangement varies with age. Nevertheless, most taxonomic descriptions continue to be based on this character.

Polyp dimorphism is considered systematically important at both the familial and generic levels. The family Xeniidae contains both dimorphic and monomorphic genera. In fact, no method

Soft-corals and gorgonians in a deep reef in Fiji.   Photo: E. Svensen

has yet been found to differentiate between specimens of the monomorphic genus *Xenia* and specimens of the dimorphic Heteroxenia in which the seasonally occurring siphonozooids have not yet developed. At the familial level, the family Paragorgiidae is differentiated from the Briareidae primarily on the grounds that the former is dimorphic.

Skeletal characters are those which refer to the axial structures and the coenenchymal sclerites. The two main types of axis, scleraxonian and holaxonian, have already been discussed in the section on morphology and anatomy. In those taxa with a non-jointed scleritic axis, divisions at the familial level are made largely on the arrangement of the canal system. The Melithaeidae and the Parisididae have a jointed scleritic axis. In genera with a holaxonian style of axis, family groupings generally reflect calcification within the axis. In the Ellisellidae, for example, the calcification is radial, in the Primnoidae it is undulated, and in the Ifalukellidae it is concentric. The axis of the Gorgoniidae is not calcified.

Sclerite form is the dominant feature of almost any taxonomic description. Although their importance lies predominantly in differentiating between genera or species, there are a number of forms, for example the "pineapple-head" clubs of some Ellisellidae and the

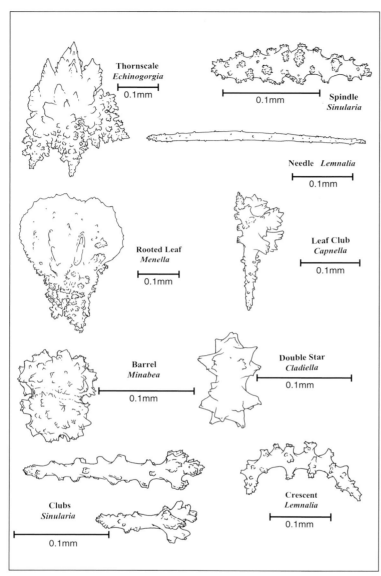

Different sklerites commonly found in Octocorals.

Drawings by Dr. P. Alderslade

In many taxa the form and arrangement of the sclerites in the polyps is of utmost importance. In the Primnoidae, which have large scale-like sclerites protecting the polyps, both the nature of the scales and how they are arranged is specifically significant. In *Dendronephthya*, anthocodial sclerites do not differ very greatly from species to species but their complex arrangement has necessitated a system of numerical formulae to characterise taxa.

The nature of the sclerites which form the polyp calyces has been used as an aid to distinguish between many of the genera in the family Plexauridae. The *Echinomuricea*, for example, have calicular thorn-scales with a single strong spike protruding from branched basal portion, whereas *Muriceides* has a single serrate spike arising from a single elongate root portion. The sclerites form a pallisade into which the polyps can retract.

Other taxa do not have polyps with a sclerite-free neck zone and so they are unable to introvert the anthocodial portion into a calyx or into the general coenenchyme. The Acanthogorgiidae, for example, have the sclerites of the branch surface continuous with those of the polyp and extending up on to the backs of the tentacles.

Colour in octocorals is present in three forms. The dull greens and browns are nearly always due to symbiotic algae in the tissues. Some taxa, such as species of *Alcyonium* have colour present in the tissue as pigment, which tends to be soluble in alcohol preservative. The colour of specimens which retain their hues in spirit is normally due to insoluble pigments chemically bound into the sclerites. In some instances, such as in *Tubipora* and *Pachyclavularia*, the colour of the sclerites is a very reliable diagnostic feature. In *Leptogorgia virgulata*, however, specimens can vary from nearly white through lemon yellow, ochre, orange, red, and purple to deep violet.

The technique of looking at sc-

scaphoids of the Gorgoniidae, which are restricted to certain families. The taxonomic importance of sclerites lies not only in their form but also in their location and arrangement within a colony. In many taxa the sclerites which lie at the surface of the coenenchyme are different from those beneath them. The surface sclerites are often asymmetrically developed with spines or leaf-like processes on their outer aspect.

Subsurface sclerites are commonly far more symmetrical.

Sclerite types maybe more or less uniformly distributed over a colony (within their layers) and in gorgonians a portion of an upper branch may have all the forms found in the colony represented. In other octocorals, however, such as *Nephthea* or *Sarcophyton* the sclerites in the upper portions of the colony are different to the basal forms.

lerite is quite simple. In selecting sclerites for examination, it is often useful, at least until the taxa are better known, to determine if different forms have been accumulated into separate layers within the coenenchyme. When a sclerite sample is finally chosen it must be cut out of the colony. Temporary preparations are simple to make by placing the sample on a glass slide and adding several drops of concentrated sodium hypochlorite to dissolve the organic matter, leaving the sclerites free to be examined under a compound microscope. If a cover-slip is applied, tapping it with a needle will usually cause the sclerites to roll about and reveal important details of their architecture. For permanent mounts the sclerites should be washed, either in a vial or on a cavity slide, and, when dried, mounted in a neutral resinous medium which has a refractive index significantly different from that of calcite (1.52), for example "Depex".

The examination of the arrangement of anthocodial sclerites is made much easier if time and facilities permit the animals to be narcotised while they are expanded. Chloretone, magnesium sulphate, magnesium chloride, formalin and menthol have all been used successfully with octocorals. In most instances, however, material to be examined has been fixed in a contracted state, but if anthocodiae are present that have not completely invaginated, accurate information can still be successfully obtained.

To enable anthocodial sclerite arrangements to be more easily observed, the polyps should be cleared in either phenol-xylene (a concentrated solution of phenol crystals in xylene), dilute sodium hypochlorite or dilute potassium hydroxide. In the latter two treatments the tissue swells and the sclerites will separate for easier examination. In sodium hypochlorite the arrangement will often disintegrate quite rapidly, but in so doing it will often reveal much more detail.

Octocorals show a high diversity in appearence. Above: *Cespitularia* sp.; below: Clove polyps.   Photos: Dr. D. Brockmann

Chapter 8

Star Polyps

Star Polyps are a group which is well-known to aquarists. From a scientific point of view, however, not a lot is known about their biology and systematics. They are unquestionably related to other members of the order Alcyonacea because of a perceived gradual progression from the encrusting Star Polyps to species which form more massive colonies. It is, though, difficult to draw exact lines between the groups. While Stolonifera formerly was regarded a separate order, this view has now been abandoned by most specialists. In accordance with the views of several scien-

Star polyps may have very delicate polyps, like this colony of "KA4-STOL-01" (picture to the left), probably a growth form of *Tubipora musica* in a reef off the Fiji Islands. The appearance of the Organ-pipe Coral, *Tubipora musica*, as seen on the picture above is probably the best-known form of this species and the best known of all Star Polyps. *T. musica* is, however, very difficult to keep in an aquarium. It is the only star polyp that produces calcareous tubes.

Photos: Scott W. Michael

tists, we have decided to use "Stolonifera" as a suborder of Alcyonacea. The reader should be aware that this taxon, as many of the other taxa in Alcyonacea, might be subject to change after future revisions of the taxonomy.

Except for a few well known species, the Star Polyps have not been very well investigated. A lot of systematic work still remains to be done in order to get an acceptable overview of the group. We must therefore expect that a lot of new information on Stolonifera will appear during the years to come. From our present understanding, the suborder Stolonifera contains five families with several subfamilies and genera (see the systematic survey to the right).

Family Cornulariidae

The species of the family Cornulariidae are those Octocorallia with a relatively simple structure. New polyps develop vegetatively from stolons, which grow from the point where the primary polyp once settled. The family is in this respect like the rest of the members of Stolonifera where the polyps are not joined laterally by layers of mesogloea and are connected only by a basal stolon. In Cornulariidae, however, the po-

lyps and the stolons are covered with a thin organic perisarc.The stolon is usually covered with a thin organic perisarc. Members of Cornulariidae do not have any sclerites. We have no information if species of this family are on offer in the aquarium trade with people being aware of it, but probably the smaller species will be found on live rock.

Family Clavulariidae

The family Clavulariidae represents an increase in complexity within the suborder Stolonifera. The simplest among its species still have a structure which is very similar to that of the family Cornulariidae. There are, however, sclerites in the tissue of these polyps and this feature separates Clavulariidae from Cornulariidae. Mostly the polyps have a cylindrical shape and are of the same height, so that appearance of the colonies is very uniform. There are, however, also polyps with the shape of a club, i.e. their upper part is thicker than the lower. According to BAYER (1981) Clavulariidae can be separated into four sub-families: Sarcodictyi-

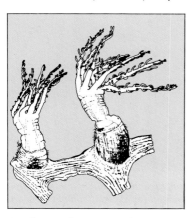

Fundamental structure of a *Cornularia*-colony (after BAYER, 1973).

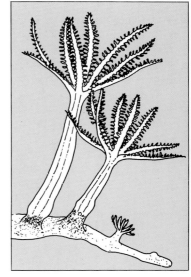

Fundamental structure of a *Clavularia*-colony (after BAYER, 1973).

inae, Clavulariinae, Telestinae and Pseudocladochoninae. The subfamilies are separated by the way the polyps are formed and by the shape of the polyps.

Subfamily Sarcodictyiinae

In Sarcodictyiinae the polyps are short and react almost flush into stolons, or producing low, conical or cylindrical calyces. *Cyanthopodium, Sarcodictyon, Scleranthe-*

"KA4-STOL-02" in the Ribbon Reef in the Great Barrier Reef.   Photo: Dr. D. Brockmann

"KA4-STOL-03" off Papua New Guinea.
Photo: Scott W. Michael

"KA4-STOL-04" off Papua New Guinea.
Photo: Scott W. Michael

"KA4-STOL-05" in a reef in Indonesia.

"KA4-STOL-06"
Photo: Scott W. Michael

"KA4-STOL-07" on live rocks in an aquarium.
Photo: Scott W. Michael

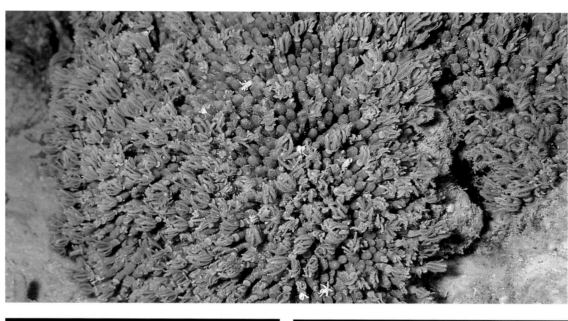

The photos above show the two main forms of *Clavularia* in the tropics. The one on the top (KA4-STOL-08) grows as an encrusting membrane stolon on top of dead corals, and has closely packed polyps that have virtually no joints between them other than the basal stolons membrane. Photo from Bunaken, Indonesia. The one in the Lower panel (KA4-STOL-09) has a mass of long, relatively hard tubes into which the polyps retract. The tubes are joined here and there by cross pieces, but there is no membrane. This form is often erroneously named "long *Anthelia*" and in Europe sold under this name.

This Star Polyp colony (KA4-STOL-10) is often imported, but so far nobody have been able to identify it with certainty. The tentacles are flattened leading to the popular name "Paddle Tentacle Stolonifera". The polyps of this specific colony has 37 pinnules down each side of the tentacle, but other forms, which have some 70 pinnules, exist (ALDERSLADE, pers. com.). This clearly illustrates how difficult taxonomic work on Star Polyps might be. ALDERSLADE (pers. com.) has noted the resemblance between these colonies and those of an animal called *Liposclera acrossota*. This species was described by BOURNE in 1914, but the type species appears to have been lost.

lia, *Tesseranthelia* and *Trachythelia* are genera mentioned by BAYER (1981). As far as we know they are not yet recorded from the reef aquarium, but this does not mean that they do not occur here.

Subfamily Clavulariinae

New polyps in Clavulariinae rarely bud off laterally, but always almost rise from the stolon and are tall, cylindrical or trumpet-shaped. Occationally, when the polyps have reached a certain height, a new lateral stolon develops. From this stolon more polyps may spring vegetatively and the colony develops inequitably in several levels. Here the polyps become connected with each other basally as well as laterally, but this does not happen very often. *Clavularia*, *Rhodelinda*, *Bathytelesto* and *Scyphopodium* are genera mentioned by BAYER (1981).

Among aquarists *Clavularia viridis* is the "best-known" Star Polyp. It was described by QUOY & GAIMARD in 1834, but nobody knows exactly, which coral it was, that these authors described. The species called *Clavularia viridis* by aquarists is really *Pachyclavularia violacea* (ALDERSLADE, pers. communication). More details are described on page 121. All in all the genus *Clavularia* is

little known. All species have relatively tall calyces into which the anthocodiae may be retracted completely. One species quite common in the Indo-Pacific is *C. inflata* (SCHENK, 1895). VERSEVELDT (1966) refers to the following species: *Clavularia rosea*, *C. magelhanica*, *C. cilindrica* and *C. frankliniana*. For all of these it is still very doubtful if they belong to the

genus, or perhaps even the family.

Several undescribed species of *Clavularia* are present in the aquarium trade. Representatives of the other genera might also, very well, be found. However, systematic sampling and investigations by experts will be needed to clarify this.

Monopodial (to the left) and sympodial (to the right) budding in the subfamily Telestinae (after BAYER, 1973).

Subfamily Sarcodictyiinae

Many of the colonies in this subfamily are small and encrusting. *Cyathopodium* spp. have low, conical calyces that arise from a narrow ribbon-like stolon rich in inseparably fused sclerites, penetrated by minute pores. Material of *Cyathopodium tenue* from Palau commonly inhabits the dead parts of other corals or grows on live rock. It is therefore likely that this species can occur ǒn material introduced to the reef aquarium. Colour of the skeleton in the same colony varies from carmine red to pale pink (BAYER, 1981). The genus *Tesseranthella* also has ribbon like stolons that produce low, conical anthosteles calyces at wide intervals. The stolon is covered by elongated, arched plates. The calcicular walls are formed by large, closely fitted plates and the aperture is closed by triangular opercular scales. The species are bright red, such as *T. rhodora* from the Caribbean (BAYER, 1981).

Subfamily Telestinae

The fact that the subfamily Telestinae often appears as the separate order Telestacea is a good example of how complicated the systematics of the order Alcyonacea are. We follow BAYER (1981) in this question, however.

In the subfamily Telestinae we find species with colonies that grow from a stoloniferous root like structure and commonly bud lateral secondary polyps. While there are no branchings in the subfamily Clavariinae, i.e. each polyp always grows into a main branch, there are the first beginnings of such lateral branchings in the Telestinae, where the species branch monopodial (see drawing on page 119). The species in the subfamily Telestinae have sclerites. BAYER (1981) mentions the genera *Carijoa*, *Paratelesto*, *Telesto*, *Telestula* and *Stereotelesteo*.

Most of the species are deep water organisms, which are only rarely or even never imported. Occasionally there are imports of *Carijoa risei* (formerly referred to as *Telesto risei* in the aquarium literature). It grows in colonies and the main branches have short side branches. It has been found at depths between 0 and 50 m from Florida to Brazil, very often in extremely dirty harbor basins. In the aquarium, however, this species may not grow properly, if the nutrient content of the water is too high. It seems that this not very robust species needs extremely fine plankton for food.

Subfamily Pseudocladochoninae

In this subfamily the polyps are similar to those found in Telestinae. However, while the branching in Telestinae is monopodial, here it is sympodial. *Pseudocladochonus* is the only genus mentioned by BAYER (1981). We have not yet heard of this genus in an aquaristic connection. THOMSON & DEAN (1931) describes *P. mosaica* from the Timor Sea, Indonesia.

Family Tubiporidae

At the moment there are two genera in the family Tubiporidae: *Pachyclavularia* and *Tubipora*. From the genus *Pachyclavularia* only *P. violacea* is known to aquarists under the incorrect name of *Clavularia viridis*. Its shape reminds people of *Tubipora musica*. VERSEVELDT (1966) questioned whether *Pachyclavularia* should in fact be placed in the family Clavulariidae, but ALDERSLADE (pers. com.) maintains that it clearly should be grouped with *Briareum* (see fact-page 121).

The Organ-pipe Coral, *Tubipora musica* is the only species of the genus *Tubipora* but Alderslade and Sprung are currently working on several points. The polyps of *Tubipora* can retract within hard tubes which are connected by lateral stoloniferous platforms forming slate like braces for support (see the picture on page 115). These stolons and the polyp tubes are formed from fused extremely calcareous sclerits, and are intensively red to violet in colour. The polyps have wide, flattened tentacles (see fact-page 122).

In Indonesia we found *Tubipora musica* in great numbers on the reef flats. They grew there at an extremely high light intensity together with *Xenia* spp. In the aquarium they are not easy to keep, but very attractive. In a 4500-litre-aquarium we placed two colonies 1.2 m below the water surface at the bottom of the decoration (NILSEN, 1991). The aquarium was lit by seven HQI-lamps of 250 watts each, and the colonies were placed in positions with strong water circulation. Evaporated water was automatically replaced by the addition of "Kalkwasser" (see vol. 1, chapter 10). Under these conditions the two colonies thrived and showed considerable growth.

Family Coelogorgiidae

In this family the polyps are contractile but not retractile. The colonies are aborescent and axial polyps arise from spreading stolons that are attached to the substratum and which branch and bud off numerous secondary polyps.

Coelogorgia is, according to BAYER (1981), the only genus in the family. The genus does very well in reef aquaria and is occasionally seen (see fact page 123).

The type species is *Coelogorgia palmosa* described from material collected from the coast of Madagascar (WRIGHT & STUDER, 1899). We present this species in the fact-page 123. THOMSON & HENDERSON (1906) describe *C. repens* from Wasin, Zanzibar. This species is rougher and has larger spicules than *C. palmosa*.

Pachyclavularia violacea
(Also called *Clavularia viridis* by many authors. Synonym: *Pachyclavularia erecta*)

Range: Widely distributed in the Indo-Pacific.

Size and growth form: Usually grows in thick, mat like colonies, which may spread over several metres in the reef. Polyps may be joined laterally at different levels by stolonic platforms.

Food: Feeds on the products of its zooxanthellae.

Description: The species was first described by QUOY & GAIMARD (1833). It may be identified by its leathery, purple membranous stolon between the polyps. The stolons does not only cover the substrate, but as in *Tubipora* they can form platforms between polyps so the colony grows at different levels. Colonies may also overgrow older parts of the colony, or animals, such as sponges. When the overgrown material dies cavities inside the colony result. The stolon consists of two layers, which are marked by different sclerites. The upper layer has straight spindle-shaped sclerites, which sometimes have the form of a "Y", while the lower layer contains sclerites, which are irregularly branched. The sclerites are purple and determine the colour of the stolon. Polyps are fluorescent white or greenish in the centre. The tentacles are light brown or fluorescent greenish. The pinnules on the tentacles are exceedingly small, and a strong lense may be needed to see them.

Aquarium maintenance:
- **General conditions:** Robust and able to grow considerably under good lighting conditions. May overgrow large areas of the aquarium decoration.
- **Lighting:** Medium to high light intensity.
- **Water circulation:** Medium.
- **Reproduction:** Can easily be achieved by cutting pieces from the stolon.

GA: +/-; TO: 0; SE: +/-

Photos

Above: Typical habitat and polyp structure of a non-fluorescent colony.

Middle: Close-up of the purple-coloured, leathery stolon with its branched tubes and its polyps retracted.

Below: A colony in an Indonesian reef.

Tubipora musica
Organ-pipe Coral

Range: Widely found in the Indo-Pacific.

Size and growth form: Usually grows in round and massive colonies of medium size, may occasionally also creep on the ground. Is usually found on reef flats in places with an extremely high light intensity.

Food: Feeds on the products of its zooxanthellae and thus does not need any additional food.

Description: Red, calcareous stolon, which has lateral, plate like connections between the zooids (see photo page 115). The zooids are variable in shape and colour, normally gray or light brown with flattened tentacles.

Aquarium maintenance:
- **General conditions:** Difficult to keep. Needs enormous light intensity and the best water quality possible.
- **Lighting:** Very high light intensity.
- **Water circulation:** Very strong.
- **Reproduction:** It is difficult or nearly impossible to induce the reproduction by cutting off parts of the stolon.

GA: +/-; TO: 0; SE: +/-

Photos
Above: Colonies on a reef flat off Bunaken, Indonesia.
Below, to the left: Colony with partly expanded polyps on the reef flat of Siladen, Indonesia.
Below, to the right: Colony in an aquarium.

Coelogorgia palmosa

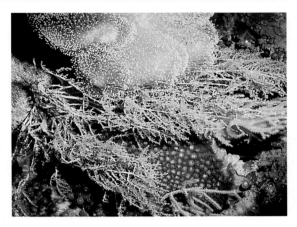

Range: Indo-Pacific, described from the Mosambique Channel, details unknown.

Size and growth form: The colony consists of a stem which rises from a broadened base attached by stolonlike processes. The stem gives off, mainly on two sides, and usually in alternate succession at obtuse angles or prependicular. These may again bear twigs, or may be beset with the club-shaped polyps which arise in spirals at wide intervals. The whole colony is rigid and brittle, only in the twigs does it exhibit a slight elasticity (WRIGHT & STUDER, 1899). According to the same authors the colonies can reach 20 cm in height. We have, however, observed colonies in aquaria that were considerable larger than this.

Food: Feeds on the products of its zooxanthellae and thus does not need any additional food.

Description: The description is adapted from WRIGHT & STUDER (1899): Colour usually pale brown with a tint of red. The polyps are not retractile. The tentacles, furnished with spicules, lie down side by side over the oral disc. The apex of the stem, like that of each branch bears a terminal polyp. In the formation of a new branch the polyp bud grows in length and then develops lateral polyps on its walls. The sclerites are distributed through the enteric mesoderm of the colony and are continued from the stem and the branches into the polyps, where they are developed to the very tip of the tentacles. They consist of straight or curved spindles, which have irregular scattered spinose warts. The length of a spicule varies from 0.12-0.37 mm and width from 0.012-0.033 mm. *Coelogorgia* is close to *Carijoa*, the principle differences are a clearer difference between the axial and lateral polyps, the absence of horny substance in the mesogloea, and the non-retractile character of the polyps.

Aquarium maintenance:

- **General conditions:** Easy to keep. Needs the best water quality possible.
- **Lighting:** Moderate to high light intensity.
- **Water circulation:** Moderate to strong.
- **Reproduction:** Can easily be cut and spread as offsprings, but it might be best to cut a small piece that contains a fraction of the stolon.

GA: +/-; TO: 0; SE: +/-

Photos

Above: Overview of a colony in "Löbbecke Aquarium", Düsseldorf.

Middle: Close up of a colony.

Below: Drawing of typical sclerites: above from a main branch, below from a polyp (drawings: Dr. P. Alderslade).

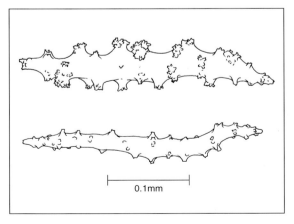

0.1mm

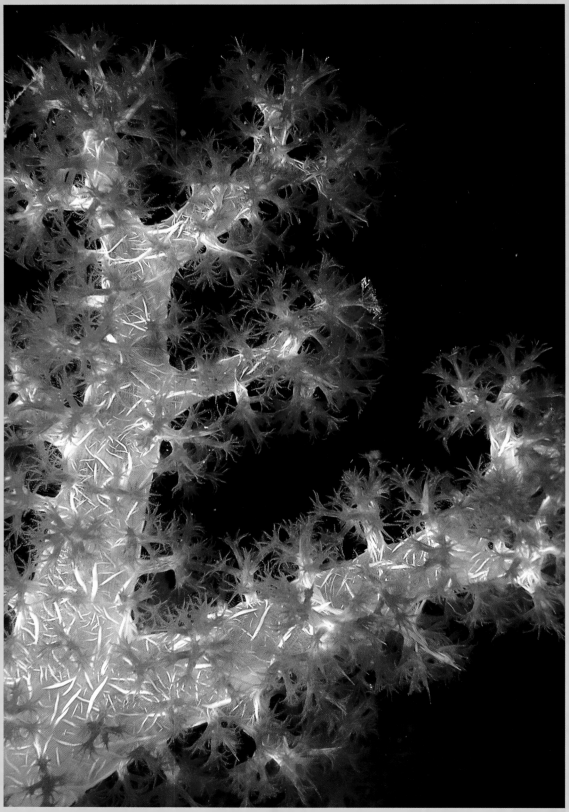

Chapter 9

Soft Corals

The soft corals of the suborder Alcyoniina form a very variable group of animals containing a large number of species. It includes large species that grow in shallow water areas where the light intensity is high, and smaller species that hang down from cave roofs beyond the reach of human beings. Thus, it is highly probable that there is a considerable number of species that nobody has ever set eye on. Nevertheless, this group is well-known to aquarists and can often be found in marine aquaria.

As with many other groups of cnidarians, not very much is known about the biology and the systematics of soft corals. In few other group is the identification of species as difficult as in soft corals. Misidentifications of soft corals are very common among aquarists.

It is utterly impossible to obtain a complete survey of the Alcyoniina, no matter which point of view is taken, or which collection of literature is cited. BAYER (1981), who

Many soft corals are particularly delicate and beautiful. Their tissues are packed with sclerites. On the left we can see a detail of a *Dendronephthya* species, which was photographed off Papua-New Guinea (photo: Scott W. Michael). The picture above, of a group of *Dendronephthya* species hanging down from the roof, was taken in a cave off the Maldives.

Polyp dimorphism: In this small colony of a *Sarcophyton* sp., taken off the Fiji-islands, the long autozooids with their tentacles and the tiny siphonozooids between the bases of the autozooids are clearly recognizable. The siphonozooids guarantee water transport from the inside of the colony to the outside and vice versa.   Photo: Scott W. Michael

is the only author, so far, to publish a comprehensive key to the soft corals, lists 45 genera, but this survey is not complete either. It does not, for example, include the genus *Nephthyigorgia*, e.g., which is a genus that is imported and kept rather frequently in aquaria.

To identify a soft coral to species level almost always requires a careful examination of the sclerites (calcareous skeletal elements). Sometimes, this is even necessary in order to identify the genus. In some cases, e.g. with the Xeniidae, an examination of the structure of the sclerites is needed even to determine if a specimen belongs to the family. Consequently, we are using scientific names only when species or genera may be determined with a sufficient degree of certainty. The help of Dr. P. Alderslade was indispensable to us in these matters.

The species in the suborder Alcyoniina are split up into families based on their structural features, i.e. the arrangement of their polyps. This is the first suborder in the order Alcyonacea, where we find dimorphism of the polyps, which means that there is more than one kind of polyp with diffe-

rent functions. One type, the autozooids, which are polyps that ingest food, develop vegetatively on the side of the mother polyp. They have a mouth and their tentacles are normally long. The other type develops a strong syphonoglyph, a ciliated groove on the inside of the mouth opening, and their tentacles are strongly reduced. These polyps are called siphonozooids. They specialise in pumping water into and out of the colony, and may have a function in the reproductive process.

Monomorphism is the rule in branching soft corals; they just have autozooids. The large, massively built species of the genera *Lobophytum* and *Sarcophyton* are always dimorphic, however, possessing both autozooids and siphonozooids. Scientists assume that the necessity for an improved water transport in the larger, massive colonies brought about polyp dimorphism.

Soft corals have special, highly active cells that produce mucus and contribute to an effective cleaning of the surface of the colony. In comparison to those of anemones, the muscle layers are not very strong. Simple nerve connections between the individual polyps have the effect that

the whole colony reacts if something touches it. The mesogloea is well developed and is a medium for the sclerites, however, this is only one of its functions. Food is taken in through the mouth, and digestion begins extracellularly in the gastrovascular cavity of the polyps. Products of digestion may be distributed via the solenrial chanals (tubes connecting the polyps), or by cell diffusion through the mesogloea.

Like most other corals, soft coral polyps also have nematocysts that contain various toxins. On the one hand, nematocysts paralyse any prey that the polyps catch with their tentacles and protect the corals against attack and, on the other, the substances they contain give them an advantage over other organisms in competing for space on the reef. These are not, however, the only toxins found in soft corals. Analyses in the Great Barrier Reef have shown that the majority of species of soft corals contain toxic terpene compounds which they release into their surroundings (COLL et al., 1982).

Terpene compounds are hydrocarbons with the general formula $C_{10}H_{16}$. They have a very characteristic smell, which can easily be detected when a box of corals is opened. Terpenes are found in the majority of the octocorallia, often as sesquiterpenes ($C_{15}H_{24}$) or diterpenes ($C_{20}H_{32}$). They may account for up to 5 % of the dry weight of a colony and, in such a high concentration, are poisonous to fish and protect the colony against predators. Thus, soft corals or gorgonians that have been partly or completely eaten by fish, are a very rare thing on a coral reef. Other terpenes have the effect of inhibiting growth of zooxanthellae in stony corals, or even killing them (SAMMARCO et al., 1982; COLL & SAMMARCO, 1986; WEBB & COLL, 1983). In the open sea, this often results in stony corals and soft corals growing in distinctly separated clumps. This is also the reason why it is so difficult to cultivate stony corals and soft corals next to each other successfully in the same aquarium, or why stony corals that are placed next to a soft coral, tend not to do well. More details about the toxicology of the coral reef can be found in MEBS (1989).

The skeleton of soft corals, like that of stony corals, consists mainly of calcium carbonate, but the calcareous material is laid down on a fine organic matrix. Sclerites have different shapes, according to where in the colony they are found. To identify a species it is necessary, therefore, to take samples from the surface, from the inside, from the stem and branches of the colony, and from the polyps. The way the examination needs to be carried out is described on page 113, chapter 7.

The largest sclerites are spindle-shaped, can be several millimetres long and are often found in the interior of the stem, there may also be polyp-supporting sclerites, e.g. in the family Nephtheidae. Most sclerites are usually not much longer than a few tenths of a millimetre and have shapes resembling a crankshaft, an anchor, a dumbbell or a club (see drawing on page 112).

All this might lead one to believe that identification of octocorals can be achieved relatively easily by means of an examination of the sclerites, but this is definitely not the case. Size and shape of the sclerites can vary, even within one species, and this variability is often dependent on the habitat where a colony grows. For example, a colony that is exposed to heavy wave action may develop a different shape compared to one that grows in calm water. It is quite conceivable that this also has consequences for the shape of the sclerites. It is not an easy task for an aquarist to remove the sclerites and to examine them. Not only do you need a basic knowledge of systematics and morphology, but also a great deal of experience with variations among the different genera of octocorals, as well as access to numerous scientific publications.

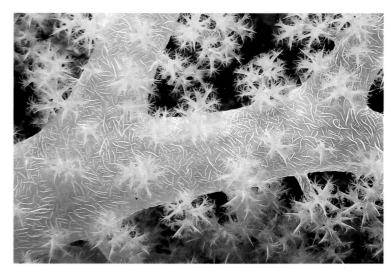

The body tissue of soft corals is supported and stabilized by different types of sclerites. The form of the sclerites is an important criterion in the systematic identification of soft corals. The picture above shows the spindle-shaped sclerites in the tissue of *Dendronephthya* spp., which is typical of these soft corals. Photo: Scott W. Michael

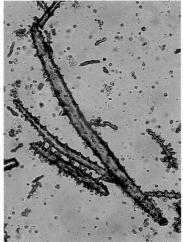

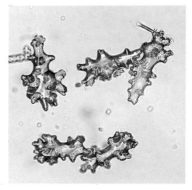

Above, on the left: Spindle-shaped sclerites supporting the polyps of *Nephthea* sp. The body tissue also contains club-shaped and windlass-shaped sclerites.

Above, on the right: The supporting, spindle-shaped sclerites removed from the body tissue, as seen through a microscope (magnification: 80x).

To the right: Club-shaped sclerites removed from the body tissue, as seen through a microscope (magnification: 400x).

Further, it is often necessary to compare one's findings with the type material. Like it or not, without such an examination, identification of most species of soft corals is next to impossible. So, we usually end up with species identification being a matter for just a few experts. As aquarists, we should be pleased if we can identify the family and genera, but even this can frequently prove a tough challenge.

We would like to deal with the families separately according to their special characteristics. As a summary, or overview, we have worked out a table of the families and genera of the Alcyoniina, based on the works of BAYER (1981), VERSEVELDT & BAYER (1988) and personal communications from ALDERSLADE. This summary (see below) is intended to provide an idea of the great variety found among octocorals.

Summary of the families and genera of soft corals (suborder Alcyoniina)

Families	Genera
Paralcyoniidae (= **Fasciculariidae**, = **Viguieriotidae**)	*Maasella* (= *Fascicularia*, = *Viguieriotes*), *Carotalcyon*, *Paralcyonium*, *Studeriotes*
Alyoniidae	*Alcyoniom, Acrophytum, Anthomastus, Bellonella, Cladiella* (= *Lobularia*, = *Microspicularia*, = *Sphaerella*), *Lobophytum, Metalcyoniun, Minabea, Malacacanthus, Parerythropodium, Sarcophyton, Sinularia, Dampia, Eleutherobia, Inflatocalyx, Ceratocaulon*
Asterospiculariidae	*Asterospicularia*
Nephtheidae	*Nephthea, Capnella* (= *Eunephthya*), *Daniela, Drifa, Duva, Gersemia, Lemnalia, Litophyton* (= *Ammothea*), *Dendronephthya* (= *Morchellana*, = *Roxasia*, = *Spongodes*), *Neospongodes, Paralemnalia, Pseudodrifa, Scleronephthya, Stereonephthya, Umbelluifera*
Nidaliidae	*Nidalia* (= *Cactogorgia*), *Agaricoides, Siphonogorgia, Chironephthya, Nidaliopsis, Nephthyigorgia, Pieterfaurea*
Xeniidae	*Xenia, Anthelia, Cespitularia, Efflatounaria, Fungulus, Heteroxenia, Sympodium*

General maintenance in aquaria

Even though identifying many soft corals is an almost hopeless task, it is a comfort to know that many of them are very suitable for our aquaria, where they can thrive and grow magnificently. From the aquatic hobby point of view, we may subdivide soft corals into two groups: species with zooxanthellae and those without.

Soft corals with zooxanthellae do best at moderate to high light intensities. If the conditions are favourable, most species will grow quickly and form large colonies, so that it becomes necessary to prune them from time to time. With soft corals that have zooxanthellae, it is quite simple to take cuttings. It is especially easy for the branching genera, which develop quickly into new colonies from cut-off branches. The mushroom-shaped *Sarcophyton* spp. take a little longer to grow into their original shape again.

Stony corals may be what many aquarists dream of, but among the soft corals, there are numerous species that are much easier to keep. They are very suitable as beautiful and highly interesting decorations for a coral reef aquarium. We would like to advise beginners, therefore, to start with soft corals that contain zooxanthellae, rather than with stony corals. Soft corals are, however, quite sensitive to changes in salinity, not being able to tolerate values of less than 30 ‰ for any length of time. We have repeatedly experienced that, over time, the salinity of the reef aquarium often decreases, resulting in degeneration among the corals and, often, an uncontrollable growth of filamentous algae. Regular testing of the salinity is most important in all reef aquaria.

It is extremely difficult to keep soft corals that do not contain zooxanthellae, e.g. the delicate *Dendronephthya* spp., alive in a normal coral reef aquarium. They need a special aquarium with a vigorous current, medium, or even low, light intensity and a regular, nearly continual, supply of live plankton of different sizes. The maintenance of such aquaria is very difficult and this is why we advise against soft corals without zooxanthellae as a matter of principle. Our knowledge about these corals is not yet sufficiently thorough to enable us to keep them successfully in our aquaria over a long period of time.

It is not only possible, but actually quite simple, to propagate soft corals in the aquarium by cutting off branches as layers. Most of these fleshy and bushy-growing soft corals with zooxanthellae tolerate this procedure without any problems. Soft corals without zooxanthellae cannot be propagated by this method. The series of pictures above shows a specimen of *Capnella imbricata* which grew from a piece of live rock and which we wanted to propagate by cuttings. A pair of sharp scissors is the most suitable tool to use for this purpose. The two pictures in the centre show the layer being cut off and removed. The pictures at the bottom prove that the remaining stub survives this procedure without any problems and that, within four weeks, a new colony has grown from the remains.

Distribution of Xeniidae from the Coral Sea to the shores of the Great Barrier Reef (After Dinesen, 1983)

Genera	Coral Sea						Great Barrier Reef — Ocean zone						Middle zone						Coastal zone					
	H	D	H	D	H	D	H	D	H	D	H	D	H	D	H	D	H	D	H	D	H	D	H	D
Sympodium			◔				◔		◑				◕		◔	◔	◔							
Efflatounaria	◑		●	◔	◔	◔	●		●	◔	●		◑		◔		●				◐			◑
Anthelia							◔		◑				◑		◔									
Cespitularia					◔		◔		◑				◑		◑		◑		◔		●		●	
Xenia	◐		◔		◔		●	◐	●	◕			●	◐	●	◕		◕	●		●		●	
Heteroxenia							◔		◔						◔				◔					

Legend:

H = reef slope   D = reef flat

◔ = low frequency, genera recorded in 1–25% of the reef sites examined

◐ = medium frequency, genera recorded in 26–50% of the reef sites examined

◕ = high frequency, genera recorded in 51–75% of the reef sites examined

● = very high frequency, genera recorded in 76–100% of the reef sites examined

Family Xeniidae

In the family Xeniidae, we meet the soft corals that are most popular among aquarists. We find monomorphic, as well as dimorphic, genera. The genus *Xenia* is always monomorphic, while *Heteroxenia* also forms siphonozooids, but only seasonally. It is not possible to separate a *Xenia* sp. from a *Heteroxenia* sp. if the latter has not yet formed a dimorphic polyp structure. Whether a coral belongs to the family or not can only be ascertained, however, by a careful examination of the sclerites. These are very small and have the shape of a minute discs or corpuscles pointed cone. It is also difficult with some Xeniidae to separate them from the star polyps (of the suborder Stolonifera) just by looking at the sclerites, as these may be very similar in the two groups. Xeniidae usually grow in mushroom-shaped colonies, but they may also be lobed or grow prostrate. All Xeniidae have sclerites, which are not very variable, as compared to those of the family Alcyoniidae. The number of rows of pinnules (tiny projections) on the tentacles, as well as the number of pinnules in each row, are the most important systematic characters in Xeniidae.

In the genus *Fungulus*, the polyps are dimorphic and may be retracted completely into the coenenchyme. Very short monomorphic polyps which are able to withdraw into the coenenchyme, are found in the genus *Sympodium*, whose colonies grow as thin pads. The colonies of the genus *Efflatounaria* have upright, finger-shaped lobes, whose polyps are also able to retract into the coenenchyme. We have not seen these genera in aquaria as yet, but they are very decorative soft corals which should definitely be tried in the reef aquarium. We found their colonies in the shallow, crystal-clear water of the Coral Sea, together with a rich fauna of other cnidarians. This corresponds with the findings of Dinesen (1983), who mentions *Efflatounaria* as the only genus of the family Xeniidae, which is really common in the nutrient-deficient areas of the Coral Sea. We also followed Dinesen (1983) in the basic survey of the distribution of the various genera of different families in a cross-section of the inner reef areas of the Great Barrier Reef and of the oceanic Flinders Reef in the Coral Sea. These studies point out which kind of environment the families and genera prefer. The environment close to the shore is, by far, richer in nutrients than that of the

Coral Sea, which has water that is extremely low in nutrients.

The genus *Anthelia* is well known to aquarists, but, unfortunately, it is a mess with respect to its systematics. The genus is polyphyletic (i.e. it has originated from several lines of descent) and will probably undergo a major revision in the near future. *Anthelia* spp. grow prostrate and their strong polyps, which possess well-developed tentacles with small side branches, are unable to withdraw into the coenenchyme. Colonies of *Anthelia* are well-known to coral reef aquarists and are among the most easily kept soft corals. In some cases, *Anthelia* species grow so profusely that they eventually cover large parts of the aquarium decorations, sides and back panes.

Anthelia species probably subsist mainly on the products of their zooxanthellae. It is also possible, however, that they take in organic substances directly from the water through their body tissue. In contrast to some *Xenia* spp., the polyps of *Anthelia* spp. do not move rhythmically of their own accord. Unfortunately, it is impossible to say anything substantial about the identification of these species. Quite often, it is also very difficult to tell *Anthelia* spp. apart from the star polyps of the suborder Stolonifera.

Among the most delicate Xeniidae are species of the genus *Cespitularia*. It is possible to identify the genus by looking at the shape of the colony, since the polyps are evenly distributed on the lobes and are often very long, usually with very small tentacles. Sometimes, *Cespitularia* spp. display beautifully fluorescing colours. Their growth may, however, be very different in our aquaria.

The genus *Xenia* is monomorphic, i.e. there is only one type of polyp. The colonies are mushroom-shaped with the polyps sitting on the rounded summit of the stalk. Some *Xenia* spp. have the ability to make pulsating movements with their autozooids, a kind of behaviour which we do not, as yet, know how to interpret.

The genus *Efflatounaria* includes extremely beautiful soft corals. Unfortunately, they are hardly ever imported. The picture of the magnificent yellow colony, above, was taken in the Myrmidon Reef, a reef in the outer Great Barrier Reef complex. The picture below shows several colonies near Rock Arch in the Flinders Reef in the Coral Sea. The colonies in the middle (the white area between the upper and the lower expanded colonies) show that the polyps may be retracted completely.

"Anthelia" spp.
Waving hand polyp

Distribution: Very common in the Indo-Pacific. No further details are known.

Size and growth form: They usually grow in mat- or crust-like colonies, which may cover large areas of the reef. The polyps may grow from 2 to 10 cm in height.

Food: They utilize the photosynthetic products of their zooxanthellae, but they probably also absorb dissolved organic compounds through the body tissue. They do not require additional feeding in aquaria, as long as they are kept under high light intensity.

Description: The colonies shown in this fact page are, at present, all grouped together as *Anthelia* spp. As the group is currently subject to revision (ALDERSLADE in prep.), we expect this will change in the future. In *Anthelia*, the polyps, which have one or more rows of pinnules along each edge of the tentacles, cannot retract into the coenenchyme. *Anthelia* spp. live in shallow water areas with high light intensity. Some species are difficult to tell apart from members of the suborder Stolonifera without microscopic examination of the sclerites.

Aquarium maintenance:
– **General conditions:** Most of the species are very hardy, grow profusely and may overgrow large areas of an aquarium if the light intensity is very high. They are, however, very sensitive to filtration through activated carbon, which might suggest that they utilize organic compounds as additional food.
– **Lighting:** High light intensity.
– **Water circulation:** Medium to strong.
– **Reproduction:** Easy to propagate by fragmentation.
GA: + ; **TO:** + ; **SE:** +/-

Photos:
– Top: Dense growth of a colony ("KA4-ALC-01") in an aquarium
– Centre: Budding of new polyps from the coenenchyme
– Bottom: Close-up of polyps

Cespitularia spp.

Distribution: Very common in the Indo-Pacific. No further details are known.

Size and growth form: They usually grow in small colonies, but in some places on the reef, they cover large areas.

Food: They feed on the products of their zooxanthellae and therefore do not require additional feeding.

Description: The polyps are distributed evenly on the lobes; heads and tentacles are small, while the stalks may be very long. Very small sclerites. The colonies sometimes have beautiful, fluorescent colours.

Aquarium maintenance:

– **General conditions:** They are among the most delicate and beautiful of soft corals. Sometimes, they are rather fast-growing and develop into large colonies. Quite sensitive to sudden changes in water conditions, which may even lead to their death, especially if activated carbon is used in the filtration system. They are generally more difficult to keep than other members of the Xeniidae. Moreover, they are very vulnerable to damage during transportation. Great care should be taken if these soft corals have to be transported, which is best done in a styrofoam container with large amounts of water in which they should be kept hanging upside down.

– **Lighting:** High light intensity.

– **Water circulation:** Medium.

– **Reproduction:** May be propagated by fragmentation, if the conditions required for their growth are met.

GA: + ; **TO:** + ; **SE:** +/–

Photos:

– Top: A colony ("KA4-ALC-04") in an aquarium

– Bottom right: Close-up of the lobes and the polyps

– Bottom left: Close-up of a colony photographed at Heron Island, GBR (photo: L. Newman & A. Flowers)

Xenia spp. – Pulse corals

Distribution: Very common in the Indo-Pacific. No further details are known.

Size and growth form: Usually forming small colonies with a diameter of about 10 cm. These may, however, occur in larger groups. Some species also grow in single colonies.

Food: They feed on the products of their zooxanthellae, but they probably also take in organic compounds through the body tissue. They do not require additional feeding.

Description: Most species develop mushroom-shaped colonies with long autozooids, which make pumping movements in their upper parts. *Xenia* spp. are monomorphic. On the reef, they will grow together with other species, but in shallow-water areas, monospecific populations will also be found.

Aquarium maintenance:

– **General conditions:** They require good water conditions. Some species seem to be very sensitive to the application of activated carbon in the filtration system and to the vicinity of other corals, especially stony corals. If conditions are favourable, they may grow very quickly and become dominant in an aquarium. Other species, like *Xenia macrospiculata* from the Red Sea, are very hardy and grow profusely in most aquaria.
– **Lighting:** High light intensity.
– **Water circulation:** Medium.
– **Reproduction:** They may be propagated by dividing colonies, but hardly ever by fragmentation.

GA: + ; **TO:** + ; **SE:** +/-

Photos:

– Top left: Beautifully growing "KA4-ALC-05" (white variant) and "KA4-ALC-06" in an aquarium owned by P. Findeisen, Witten/Germany.
– Bottom left: "KA4-ALC-07" sp. in an aquarium at the Löbbecke Museum and Aquazoo, Düsseldorf/Germany
– Bottom right: Beautiful and delicate polyps of a "KA4-ALC-08"

"KA4-ALC-09" off Papua-New Guinea
Photo: Scott W. Michael

"KA4-AC-10" on the Great Barrier Reef
Photo: Scott W. Michael

"KA4-ALC-11" in an aquarium
Photo: Scott W. Michael

"KA4-ALC-12" in an aquarium
Photo: Scott W. Michael

"KA4-ALC-13" in our experimental aquarium set-up

"KA4-ALC-14" on an Indonesian reef

The genus *Heteroxenia* is dimorphic, i.e. it has autozooids and siphonozooids. A close-up view reveals the fact that there are tiny siphonozooids between the bases of the long, fully expanded autozooids.

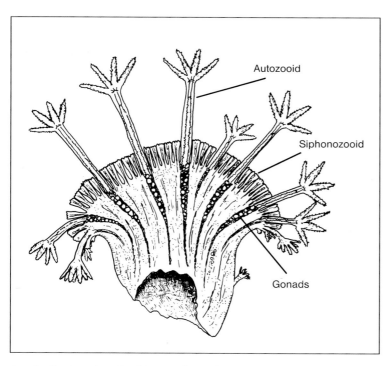

Autozooid

Siphonozooid

Gonads

Longitudinal section of a *Heteroxenia* species.

Drawing simplified after BAYER (1973)

In Indonesia, we observed strongly pulsating colonies in shallow water at extremely high light intensity. In the aquarium, however, this pulsating movement seems to disappear in many of the central Indo-Pacific species after a time. A quite different situation applies to the beautiful "Red Sea" Xenia, probably *Xenia macrospiculata*. This species grows like crazy, given right conditions, and can be easily cultivated. Its pumping activity does not seem to decrease with age, but, according to J. Sprung (pers. com.), the activity of the polyps is correlated with pH. High pH makes them pump vigorously, while a decrease in pH leads to a cessation of the pumping. As *Xenia* spp. have only one type of polyp, but are also occasionally found growing in rather large colonies, it is very possible that the purpose of this pulsating movement is to provide the necessary water circulation in the colony.

We have noticed that the polyps contract when one attempt to feed them, and this might be interpreted as an active intake of food. On the other hand, it is interesting to note that laboratory examinations showed the mesenteries of the Xeniidae to have no alimentary system and that no food was taken in (GOHAR, 1940 and 1948).

Xenia spp. are quite popular with aquarists, yet they are not always easy to keep. Whether they thrive in a coral reef aquarium or not, seems to depend very much on the general conditions of this aquarium and on the kind of company they are kept with. Just as in *Anthelia* spp., we have noticed that *Xenia* spp. do not do very well if an aquarium filtered intensively with activated carbon. We have found that it is equally difficult to make *Xenia* spp. grow in an aquarium that is dominated by *Acropora* stony corals. *Xenia* spp. are perhaps the most delicate soft corals and create incredibly beautiful and unusual effects in an aquarium.

At first glance, the genus *Heteroxenia* might be regarded as being identical to the genus *Xenia*. Indeed, in most cases, they will probably be wrongly identified as *Xenia* spp. *Heteroxenia* spp. are, however, dimorphic, having both autozooids and siphonozooids. The autozooids are large and easily recognizable. Moreover, they also possess gonads and produce gametes. The siphonozooids are small and do not protrude from the coenenchyme to any extent. They specialise in water movement. To tell *Heteroxenia* from *Xenia* spp., it is necessary to determine if there are any siphonozooids between the large polyps. *Heteroxenia* is very much rarer on the Great Barrier Reef than *Xenia*.

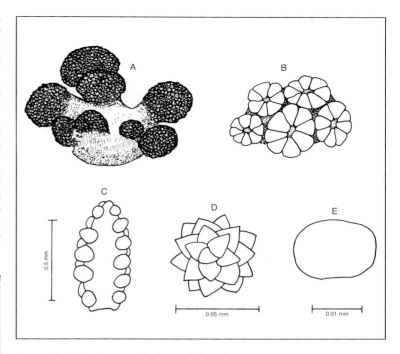

Asterospicularia: A - overall shape of the colony;
B - five polyps with retracted tentacles;
C - tentacle with expanded pinnules;
D - star-shaped sclerite;
E - oval, disc-like sclerite.
Drawings A and B after UTINOMI **(1951);**
Drawings C, D and E after GAWEL **(1976)**

Family Asterospiculariidae

From the point of view of the marine aquarist, the family Asterospiculariidae is of hardly any significance at all. With *Asterospicularia* as its only genus, containing the two species *Asterospicularia laurae* and *A. randalli*, it is a monotypic family (UTINOMI, 1951; GAWEL, 1976).

Asterospicularia spp. grow in a bushy shape with dome-shaped lobes on the thick branches. The polyps are low and monomorphic. There are two types of sclerites: star-shaped ones and oval, almost-disc-like ones. The oval type is known in the Xeniidae as well, but the family Asterospiculariidae may be separated from the other families in the Alcyoniidae by their star-shaped sclerites (astrum = Latin: star; and spiculum = Latin: point, lance). In Guam, populations of *A. randalli* were found with a population density of up to 24 colonies per square metre (GAWEL, 1976), stretching from low tide level down to a depth of about 7 metres.

Asterospicularia randalli off Guam   Photo: M. Gawel

The family Nephtheidae includes many interesting and easy-to-keep soft corals, but there are also species which are next-to-impossible to keep alive in an aquarium. Some of the species are among the most beautiful and impressive soft corals in the reef, with fantastic colours and shapes, growing in the most enchanting spots in caves and under overhanging rocks.

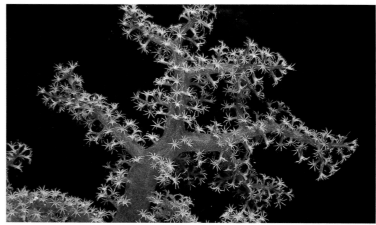

Treelike branching ...   Photo: Scott W. Michael

The large gastrovascular canals in the stalk are characteristic of the family Nephtheidae. The picture shows a cross-section through the stalk (diameter about 1 cm) of a *Nephthea* species. The canals, which fill the larger part of the interior, may be easily discerned. It is also rather easy to see that the outer tissue and the inner walls are full of sclerites.

This family has some typical characteristics and is easy to tell apart from the soft corals of the family Alcyoniidae. The colonies are branched and, in some cases, may grow to an extraordinary size, with gastro-vascular channels, through which water flows in and out, running through the whole stalk. When the colonies pump out water, they collapse and are greatly reduced in size. There is only one type of polyp and it is not able to retract into the coenenchyme. The polyps are of-

... umbrella- or mushroom-shaped branching ...

... ball-shaped branching.   Photo: Scott W. Michael

The best-known species of the family Nephtheidae are found in the genus *Dendronephthya*. Here, a group of colonies photographed off the Fiji-Islands really show the beauty of the genus. Photo: Scott W. Michael

Distribution of Nephtheidae and Nidaliidae from the Coral Sea to the shores of the Great Barrier Reef (After DINESEN, 1983)

Genera	Coral Sea H	D	H	D	H	D	Ocean H	D	H	D	H	D	Middle H	D	H	D	H	D	Coastal H	D	H	D	H	D
Siphonogorgia	◕		◔																					
Scleronephthya			◔																					
Stereonephthya	◕		◑		◑		◑		◑		◑		◑		◑									
Lemnalia	●		●	◕	●	◔	●		●		●		◑		●		◔		◑		◑			
Nephthea	●		◕	◑	◔		◕		●	◔	●		●	◑	●		◑				◔			
Paralemnalia	◑		◑		◑	◔	●		●	◑	●	◔	◕		●	◑				◔				
Capnella	◑		◑	◕	◕	◑	◕		◑		◑		◑	◔	●									
Dendronephthya		◕	◕		◑		◑		◔		◔		◑		◔		◑				◑			

Legend: H = reef slope D = reef flat

◔ = low frequency, genera recorded in 1-25% of the reef sites examined

◑ = medium frequency, genera recorded in 26-50% of the reef sites examined

◕ = high frequency, genera recorded in 51-75% of the reef sites examined

● = very high frequency, genera recorded in 76-100% of the reef sites examined

This soft coral is usually sold under the name *Litophyton*. The generic name *Litophyton* is often used among aquarists, but it is hardly possible at all, however, to separate between *Litophyton* and *Nephthea* spp. Both belong to a complex of systematically highly ill-defined species, which also includes the genera *Neospongodes* and *Stereonephthya*. We have taken samples of the colonies shown here at the premises of Kölle-Zoo, Stuttgart. Until the question of their identity is settled, we will refer to this soft coral as "KA4-ALC-15".

On the left: "KA4-ALC-16", a *Stereonephthya* sp. In this species, the polyps are spread over the whole stem and branches. Samples of the colonies shown here were taken at Kölle-Zoo, Stuttgart. On the right: "KA4-ALC-17" was classified by Dr. Alderslade as a member of the "*Nephthea-Litophyton-Neospongodes* group". Looking at the arrangement of the polyps, it is, however, likely that this species belongs to the genus *Neospongodes*. Samples were taken at Aqua Design, Oldenburg.

ten arranged in clusters on the branches, which may be spread, as in the genus *Neospongodes*, or close to each other forming an umbrella-shaped roof, or gathered in the form of a ball. The kind of branching and its density are also important criteria for the systematic subdivision of the family.

BAYER (1981) mentions 16 genera, among which we find *Litophyton*, *Nephthea*, *Lemnalia* and *Dendronephthya*, all well-known in the marine aquatic hobby. *Litophyton arboreum* FORSSKÁL 1785 is the type species (the species on which the family description was originally based) of this family, but, unfortunately, the type material (the specimen or specimens on which the original description was based) has been lost. Today, no-one really knows which coral FORSSKÁL had in front of him in those days and there is great confusion as to which genera are really valid. A revision of the family is being worked on at present by VAN OFWEGAN (ALDERSLADE pers. com.).

The genus *Litophyton* when expanded can look like the genus *Capnella*. The two can only be separated by looking at their sclerites. In *Litophyton*, the branches are soft and very flexible. The systematic distinction between *Litophyton* and *Nephthea* is very vague, though, and a revision is urgently needed. One result of such a revision could be that *Litophyton* could turn out to be a synonym of *Nephthea*.

Aquarists should keep in mind that the soft coral that is very commonly kept in Europe under the name "*Litophyton arboreum*", and which usually reproduces profusely by budding and by forming daughter colonies, is not a *Litophyton* sp. at all, but *Capnella imbricata* (QUOY & GAIMARD, 1833). We have kept this species in aquaria for years and have also found perfectly identical colonies in aquarium shops. After Dr. Alderslade had examined a colony, he informed us that the species was really *Capnella imbricata*. The tropical species of *Capnella* (there are also species

"KA4-ALC-18", a *Lemnalia* sp.   Photo: Scott W. Michael

"KA4-ALC-19", another *Lemnalia* sp.   Photo: Scott W. Michael

"KA4-ALC-20", a *Paralemnalia* sp. Samples of the colony were taken at Kölle-Zoo, Stuttgart.

A colony off Madang, Papua-New Guinea
Photo: Scott W. Michael

A colony off the Fiji-Islands
Photo: Scott W. Michael

A colony with closed and expanded polyps
in a cave off the Maldives

A colony with partly contracted polyps
Photo: T. Luther

known from other ocean regions) have strong, thorny, club-shaped sclerites. Thus, the polyps are unable to contract, making the colonies feel rough and coarse to the touch (see fact-pages 144-145).

The surface of the stalk in the genus *Lemnalia* is densely covered with sclerites and the colony has stiff branches, but the genus differs from *Capnella* in the arrangement of the polyps. In *Capnella*, the polyps sit at the end of small branches, while in *Lemnalia*, they are found along the third branchings.

In the genus *Paralemnalia*, the colonies have distinctly finger-shaped branches which grow together at the base and turn towards the light. The polyps can be found separately (often, not close together) along the whole of the branches.

The genera *Capnella*, *Lemnalia* and *Paralemnalia* do very well in a coral reef aquarium, but they require a great deal of light and space to thrive.

In the genera *Nephthea*, *Stereonephthya*, *Dendronephthya* and *Scleronephthya*, the colonies are able to pump large amounts of water in and out of their bodies; they, thus, have the ability to change their size considerably. The genera *Nephthea* lives on the products of photosynthesis carried out by their zooxanthellae. The genera *Scleronephthya* and *Dendronephthya*, on the other hand, do not have any zooxanthellae, and this is why they are rather difficult to keep alive over a longer period in an aquarium.

In *Nephthea* spp., many polyps are arranged regularly in small lobes at the end of a branch. In *Stereonephthya*, however, they are distributed over the whole branch.

Stereonephthya are delicate soft corals which are difficult to keep, in spite of the fact that they have zooxanthellae which photosynthesize. We have repeatedly seen *Stereonephthya* mislabelled and sold in aquarium shops as "*Lemnalia*".

Neospongodes is very closely related to *Stereonephthya*, but in

"KA4-ALC-21", a *Scleronephthya* sp. in an aquarium

that genus the polyps are only on the branches and not distributed all over the surface of the colony.

Dendronephthya spp. are well known to aquarists and are imported on a regular basis. The polyps are arranged in groups or clusters bearing different numbers of polyps (two to ten) in each group. The polyps sit on the distal end of the branches or the lobes. In this genus, we find clearly recognizable sclerites on the inside, as well as on the surface, of the colony. *Dendronephthya* species are beautifully coloured and look magnificent and most attractive to naturalists, as well as to aquarists. Yet, they are probably among the soft corals that are most difficult to keep. We have yet to see one single colony being kept in a closed reef aquarium for more than a few months at most. They are totally dependent on plankton for food.

Often, small coral crabs of the

genus *Porcelanella* are imported together with *Dendronephthya* species. Their symbiotic relationship may be observed at close quarters in aquaria, if living conditions for the corals are favourable.

The species of the genus *Scleronephthya* are even more beautiful than those of the genus *Dendronephthya*. They differ from them by having very contractile polyps that do not have supporting sclerites. Occasionally, it is possible to find *Scleronephthya* on offer in the aquarium trade. These soft corals are, however, just as difficult to keep as their close relatives in the genus *Dendronephthya*.

All in all, the family Nephtheidae is an assemblage of beautiful soft corals with different demands concerning their aquarium maintenance. Many of the genera in the family are not mentioned in this book because little or nothing is known about them.

Capnella **spp.**
Kenya tree
(Sometimes wrongly referred to as *Litophyton arboreum* or *Litophyton* sp. in older aquarium literature.)

Distribution: Very common in the Indo-Pacific; details unknown.
Size and growth form: Of medium size; only slightly branching colonies.
Food: Feed mostly on the products of their zooxanthellae.
Description: The polyps are found on small brushes at the ends of the branches. They cannot be retracted and are filled with club-shaped sclerites that are equipped with leaves and spines. The interior of the stalk is interspersed with numerous sclerites. The colonies feel very rough to the touch when they are retracted. *Capnella imbricata*, which was first described by QUOY & GAIMARD (1833), is the type species of the genus. ROXAS (1933) writes: "Colonies tree-like, usually branching, with polyps arranged in lobes around the terminal branches. In contracted specimens, the polyps may be so compactly arranged as to appear to be overlapping each other. Polyps are from 1.8 to 2.2 mm high and 0.8 to 1.5 mm wide. Tentacles are short, blunt, with about twelve pairs of closely packed pinnules. Armature of polyps consists of capstan-like sclerites (0.075 to 0.1 mm high and 0.06 to 0.075 mm wide) and foliaceous clubs (0.12 to 0.17mm long and 0.04 to 0.07 mm wide). Sclerites of stem cortex are similar to the capstan-like sclerites of the lower portions of the polyps, forming a densely packed layer. Inner cortical sclerites are few, in the form of small, smooth, four-rayed sclerites (0.16 mm long and 0.14 mm wide). Stalk canal walls full of 4-rayed sclerites (0.18 to 0.22 mm long and 0.16 to 0.2 mm wide), irregular, thick or barrel-shaped sclerites (0.17 to 0.28 mm long and 0.16 to 0.24 mm wide) with very numerous, rounded, compactly arranged warts. Basic form of canal-wall sclerites is the four-rayed type, which, by growth and wart formation, may transform into irregular, rounded or barrel-shaped sclerites with prominent and heavy warting. Colour in life, from very light brown to light green." Note: The "4-rayed sclerites" in stalk canals mentioned above are actualle 6-8 rayed sclerites, so Roxas was wrong, (ALDERSLADE, pers. com.).

Photos
– Top: Colony of *Capnella* sp. "KA4-ALC-22"
– Bottom: Colony of *Capnella* sp. "KA4-ALC-23"

Capnella imbricata

Aquarium maintenance:
- **General conditions:** The species most commonly seen in aquaria is *C. imbricata*, which, however, is usually referred to as *Litophyton arboreum* by mistake. Growth is very fast. There are several species that are occasionally on offer in the aquarium trade. All of them do very well in aquaria and may be kept successfully for a long time.
- **Lighting:** High light intensity.
- **Water circulation:** Medium to strong.
- **Reproduction:** *C. imbricata* and, perhaps, the other species as well, develop daughter colonies on their branches, but it may also be propagated by cutting off fragments (see photo page 129).

GA: + ; **TO:** + ; **SE:** +

Photos:
Capnella imbricata
- Top right: Fully expanded colony
- Right: The formation of a daughter colony
- Bottom left: Sclerites from the outer layer of the stem (magnification 200x)
- Bottom right: Sclerites from the polyps (magnification 400x)

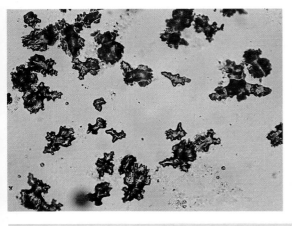

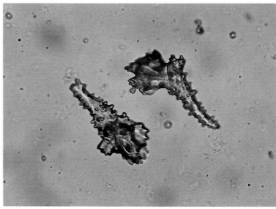

Nephthea spp.
Broccoli coral

Distribution: Very common in the Indo-Pacific. No further details are known.

Size and growth form: Branching colonies of medium size.

Food: Feed on the products of their zooxanthellae.

Description: Monomorphic. At the ends of the branches, there are bundles of more than ten polyps. The polyps are protected by large sclerites which make the colonies feeling rough to the touch. May easily be confused with *Capnella* spp. *Litophyton* is possibly a synonym of *Nephthea*.

Aquarium maintenance:
- **General conditions:** Regularly seen in the aquarium trade. They develop into large, branching colonies, if the light intensity is sufficiently high. Easily kept.
- **Lighting:** High light intensity.
- **Water circulation:** Medium to strong.
- **Reproduction:** May be propagated by cutting off fragments.

GA: + ; **TO:** + ; **SE:** +

Photos:
On the left:
- Top: Large colony on the Myrmidion Reef, Great Barrier Reef
- Bottom: Colony of *Nephthea* sp. "KA4-ALC-24"

On the right Nephthea sp. "KA4-ALC-24"
- Top left: With polyps open
- Top right: With polyps closed
- Bottom left: Supporting sclerites in the lobes (magnification: 12x)
- Bottom centre: Supporting sclerites in the polyps (magnification 200x)
- Bottom right: Sclerites from the stalk (magnification 200x)

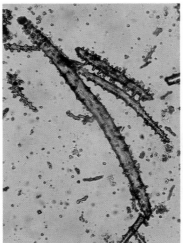

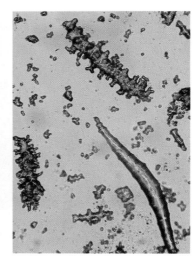

Dendronephthya spp. – Strawberry corals

Distribution: Very common in the Indo-Pacific.

Size and growth form: Colonies of up to 2 m in size, but usually smaller. Form three different types of branching (see page 138).

Food: Do not contain zooxanthellae and are totally dependent on phytoplankton as food.

Description: The colonies have the ability to change their size dramatically by pumping water in or out with their gastro-vascular canals. Polyps cannot be retracted. Each polyp is protected by large, thorny sclerites of more than 1 mm size, which are found beneath the ectoderm of the polyp stalk. Polyps are arranged in groups or balls on the ends of the lobes and on the branches. The ends of the lobes and the polyps often display beautiful colours. The stalk has large sclerites, which are clearly visible. They often grow on reef edges, hanging down from cave roofs, or overhanging rocks.

Aquarium maintenance:

- **General conditions:** Often on sale in aquarium shops and look attractive with their beautiful colours and delicate shapes. They do, however, belong to the most difficult of all Cnidaria and should, in general, neither be caught nor kept. If kept, a special aquarium is an absolute must (e.g. a cave aquarium, see vol. 1, page 149), where the light and water movement are correct. They have to be fed almost continuously in aquaria in order to stand a chance of survival. Cultures of different plankton should be tried. *Dendronephthya* soft corals need the full attention of an experienced aquarist and are not at all suitable for beginners.
- **Lighting:** Low to medium light intensity.
- **Water circulation:** Very strong, alternating.
- **Reproduction:** By polyp- or group-polyp bail-out; there is, however, little chance that these soft corals can be propagated in the aquarium.

GA: - ; **TO:** + ; **SE:** -

Photos to the right:

- Top left: Fully expanded colonies off the Fiji-Islands
  Photo: Scott W. Michael
- Top right: Colony off Papua-New Guinea
  Photo: Scott W. Michael
- Centre left: Colony on the floor of a cave off the Fiji-Islands
  Photo: Scott W. Michael
- Centre right: Detail of a ball-shaped colony
  Photo: Scott W. Michael
- Bottom left: Detail of the stem and polyps
  Photo: Scott W. Michael
- Bottom right: Often, little coral crabs of the genus *Porcellanella* are introduced into the aquarium with *Dendronephthya* spp.

Photos above:
- Top: Colony on the Great Barrier Reef
- Bottom: Colony off the Maldives

Close-up of a *Nephthyigorgia* colony off the Fiji-Islands. The thickness and the large numbers of supporting sclerites in the body tissue are remarkable.   Photo: Scott W. Michael

Family Nidaliidae

In the family Nidaliidae, we find corals that represent a kind of transitional stage between soft corals and gorgonians. The genera *Agaricoidea*, *Nidalia* and *Pieterfaurea* have monomorphic colonies and are of little interest for the aquarist. More details and information on these genera may be found in VERSEVELDT & BAYER (1988).

The genera *Chironephthya* and *Siphonogorgia* are frequently found on the reef. It therefore comes as no surprise to find them in the aquarium trade from time to

time. *Chironephthya* is often regarded as a synonym of *Siphonogorgia*, but this is not correct, as there are clear systematic differences between them (ALDERSLADE, pers. com.).

Chironephthya spp., with their heavily branched colonies that resemble small trees, remind us of *Dendronephthya*. Nearly all of the strong, spindle-shaped sclerites are found on the surface of the colony. This is why the inner parts of a colony, which have large canals, collapse completely if the water is pumped out of the colony. The polyps which primarily sit on the branches (and not on the stalk), are reinforced by sclerites and are able to retreat into their calyces. We have not, as yet, heard of anyone keeping *Chironephthya* successfully in an aquarium. It is very well possible, however, that these beautiful

corals have been mistaken for *Dendronephthya*-species. They are probably as difficult to keep and, as they have no zooxanthellae, they require small live food.

In the genus *Siphonogorgia*, the corals have slim branches and a shape that is very similar to that of the gorgonians. However, they lack the inner skeleton of gorgonin, which is typical of the gorgonians. The stalk is densely filled with large, spindle-shaped sclerites, which give the colony great stability. Thin gastrovascular canals are only found in the very centre of the stalk. The polyps sit on the branches and are reinforced with small sclerites. There are no, or hardly any, calyces.

The genus *Nephyigorgia* also belongs to the family Nidaliidae. It was first collected in 1910 in "Shark Bay" in West Australia at a depth of 15 m (KÜKENTHAL, 1910). Another species, which is, as yet, unidentified but quite common in the aquarium trade (at least, in Europe) under the name of *Alcyonium* sp., most likely also belongs in this genus. This soft coral, which is among the more challenging aquarium animals, is incredibly beautiful (see fact-page 180).

Unfortunately the corals in the family Nidaliidae are not among the easiest corals to keep in the modern coral reef aquarium. Mixed with photosynthetic corals, they will soon die from starvation. All in all they are challenge for the advanced aquarist who can give them a special aquarium and meet their requirements.

The family Nidaliidae is virtually unknown to aquarists. This is an example of how little we still know about soft corals. The picture shows a thick rowth of *Chironephthya* spp. under a cave roof off the Fiji-Islands. A gorgonian of the family Ellisellidae is shown growing at the bottom of the cave.   Photo: Scott W. Michael

Chironephthya spp.
(Often mistaken for *Dendronephthya* in aquarium literature.)

Distribution: Very common in the Indo-Pacific.

Size and growth form: Medium-sized, tree-shaped colonies.

Food: Lack symbiotic algae and are totally dependent on plankton as food. In aquaria, they have to be fed almost continuously with live plankton.

Description: Long, spindle-shaped sclerites are only found on the surface of the colony. As there are hardly any sclerites in the gastrovascular canals, the stalk may be compressed and collapse when a colony dies. Colonies have the ability to change their size dramatically by pumping water in or out with their gastrovascular canals. The polyps are heavily equipped with sclerites, but may be retracted into well-developed calyces. They do not have any zooxanthellae. The colours are varied (white, yellow, red or orange). They grow in places with strong water circulation, often hanging down from cave roofs in shallow water, or from overhanging rocks in water of medium depth.

Aquarium maintenance:
– **General conditions:** Only occasionally found in aquarium shops. Very difficult to keep. If kept, a special aquarium is an absolute must (e.g. a cave aquarium, see vol. 1, page 149), where the light and water movement are correct. They have to be fed almost continuously in aquaria in order to stand a chance of survival. Not at all suitable for beginners!
– **Lighting:** Low to medium light intensity.
– **Water circulation:** Strong to very strong and alternating.
– **Reproduction:** Unknown; there is little chance that these soft corals can be propagated in the aquarium.

GA: - ; **TO: +** ; **SE: -**

Photos:
On the left:
– Top: Colony on a reef in the Maldives
– Bottom: Colony on a Maldive reef at a depth of 15 m

On the right:
– Top left: White colony hanging down from overhanging rock in water of medium depth off the Maldives
 Photo: Scott W. Michael
– Top right: Colony off the Fiji-Islands
 Photo: Scott W. Michael
– Centre left and right: Details of the polyps and branches
 Photos: Scott W. Michael
– Bottom left: Close-up of the polyps
 Photo: Scott W. Michael
– Bottom right: Acoelomate flatworms on a colony off Papua-New Guinea Photo: Scott W. Michael

***Nephthyigorgia* spp.**
Devil's hand
(Referred to as *Alcyonium* spp. by many authors in older aquarium literature.)

Distribution: Indo-Pacific; no further details known.

Size and growth form: Small branching colonies that remind one of the shape of a hand.

Food: Lack symbiotic algae and are totally dependent on plankton as food.

Description: The colonies are brittle and have some more or less conical or finger-shaped branches, which are usually arranged in one plane. Long, spindle-shaped sclerites are mainly found on the surface of the colony and are easily recognisable. Polyps can be found all over the colony, except for the lower part of the stalk. The polyps may be retracted into well-developed calyces. The colours are magnificently red, orange, white or yellow.

Aquarium maintenance:

– **General conditions:** These soft corals are occasionally imported from Indonesia or Sri Lanka. They are very difficult to keep over a long period. They open, if they do open at all, only after they have been in an aquarium for a long time. They need ample supplies of live and frozen plankton of different sizes and strong water movement. They should therefore be kept in a special aquarium, where it is possible to provide these conditions.

– **Lighting:** Low to medium light intensity.

– **Water circulation:** Strong to very strong and alternating.

– **Reproduction:** Unknown; there is little chance that these soft corals can be propagated in aquaria.

GA: +/- ; **TO:** + ; **SE:** +/-

Photos:

– Top: An expanded and a contracted colony of "KA4-ALC-25" in an aquarium

– Bottom: Colony of "KA4-ALC-26" at the Löbbecke Museum and Aquazoo, Düsseldorf, Germany

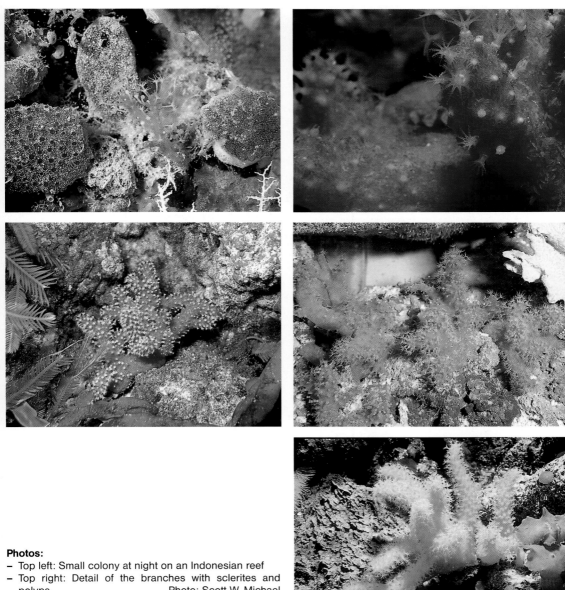

Photos:
- Top left: Small colony at night on an Indonesian reef
- Top right: Detail of the branches with sclerites and polyps
  Photo: Scott W. Michael
- Centre left: Small colony in a cave in an aquarium
- Centre right: A group of colonies at the bottom of a cave in our experimental aquarium set-up
- Bottom right: Yellow colony in an aquarium

Siphonogorgia spp.
(Often mistaken for gorgonians in aquarium literature.)

Distribution: Very common in the Indo-Pacific.

Size and growth form: Medium-sized colonies that are reminiscent of gorgonians.

Food: Lack symbiotic algae and are totally dependent on plankton as food.

Description: Stalk and branches are densely covered with large, spindle-shaped sclerites, which give the colonies a high degree of stability. The gastrovascular canals are only found in a small central area of the stalk and branches. The polyps are equipped with sclerites. They may be retracted, yet calyces are barely developed, or non-existent. These soft corals grow in reef zones of medium to great depth, in caves or under overhanging rocks. Some colonies resemble gorgonians and can be mistaken for such underwater.

Aquarium maintenance:

- **General conditions:** These soft corals are only occasionally imported. They are difficult to keep over a long period. They need large quantities of live and frozen plankton of different sizes and strong water movement. A special aquarium, where it is possible to provide these conditions, is an absolute must. Not at all suitable for beginners!
- **Lighting:** Low to medium light intensity.
- **Water circulation:** Strong to very strong and alternating.
- **Reproduction:** Unknown; these soft corals can probably not be propagated by cuttings.

GA: - ; **TO: 0** ; **SE:** -

Photos:
- Top: "KA4-ALC-27" off the Philippines
  Photo: O. Gremblewski-Strate
- Centre: "KA4-ALC-28" on the Great Barrier Reef
- Bottom: "KA4-ALC-29" in a cave off the Maldives

Family Alcyoniidae

The family Alcyoniidae is the most important family of soft corals from the aquarists point of view. Here we find the large branching or mushroom-shaped soft corals that may grow to gigantic sizes, even in aquaria. In many shallow waters of tropical regions, this family may be the dominating one with, in some cases, individual colonies reaching diameters of up to one metre. The well-developed coenenchyme, into which the polyps may retract completely, is typical of these soft corals. The Alcyoniidae contains monomorphic, as well as dimorphic, genera.

Five out of a total of 14 genera (BAYER, 1981) are of special aquarium interest: *Lobophytum*, *Sarco-*

"Field of Dreams" - A dense population of *Sarcophyton crassoacule* off Papua-New Guinea.   Photo: Scott W. Michael

phyton, *Cladiella*, *Alcyonium* and *Sinularia*. Each genus contains a vast number of species and there is no hope whatsoever for aquarists of identifying them. Many of the species are very decorative, even if they are only yellow, beige or brownish in colour. The colonies form different shapes and polyp structures. Many grow very quickly and must be cut back now and then in order to prevent the aquarium from becoming completely overgrown. Species iden-

Distribution of Alcyoniidae from the Coral Sea to the shores of the Great Barrier Reef   (After DINESEN, 1983)

Genera	Coral Sea H	D	H	D	H	D	Ocean zone H	D	H	D	H	D	Middle zone H	D	H	D	H	D	Coastal zone H	D	H	D	H	D
Alcyonium	◑		◔		◔				◔		◔		◔	◑	◔				●		●		●	
Cladiella	◔		◔		◔		◔		◑				◔		◔		◑		◔				◑	
Lobophytum	●	◑	●	◑	●	◑	◑		●	◑	◑		◑	●	◑	●	◔		◑	◑	◔	◑	◑	●
Parerythropodium	◑		◑	◔	◔		◔		◑		◔				◔				◑		◔			
Sarcophyton	●		●	◑	●		◑		●		●	◔	●	◑	●		●		◑		●	●	●	●
Sinularia	●		●	◑	●	◔	●		●	◔	●	◔	●	◑	●	◔	◑	◑					◑	●
Miabea				◔																				

Legend: **H** = reef slope   **D** = reef flat

◔ = low frequency, genera recorded in 1-25% of the reef sites examined

◑ = medium frequency, genera recorded in 26-50% of the reef sites examined

◕ = high frequency, genera recorded in 51-75% of the reef sites examined

● = very high frequency, genera recorded in 76-100% of the reef sites examined

"KA4-ALC-30" in the shallow water
of the Coral Sea

"KA4-ALC-31" is often on sale in aquarium shops.
It is only slightly folded.

"KA4-ALC-32" off the Maldives
Photo: Dr. D. Brockmann

"KA4-ALC-33" in an aquarium owned
by Kenneth Olsen, Oslo.

"KA4-ALC-34", shown here in an aquarium owned by Aqua-Design, Oldenburg, was regarded as a variety of *Sarcophyton glaucum* for a long time. It will probably be described as a distinct species in the near future (ALDERSLADE, pers. com.). It is often found on offer in aquarium shops. It is not difficult to keep in the aquarium and may attain a diameter of more than 50 cm. It needs a lot of space and a high light intensity.

tification remains extremely difficult, though, and is a matter for a just few specialists. For those aquarists who, nevertheless, like to go into detail into this difficult field of knowledge, the group offers excellent opportunities for systematic studies, including that of the sclerites. A good place to start is to study the many scientific papers on soft coral systematics given in the list of references at the end of the book. We only deal briefly with the most important genera in this text. The reader will find more information profiling these genera - and, in some cases, their species - in the fact pages, which include detailed descriptions and illustrations.

It makes a great deal of sense to distinguish between monomorphic and dimorphic species in the Alcyoniidae. Among the dimorphic types, we find for excample the well-known genera *Sarcophyton* and *Lobophytum*, both with an unknown number of species. *Sarcophyton* species are more or less clearly mushroom-shaped, but with a marked main stalk, which is often quite thick and bears no polyps. They also have a very sturdy capitulum that is densely covered with polyps. The autozooids may be more than 10 mm long when they are fully extended, but there are species, however, in which they are considerably smaller. The rim of the capitulum may be more or less folded, yet, in its centre, there are never any folds or lobes.

Sarcophyton spp. are among the best known and most popular soft corals for marine aquaria. With their beautiful shape - often mushroom-like - and slender growth, they are real eye-catchers. J. VERSEVELDT, a late biologist from the Netherlands and an authority on soft corals, who published the largest number of articles on soft corals, mentioned 35 valid species and 50 invalid species, subspecies or varieties in 1982. The most commonly mentioned species in an aquarium connection is, undoubtedly, *Sarcophyton trocheliophorum*. According to VERSEVELDT (1982), this species is

"KA4-ALC-35" (above) and "KA4-ALC-36" (below) off Papua-New Guinea
Photo: Scott W. Michael

"KA4-ALC-37" in an aquarium   Photo: Scott W. Michael

"KA4-ALC-38", a *Lobophytum* sp., in an aquarium owned by P. Findeisen, Witten. The dimorphic polyp structure and the highly lobed form of this species are remarkable.

"KA4-ALC-39", a *Lobophytum* sp., is often found in the aquarium trade. It is possible that it is identical to "KA4-ALC-38".

widespread in the warmer Indian Ocean and in the West Pacific. Personally, we know this species only from books and articles and have never been able to verify its identity from samples collected from aquarium-kept specimens. There are soft corals sold in aquarium shops under the names of *Sarcophyton glaucum*, *S. ehrenbergi* and *S. lobulatum* and, whereas the first two are valid species, *S. lobulatum* is probably a synonym of *S. ehrenbergi*. There is no point at all in trying to identify a species by the shape of the colony. As with most other groups of soft corals, the only way to determine the species of these soft corals is to examine their sclerites. VERSEVELDT (1982) is an excellent source of information about the genus *Sarcophyton* for anyone who wants to study this genus in detail.

In the profiles on pages 164 to 168 we present three *Sarcophyton* spp. that were identified by Dr. Alderslade by means of microscopic examination. For two species, we also show sclerites that were taken from inside the body and from near the surface. This is done to illustrate how little sense it makes to call one coral "*ehrenbergi*" and the other "*glaucum*" without a careful morphological examination of the sclerites. The two different types of shape that are shown for *S. ehrenbergi* may be the reason why the colonies were assigned to two species. But, who is really capable of distinguishing between *S. glaucum* and the mushroom-type colony of *S. ehrenbergi*?

As the name indicates, the genus *Lobophytum* has a strongly lobed colonies, which we have, mostly, found to grow low and to be of a light yellow or beige colour. Usually, there is no real stalk and, occasionally, the colonies grow out from a low platform. The polyps are more or less separated and are sometimes of a chalk-white colour, which makes them very decorative. This genus is very common on the reef. *Lobophytum* spp. are among the more beautiful soft corals and are rather easy to keep. Some species are described in the profiles on pages 169 to 171.

Of the monomorphic genera of the family Alcyoniidae, *Parerythropodium* is, perhaps, the most delicate. To our regret, it is only very rarely on offer in the aquarium trade. The genus grows nearly prostrate and has a coenenchyme which is about 2 mm thick and sports beautiful autozooids of 2 to 3 cm length, with a little ring of tentacles. There is hardly any danger of mistaking this genus for another of this family. *Parerythropodium* may grow quite quickly in aquaria if conditions are favourable. On the other hand, we have also experienced situations where it has been really difficult to get them to thrive, and we have no idea what causes this kind of variability. It is, however, very likely that other corals they were kept together with, and/or the degree of organic nutrients dissolved in the water, contributed to the situation.

The genus *Dampia* was discovered and described only relatively recently. It is monotypical, with *D. pocilloporaeformis*, from the Dampier Archipelago, Western Australia, as its only species. It may be assumed, however, that it is quite common in large areas of the Indo-Pacific. The surfaces of the crust-like growing colonies are strongly folded in adult colonies. The monomorphic polyps may be retracted completely into their calyces, which is not a common phenomenon in leather corals. Further information may be found in ALDERSLADE (1983).

We find particularly beautiful species in the genera *Eleutherobia* and *Minabea*, both of which grow in finger-shaped colonies that display a bright yellow or red colour. Whereas there is only one type of polyp in *Eleutherobia*, *Minabea* is dimorphic. These beautiful soft corals are only imported occasionally. There is no information about their maintenance in aquaria that we can pass on. However, as these corals have no zooxanthellae, they are probably

"KA4-ALC-40", a *Lobophytum* sp. with clearly dimorphic polyp structure, on a reef flat off the Maldives

"KA4-ALC-41" is a *Parerythropodium* species. It grows in crust-like fashion and has large, monomorphic polyps. Some authors refer to it as "*Alcyonium fulvum*". Yet, according to BAYER (1981), *Alcyonium* spp. always grow erect and have lobes.

difficult to keep alive over a long period.

By comparison, the three genera *Cladiella*, *Alcyonium* and *Sinularia* are rather easy to keep and are well known in the hobby. All these three genera are monomorphic and are quite regularly on offer in aquarium shops. *Alcyonium* is not really regarded as a common species, but this is probably due to errors in identification.

Often, but not invariably, *Cladiella* species have a white surface,

which contrasts with their brown polyps. The colonies are only slightly branched. The sclerites are small and of the same size all over the colony. Many species of this genus are on offer in the aquarium trade and all seem to grow quickly and to do well under strong light. Some species, however, prove to be quite delicate and die if we try to propagate them by cutting off branches. Some species are described in the profiles on pages 172 to 173.

Alcyonium, as well as *Sinularia*,

Penis corals are beautiful, but the polyps are hardly ever seen, as they are nocturnal. All the species shown here probably belong to the genus *Eleutherobia*. If the polyp structure is dimorphic, however, penis corals may also belong to the genus *Minabea*. We have no information that penis corals have ever been kept in aquaria. The pictures show "KA4-ALC-43" (above, on the left) off the Maldives and "KA4-ALC-44" (above on the right) on the Great Barrier Reef.

colonies have finger-shaped lobes and most species grow upright. *Alcyonium* species often have sclerites only at the base of their stalk; the rest of the colony is clear of sclerites. This gives the colony a soft and flabby texture. In *Sinularia*, numerous small club-shape sclerites are distributed all over the surface of the colony. However, in the interior of its base, we find large spindles. Some species of *Sinularia* may reach diameters of over 1 m on the reef and grow into enormous colonies, as, e.g. those of *Sinularia flexibilis*, one of the most common species found in the central Indo-Pacific.

The characteristic feature of *Sinularia flexibilis* is its long and slim finger- or tube-like lobes, which we also know from *S. mollis*, *S. procera* and *S. sandensis*. *S. flexibilis* is, by far, the most common species among these. To identify it with any certainty, it is necessary to examine the sclerites. *S. flexibilis*, which is occasionally found on offer in aquarium shops, is described in more detail in the profile on page 177.

The *Sinularia* species which is probably most easily recognized, is *S. dura* (its profile appears on page 174). Among aquarists, it is sometimes mistakenly called *Lobophytum crassum*. *S. dura* usually grows in saucer-shaped colonies and has only a few polyps. It has numerous sclerites, however, and these give the body tissue a certain stiffness.

Sinularia cf. *notanda* (see page 179 for its profile) is a beautiful and rather rare species. It is heavily branched and does not look like a typical *Sinularia* species at first sight. If we examine it more closely, though, we find the thick layer of sclerites which is typical of the genus.

Sinularia brassica (see its profile on page 176) is another species that is commonly found on the reefs and is often seen in the trade. It does, however, have an extremely variable appearance and is closely related to *S. dura*.

In aquarium shops, we often find a *Sinularia* species on offer as *S. asterolobata*, which it is definitely not, as *S. asterolobata* has soft and flexible lobes without any sclerites. So far, we have not been able to identify this species with any degree of certainty, which is why we provisionally refer to it as "KA-ALC-46". The small polyps make remarkable movements which may easily be observed in the coral reef aquarium. These movements, in which the tentacles are folded towards the centre of the polyp, are rather slow. Fur-

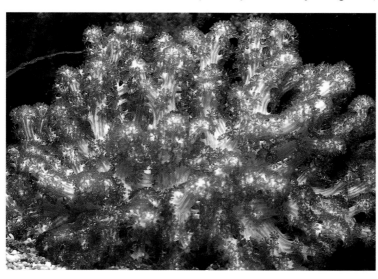

"KA4-ALC-45", a typical *Cladiella* sp., with white branches and brown polyps
Photo: Dr. D. Brockmann

ther, the single polyps in a colony only show these movements every, or every other, second. We have, to date, never seen this kind of movement in any other *Sinularia* species. This phenomenon therefore calls for more detailed study.

As in many other soft corals of the family Alcyoniidae, small crabs may occasionally be brought into our aquaria with *Sinularia* colonies. The crabs tend to have the same colour as the body tissue of the corals and live all their life between the coral lobes without (usually) causing any harm to their hosts.

Finally, we would like to point out that the genus *Sinularia* includes a host of species, most of which may only be identified by a thorough examination of their sclerites. Interested readers who would like to know more about this subject, should turn to VERSEVELDT (1980).

Family Paralcyoniidae

At the beginning of this chapter, we pointed out how octocorallia develop higher complexity in their overall structure and, especially, in that of their branches, in a step-by-step manner. This special kind of complexity is highest in the Paralcyoniidae, which are corals that are able to retract their long branches, bearing side branches and polyps, completely into the stalk or foot of the colony. This behaviour is similar to what we can observe when anemones contract. This family includes the genera *Maasella*, *Carotalcyon*, *Paralcyonium* and *Studeriotes*.

One *Studeriotes* species may be found in aquarium shops and is described in the profile on page 181. *Carotalcyon* have the same life style as *Studeriotes* species and their branches are able to withdraw completely into a kind of case which is dug into the substratum. The genus *Carotalcyon* is dimorphic, while *Studeriotes* is monomorphic.

In "KA4-ALC-46", which is probably the most remarkable *Sinularia* spp., we can observe an unusual movement of the polyps. This species is occasionally found on offer in aquarium shops. It survives very well in aquaria and grows quickly if water and lighting conditions are suitable.

"KA4-ALC-47" is very similar to the *Sinularia* species shown above, but in this species, we cannot observe the unusual movement of the polyps. These polyps are very small and of the same colour as the lobes, usually a bright, intense yellow. This species does very well in aquaria when the intensity of the light is high, and may be easily propagated by cutting off layers. It is quite regularly on sale in aquarium shops.

Sarcophyton ehrenbergi

Distribution: Very common in the Indo-Pacific.

Size and growth form: Medium-sized, laterally compressed colonies with a deep disk.

Food: Feeds on the products of its zooxanthellae, but also makes use of other food sources.

Description: This dimorphic coral was first described by MARENZELLER (1886). The distance between the autozooids is 0.6 - 1 mm. There are no sclerites in the autozooids. One, two or no siphonozooids between the autozooids. If the disk of a colony is cut in two halves and torn apart, the two parts are always connected by a sticky, filamentous mucus.

Description of the sclerites:
(From VERSEVELDT, 1982); ① Surface of the disk has clubs, 0.07 to 0.26 mm long. The heads are wide; they consists of big, blunt prominences and warts. The handles have spines, often zoned. ② Interior of the disk has slender spindles and rods or needles, covered with widely spaced, antler-like promiences, which are not arranged in girddles. The spicuels are usually not longer than 0.44 mm. ③ The surface of the stalk has clubs, the majority of which are 0.09 to 0.15 mm long. A striking feature is the wide head, composed of big warts. ④ The internal of the stalk has spindles, thick or slender, up to 0.30 to 0.40 mm long, sometimes up to 0.45 mm. They are covered with volcano-shaped, sometimes prominences, which are zoned in the middle part of the spicule. Drawings of the sclerites to the right: Dr. P. Alderslade.

Aquarium maintenance:
– **General conditions:** This species is among the most desirable leather corals. It is often said to be rare, but is, in fact, quite common in reef habitats of the Indo-Pacific. It keeps well in aquaria and grows beautifully, once the mushroom-like shape has developed. It may, however, also grow in different shapes.
– **Lighting:** High light intensity.
– **Water circulation:** Medium to strong.
– **Reproduction:** It may be divided into two halves, or cut into more parts. This, however, destroys the regular shape of the colony.

GA: + ; **TO:** + ; **SE:** +

Photos:
– Top: A colony which contains all of the sclerites described, but which - even so - has a slightly atypical form
– Centre: A colony which only has some of the sclerites described, but which spots the typical mushroom-like shape
– Bottom: Close-up of the autozooids and siphonozooids

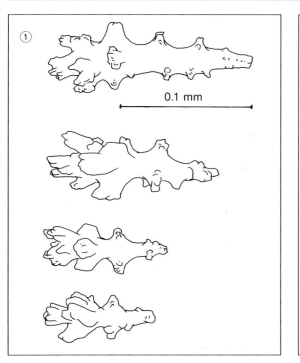

0.1 mm

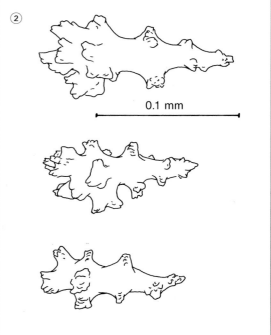

0.1 mm

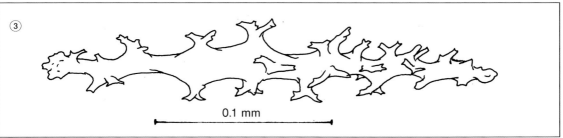

0.1 mm

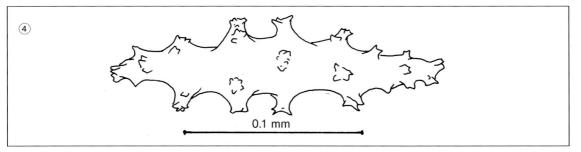

0.1 mm

Sarcophyton glaucum

Distribution: Very common in the Indo-Pacific.

Size and growth form: The diameter of the disk reaches up to 1 m.

Food: Feeds on the products of its zooxanthellae, but probably also makes use of other food sources.

Description: This species was first described by Quoy & Gaimard (1833). The autozooids at the periphery of the disk may be 4 cm long; at this point, the distance between the autozooids is 1.0-1.7 mm. In the central area of the disk, the distance is larger: about 3.5-5.0 mm. Between the autozooids in the central area of the disk, there are three to eight siphonozooids; at the periphery, only three to four. This species is very variable in its shape. Quite common in its natural surroundings.

Description of the sclerites:

① Surface of the disk - club-shaped, 0.1-0.5 mm long. ② Surface of the stalk - club-shaped, 0.09-0.28 mm long. ③ Interior of the disk - spindle-shaped, up to 0.75 mm long. ④ Interior of the stalk - variable in form, up to 2.30 mm long; may be recognized with the naked eye. Drawings of the sclerites to the right: Dr. P. Alderslade.

Aquarium maintenance:

– **General conditions:** Easy to keep, this species is often found on offer in aquarium shops. As with all other *Sarcophyton* spp., the beautiful shape of the colony will be marred for some time after cuttings have been taken.

– **Lighting:** High light intensity.

– **Water circulation:** Medium to strong.

– **Reproduction:** May be fragmented by cutting off portions. This, however, is detrimental to the regular shape of the colony.

Ga: + ; **TO: +** ; **SE: +**

Photos:

– Top: Overall view of a colony

– Bottom: Close-up of the autozooids and siphonozooids

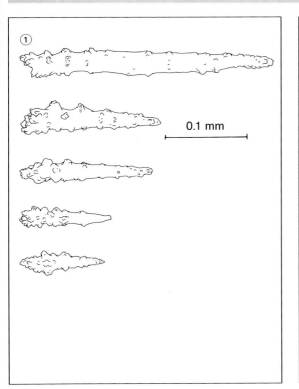

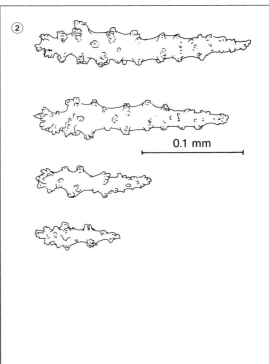

0.1 mm

0.1 mm

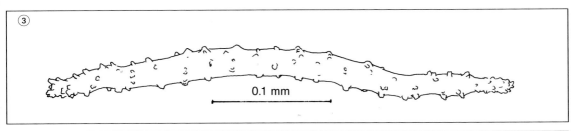

0.1 mm

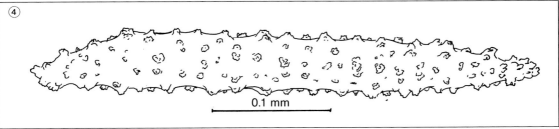

0.1 mm

Sarcophyton tenuispiculatum

Distribution: Very common in the Indo-Pacific.

Size and growth form: Large, tubular colonies. We have seen colonies in aquaria that have attained a diameter of more than 50 cm.

Food: Feeds on the products of its zooxanthellae, but probably also makes use of other food sources.

Description: This species was first described by THOMSON & DEAN (1931). It is one of the most beautiful species in the genus. The autozooids at the periphery of the disk are often arranged in rows at a distance of about 1.00-1.30 mm from each other. The distance between the rows is 1.50-2.00 mm. In the central area of the disk, the autozooids are not arranged in rows and are 1.50-2.00 mm apart.

Description of the sclerites:

① Surface of the disk - club-shaped, 0.10-0.45 mm long. ② Surface of the stalk - club- and baton-shaped, 0.10-0.25 mm long, with long thorns. ③ Interior of the disk - needle-shaped or slenderly baton-shaped, with a length of up to 0.55 mm and a thickness of 0.03-0.05 mm; also, large club-shaped sclerites as on the surface of the disk. ④ Interior of the stalk - oval and spindle-shaped, 0.23-0.33 mm long, with long thorns; in addition, there are slenderly baton-shaped sclerites of up to 0.60 mm length as in the interior of the disk.

Aquarium maintenance:

- **General conditions:** This species is very hardy, but needs a lot of space.
- **Lighting:** High to very high light intensity.
- **Water circulation:** Medium to strong.
- **Reproduction:** The colonies may be divided, but this will mar their shape. Small fragments of the disk may be cultivated.

GA: + ; **TO: +** ; **SE: +**

Photos:

- Top: A colony as seen from the side
- Centre: A colony as seen from above
- Bottom: Close-up of the autozooids

***Lobophytum* spp.**
continued on page 170

"KA4-ALC-48" off Papua-New Guinea.   Photo: Scott W. Michael

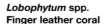

Lobophytum spp.
Finger leather coral

Distribution: Very common in the Indo-Pacific. Yet, details are unknown.

Size and growth form: These species may develop into large, encrusting colonies with fleshy lobes. They may overgrow large areas.

Food: Feed on the products of their zooxanthellae, but probably also make use of other food sources.

Description: Dimorphic with small autozooids and siphonozooids, which do not quite attain 1 cm in length. Sometimes, a short sterile stalk is produced. The coenenchyme is folded, or grows in finger-shaped lobes.

Description of the sclerites:
① Interior of the base of the colony - usually cylindrical, with whorls and thorns, less than 0.5 mm long. ② Surface of the colony - slenderly club-shaped.

Aquarium maintenance:

– **General conditions:** There are several species to be found on sale in aquarium shops. Not all of these open their polyps in aquaria, particularly if there are stony corals associated with them. They need a lot of space and seem to be slightly more delicate than the other genera in the family.

– **Lighting:** High light intensity.

– **Water circulation:** Medium to strong.

– **Reproduction:** These corals may be fragmented by cutting off layers, which, however, sometimes hurts the mother colony.

GA: + ; **TO:** + ; **SE:** +/-

Photos:

On the left: "KA4-ALC-49" in an aquarium
– Top: The whole colony
– Centre: Close-up of the finger-shaped lobes
– Bottom: Close-up of the autozooids (closed) and the siphonozooids (open)

On the right:
Left row
– Top: "KA4-ALC-50" with white polyps in an aquarium
– Centre: "KA4-ALC-51" in an aquarium
– Bottom: "KA4-ALC-52" in an aquarium
Right row
– Top: "KA4-ALC-53" in an aquarium
– Bottom: Close-up of the polyps of "KA4-ALC-53"

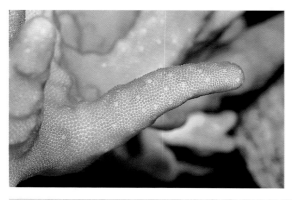

Cladiella spp.
Cauliflower coral

Distribution: Very common in the Indo-Pacific. Details are not known.

Size and growth form: May grow into large colonies in the sea, but only into medium-sized colonies in aquaria.

Food: They feed on the products of their zooxanthellae.

Description: Monomorphic, most often growing flat and crust-like. Lobes are often very flat and barely finger-shaped. The colony feels slimy to the touch. The polyps are dark (often brownish).They may be retracted completely into the coenenchyme. *Cladiella* spp. may easily be confused with *Alcyonium* spp., which, however, possess clearly finger-shaped lobes.

Description of the sclerites:

These are the same all over the colony. Usually, they have a regular shape like that of a dumbell or a windlass, and are less than 0.2 mm long.

Aquarium maintenance:

- **General conditions:** These corals can grow very quickly, but they are sensitive against fragmentation. Thus, they are among the leather corals of the family Alcyoniidae that are more difficult to keep. If environmental conditions are favourable for them, colonies may grow to a remarkable size.
- **Lighting:** High light intensity.
- **Water circulation:** Medium to strong.
- **Reproduction:** They may be fragmented by cutting, but this, however, is not always successful, and we have experienced that a complete colony died after fragmentation.

GA: + ; **TO:** + ; **SE:** +/-

Photos:
On the left: "KA4-ALC-54" in an aquarium
- Top: The whole colony
- Bottom: Close-up

On the right:
Top row: "KA4-ALC-55" in an aquarium
- Left: General view of a colony
- Right: Close-up
Bottom row: "KA4-ALC-56" (perhaps identical with "KA4-ALC-45") in an aquarium
- Left: General view of a colony
- Right: Close-up

Sinularia dura
(Often referred to as *Lobophytum crassum* in older aquarium literature.)

Distribution: Very common in the Indo-Pacific, yet, details are unknown.

Size and growth form: Usually small to medium-sized leaf-shaped colonies.

Food: Feeds on the products of its zooxanthellae.

Description: This species was first described by Pratt (1903). Because of its shape, which resembles a leaf, but is also cuplike, this species is easy to identify. There are, however, some other *Sinularia* spp. with this form, e.g. *S. fungoides*. These corals are flesh-coloured and the polyps are small with a rather large distance between them.

Description of the sclerites:
① Surface of the polypary - club-shaped, 0.1-0.2 mm long.
② Surface of the stalk - club-shaped, 0.1-0.2 mm long.
③ Interior of the polypary and the stalk - spindle-shaped, up to 5.6 mm long. Drawings of the sclerites to the right: Dr. P. Alderslade.

Aquarium maintenance:
- **General conditions:** Quite often on offer in aquarium shops. This species grows quite well under strong light. The colonies do not grow particularly tall but, rather, develop into a leafy shape or that of a flat cup.
- **Lighting:** High light intensity.
- **Water circulation:** Medium to strong.
- **Reproduction:** May easily be fragmented by cutting off small pieces of the body tissue.

GA: + ; **TO:** + ; **SE:** +

Photos:
- Top: Colony on a reef wall off Indonesia
- Centre: Colony in an aquarium
- Bottom: Close-up

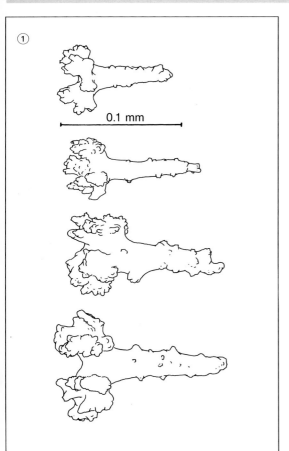

0.1 mm

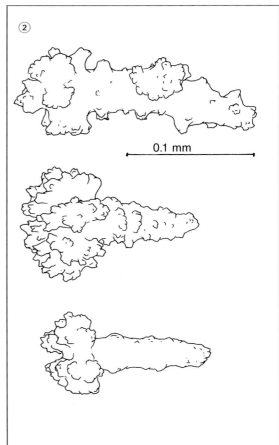

0.1 mm

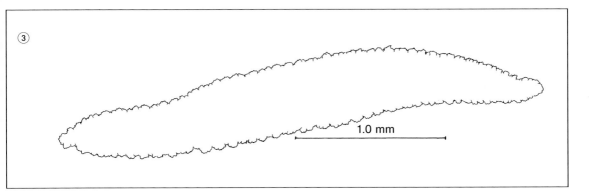

1.0 mm

Sinularia brassica

Distribution: Very common in the Indo-Pacific, yet, details are unknown.

Size and growth form: Usually small to medium-sized leaf-shaped colonies.

Food: Feeds on the products of its zooxanthellae, but probably also makes use of other food sources.

Description: This species was first described by MAY (1898). It is closely related to *Sinularia dura*, having the same type of sclerites. It may very well turn out to be the same species and, thus, a senior synonym of *S. dura*. It has a variable form, but usually develops finger-shaped lobes.

Description of the sclerites:
① Surface of the polypary - club-shaped, 0.15-0.2 mm long. ② Interior of the polypary and stalk - spindle-shaped, up to 3.25 mm long and 0.65 mm thick (VERSEVELDT, 1980).

Aquarium maintenance:
- **General conditions:** Quite often on offer in aquarium shops. This species grows quite well under strong light, forming leaf- shaped colonies.
- **Lighting:** High light intensity.
- **Water circulation:** Medium to strong.
- **Reproduction:** May easily be fragmented by cutting off small pieces of the body tissue.

GA: + ; **TO:** + ; **SE:** +

Photos:
- Top: Colony in an aquarium
- Centre: Close-up of the above colony
- Bottom: Another colony in an aquarium

Sinularia flexibilis

Distribution: Indo-Pacific; Vanokoro-, Fiji-Islands, Samoa, Philippines, Malayan Archipelago, Great Barrier Reef, Vietnam, Palau, New Caledonia and the Ryukyu Islands.

Size and growth form: The species may develop large, branching, monospecific stands which may cover whole areas.

Food: Feeds on the products of its zooxanthellae, but probably also makes use of other food sources.

Description: This species was first described by Quoy & Gaimard (1833). It is one of the few *Sinularia* spp. that develop slender finger-or tentacle-like lobes. It is, by far, the most common species with that form.

Description of the sclerites:
There are no sclerites on the end branches, but their numbers gradually increase towards the base. ① Surface of the stalk - club-shaped, with smaller sclerites usually having an oval form and being equipped with blunt thorns, variable in length, the shorter ones being 0.07-0.13 mm, the longer ones, which are also rarer, being 0.17-0.25 mm long. ② Interior of stalk - spindles 1.3-2.0 mm.

Aquarium maintenance:
- **General conditions:** This species grows well. It produces copious amounts of mucus. It needs a lot of space to grow well and to develop its long lobes.
- **Lighting:** High light intensity.
- **Water circulation:** Medium.
- **Reproduction:** May very easily be fragmented by cutting off branches.

GA: + ; **TO:** + ; **SE:** +

Photos:
- Top: Monospecific stands off Green Island, Great Barrier Reef
- Centre: Colony in an aquarium
- Bottom: Close-up of branches and polyps

Sinularia mollis

Distribution: Indo-Pacific; it was found off the Bantayan Island, the Philippines and the Ryukyu Islands; further details are not known.

Size and growth form: Medium-sized.

Food: Feeds on the products of its zooxanthellae, but probably also makes use of other food sources.

Description: This species was first described by KOLONKO (1926). The shape of the specimen shown in the pictures on this page reminds one of *S. flexibilis*. It has long, slender lobes and a fleshy stem.

Description of the sclerites:
No sclerites on the surface of the lobes and only a few in their interior. ① Polyps - club-shaped with a few flat protrusions, 0.05-0.08 mm long. ② Surface of the stalk - club-shaped with a broad, thorny head and a thorny or spiny shaft, 0.14-0.19 mm long; a few are somewhat longer, 0.25 mm. ③ Interior of the stalk - spindle-shaped, up to 5.60 mm and 0.7 mm thick.

Aquarium maintenance:
– **General conditions:** This species is hardy and grows well. It needs a lot of space to develop well. It is only rarely on sale in aquarium shops.
– **Lighting:** High light intensity.
– **Water circulation:** Medium to strong.
– **Reproduction:** May very easily be fragmented by cutting off branches.

GA: + ; **TO:** + ; **SE:** +

Photos:
– Top: Colony in an aquarium
– Bottom: Close-up of branches

Sinularia cf. *notanda*

Distribution: Western Indo-Pacific (?); it was found off Madagascar and the Seychelles; further details are not known.

Shape and height: Medium-sized, branching and slightly bushy.

Food: Feeds on the products of its zooxanthellae, but probably also makes use of other food sources.

Description: This species was first described by TIXIER-DU-VAULT (1966), however the original description is poor and the specimen is missing so we take our characters from Verseveldt's 1976 interpretation. The stiff, hard stalk has fine, longitudinal furrows and low lobes which, again, have conical branches that are 5-6 mm thick at the base and up to 10 mm long. The lobes and the branches are covered with polyps.

Description of the sclerites:
① Interior of the lobes - bizarre-shaped (see the drawings below right). ② Coenenchyme of the stalk - mostly normal spindle-shaped sclerites, 4-5 mm long. ③ Surface of the stalk - short, warty clubs and cylinders 0.11-0.16 mm long.

Aquarium maintenance:
- **General conditions:** This species is hardy and grows well. It needs a lot of space to develop well. It is among the rarer species.
- **Lighting:** High light intensity.
- **Water circulation:** Medium to strong.
- **Reproduction:** May very easily be fragmented by cutting off branches.

GA: + ; **TO:** + ; **SE:** +

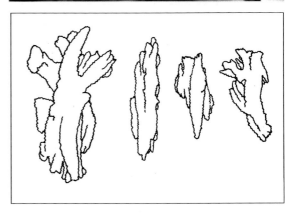

Photos:
- Top: Colony in an aquarium
- Centre: Close-up of the lobes and the branches
- Bottom: Sclerites from the lobes (drawing after VERSE-VELDT, 1976)

Alcyonium spp.
(Often referred to as *Cladiella* spp. by authors in older aquarium literature.)

Distribution: Details are not known, but, very probably, these species occur all over the tropical Indo-Pacific. Some species come from colder waters, like e.g. the well-known "dead man's finger", *Alcyonium digitatum* from the North Sea.

Shape and height: Large branching colonies.

Food: Feed on the products of their zooxanthellae, but they probably also make use of other food sources.

Description: Monomorphic, growing upright with well developed finger-shaped lobes and branches. The polyps are found on the lobes and branches. The coenenchyme may be white and contrasts with the colour of the polyps, which often leads to confusion with *Cladiella* spp.

Description of the sclerites:
Spindle-shaped (there are no sclerites having the shape of anchors, dumbells or clubs), up to 1 mm long.

Aquarium maintenance:
– **General conditions:** Some of the species may be found on offer in aquarium shops. *Alcyonium* spp. grow very well and develop beautiful large colonies.
– **Lighting:** High light intensity.
– **Water circulation:** Medium to strong.
– **Reproduction:** These species may be fragmented by cutting off branches, but, in some cases, this may result in damage to the mother colonies.

GA: + ; **TO:** + ; **SE:** +/-

Photos:
– Top: Colony of "KA4-ALC-57" in an aquarium
– Centre: Colony of "KA4-ALC-58" in an aquarium
– Bottom: Colony of "KA4-ALC-59" in an aquarium

Studeriotes sp.
(Referred to in aquarium literature as *Sphaerella krempfi* by many authors).
Christmas tree coral

Distribution: Indo-Pacific; details are not known.
Shape and height: Aquarium colonies are usually not taller than 30 cm if fully expanded, and less than 5 cm when retracted. Details about their size in their natural surroundings are not known.
Food: Plankton.
Description: The long branches may be retracted into the stalk, which is buried into the bottom sand or mud. The branches are whitish to brownish with small, thinly scattered brown polyps. Monomorphic. This species does not possess any zooxanthellae. Sometimes, black specimens (or species ?) are on offer in aquarium shops.
Aquarium maintenance:
- **General conditions:** A very interesting species, which is, however, difficult to keep and therefore quite rare in our aquaria. It needs large quantities of food. ACHTERKAMP (1991) suggests that it should be fed twice a day. This species is best kept in a special aquarium (sand zone aquarium) by experienced aquarists, who are in a position to feed them small live plankton.
- **Lighting:** Low to medium light intensity.
- **Water circulation:** Strong.
- **Reproduction:** Unknown.
GA: +/- ; **TO:** + ; **SE:** +/-

Photos:
- Top: Colony in an aquarium   Photo: H. Nooijen
- Bottom: Close-up of branches and polyps

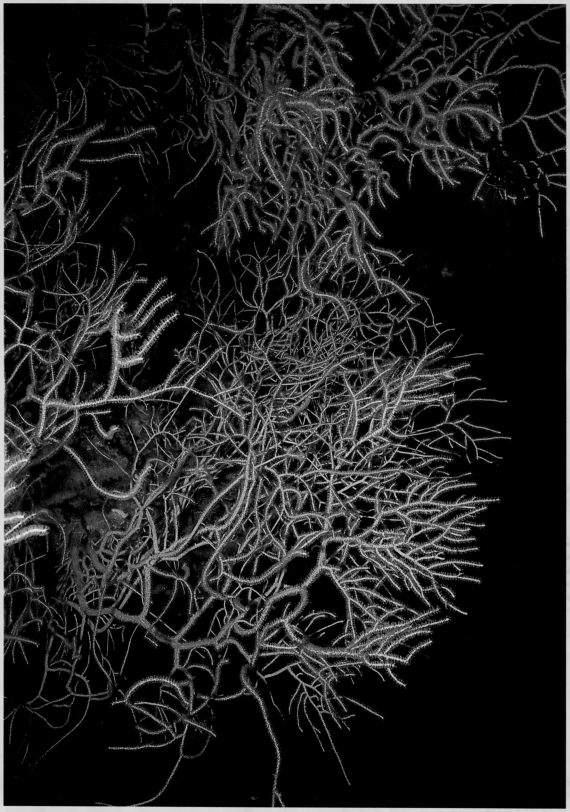

Chapter 10

Scleraxonia

Octocorals with an axis that contains sclerites

Although BAYER (1981) stated that such traditional subdivisions as this should only be retained as a convenience at a quasi-subordinal level, we have decided to continually use the taxon Scleraxonia for gorgonian-like octocorals with a scleritic axis. As Dr. ALDERSLADE points out in his introduction to the subclass Octocorallia (chapter 7), suborders of the order Alcyonacea cannot be positively distinguished from each other by strictly defined criteria. Instead, there are gradual transitions between the taxa. If we restrict our examination just to external appearance, the term "gorgonian" is obviously suitable for the members of both the suborders Scleraxonia and Holaxonia (and a few soft corals). However, looking at the internal structure of gorgonian-like octocorals, it is convenient to subdivide those with an axis into the suborders Scleraxonia and Holaxonia while bearing in mind that the family Keroididae bridges the two groups.

Members of the suborder Scleraxonia look very similar to gorgonians of the suborder Holaxonia, yet their skeletal axis contains sclerites, may be articulated, and is usually softer. In the genus *Subergorgia*, there are species which develop large fans or bushes (photo on the left: Scott W. Michael). Smaller colonies of scleraxonian corals often grow in small caves or under overhanging rocks, like the melithaeid in the picture above (photo: E. Svensen).

Comparative anatomy of members of the suborder Scleraxonia

Family/Genus	Cortex/Medulla	Polyps
Briareidae *Briareum*	Cortex not separated from the medulla by a ring of boundary canals. Both layers extensively penetrated by solenia. Cortex sclerites colourless. Medulla sclerites magenta, often branched. Sclerites easily separated; axis fragile.	Monomorphic
Paragorgiidae *Paragorgia*	Sclerites of cortex and medulla different shape and sometimes different colour. Cortex not separated from the medulla by a ring of boundary canals. Both layers extensively penetrated by solenia. Sclerites easily separated; axis fragile.	Dimorphic
Anthothelidae *Anthothela* *Semperina* *Iciligorgia* *Solenocaulon* *Homophyton* *Alertigorgia* *Callipodium* *Diodogorgia* *Erythropodium* *Titanideum* *Tripalea*	Sclerites of cortex and medulla sometimes of different shape and colour. Cortex separated from medulla by boundary canals. Medulla, unlike the cortex, is little penetrated by solenia. Sclerites easily separated; axis fragile.	Monomorphic
Sibogagorgiidae *Sibogagorgia*	Sclerites of cortex and medulla have different shape and colour. Cortex separated from medulla by boundary canals, and both layers penetrated by solenia. Sclerites of the medulla enmeshed in small amounts of gorgonin but easily separated; axis fragile.	Dimorphic
Parisididae *Parisis*	Axial medulla jointed. Nodes of smooth, lobate rods embedded in a gorgonin matrix. Internodes of inseparable fused, tuberculate sclerites. Branching from the interodes. Cortex thin, and easily scraped off. All colonial sclerites colourless. Axis brittle.	Monomorphic
Melithaeidae *Melithaea* *Acabaria* *Clathraria* *Mopsella* *Wrightella*	Axial medulla jointed. Smooth rod-like sclerites embedded in a gorgonin matrix in the nodes, and inseparable fused in the internodes. Branching from the nodes. Cortex thin, soft, and easily scraped off. Colonial sclerites commonly brightly coloured. Axis brittle.	Monomorphic
Coralliidae *Corallium*	Axial medulla hard, not articulated, and formed from inseperably fused sclerites. Cortex thin, soft, and easily be scraped off.	Dimorphic
Subergorgiidae *Subergorgia*	Medulla formed from a network of smooth anastomosing rod-like sclerites embedded in a dense gorgonin matrix. Cortex thin, soft, and containing tuberculate sclerites. Axis very strong and flexible.	Monomorphic

In principle, the substance of scleraxonian gorgonians is divided into two layers, both containing sclerites; an outer cortex and an inner medullar. The polyps lie in the cortex. If the sclerites in the medulla are unconsolidated, that is free or loosely bound, the colony can be easily broken. If the sclerites are consolidated by being cemented together by horny or calcareous material, the colonies are general much stronger.

In holaxonians there may be three layers; an outer scleritic coenenchyme, an axial cortex, and an inner axial medullar or central chord. The polyps lie in the outer coenenchyme, and the axial cortex is usually scleroproteinous (horn-like gorgonin) and maybe heavily calcified. If a central chord is present it may consist of horny material alone, or horny material and calcarious deposits, and it may be hollow and cross-chambered. In the family Keroididae these three layers are present, but the axial cortex contains sclerites so placing the group in a somewhat intermediate position between the Scleraxonia and the Holaxonia.

Whether the axial structure is purely of horny proteinaceous construction or of sclerites with or without gorgonin, the skeletal structure is not built by any individual polyps, but is a product of the whole colony, and forms a special part of the coenenchyme (BAYER, 1973). Sclerites also occur in the coenenchyme and these are commonly more densely situated in the Scleraxonia and Holaxonia than in the majority of soft corals, although there is considerable variation. The sclerites of the coenenchyme often have beautiful colours and greatly contribute to the external coloration of the colony.

As in all other octocorals, the coenenchyme of scleraxonian corals is permeated by thin canals (solenia). Although, commonly, there are different sclerites in the separate layers, in some groups the boundary of the layers is difficult to detect, while in others the cortex is clearly separated from the medulla by a ring or network of boundary canals. In some groups, fine solenia, penetrate both layers of the colony, horizontally and vertically, while in others the solenia are confined to the cortical layer only. Water, nutrients and metabolic waste are transported through these solenial canals.

The polyps grow in the coenenchyme and develop from the endodermal walls of the solenia. Most families of the Scleraxonia are monomorphic, that is there is only one type of polyp. Only the families Coralliidae, Paragorgiidae and Sibigagorgiidae have dimorphic polyps. The most important characteristics in the systematics of the Scleraxonia are the colonial form, the structure of the axis, the arrangement of the canals, the shape of the sclerites and their arrangement in the polyps. With Dr. Alderslade´s help we have tried to summarize these data in a table (see page 184). The systematic characteristics of the Scleraxonia are highly complicated and rarely available to most aquarists. The table is therefore supposed to convey useful background information about the anatomy of the group.

From the point of view of the aquarist, there are not many species which could seriously be considered for a coral reef aquarium, except for a few that contain zooxanthellae. The coral reef species of the families Subergorgiidae and Melithaeidae are especially appealing, on the one hand, because they have such beautiful colours and, on the other, because some grow to rather large sizes. These larger species are not, however, suitable for the coral reef aquarium, because, in addition to their size, their preferences concerning food and water circulation mean that they cannot be kept successfully, at least, not at the moment.

BAYER (1981) divides the Scleraxonia into eight families (see the summary above).

Systematics of the suborder Scleraxonia

Family Briareidae
Family Anthothelidae
    Subfamily Anthothelinae *
    Subfamily Sempererinae
    Subfamily Spongiodermatinae
Family Subergorgiidae
Family Paragorgiidae
Family Sibogagorgiidae
Family Coralliidae
Family Melithaeidae
Family Parisididae

The taxum marked with an asterisks (*) is not dealt with in this chapter.

Family Briareidae

The family Briareidae is monotypic, with the genus *Briareum* as its only representative. Physiologically, *Briareum* differs from other scleraxonians in that the outer layer of the coenenchyme (cortex) is not separated from the medulla by a ring of boundary canals, and both layers are extensively penetrated by solenia. The sclerites of both layers are not consolidated, and are easily separable. Although there are traces of gorgonin in the medulla, the amount is insignificant, and colonies are easily broken. The gastric cavities of the polyps lie only in the cortex, and

Briareum asbestinum: close-up of the polyps   Photo: Scott W. Michael

Briareum asbestinum: Rod-shaped colony with partly contracted polyps (left) and expanded polyps (right)   Photos: Scott W. Michael

Like the Caribbean species *Briareum asbestinum*, the species from the Indo-Pacific also have zooxanthellae. The fact that Dr. Alderslade has successfully kept several Indo-Pacific species in small, simple, undergravel-filtered aquaria indicates that they should do very well in a modern coral reef aquarium.

Family Anthothelidae

Except for a few species, corals in the family Anthothelidae have no zooxanthellae and must therefore be considered as difficult to keep alive for any length of time in aquaria, since, unless they are given plenty of plankton and strong water movement, they will soon die. The axis is different to that of the Briareidae as the cortex is separated from the medulla by boundary canals, usually forming a network, and the medulla, unlike the cortex, is little penetrated by solenia. Solenial canals may perforate the medulla in the terminal branches, but there is little penetration proximally. The axis is weak and breaks easily as, in general, the sclerites are unconsolidated, although, in some genera, groups of sclerites may occur fused together with calcareous material. The polyps are monomorphic. Several anthothelid genera grow as thin, encrusting mats, unlike the normal image of a gorgonian. However, these show the same layers as the axis of an erect, branched genus. As shown in the systematic survey on page 185, there are three subfamilies in the Anthothelidae, one of which, the Anthothelinae, will not be dealt with here.

The genus *Briareopsis*, established by BAYER in 1993, in many ways bridges between the families Briareidae and Anthothelidae. Although the cortex is not easily differentiated from the inner medulla, as boundary canals are indistinct, and the medulla is per-

do not penetrate into the medulla.

Briareum includes several species, of which *Briareum asbestinum* from the Caribbean Sea is the best known. This is one of the most attractive scleraxonians and is rather easy to keep. It contains zooxanthellae and may grow in branching, as well as prostrate, forms. In the last few years, this species has been imported quite often and has become more and more popular among aquarists.

An unknown number of species of the genus *Briareum* occur in the Indo-Pacific. These are often referred to as species of *Sole-nopodium*, which is considered to be a synonym of *Briareum* (BAYER, 1961). A revision of the genus is badly needed.

Briareum stechei grows as a tangled mass of tube-like branches. The colonies are always hollow, that is they have an outside and an inside, the lining of the cavity being formed by the medulla. The sclerites of the medulla are magenta-coloured, while those of the cortex are colourless giving the surface a pale pinkish-brown colour. The arrangement of these colours is typical of the genus in general.

Briareum asbestinum
Corky sea fingers

Distribution: Common in the Caribbean.
Size: Crust-like or digitate colonies of medium height and up to 60 cm.
Food: Feeds on the products of its zooxanthellae.
Description: This species is often found on reef flats and inner reefs. Colonies usually have a crust-like base, from which two or more cylindrical branches may grow. The large polyps have their gastric cavities embedded in the cortex. When fully expanded, they make the colonies look hairy. There are transparent sclerites on the surface and magenta ones in the interior. The medulla is not separated from the cortex by boundary canals, but is penetrated by solenial canals and by thicker endodermal canals. The polyps and the tentacles are very similar to those of *Pachyclavularia violacea* (see page 121). The sclerites, both in the cortex and medulla, are easily separated and only insignificant amounts of gorgonin are present.
Aquarium maintenance:
− **General conditions:** Easy to keep, but this species needs high light intensity, a moderate current and high water quality.
− **Lighting:** High light intensity.
− **Water circulation:** Medium to strong.
− **Reproduction:** May easily be propagated by cutting off layers of tissue.
GA: + ; TO: + ; SE: +

Photos:
Top: Rod-shaped colony off the Cayman Islands
Photo: Scott W. Michael
Bottom on the right: Crust-like-growing colony off the Cayman Islands
Photo: Scott W. Michael
Bottom on the left: A colony in an aquarium

Iciligorgia schrammi is the largest of the non-photosynthesizing scleraxonian corals of the Caribbean. It lives in clear water with a moderate current. The bottom picture shows that the tiny polyps are on the sides of the branches.

Photos: Scott W. Michael

forated by solenia, the genus was tentatively placed in the Antholthelidae because the sclerites and gross colonial morphology are more consistent with that family. There is only one species, *Briareopsis aegeon*, and it has only been found in the freezing waters of the South Shetland Islands at between 300-686 m.

In the Caribbean Sea, we find the genus *Iciligorgia*, which is a monotypic genus, with *Iciligorgia schrammi* as the only species. These large corals, swaying with the movement of the water, represent the subfamily Semperininae. *I. schrammi* branches only in one plane, which results in the colony developing a fan-like shape. The thickened, fistulose ends of the branches are a typical feature of this species. It grows in deeper areas of the reef, most often at about 10 m depth (COLIN, 1978), has no zooxanthellae, grows in long rows and develops colonies of a diameter of up to 2 m.

The subfamily **Spongiodermatinae** includes, among others, the frequently imported *Diodogorgia nodulifera* from the Caribbean, a coral which is, from an aquaristic point of view, perhaps the most interesting species of the family Anthothelidae. In spite of the fact that the species does not contain zooxanthellae, *D. nodulifera*, which occurs in several colour morphs, is not too difficult to keep in a coral reef aquarium (see fact page 189).

Erythropodium caribaeorum from the Caribbean, grows prostrate in mat-like forms in shallow water areas and contains zooxanthellae. When their polyps are fully expanded, the colonies look like hairy carpets. This species is very durable in reef aquaria, where it can quickly grow to cover large areas and almost overgrow other corals. We have never seen *E. caribaeorum* on offer in the aquarium trade in Europe, but believe it to be more common in the States. As it is really common in shallow water, often in front of the actual reef, and easy to keep, we think it might be a most valuable addition to a coral reef aquarium.

Diodogorgia nodulifera
Colourful sea rod

Distribution: Caribbean Sea, including Florida and the Bahamas. According to HUMANN (1993), this species inhabits a wide range of habitats, such as patch reefs with sandy or rocky substrates, or caves or overhanging walls in moderate to greater depths.

Size: Small, thinly branching colonies and thick rod-shaped ones. Usually not higher than 10-30 cm.

Food: Feeds on plankton and other small organisms.

Description: This species grows on reef flats in water of medium to greater depth, on sandy, as well as on rocky, substrates and also in the shade of overhanging rocks. It contains no zooxanthellae. The colouration is variable and includes the following combinations: ① Yellow to orange branches with violet or purple calyx rims; ② red branches with red calyx rims; ③ red branches with yellow calyx rims. The polyps are always white or transparent. As in other members of the family, the medulla and cortex consist of layers of different types of sclerites. It is the colour of the sclerites that gives the species its different colour morphs.

Aquarium maintenance:

— **General conditions:** This species is not easy to keep, but it is one of the most enduring non-photosynthesizing sleraxonians. It is best kept in a special aquarium set up specifically for this type of animal. It has to be fed regularly, preferably with live plankton.

— **Lighting:** Low to medium light intensity.

— **Water circulation:** Strong to very strong and alternating.

— **Reproduction:** Unknown; it is probably impossible to propagate this species by cutting off layers.

GA: +/- ; **TO:** + ; **SE:** +/-

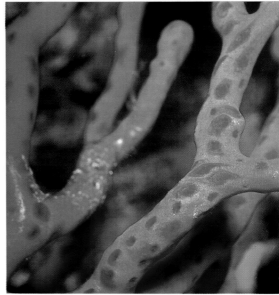

Photos:
Top: Yellow colony with partly expanded polyps in an aquarium
Bottom: Close up of a bright red colony
Photo: Scott W. Michael

Erythropodium caribaeorum
Encrusting gorgonian

Distribution: Caribbean Sea, including Florida and the Bahamas, where it, according to HUMANN (1993), inhabits most reef habitats, but is most common in shallow fringing, patch and back reef areas.

Size: Crust-like colonies of medium size.

Food: This species feeds on the products of its zooxanthellae.

Description: This coral mostly grows in mat-like colonies in shallow water areas. The polyps have small, hair-like tentacles. When the polyps are retracted, the coenenchyme is smooth and leather-like. The colour of the colony is tan-like and the underside is reddish; the polyp mouth often looks whitish.

Aquarium maintenance:

— **General conditions:** This species is easy to keep, but it needs high illumination, demands particular conditions with regard to water circulation and requires the best water quality possible. It may easily cover large areas in the aquarium. It is only rarely on offer in the aquarium trade in Europe, but more commonly seen in the States.

— **Lighting:** High light intensity.

— **Water circulation:** Medium.

— **Reproduction:** May be easily propagated by cutting off fragments of tissue.

GA: + ; **TO:** + ; **SE:** +

Photos:

Top: Habitat off the Cayman Islands

Photo: Scott W. Michael

Centre: Colony with expanding polyps, photographed off the Cayman Islands.   Photo: J. Cairns-Michael

Bottom on the left: Colony with retracted polyps, photographed off the Cayman Islands.   Photo: Scott W. Michael

Bottom on the right: Close-up of the "hairy" polyps

Photo: Scott W. Michael

The genus has now also been found in the Indo-Pacific. *E. hicksoni* occurs in the temperate waters of the southern coast of Australia, and a new species from the Solomon Islands is under description (ALDERSLADE, pers. com.).

Family Subergorgiidae

The family Subergorgiidae is monotypic, with the genus *Subergorgia* as its only representative. Some species may grow into gigantic fan-shaped colonies. The subergorgiid axial structure is quite different to the structures we have mentioned so far. The axis is very strong and flexible, and able to withstand even strong currents, because the medulla is made up of smooth, branched, anastomosing sclerites that are embeded in a robust gorgonin matrix.

Subergorgia mollis is very common in the Indo-Pacific (see also the profile on page 192). We found colonies of over a metre in size off "Wotanabe Bommie" at Flinders Reef in the Coral Sea. Here, the current is strong and the water is crystal-clear and poor in nutrients. The large coral fans grew nearly perpendicularly from the reef walls, at right angles to the direction of the current. Colonies up 2 m have been observed in other parts of the world (ALDERSLADE, pers. com.). Another Indo-Pacific species is *S. suberosa*.

Family Melithaeidae

Many species of the family Melithaeidae grow into large, fan-shaped colonies, and need to be flexible enough to withstand strong currents. On the reef, these species are very often found on the reef slope at depths of 5 to 6 m and over. They can be found in shallower waters but only in shel-

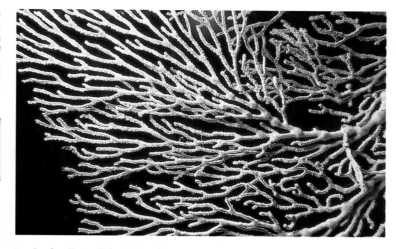

In the family Melithaeidae, the branches are articulated and connected by horny nodes. Because of this structure, the colonies are very flexible and yet stable enough to grow into large fans. The knot-like nodes are easily seen on the right.

tered areas like canyons and caves. Now and then, we have found isolated specimens under relatively strong light, but most species grow in places where the light is moderate to low. Water current is of vital importance for these corals, as it supplies them with large amounts of plankton.

In some respects the melithaeid axial skeleton is similar to that found in the Subergorgiidae, but it has extra complexities. For a start, the axis is jointed, being made up of alternating horny joints (nodes) and calcareous joints (internodes). These nodes are constructed from numerous smooth, rod-shaped sclerites which are tightly bound in a gorgonian matrix. The internodes are formed from similarly shaped sclerites, but these are fused together to form porous, rigid sections. The nodes, which appear as small knots regularly distributed over the branches and placed at each branch junction, are relatively soft and provide the colonies with the necessary flexibility. The polyps are small and they are situated in the outer cortex, which is very thin and easily damaged. The sclerites contain pigments

Acabaria sp. off Indonesia. Some of the polyps are partly retracted.

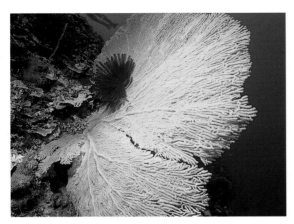

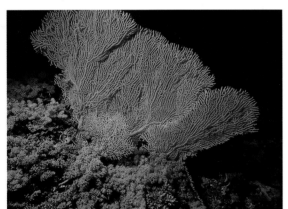

Subergorgia mollis

Distribution: Very common in the Indo-Pacific. No further details are known.

Size: This species may not only develop small fans, but also large ones with diameters of several metres.

Food: Feeds on plankton.

Description: This coral usually grows on reef walls at right angles to the direction of the current. The medulla contains sclerites, partially fused, and bound in a gorgonin matrix. The cortex is separated from the medulla by boundary canals, but the medulla lacks solenial canals. This species has no zooxanthellae. The colony colour varies from orange to yellow-brown to bright yellow.

Aquarium maintenance:

– **General conditions:** This coral is difficult to keep. Small colonies are sometimes found on offer in aquarium shops. It needs strong water circulation and large amounts of planktonic food.

– **Lighting:** Low light intensity.

– **Water circulation:** Very strong.

– **Reproduction:** Unknown.

GA: - ; **TO:** + ; **SE:** -

Photos:

Top: A colony with expanded polyps near "Wotanabe Bommie" in the Coral Sea

Centre: Dark orange colony with expanded polyps on the Myrmidion Reef, Great Barrier Reef; in the foreground, there are soft corals that probably belong to the genus *Efflatounaria*.

Bottom: A young colony on the Great Barrier Reef; this is what colonies may look like when they are imported.

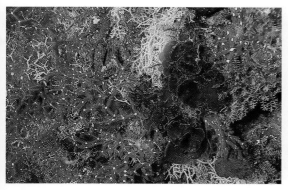

Clathraria maldivensis: growing together with other *Clathraria* spp. on a reef wall in the Maldives (left). Right: Close-up with partly closed polyps

which give the species of the family their beautiful colours: red, orange, pink, yellow and white.

According to BAYER (1981) the family contains the following genera: *Melithaea*, *Clathraria*, *Mopsella*, *Wrightella*, and *Acabaria*. On the whole, these genera are very similar and can only be told apart by a close examination of their sclerites. We have to point out, however, that the systematics of these genera are anything but clear. There are many intermediate species, and the distinct possibility that a revision will lead to the conclusion that they all belong to a single genus (ALDERSLADE, pers. com.).

The genus *Melithaea* is possibly the most common in the family, with *M. ochracea* as the most common species. Some *Acabaria* and some *Clathraria* species may be identified by the fact that the colour of the nodes stands out in strong contrast to the colour of the rest of the colony.

We have never heard of species of the family Melithaeidae being kept in aquaria. Looking at their life style in the sea, and bearing in mind the fact that none of these species have zooxanthellae, we believe them to be very difficult to keep in aquaria.

Dense growth of scleraxonian corals from the family Melithaeidae in the Red Sea   Photo: E. Svensen.

Clathraria sp.: The tiny polyps are found only on the sides of the branches.   Photo: Dr. D. Brockmann

Chapter 11:

Holaxonian Corals

At first sight, the corals of the suborder Holaxonia are difficult to distinguish from the corals of the suborder Scleraxonia. As a rule, holaxonian corals have a stronger axis that always contains significant amounts of gorgonin. There is, however, no distinct dividing line (neither anatomically, nor systematically) between the species of the Holaxonia and Scleraxonia and, as we mentioned at the beginning of the previous chapter, the two groups are bridged by the family Keroididae. The term "gorgonian" can be used in connection with both suborders. The structure of the corals in this group varies considerably; sufficiently to divide the suborder into nine families.

Holaxonian corals are very common in all the oceans of the world, but are most numerous in the tropical seas. Among these tropical holaxonian corals, we find quite a number of animals

Most of the holaxonians that are best suited to be kept in aquaria are found in the Caribbean. They are referred to as "photosynthesizing gorgonians", because they have zooxanthellae. The underwater world of the Caribbean (see the picture on the left) differs considerably from that of the Indo-Pacific, but it is as beautiful and interesting. Holaxonians have tiny polyps (top picture) that arise from the coenenchyme. The coenenchyme encloses an axial skeleton, which usually consists of gorgonin often impregnated with non-spicular calcium carbonate. A large number of species from the Indo-Pacific are magnificently coloured, yet they are often difficult to keep in aquaria.

Photos: Scott W. Michael

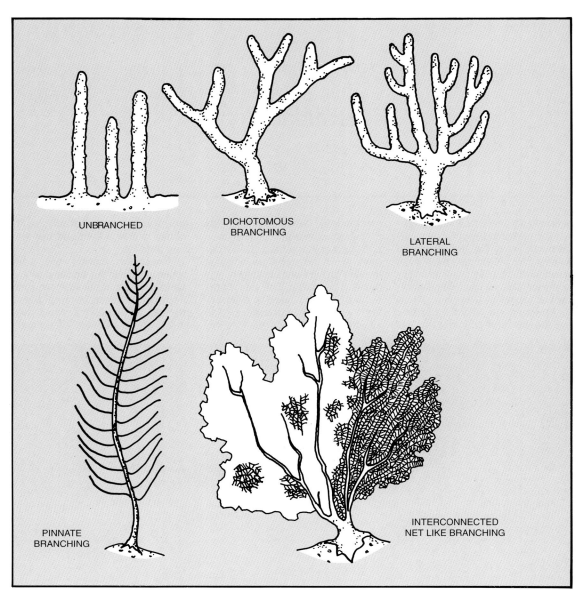

UNBRANCHED

DICHOTOMOUS
BRANCHING

LATERAL
BRANCHING

PINNATE
BRANCHING

INTERCONNECTED
NET LIKE BRANCHING

that are very interesting for the aquarist and are easy to keep.

Just as in some of the scleraxonian corals, the axis consists of two parts, the medulla, more commonly called the central chord, and the cortex (see the drawing on page 197). With the exception of the family Keroeididae, there are no sclerites to be found in the axis. The central chord is either solid, or hollow and cross chambered, and sometimes calcified. The cortex may be pure gorgonin, and is generally calcified with va-

rious amounts of amorphous or crystalline calcium carbonate. The gorgonin is present as lamellae or fibre bundles.

The axial skeleton is covered by the coenenchyme, the sclerites of which have different colours and are generally responsible for the colouration of the colonies. Many species are intensely red or yellow. In some, especially from the Caribbean, the endodermal cells contain zooxanthellae. In these cases, the colour is usually brown or brown

and yellow hues, as in soft corals with zooxanthellae. There is only one type of polyp which develops from the coenenchyme, thus, holaxonian corals are described as monomorphic.

The formation of colonies shows a higher degree of development in holaxonian than in scleraxonian corals. This can be seen in the great regularity of the branching and in the arrangement of the polyps (BAYER, 1973).

There are at least eight different types of branching (ALDERS-

LADE, pers. com.):

- unbranched,
- dichotomous,
- pseudodichotomous,
- quasidichotomous,
- sympodial,
- lateral,
- pinnate,
- interconnected (net-like).

Species which usually form bushes, may also develop in very flat forms if they are exposed to a unilateral current. The arrangement of their polyps in relation to the direction of the current is ideal for the collection of plankton. Polyps may be placed on one or both sides of the branches, or all around.

Like most other cnidarians, holaxonian corals have to endure commensalism and parasitism, i.e. there are numerous other organisms that live between the branches of a colony. Some of these are harmful and feed on the tissue of the colony, while others are completely harmless. In certain cases, parts of a colony may change their appearance completely owing to the influence of such "guests". On several occasions, we have noticed symbiotic barnacles, which have survived for quite a long time in our aquarium, between the branches of holaxonian corals from the Caribbean. In other cases, we have observed parasitic nudibranchs, which, however, have not survived in our aquarium. We think that it is highly interesting to observe such natural assemblages of species in coral reef aquaria. We should also bear in mind that not all associated animals are, by any means, harmful to reef aquaria.

Compared to the Scleraxonia, the Holaxonia contain more species that are easy to keep in reef aquaria. This holds true especially for species containing zooxanthellae from the Caribbean Sea, where photosynthetic gorgonians inhabit the ecological niches which are dominated in the Indo-Pacific by soft corals, a group that is completely missing in the Caribbean. Divers in the

Systematics of the suborder Holaxonia

Family Keroeididae

Family Acanthogorgiidae

Family Plexauridae

     Subfamilies Plexauriinae, Stenogorgiinae

Family Gorgoniidae

Family Ellisellidae

Family Ifaukellidae *

Family Chrysogorgiidae *

Family Primnoidae *

Family Isididae

     Subfamilies Isidinae, Muricellisidinae *,

          Kertoisidinae * , Mopseinae *

(* not dealt with in this volume)

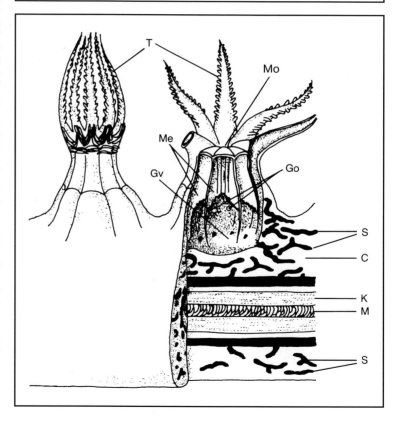

Basic structure of a holaxonian gorgonian coral, after BAYER (1956) and BARNES (1980). T = tentacles; Mo = mouth; Me = mesenteries; Gv = gastro-vascular cavity; Go = gonads; S = solenia; C = coenenchyme; K = cortex; M = medulla.

"KA4-HOL-01" off the Maldives

"KA4-HOL-02" off Papua-New Guinea   Photo: Scott W. Michael

"KA4-HOL-03" in the Coral Sea   Photo: E. Svensen

Caribbean Sea immediately notice the large bush-, branch- or fan-like gorgonians, which, before the era of the modern coral reef aquarium, were thought impossible to keep. Today, we know the opposite to be true and some of the species must be regarded as being among the easiest of all corals to keep.

In the Indo-Pacific, there are only very few species of Holaxonia which contain zooxanthellae. These few photosynthetic species are, however, very durable in the reef aquarium. The species which do not photosynthesize are usually colourful, often fan-shaped colonies that grow in strong currents, under overhanging rocks, or in places reached only by moderate or low levels of light. Although many have beautiful colours, like most scleraxonians, they cannot be kept alive in an aquarium for a long period of time unless given large quantities of plankton; not even modern aquarium technology can meet their demands. In most cases, we cannot provide the food and/or the water circulation they require. Anyone who wants to try and keep the non-photosynthesizing species of Holaxonia should provide them with a specially equipped aquarium with the strongest water movement possible and supply them with plenty of food.

Family Keroeididae

From the systematic point of view, the family Keroeididae holds a very special position. In this family, the central chord is hollow and cross chambered. The cortex, however, consists of smooth sclerites, which are cemented together with gorgonin, a phenomenon which we also know from the family Subergorgiidae of the suborder Scleraxonia. This is the reason why the Keroeididae are also regarded as the link between the scleraxonians and holaxonian corals. The family includes the genera *Keroeides, Ideogorgia, Lignella, Thelogorgia,* and *Pseudothelogorgia*, with a tropical distribution and found at depths of 50 metres and more. From the point of view of the aquarist, they are of no special interest.

Family Acanthogorgiidae

The main range of the family Acanthogorgiidae is the Indo-Pacific. According to BAYER (1981), this family includes the genera *Acanthogorgia, Acalycigorgia, Anthogorgia, Calcigorgia, Cyclomuricea, Muricella* and *Versluysia*. Aquarists will find *Acanthogorgia* the most important genus. None of the genera is found often on sale in the aquarium trade. On coral reefs, however, the family is very common.

The species of the genera *Acanthogorgia* and *Acalycigorgia* (which is probably a variation of the *Acanthogorgia*; ALDERSLADE, pers. com.), in particular, may be observed in caves or in the lower areas of reef slopes, where they grow as large, fan-shaped, rather densely branching colonies. They are usually found in places where water circulation is strong.

As a rule, these species have an axis of pure gorgonin, and a wide chambered central chord. The polyps cannot be retracted into the coenenchyme, so they fold their tentacles over the mouth when contracting. The polyps are also reinforced with strong supporting sclerites.

Corals of the family Acanthogorgiidae are very difficult to keep alive in aquaria for a long time. None of the species has zooxanthellae and they all have very precise demands with regard to food and water circulation. For anyone who wants to try and keep these corals, an aquarium especially equipped for that purpose is a must.

"KA4-HOL-04", an *Acalycigorgia* species on the Osprey Reef, in the Coral Sea

Family Plexauridae

In the suborder Holaxonia, the family Plexauridae is the one with the highest number of genera and a vast number of species, some of which are of great interest for the coral reef aquarium. Members of this family also have an axis with a wide, chambered central chord, but the axial cortex usually has locules containing non-crystalline calcium carbonate.

The family includes species with and without zooxanthellae. Some authors describe certain genera as belonging to the Muriceidae or the Paramuriceidae (= Muricidae without the genus *Muricea*). We, however, follow BAYER (1981), who holds the opinion that these can be included in the family Plexauridae, and who divides the family into two subfamilies.

Subfamily Plexauriinae

BAYER (1981) subsumes the following genera into this subfamily: *Plexaura, Anthoplexaura, Eunicea,* *Euplexaura, Muriceopsis, Plexaurella, Psammogorgia* and *Pseudoplexaura,* but *Muricea* should be added to these.

The species of the genus *Plexaura* generally have thick, bushy branches, with the outer layer of the coenenchyme containing sclerites composed mostly of spindles and clubs, and an inner layer of spiny spindles that are usually purple. We have, at least, three species in the genus *Plexaura,* i.e. the Black Sea Rod *Plexaura homomalla* and the Bent Sea Rod *P. flexuosa,* both of which are found in the Caribbean Sea. They have zooxanthellae, which makes them easy to keep in aquaria. Both species grow in the form of a bush or, at least, of an open fan, and are very decorative. *P. homomalla* tends to branch laterally (only occasionally dichotomously) compared to *P. flexuosa,* which tends to branch dichotomously (HUMANN, 1993). Both species require a lot of space in aquaria and moderate, yet continual, water circulation. In addition the genus contains the species *P. nina.*

According to COLIN (1978), there are two variants of *Plexaura*

"KA4-HOL-05", a *Pseudoplexaura* species, off the Cayman Islands in the Caribbean
Photo: Scott W. Michael

homomalla: one is dense and bush-like in form, with thick branches, and is found at depths between 0 and 30 m, and another, with thinner branches, at depths of 15 to 50 m. In the zone between 15 and 30 m depth, the two variants overlap (see fact page 205).

Plexaura homomalla became of special scientific interest when it was found that it contains a high amount of Prostaglandin A₂, a fatty acid derivative with a hormone-like effect. This substance may amount to 8% of the dry weight of a colony and, in the sea,

prevents fish from feeding on these corals. Prostaglandin A₂ controls a number of human physiological processes, e.g. the contraction and dilation of blood vessels and the bronchial musculature. It also influences diuresis and sugar level, protects the lining of the stomach and is a mediator in cases of inflammations, allergies, sensitivity to pain, etc. (Mebs, 1989).

Species of *Pseudoplexaura* resemble those of *Plexaura*, but their colonies usually have a somewhat slimmer appearance. The

genus may usually be distinguished from *Plexaura* by its lack of calyces. Although it must be said that in *Plexaura* they are not well developed. Humann (1993) mentions four species in this genus, which may, however, only be distinguished by an examination of their sclerites.

Pseudoplexaura species have zooxanthellae, too, and are easily kept in aquaria, where they require a great deal of space. We have successfully kept them in our aquaria for several years, where they have grown very rapidly, often needing to be pruned to prevent other corals from being overgrown. The branches that have been cut off have been "implanted" in other places in the aquarium decoration where they have quickly attached to the substrate. It would, perhaps, be a most fascinating idea to set up an aquarium according to zoogeographical guidelines, which would contain corals exclusively from the Caribbean and in which branching gorgonians would be dominant. Such an aquarium might have a relatively flat sand bottom with some live rock projecting from it. It is our hope that more aquarists will turn to special aquarium types such as this, thus learning about the variations that are possible on the theme of the "mixed" coral reef aquarium. See fact page relating to this genus on pages 206 and 207.

The number of Caribbean Sea species belonging to the genus *Eunicea* is not precisely known. Many of the species may be identified by their large protruding calyces, which can easily be seen and which give the branches a bony and coarse surface. But others such as *E. knighti*, *E pinta*, or *E. palmeri* have little or no development of the calyces. Without a detailed examination of the sclerites, however, the individual species can hardly be told apart. Humann (1993) thinks that the species *Eunicea mammosa*, *E. succinea*, *E. calyculata* and *E. fusca*, may, perhaps, be distinguished from each other by the form of their colonies. However,

Plexaurella nutans off the Cayman Islands in the Caribbean
Photo: Scott W. Michael

this character may vary considerably depending on environmental conditions, so species identification based on this criterion alone is, from our point of view, most doubtful.

Eunicea mammosa (Swollen Knob Candelabrum) has large, close-set, swollen, tubular/cylindrical calyces and is usually light beige in colour. The colonies are normally compact with stout branches. This species inhabits most reef environments, but is most commonly found in the northwestern parts of the Caribbean (HUMANN, 1993).

E. succinea (Shelf Knob Sea Rod) has diagonally placed calyces which usually project diagonally upwards, with the lower part of the calyx forming a protruding lip. According to HUMANN (1993), there are two growth forms: one (*E. s. succinea*) is low, wide candelabrum-shaped, with thick end branches, while the other (*E. s. plantaginea*) is tall and bushy, with thin end branches and with the lower calyx lips more upturned.

While the majority of the *Eunicea* spp. branch only in one plane, *E. calyculata* (Warty Sea Rod), branches on numerous levels. The branches are thick, cylindrical and non-tapering and look bushy when the polyps are expanded. The calyces are low and gaping. This species is widespread in the Caribbean and inhabits most reef environments. *E. fusca* (Doughnut Sea Rod) has low, circular, swollen calyces with a distinct round opening in the middle when the polyps are fully contracted. The colonies are, according to HUMANN (1993), often low, bushy and shrub-like, occasionally taller with widely spaced branches. The branches are light to dark grey, while the polyps are yellow-brown to brown. This species is found on shallow, turbulent, hard substrata and patch reefs.

The genus *Plexaurella* is known only from the Caribbean Sea and the coasts of Florida. HUMANN (1993) mentions six species in the genus, with *Plexaurella nutans* (Giant Slit-Pore Sea Rod) being

One of the most common Indo-Pacific genera from the subfamily Plexauriinae is *Euplexaura*. Colonies may develop into gigantic fans.

"KA4-HOL-06" in the Coral Sea   Photo: E. Svensen

"KA4-HOL-07" on Flinder's Reef, in the eastern part of the Great Barrier Reef

"KA4-HOL-08" off the Maldives   Photo: I. Erga

"KA4-HOL-16", a *Villogorgia* species, off the Maldives

the most common. It grows into very tall colonies, with thick stalks and sparse, dichotomous branches, with their tips usually slightly enlarged. *P. nutans* will only develop to its full size in a very large aquarium. The other species may only be identified with certainty by an examination of their sclerites. The genus, however, is, in general, easily recognized when the polyps are retracted, since, in this position, only an elliptical opening with a slightly raised calyx remains. The maintenance of these species in aquaria is very similar to that of the other photo-synthesizing gorgonians from the Caribbean: a great deal of light and moderate, yet continual, water circulation.

Muricea species remind us somewhat of *Eunicea* species, but the branches of *Muricea* colonies feel coarse to the touch. This is due to the rather strong, protruding calyces, which have projecting, spinous, spindles in the walls. *Muricea* (as well as *Eunicea*) species also contain zooxanthellae.

The genus *Muricea* includes six species, with *Muricea muricata* (Spiny Sea Fan) as the most common one. *M. muricata*, which often has a light beige colour, branches laterally and tightly with only occasional dichotomous secondary branching, all in a single plane (HUMANN, 1993). *M. pinnata* (Long Spine Sea Fan) is "pinnately" branched and can grow on one or more levels, which results in a very bushy shape; the colours are whitish to light grey or yellow-brown. *M. elongata* (Orange Spiny Sea Rod), as well as *M. laxa* (Delicate Spiny Sea Rod), branch laterally on several levels and have a clearly bushy appearance. Both species also have calyces with conspicuously strong and elevated supporting sclerites.

In the genus *Muriceopsis* we find large, pinnate, bushy colonies, which develop large numbers of side branches slanting upwards from a central branch. Thus, the small branches are not always in the same plane, as is the case with *Pseudopterogorgia* spp. from the family Gorgoniidae (see page 213), but develop on several levels. The polyps are

small and arranged on all sides of the main branches, as well as the side branches. The colour of the coenenchyme is often purple or grey-purple. The number of species in the genus is not known, but HUMANN (1993) refers to *M. flavida* (Rough Sea Plume) as the most common species.

The holaxonian corals with zooxanthellae from the subfamily Plexauriinae, which may be kept in aquaria, come from the Caribbean. Yet, there are also many interesting representatives of this subfamily in the Indo-Pacific, where the genus *Euplexaura* is the most common. These are large, fan-shaped holaxonian corals without zooxanthellae, although on the reef, they are common in less than 10 metres of water. *Euplexaura* species are magnificent and it is fascinating to see them sway in the water current. Unfortunately, they are very delicate aquarium animals.

Subfamily Stenogorgiinae

While the subfamily Plexauriinae includes a large number of photo-synthesizing holaxonian corals and is common in the Caribbean Sea, the species of the Stenogorgiinae are most common in the Indo-Pacific. This subfamily includes a large number of genera; BAYER (1981) assumes that there are as many as 22. There is hardly any hope for an aquarist ever attaining an overview of this sophisticated complex of genera and species. Nevertheless, it is not improbable at all that, now and then, specimens of these corals may, by chance, be on sale in the aquarium trade. None of these species has zooxanthellae; thus, they are among the "difficult" holaxonian corals, which have exacting demands concerning food and water circulation.

Astrogorgia sp. and *Villogorgia* sp. are two examples of genera from the Indo-Pacific. Occasionally, gorgonians from the genus *Echinogorgia* are imported, at least one species of which is quite commonly on sale in aquarium shops. Its coenenchyme is light red, while the polyps are bright yellow. Tiny bristle stars can often be found living among their branches. This species requires a strong current, low light intensity and daily feeding to survive in aquaria. Like most of the gorgonians that do not photosynthesize, it must be classified as difficult to keep.

In the Caribbean Sea, we find the fan-shaped, bright yellow *Heterogorgia uatumani*. It lives at relatively great depths and is most common in the northwestern part of the Carribbean (HUMANN, 1993).

One species from the Caribbean is very special: *Swiftia exserta*. It is imported relatively often and has proved to be quite enduring, in spite of the fact that it has no zooxanthellae. With its thin yellow branches and dark red polyps, it looks extremely attractive. *Swiftia exserta* is the only holaxonian coral which we know to have spawned in aquaria (see pages 50 and 51). See fact page 210 for more details.

"KA4-HOL-17" an *Astrogorgia* species, photographed in the Coral Sea.
Photo: E. Svensen

"KA4-HOL-18", an *Echinogorgia* species, is occasionally imported. It does not do well in aquaria, however, and needs strong water circulation and daily feeding to survive. Quite often, beautifully coloured small brittle stars are found among the branches (see bottom picture, on the left).

Plexaura flexuosa
Bent Sea Rod

Distribution: Caribbean Sea, including Southern Florida and the Bahamas.

Size and growth form: This coral usually grows in flat vertical planes with dichotomous branching, but it may also develop in a bush-like form with thick branches branching in all directions; 15 - 40 cm high.

Food: It feeds mainly on the products of its zooxanthellae.

Description: The end branches are 2.5-4.5 mm wide. Inner layer of the coenenchyme contains purple capstans and short rods, middle layer composed of short spindles, outer layer has large leaf-clubs, with serrate folia. Acanthocodia without collaret (BAYER, 1961). Colours vary considerably: light yellow, brownish-yellow or brown, sometimes even purple to purple-red. The polyps are usually lighter coloured than the stalk. When the polyps are retracted, the rims of their aperture are only slightly raised, with a small lip around the inside of the opening (HUMANN, 1993).

Aquarium maintenance:

- **General conditions:** Easy to keep; does best in a sand zone aquarium. It should be allowed to develop into the open water zone without disturbance from other corals. Needs plenty of space.
- **Lighting:** High light intensity required.
- **Water circulation:** Medium strength, but continuous flow.
- **Reproduction:** This coral may be reproduced by fragmentation. Nothing is known about its sexual reproduction in aquaria.

GA: + ; **TO:** + ; **SE:** +

Photos:

Colonies at different locations off the Cayman Islands

Photos: Scott W. Michael

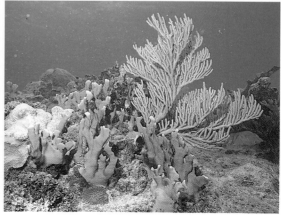

Plexaura homomalla
Black Sea Rod

Distribution: Caribbean Sea, including Southern Florida and the Bahamas.

Size and growth form: This coral usually grows as a flattened bush, although it may also develop lateral branches with finger-shaped protrusions; 15 - 60 cm.

Food: It feeds mainly on the products of its zooxanthellae.

Description: The end branches are 2.5-5.0 mm wide. Inner layer of the coenenchyme contains purple capstans, middle layer composed of spindles, and outer layer with large asymmetrical leaf-clubs having serrated leaves. Polyps with a distinct transverse collaret (BAYER, 1961). Colours vary considerably: light yellow, brownish-yellow or brown, sometimes even purple to purple-red, but the polyps always stand out in contrast to darker stalks. When the polyps retract, the area around them is almost flat or protrudes only slightly.

Aquarium maintenance:
- **General conditions:** Easy to keep; does best in a sand zone aquarium. It should be allowed to develop into the open water zone without disturbance from other corals. Needs plenty of space.
- **Lighting:** High light intensity required.
- **Water circulation:** Medium strength, but continuous flow.
- **Reproduction:** This coral may be reproduced by fragmentation. Nothing is known about its sexual reproduction in aquaria.

GA: + ; **TO:** + ; **SE:** +

Photos:
Above and below on the right: Colonies at two different locations off the Cayman Islands
Bottom left: Detail of branches   Photos: Scott W. Michael

Pseudoplexaura spp.
Porous Sea Rods

Distribution: Caribbean Sea, including Southern Florida and the Bahamas.

Size and growth form: These corals grow into bushy forms with short stems and thick, finger-shaped branches, up to 2 m high.

Food: They feed on the products of their zooxanthellae.

Description: The genus has a sclerite composition where the outer layer contains smooth leaf-clubs or smooth-headed wart-clubs, spiny spindles, and capstans, all colourless. Middle rind with white or purple spindles. The polyps lack sclerites and are fully retractile, resulting in gaping, elliptical pores on the branches (BAYER, 1961). These corals are quite common in the area where they are found. There are four species (HUMANN, 1993), which are very similar and can only be distinguished by a detailed examination of their sclerites. The genus may be identified by the fact that oval or round openings can be seen as pores when the polyps are retracted, as there are no protruding calyces. These corals have large polyps and thick branches.

Photos:
Top: "KA4-HOL-09" off Cuba   Photo: E. Svensen
Bottom left: "KA4-HOL-10" off the Cayman Islands
                                        Photo: Scott W. Michael
Bottom right: "KA4-HOL-11" off the Cayman Islands
                                        Photo: Scott W. Michael

Aquarium maintenance:

- **General conditions:** Very easy to keep; fast-growing; if the light conditions are favourable, these corals grow into large, bushy colonies, which may have to be clipped to limit their size. Very good species for a Caribbean aquarium, but requires ample space and is best kept in a very large aquarium.
- **Lighting:** High light intensity.
- **Water circulation:** Medium to strong.
- **Reproduction:** These corals may be reproduced by fragmentation. Nothing is known about their sexual reproduction in aquaria.

GA: + ; **TO:** + ; **SE:** +

Photos:

Top: "KA4-HOL-12" in our experimental aquarium set-up
Bottom left: "KA4-HOL-13" in an aquarium owned by K. Grube, Berlin, Germany
Bottom right: Close-up of the polyps of "KA4-HOL-13"

Eunicea spp.
Knobby Sea Rods

Distribution: Caribbean Sea, including Southern Florida and the Bahamas.

Size and growth form: These corals usually grow as medium-sized bushy colonies (15 - 60 cm high) that branch laterally in a flat plane resembling a candelabrum, or as colonies which are flat, yet always with a knotty surface.

Food: They feed mainly on the products of their zooxanthellae.

Description: Some of the species in the genus, such as *Eunicea fusca*, have calyces that clearly protrude when the polyps are retracted. This makes these species look rather rough. Others, like *E. pinta*, *E. palmeri*, *E. tourneforti* and *E. knighti* have calyces developed little if at all. Outer layer with small, colourless clubs and purple, warty spindles; middle layer with large, colourless white or purple spindles (BAYER, 1961). The colours of the colonies vary from light brown to yellow brown, purple-red, purple or grey.

Aquarium maintenance:

- **General conditions:** Easy to keep, but they need a large aquarium with an abundant sand zone. They should be allowed to grow into the free water zone without competition from any other corals.
- **Lighting:** High light intensity.
- **Water circulation:** Medium to strong.
- **Reproduction:** These corals may be reproduced by fragmentation. Nothing is known about their sexual reproduction in aquaria.

GA: + ; **TO:** + ; **SE:** +

Photos:

Top: "KA4-HOL-14" off the Cayman Islands
Bottom left: This close-up clearly shows the knots on the branches when the polyps are retracted.
Bottom right: Close-up of the branches with partly retracted polyps   Photos: Scott W. Michael

Muricea spp.
Spiny Sea Fans

Distribution: Caribbean Sea, including Southern Florida and the Bahamas; Southern California to Panama.

Size and growth form: These corals usually grow densely branched and bushy with the form of an open fan. They are medium-sized (15 - 45 cm high) and look prickly.

Food: They feed mainly on the products of their zooxanthellae.

Description: *Muricea* spp. have branches that are hard and prickly, with numerous, close-set, tubular or shelf-like, lower calycular rims (edges; BAYER, 1961). The branching varies from lateral in one plane (*M. muricata*), to lateral in several planes (*M. elongata* and *M. laxa*), to openly pinnate (*M. pinnata*). The protruding calyces have sharp terminal spikes, which makes the colonies prickly to the touch.

Aquarium maintenance:
- **General conditions:** Easy to keep; is best kept in a Caribbean aquarium with large sand and rock areas.
- **Lighting:** High to medium light intensity, depending on the species: *M. laxa* and *M. pinnata* live in deeper water and therefore need less light than the other two species from shallower water.
- **Water circulation:** Medium to strong, but always continuous.
- **Reproduction:** These corals may be reproduced by fragmentation. Nothing is known about their sexual reproduction in aquaria.

GA: + ; TO: + ; SE: +

Photo:
Top: "KA4-HOL-15" in an aquarium
Bottom: Close up of the brancges Photo: A. Flowers and L. Newman

Swiftia exserta
Red Polyp Octocoral
(Referred to as *Ellisella* by Fossà & Nilsen, 1992b.)

Distribution: Florida; sometimes also found off the Bahamas and in the Caribbean Sea.
Size and growth form: Bushy, medium-sized colonies; 15 - 45 cm high.
Food: Feeds on plankton.
Description: Bushy, occasionally fan-shaped, colonies with thin branches and long protruding calyces. The branches are yellow, orange or red; the polyps are dark red. Off Florida, the species lives in deeper reef zones on rocky or sandy ground. In deeper caves in the Caribbean, it develops into fan-shaped colonies.
Aquarium maintenance:
- **General conditions:** In general, *S. exserta* must be regarded as difficult to keep, but it is among the hardiest non-photosynthesizing octocorallia. If provided with sufficient food, e.g. *Artemia* and frozen plankton, it can live a long time in a reef aquarium. On principle, it should be regarded as being only suitable for the experienced aquarist, since this species is best kept in a special aquarium.
- **Lighting:** Low to medium light intensity.
- **Water circulation:** Strong.
- **Reproduction:** There is not much chance of reproducing this species by fragmentation.
GA: +/- ; **TO:** + ; **SE:** +/-

Photos:
Top: Colony in an aquarium
Bottom left: Close-up of the branch structure
Bottom right: Close-up of the polyps

Gorgonia flabellum is a very common gorgonian off the Bahamas, where this photograph was taken, but it is not so abundant in other places in the Caribbean. Photo: Scott W. Michael

Family Gorgoniidae

In the family Gorgoniidae, we find gorgonians with a narrow, chambered, central chord and a cortex of pure gorgonin with little loculation. Many of the genera include species that grow in the shape of a fan. BAYER (1981) mentions the following genera as members of the family: *Gorgonia*, *Adelogorgia*, *Eugorgia*, *Eunicella*, *Hicksonella*, *Leptogorgia*, *Lophogorgia*, *Olindagorgia*, *Pacificigorgia*, *Phycogorgia*, *Phyllogorgia*, *Pseudopterogorgia*, *Pterogorgia* and *Rumphella*. Since then, *Lophogorgia* has been found to be a junior synonym of *Leptogorgia* (GRASSHOFF, 1992). Some of these genera are very interesting for the coral reef aquarium, as they are hardy and common in the trade, while others

are almost never imported and are very difficult to keep alive.

Perhaps the best-known of all gorgonians are the sea fans of the genus *Gorgonia*. The most popular among these, *Gorgonia ventalina*, *G. flabellum* and *G. mariae*, which are all endemic to the Caribbean Sea, form medium to large fans that grow in a single plane. All *Gorgonia* species contain zooxanthellae and are the most clearly fan-shaped of all the holaxonian corals. They are also the characteristic species of the fauna of the Caribbean Sea. We have to bear in mind, however, that, unlike the other holaxonians of the Caribbean, the genus *Gorgonia* is protected in the USA and may not be collected or exported without special permits. Occasionally, colonies are introduced into aquaria with pieces of live rock, or as secondary organisms on the base of other corals. In general, *Gorgonia* spp. do very well in

aquaria, where, given intense light, strong water movements and good water conditions and circulation, they grow excellently.

While *Gorgonia ventalina* (Common Sea Fan) is found all over the Caribbean, *G. flabellum* (Venus Sea Fan) is only common off the Bahamas and is less common than *G. ventalina* in other areas of the Caribbean and off Southern Florida. The two species are difficult to tell apart, but may be separated by the shape of the cross-section of the interconnected network of branches. In *G. flabellum*, the inner edges of the branches are distinctly flattened at right angles to the fan's surfaces, while in *G. ventalina*, the branches are round or slightly flattened on the outer surface (HUMANN, 1993). *G. flabellum* may reach the same maximum size as *G. ventalina* and grow to a diameter of up to 2 m. It is often found in shallow water with a strong surf

Gorgonia ventalina
Common Sea Fan

Distribution: Caribbean Sea, including Southern Florida and the Bahamas.

Size and growth form: Large fan-shaped colonies that grow in single planes, and measure up to 2 m in height. It usually lives on the outer reef slopes in clear waters and at right angles to the wave surge.

Food: This species feeds mainly on the products of its zooxanthellae, but probably also takes in small plankton.

Description: *G. ventalina* may be mistaken for *G. flabellum* (see page 211). The branches of *G. ventalina* anastomose, forming uniplanar, reticulate, fan-shaped colonies, or in other words the dense network of interlaced branches which are rounded or flattened on their outer surfaces in such a way that they form fans arranged in one plane. It usually lives on the outer reef slopes at right angles to the wave surge. In Florida, the species is always purple, while in other locations, it is commonly purple, but, occasionally, yellow or brownish.

Aquarium maintenance:

- **General conditions:** High light intensity and good water circulation are absolutely necessary. This species should be kept in a special aquarium. The genus *Gorgonia* is protected by law in the USA!
- **Lighting:** High light intensity.
- **Water circulation:** Strong; it may be an advantage if the surf of the sea is reproduced in the aquarium.
- **Reproduction:** Unknown. It therefore makes sense to carry out experiments to try to reproduce this species by fragmentation.

GA: +/- ; **TO:** + ; **SE:** +/-

Photos:
Top: Colony on a reef off Florida
Bottom left: Colony in our experimental aquarium set-up

and is rare at depths below 10 m. Its colour is usually some kind of yellow. See fact page 212 for more information on *G. ventalina*.

Gorgonia mariae (Wide-Mesh Sea Fan) is considerably smaller than the two other previous species and only reaches a maximum size of 30 cm. It develops in several small fans, which grow in one and the same plane, so that the whole colony, itself, looks like a single fan. The interconnected branches are, however, widely spaced out, in contrast to the tightly meshed network found in the other two species. *G. mariae* is not very common in the Caribbean Sea and has not been found off Florida and the Bahamas. It is known to occur in different types of reef areas, yet, it is most common in deeper water down to

On the right: *Pseudopterogorgia* species (these specimens were seen off Cuba) are probably the largest and the most common gorgonians in the Caribbean.   Photo: E. Svensen

The series of pictures below shows a *Pseudopterogorgia* species retracting its polyps. Photos: J. Cairns-Michael

Pseudopterogorgia spp.
Sea Plumes

Distribution: Caribbean Sea, including the Bahamas and Southern Florida, to Brazil.

Size and growth form: The different species exhibit varying growth forms. Some grow into very large, bushy colonies (2 m high), with broadly spread primary and secondary branches, while e.g. the pinnate branches of *P. bipinnata*, grow in a single plane and remain smaller (up to 60 cm high). Found on moderate to deeper patch reefs in clear waters.

Food: They feed mainly on the products of their zooxanthellae, but probably also take in plankton.

Description: These species grow in all reef zones. Most colonies are bushy with pinnate branches and the polyps are usually arranged in rows or ribbons, yet distributed rather at random. There are no calyces, or only rudiments of calyces, so that the branches look rather smooth when the polyps are retracted. The genus includes about 15 species, which can only be distinguished by a close examination of the sclerites - except for *P. americana* and *P. bipinnata*. The popular name for *P. americana* is "Slimy Sea Plume", which refers to the fact that this species produces considerable amounts of slime and therefore feels slippery. *P. bipinnata* develops pinnate branches which are arranged in one plane. It remains smaller than the other species and is mostly found in medium to deeper reef zones.

Photos:
Top: Colony of *P. americana* in an aquarium
Bottom left: Close-up of polyps of *P. americana*
Bottom right: "KA4-HOL-19" off the Cayman Islands
Photo: Scott W. Michael

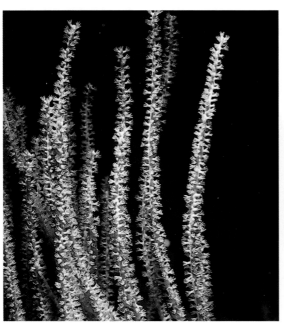

Aquarium maintenance:
- **General conditions:** Very easy to keep, but because of the size these corals can reach, they are best kept in a special aquarium where the colonies may grow unimpeded by other corals.
- **Lighting:** Moderate to high light intensity.
- **Water circulation:** Strong.
- **Reproduction:** These corals may be easily reproduced by fragmentation. Nothing is known about their sexual reproduction in aquaria.

GA: + ; **TO:** + ; **SE:** +

Photos:
Top and bottom right: *P. bipinnata* in its natural habitat off the Cayman Islands
Bottom left: Close-up of the branch structure of *P. bipinnata*
Photos: Scott W. Michael

Pterogorgia spp.
Sea Whips

Distribution: Caribbean Sea, including Southern Florida and the Bahamas.

Size and growth form: Medium-sized colonies, 30 - 60 cm high, bushy and highly branched, often with quite flattened and narrow branches.

Food: These gorgonians feed mainly on the products of their zooxanthellae.

Description: These gorgonians grow in bush-shaped colonies. The genus includes three species, of which *P. citrina* is the most common. In this species, the polyps are arranged along the flattened edges of the branches. *P. anceps* branches have an X- or Y-shaped cross-section. In this species and in *P. guadalupensis,* the polyps grow from slits along the edges of the branches. All three species are found in shallow waters close to the shore.

Aquarium maintenance:

- **General conditions:** These gorgonians are more delicate than most other Caribbean gorgonians with zooxanthellae. They are best kept in a sand zone aquarium.
- **Lighting:** High light intensity.
- **Water circulation:** Medium and continuous.
- **Reproduction:** Unknown. They are probably difficult to reproduce by fragmentation. Nothing is known about their sexual reproduction in aquaria.

GA: + ; **TO:** + ; **SE:** +/-

Photos:

Top: *P. anceps* in an aquarium
Centre: Close-up of polyps of *P. anceps*
Bottom left: Close-up of polyps of *P. citrina*
Bottom right: *P. citrina* in an aquarium

50 m. Here, it occupies an ecological niche with a low light intensity, where other species of the genus are quite rare. From the aquarist's point of view, it is of no importance.

In contrast to this, the genus *Pseudopterogorgia*, (Sea Plumes) which may grow in large, bush-shaped colonies, is very interesting for the coral reef aquarium. We have kept *P. americana* (Slimy Sea Plume) for a long time in an aquarium and can verify that it grows really quickly. In fact, we had to prune the colony regularly to prevent it from overgrowing other colonies. This species forms colonies with bushy clusters of long, feather-like plumes.

Pseudopterogorgia bipinnata (Bipinnate Sea Plume) is a very common species and is also found quite often on offer in aquarium shops. While the other species of the genus grow like bushes with branches in many different planes, *P. bipinnata* grows only in one plane, with clearly pinnate branches.

Pseudopterogorgia species often grow very large, so that one colony may completely fill up an aquarium. It does not, therefore, make sense to associate *Pseudopterogorgia* species with too many other corals. We would, again, recommend a biotope aquarium of the Caribbean type with lots of sand on the bottom and continual water circulation. Under these conditions, the beauty of these holaxonians is shown to their best advantage. See fact page 214/215 for more information on the genus.

The species of the genus *Pterogorgia*, have a special structure. Like many other holaxonians of the Caribbean, they grow into a bushy shape and have zooxanthellae, however. The form of the branches and the arrangement of the polyps are characteristic of *Pterogorgia*, however. The branches are flat and wide, often having a brownish-yellow colour, with the polyps arranged along the edges of the branches.

The common popular name for this group is "Sea Whips" which is

"KA4-HOL-20", a *Rumphella* species, in the Coral Sea.   Photo: E. Svensen

most misleading. "Whips" are, from a taxonomic point of view, unbranched colonies, or more rarely colonies with a few long, thin, branches. *Pterogorgia* spp. are branching and often bushy and therefore do not fit into the term "whips".

COLIN (1978), as well as HUMANN (1993), refer to three species in the genus *Pterogorgia*. In *Pterogorgia citrina* (Yellow Sea Whip), the polyps grow individually along the edges of the branches. This distinguishes it from *P. guadalupensis* (Grooved-Blade Sea Whip) and *P. anceps* (Angular Sea Whip), where the polyps grow from a lengthways depression along the edge of the branches. In contrast to the other two species, *P. citrina* grows in rather small colonies and is the most common of the three, not only on the reef, but also in aquaria. The cross-section of the branches of *P. guadalupensis* is rather flat, and the wide and flat branches taper towards their tips. In *P. anceps*, the cross-section of the branches has the

shape of an "X" or a "Y". In *P. citrina* the branches also taper towards their tips, but they are often twisted as well so that they look like a spiral. Thus, these three species are not too difficult to tell apart. See fact page 216 for more information on the genus.

In the Caribbean Sea, we find several species of the family that do not have any zooxanthellae and these are less interesting for the aquarist, as they are extremely difficult to keep. The genus *Leptogorgia* includes three species, *L. virgulata*, *L. hebes* and *L. miniata*, all of which grow on hard ground mixed with a small amount of sand; they are rarely seen in the trade.

Leptogorgia virgulata is common along the coasts of Florida and grows in long, stiff and only slightly branching colonies with highly variable colouration, ranging from violet and purple, to orange and yellow.

Leptogorgia hebes, also known only from the coasts of Florida, is a strongly branching type, with

Rumphella spp.

Distribution: Widespread in the Indo-Pacific. No details are, however, known.

Size and growth form: Medium-sized to large colonies, often bushy with large, slender, rounded branches.

Food: These gorgonians feed mainly on the products of their zooxanthellae.

Description: The axis is made of gorgonin and the colonies are bushy with rounded branches. The colour is grey, light yellow or light brown. The systematics of the genus are not very clear. The most common species is *R. aggregata*, first described by NUTTING (1910). Two other species have been described: *R. suffruticosa*, first described by DANA (1846) (this is possibly a synonym of *R. aggregata*), is hardly known at all. Only one specimen of *R. antipathes*, first described by LINNÉ (1758), is known from Ambon, Indonesia. *R. antipathes* has a more calcified base and has shorter branches than *R. aggregata*.

Aquarium maintenance:
- **General conditions:** These gorgonians are very hardy. They may be kept in aquaria for years if conditions are suitable.
- **Lighting:** High light intensity.
- **Water circulation:** Strong.
- **Reproduction:** These corals are easy to reproduce by fragmentation. Nothing is known about their sexual reproduction in aquaria.

GA: + ; **TO:** + ; **SE:** +

Photos:
Top: *R. aggregata* in the Coral Sea
Centre: "KA4-HOL-21": the picture and the specimen were taken at Biotop Aquaristics, St. Augustin-Hangelar, Germany
Bottom: "KA4-HOL-21": Close-up of the colony with its polyps partly retracted

the polyps arranged in rows along the branches. There are furrows between the rows of polyps, which clearly separate them. The colonies are most commonly red or orange, but they may also be purple.

Leptogorgia miniata is less common than the other two species, but is found in the same areas. It grows in openly branching colonies, which are often purple or orange in colour. The polyps are white or transparent and are arranged along the edges of the branches.

Among the representatives of the family from the Indo-Pacific, the genus *Rumphella* is of special interest for the aquarist. It includes some of the few species of holaxonians from the Indo-Pacific which contain zooxanthellae and are therefore widespread on the reef. Thus, *Rumphella* species are very suitable for aquaria. The colonies branch profusely and are often brown or light beige in colour. Colonies in the Carl Hagenbeck's Tierpark Aquarium Zoo in Hamburg, Germany, have been kept in aquaria for more than 12 years.

We do not know for certain how many species the genus *Rumphella* contains. A revision of the genus is therefore absolutely essential. *R. aggregata* is mentioned most often by authors writing about the genus. Other species that have been described are *R. antipathes* and *R. suffruticosa*, but we do not really know if these species are valid, since very little is known about them (ALDERSLADE pers. com.). We have featured the genus on fact page 218.

There is one very special species included in the genus *Hicksonella*, i.e., *H. expansa* in which the branches are leaf-shaped. When we saw the species in the Coral Sea ourselves, we confused it with a colony of hydroids of the genus *Millipora*. *H. expansa* is only found off Australia and in the Coral Sea. See ALDERSLADE (1986) for a description of this unique species.

A more popular species is *Hicksonella princeps*. It grows in a

This leaf-shaped *Hicksonella expansa*, which is a rather rare species, was photographed at Flinder's Reef in the Coral Sea.

Many holaxonians from the family Ellisellidae have branches with a slim and delicate structure, especially *Ctenocella pectinata*, which is shown in this photo taken on the Great Barrier Reef. Photo: E. Svensen

On the left: The colonies of *Junceella fragilis*, seen here off Papua-New Guinea, consist of only one branch, as in the other *Junceella* species, which are commonly called sea whips. To the right is the coral formerly known as *"Ellisella barbadensis"*. As all *Ellisella* colonies repeatedly fork, the *Ellisella* spp. of the caribbean are under revision and at least one species (*E. elongata*) has been transferred to the new genus *Viminella*. Photos: Scott W. Michael

bush-like form, has cylindrical branches and reminds us of *Rumphella* species.

Family Ellisellidae

The holaxonians of the family Ellisellidae often have thin red, orange-red or white branches. The central chord of the axis is calcareous and not chambered, and the cortex is heavily calcified. Among other sclerites, the coenenchyme contains small, dumbbell-like sclerites measuring up to 0.1 mm in length. The polyps are small and numerous. Most of the species tend to live in rather shallow water. None of the species contain zooxanthellae.

Like the other non-photosynthesizing holaxonians, the Ellisellidae have exacting demands with regard to food, lighting and water circulation, if they are to thrive in an aquarium. Nevertheless, some species are rather often imported, but can only be kept in a special aquarium where live food, medium to weak light and a strong and varying current are provided. Keeping these delicate colonies in a show aquarium mixed with photosynthetic corals is tantamount to killing them within a few weeks or months.

BAYER & GRASSHOFF (1994) revised the family at the generic level and proposed four genera: *Ctenocella*, *Junceella*, *Nicella*, and *Risea*. *Ctenocella* was divided into the subgenera: *Ctenocella* s.s., *Viminella*, *Ellisella*, *Umbracella*, *Verucella*, and *Phenilia*. The genus *Junceella* was divided into the two subgenera: *Junceella* s.s., and *Dichotella*.

On the coral reefs of the Indo-Pacific, the genera *Ellisella* and *Junceella* are the most common. The two are popularly referred to as Sea Whips or Whip Corals, na-

Nicella schmitti with retracted polyps Photo: Scott W. Michael

"KA4-HOL-22" off Cebu in the Philippines
Photo: O. Gremblewski-Strate

"KA4-HOL-23" in an aquarium
This species is often imported from the Indo-Pacific.

"KA4-HOL-24" at a depth of 20 m
off the Maldives

"KA4-HOL-25" off Papua-New Guinea
Photo: Scott W. Michael

Close-up of the polyps of a *Nicella* species, probably *Nicella schmitti*
Photo: J. Cairns-Michael

Colonies of *Isis hippuris* at "Shark Bommie" on Flinder's Reef, in the Coral Sea. A multitude of stony corals and soft corals, as well as green calcareous algae from the genus *Halimeda* (Cactus Seaweeds), grow in the vicinity.

mes which allude to the branching structure of the colonies. *Junceella* species always consist of one single branch with no side branches, whereas *Ellisella* colonies repeatedly fork.

In the genus *Nicella*, which is widespread in the Caribbean Sea, we, once more, find two species, i.e. *N. goreaui* and *N. schmitti*. *N. goreaui* grows as a fan which is composed of some lateral branches and finger-shaped twigs. The colour of the colonies is light red to orange-red, while the polyps are white. *N. schmitti* has short, whip-like branches that arise from a a basal stem. These branches are lateral, as well as finger-shaped. The colour of the colonies and of the polyps are the same as in *N. goreaui*. Both species are difficult, if not impossible, to keep longterm in aquaria.

Family Isididae

In the family Isididae, the skeletal axis is articulated. It is divided into segments of pure horny gorgonin and solid, non-spicular calcium carbonate. The central chord in the horny nodes is solid and not chambered. In the calcareous internodes it may be solid or hollow, but if hollow it is never chambered.

Isis hippuris is common in the central and the eastern areas of the Indo-Pacific and contains zooxanthellae. We found it at several locations on the upper reef zones of the Coral Sea, where the light intensity was high. *I. hippuris* grows in a wide variety of forms. Most often it has thick or thin main branches, with more or less developed side branches. *Isis reticulata* is most probably a synonym of *I. hippuris*.

Isis hippuris is very well known, and its skeletal structure, of alternating sections of black gorgonin and white calcium carbonate, was described in natural history publications as early as the 18th century. We have never heard of *I. hippuris* being kept in aquaria. Looking at its way of life, however, we would expect it to be easy to keep.

Close-up of the branches and polyps of *Isis hippuris*

Chapter 12:

Blue Corals and Sea Pens

In the subclass Octocorallia, the corals of the order Helioporacea contain a few described species of which one, *Heliopora coerulea*, the blue coral, must be regarded as numerous on reefs in the central Indo-Pacific and a commonly seen and easily kept species for the reef aquarium. The sea pens of the order Pennatulacea are often nocturnal feeders. They are most often found on muddy or sandy bottoms and are rarely seen in the trade. In contrast to *H. coerulea*, they are very difficult to keep in captivity for a long period of time unless given a special aquarium.

Above: Sea pens, like this *Pteroeides* (?, KA4-PEN-01) species, are occasionally found on sale in shops. They are, however, only suited for a special aquarium, e.g. a sand zone aquarium.

On the left: On some reef flats, as on this reef edge in the coral island of Siladen, North Sulawesi, the blue coral, *Heliopora coerulea*, dominates the scenery.

Order Helioporacea

The order Helioporacea contains two families, the Lithotelestidae and the Helioporidae. The genus *Epiphaxum*, with four known species, belongs to the family Lithotelestidae (BAYER, 1992).

Epiphaxum auloporoides is known from fossil finds from Denmark, while *Ephiphaxum micropora* (= *Lithotelesto micropora*) is known also from Barbados. The most recently described species are *Ephiphaxum breve*, found in the Gulf of Mexico and the Great Bahama Bank, and *Ephiphaxum septiferum*, which lives off Madagascar.

All *Epiphaxum* species come from deep water, where they live at depths of 40 - 50 metres down to several hundred metres. The colonies are small and have a prostrate, network-like stolon, from which the polyps develop. The polyps are cylindrical and rise as little tubes along the stolon. The stolon, as well as the polyps, has a skeleton of aragonite (a special orthorhombic form of calcium carbonate) while the sclerites are calcite. *Epiphaxum* species are of no significance for the reef aquarium.

The blue coral, *Heliopora coerulea*, is found on the reefs of the central Indo-Pacific and belongs to the family Helioporidae. It is far better known than the rest of its relatives in the family Lithotelestidae. It is the only species in the genus and is more or less a living fossil that shows little change in morphology as compared to 150-million-year-old fossils of the Lower Cretaceous Period (COLGAN, 1984). The blue coral reminds us of a stony coral, yet it is a very special octocoral, being the only such species which has a massive skeleton of calcium carbonate which is not made of fused sclerites.

The colour of its calcium skeleton is blue and BOUILLON & HOUVE-NAGHEL-CREVECOEUR (1970), who

Small colonies of the blue coral, *Heliopora coerulea*, are often imported on live rock, like the one in this picture taken in 1988. Since then, the colony has grown profusely and has covered more than half the back of our aquarium.

This colony in an aquarium owned by F. Jørgensen, Stavern, Norway, grew bubbles at the ends of the columns. This phenomenon is quite normal, but we do not know why the bubble tissue was extremely soft in this special case.

discuss the chemical nature of the colouring matter, conclude that it is composed primarily of biliverdin IX and secondary oxidation products (autoxidation?) thereof. Biliverdin is one of the bile pigments which also occur in human and animal bile as a breakdown product of haemoglobin. The blue pigment of *Heliopora* is unique in nature.

The colonies are very sturdy and have thick, slate-like branches, which are perforated by a large number of small cylindrical canals. In nature, the species forms many different colony shapes and is highly variable in growth form.

Heliopora coerulea makes higher temperature demands than hermatypic stony corals and is not found in places where the temperature falls below 22 °C. The fact that it does not tolerate colder water is probably the main reason why it is not as widespread as it once was in ancient times when it was found in all the world oceans. Today, it is found only in the western and central parts of the Indo-Pacific, from the Red Sea to the Islands of Samoa. This restricted distribution is probably linked to the species' limited larval dispersal ability. We found that the species dominated the windward side of an Indonesian reef flat (see fig. page 224), where it grew interspersed with *Acropora* spp. and a few soft corals. The colonies there were continually washed over by the surf and were probably the most important reef builders at that location.

The reproductive biology of *Heliopora coerulea* corresponds very well with that of the other Octocorallia, having, for example, separate sexes. WEINGARTEN (1992) observed that the blue coral had a synchronous annual life cycle of oocytic development and that it seemed to follow the general octocorallian reproductive characteristics. The gametes are, typically, released in January, immediately after full moon, when the temperature is at the summer maximum. At the borders of the area where it is found, it takes more than one year for the gametes to mature. This coral broods

Close-up of *Heliopora coerulea* with its polyps expanded.

In a shallow lagoon off Kanifinolhu, Maldives, enormous rows of colonies of *Heliopora coerulea* account for the major part of the coral fauna.

its larvae, which are, as in other brooding octocorals, able to settle almost immediately after release. The larvae do, however, lack zooxanthellae, which might be one reason for limiting the species' ability to disperse (WEINGARTEN, 1992). The same author suggests that the blue coral is a good candidate for breeding in reef aquaria.

Heliopora coerulea is imported frequently and offered as separate colonies (often sold as a "stony coral", though). The species is also very common on live rock, where, quite often, seemingly dead blue skeletons develop into magnificent colonies. *Heliopora coerulea* is among the species of corals that do very well in coral reef aquaria. Within a short time, it can grow considerably, changing from a prostrate way of life on live rock, to colonies which grow in an upright, columnar shape. It is, however, sometimes sensitive to light. We have kept colonies that, once adapted to very strong light, could tolerate this well and grew profusely almost directly below the metal halide lamp. On the other hand, we have also seen colonies that bleached heavily in strong light, but recovered as soon as they were placed at the bottom of the tank under moderate light intensity.

Systematic overview of Pennatulacea

(After WILLIAMS, 1995)

Order Pennatulacea
  Family Veretillidae
    Lituaria, Cavernularia, Veretillum, Cavernulina
  Family Echinoptilidae
    Actinoptilum, Echinoptilum
  Family Renillidae
    Renilla
  Family Kophobelemnidae
    Kophobelemnon, Sclerobelemnon, Malacobelemnon
  Family Funiculinidae
    Funiculina
  Family Protoptilidae
    Distichoptilum, Protoptilum
  Family Stachyptilidae
    Stachyptilum
  Family Scleroptilidae
    Scleroptilum
  Family Chunellidae
    Calibelemnon, Amphiacme, Chunella
  Family Ombellulidae
    Ombellula
  Family Anthoptilidae
    Anthoptilum
  Family Halipteridae
    Halipteris
  Family Virgulariidae
    Stylatula, Acanthoptilum, Scytalium, Virgularia, Scytaliopsis
  Family Pennatulidae
    Pennatula, Ptilosarcus
  Family Pteroeididae
    Gyrophyllum, Sarcoptilus, Crassophyllum, Pteroeides

Order Pennatulacea

The sea pens were until recently poorly known. KÜKENTHAL (1915) provides a survey of some genera and this source together with KÜKENTHAL & BROCH (1911) and HICKSON (1916) were until the mid nineties the last major scientific works on systematics and evolution of the group. The order is not mentioned by BAYER (1981), who, to date, has produced the most complete survey of the Octocorallia. Sea pens are briefly mentioned in popular books such as FAULKNER & CHESHER (1976), GEORGE & GEORGE (1979), GOSLINER et

al. (1996) and COLIN & ARNESON (1995). WILLIAMS (1993) discusses the sea pens of the coral reefs from an evolutionary point of view.

Definitely the best paper on sea pens is that by WILLIAMS (1995) which presents a synopses of the known genera of Pennatulacea and includes new morphological and distributional data from recent collected material. The paper also has a key to the families and genera in Pennatulacea. The short overview of the most important families, beginning on the next page, is based on this paper.

The main morphological difference between the sea pens and the other Octocorallia is that, in

addition to the common autozooids and the siphonozooids, they also possess an oozooid, the primary, axial polyps. Each oozooid consists of two parts: a "foot" or peduncle, which is dug into the sand or mud bottom, and an upright part, the rachis, which sways freely in the water and bears the autozooids, with well developed tentacles, and the smaller siphonozooids, with reduced or absent tentacles. Some sea pens (like in the genus *Pennatula*) also have additional mesozooids, which are an intermediat in form between autozooids and siphono-zooids. These are specialised polyps through which the water, which streams in through the siphonozooids, subsequently passes out of the colony. All secondary zooids are formed by lateral budding of the body wall of the oozooid. Many, but not all, sea pens have a axis interior in the colony (see table 231).

In the some genera, among them *Cavernularia* and *Veretillum* (= *Policella*), the autozooids and siphonozooids are distributed on the rachis more or less at random and the symmetry of the colony is radial. In other genera such as *Ombellula* (a genus that contains deep sea species only) the autozooids and siphonozooids are arranged in a terminal cluster or the colony have a single large polyp on the end of a long stalk and the symmetry of the colony is bilateral. In a large number of species, among them *Ptilosarcus* and *Pteroeides* spp., the colonies have the form of a feather and are bilaterally symmetrical. The autozooids, which have large, spiky sclerites for protection, are placed at the rims of the leaf-shaped structures ("polyps leaves"), while the siphonozooids are usually found on rachis (the main axis).

Most sea pens are known from greater depths, some species living deeper than 6100 m. In tropical seas, however, some also exist in shallow water areas. They prefer sandy or muddy ground there, where they can dig themselves in easily. In the sea, colonies usually expand at times when the flowing tide carries large amounts of plankton. If they are disturbed, the colonies may react by using the peduncle to pull the rachis down below the level of the sand. Only a few species are unable to do this.

One of the characteristics of the sea pens is their bioluminescence, i.e. the ability of colonies to emit biologically-produced light. If an expanded colony is touched, it lights up for a moment in a beautiful blue, yellowish or green fluorescent colour. This light then spreads gradually over the colony from the point where it was touched. It is not at all improbable that the purpose of this bioluminescence is to deter preda-

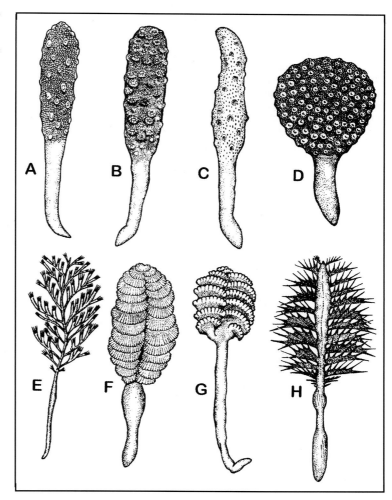

Four tubular (A-D) and four pinnate (E-H) sea-pens; A) *Lituaria hicksoni*, B) *Cavernulina darwini*, C) *Veretilum manillensis*, D) *Carvernularia malabarica*, E) *Pennatula phosphorea*, F) *Ptilosarcus undulatus*, G) *Gyrophyllum sibogae* and H) *Pteroeides* sp. All genera are shallow water genera and can be expected to show up in the trade.   After WILLIAMS (1995)

tors. There is also no doubt that it is extremely interesting to observe this phenomenon in a special aquarium.

Of the about 436 described species of sea pens about 200 species in 32 genera seem to be valid. We have listed the families and genera in a systematic overview at page 228. Many of the genera have a near cosmopolitan distribution. Some sea pens live in deep water only while others can be found from the surface down to several thousand metres. These and other valuable infor-

mation are included in table 9 on page 231.

Family Veretillidae

In the Veretillidae, the colonies are cylindrical, capitate (with swollen tips), clavate (club-shaped) or elongated with an erect rachis (shaft or stalk) that does not lie on the substratum. The autozooids are free (not fused to any degree), evenly distributed on all sides of rachis and lack calyces.

The family includes four genera, all of which can appear in

the trade. Among these are *Cavernularia*. Most of the cylindrical sea pens imported and sold in aquarium shops are commonly (but wrongly) referred to as "*Cavernularia obesa*", which is the type species of the genus. *Cavernularia* spp. can have a conspicuous or rudimentary axis, or lack an axis completely. All species exhibit radial symmetry throughout the length of the rachis. There are numerous siphonozooids between the autozooids, while the sclerites are smooth spindles, rods or are oval-shaped; these ovals are often minute in the peduncle. There are 13 species which are considered to be valid (WILLIAMS, 1989, 1995).

Four described species of *Cavernulina* are considered valid today. These are very close to those in *Cavernularia* and the two genera can only be separated by the presence of branched and bilobed sclerites in *Cavernularia*, which are lacking in *Cavernulina*.

In the genus *Veretillum*, where about 7 valid species exist, the colonies are cylindrical or slightly clavate, with radial symmetry throughout the rachis and autozooids evenly distributed over its surface. The siphonozooids are numerous and sometimes situated in longitudinal rows. The axis can be absent or present, and the surface sclerites are small, irregularly-, bone- or biscuit-shaped plates. The interior sclerites of the peduncle are minute ovals in shape and are usually numerous. Sclerites may be absent from the rachis altogether and polyp sclerites may be present or absent (WILLIAMS, 1995).

The 10 described species of *Lituaria* are all considered valid and are cylindrical to clavate, with radial symmetry throughout the rachis and autozooids evenly distributed over its surface. The axis is present in the rachis and sometimes has longitudinal furrows or outgrowths. The siphonozooids are numerous and the sclerites are, mostly, short tuberculate capstans, or irregularly-shaped broad plates. The interior of the peduncle lacks sclerites.

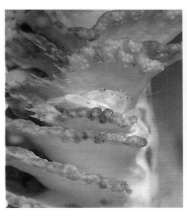

Sea pens are often hosts for other organisms. In the colony above a crab has made itself at home. Brittle stars also frequently take up residence with sea pens (below).

Tubular and cylindrical sea pens appear more often on sale than pen-shaped ones. They are imported from Indonesia and Singapore fully unfolded and many of the imported colonies attain a size of about 40 cm or more, with their colours ranging from grey-white, to lightly flesh-coloured, to yellow or orange. The large autozooids trap plankton easily, including rather large organisms like shrimps or *Artemia salina*. In aquaria, the species also accept finely minced shrimp or fish meat (WILKENS, 1980).

According to WILKENS, "*Cavernularia obesa*" is easy to keep. We think, however, that none of the sea pens are easy to keep. Yet, we agree that, among the species that are imported, the cylindrical species of the family Veretillidae are probably among the hardiest. When we put a colony in the filter chamber of our aquarium - a chamber that had a relatively thick layer of coral gravel and a steady flow of water - and fed it several times a week with liquid food, the colony expanded daily and showed no sign of deterioration for months. The heavy feeding was, however, too risky for the general health of the aquarium and, when it was reduced, the sea pen's condition rapidly declined.

Family Virgularidae

In this family, the proximal portions of adjacent autozooids are fused to some degree, forming thin polyp leaves situated along the rachis in two opposite longitudinal series. The autozooids lack spiculiferous calyces (i.e. cups bearing spicules), a character which separates this family from the Pennatulidae.

Colonies of *Scytalium* are fo-

Table 9
Interesting characteristics of Sea Pens.

Modified from WILLIAMS (1995)

BL = bilateral, R = radial, P = present, A = absent, Rr = Raised ridges

Genus	Sym-metry	Axis	Polyp leaves	Depth (m)	Distribution
Acanthoptilum	BL	P	P	3-529	California, Gulf of Mexico
Actinoptilum	R	A	A	12-333	West South Africa to southern Mozambique
Amphiacme	BL	P	A	818-1200	East Africa and western Indian Ocean
Anthoptilum	BL	P	A	155-3150	Near cosmopolitan distribution
Calibelemnon	BL	P	A	100-1275	Indo-Pacific; southeastern Africa to Hawaii
Cavernularia	R	P/A	A	3-320	East Atlantic, S. Europe, Mediterranean, W. Africa, Indo-Pacific east to Marquesas, north to Japan
Cavernulina	R	P	A	30-62	Indo-Pacific and eastern Pacific
Chunella	BL	P	A	818-1200	Indo-West Pacific; East Africa to Irian Jaya
Crassophyllum	BL	P	P	30-650	Mediterranean and the West African coast
Distichoptilum	BL	P	A	650-4300	Near cosmopolitan distribution
Echinoptilum	R/BL	A	A	50-628	Indo-Pacific; eastern Africa to Hawaii
Funiculina	P	BL	A	60-2600	Cosmopolitan
Gyrophyllum	P	BL	P	520-1266	Widespread; North Atlantic, Madagascar, Malay Archipelago, Tasmania
Halipteris	P	BL	Rr	36-1950	Near cosmopolitan distribution
Kophobelemnon	P	BL	A	36-4400	Near cosmopolitan distribution
Lituaria	P	R	A	3-150	Indo-West Pacific; s.e. Africa, India, Mergui , Andaman- and Malay Arch., Philippines, s. China, Taiwan, Japan, PNG, Australia
Malacobelemnon	P	BL	A	42-60	Western Indian and western Pacific Ocean; s.e. Africa and e. Australia
Ombellula	P	BL	A	210 - >6100	Cosmopolitan
Pennatula	P	BL	P	18-2815	Near cosmopolitan distribution
Protoptilum	P	BL	A	250-4000	Northern Atlantic, Indo-Pacific and eastern Pacific
Pteroeides	P	BL	P	9-320	Eastern Atlantic, Mediterranean, Indo-West Pacific
Ptilosarcus	P	BL	P	0-68	Eastern Pacific; from Gulf of Alaska to Peru
Renilla	A	BL	A	0-70	Pacific and Atlantic coasts of North-, Central- and South America
Sarcoptilus	P	BL	P	0-145	Southern Australia and New Zealand
Sclerobelemnon	P	BL	A	10-472	Indo-West Pacific and western Atlantic; Gulf of Mexico, Trinidad, Surinam, Red Sea, Indian Ocean, Australia, PNG, Malay Arch., Philippines, Taiwan and Japan
Scleroptilum	P	BL	A	510-4200	Scattered in the Atlantic-, Indian- and Pacific Oceans
Scytaliopsis	P	BL	P	? - 460	Western Indian Ocean; Red Sea to southeastern Africa
Scytalium	P	BL	P	18-180	Indo-West Pacific; Red Sea, s.e. Africa, Indian Ocean, Malay Arch., Philippines, China, Taiwan, Japan
Stachyptilum	P	BL	A	36-950	Pacific Ocean; Malay Arch., Japan, and Oregon to central America
Stylatula	P	BL	P	0-1020	Northern and western Atlantic and eastern Pacific Oceans
Veretillum	P/A	R	A	6-220	Eastern Atlantic, S. Europe and Mediterranean, west coast of Africa, Indo-West Pacific
Virgularia	P	BL	P	0-1100	Widespread in the Atlantic- Indian- and Pacific Ocean

und in the Red Sea and the Indo-West Pacific. They vary from elongated and slender, to more stout and robust, with bilateral symmetry throughout the rachis. An axis is present throughout the colony and the polyp leaves are thin and fleshy, with the broadest part of each leaf being where it joins the rachis. The autozooids are tubular. The siphonozooids are found on the rachis between the polyp leaves. They are exclusively small oval-shaped plates distributed through all parts of the colonies. There are three valid species: *Scytalium tentaculatum* (known from the Phillipines) with a digitiform (finger-like) process on each calyx, *S. martensi* (known from the Indian Ocean, China and Japan) with a naked ventral region along the rachis and *S. sarsi* (known from the Indian Ocean, the Philippines and the Red Sea) lacking the naked ventral region along the rachis.

In *Virgularia*, the colonies are long, slender and vermiform (worm-shaped), or more stout, robust and rigid. The polyp leaves are relatively short and congested, or sometimes with intervals of bare rachis between adjacent leaves. The number of autozooids varies from three to 100 on each polyp leaf and the siphonozooids are sparsely distributed on the leaves below the free parts of the autozooids or, more commonly, on the rachis between the polyp leaves. Sclerites are absent, except for minute oval bodies in the interior of the peduncle. The 20 or so valid species are widespread in the Atlantic, Indian Ocean and in the Pacific. Two of the most common and well known species are: *Virgularia gustaviana* from the Indo-West Pacific and *V. juncea* from the eastern Indian Ocean and Australia.

Family Pennatulidae

This family shows the same characters as the previous two families, but the autozooids are tubular, with spiculiferous calyces, having one, two or eight terminal teeth. Two genera, *Pennatula* and

Cavernulina sp. (*Cavernularia* sp.?) is a very common sea-pen seen is the

Ptiloscarus, are placed in this family. *Pennatula* spp. are feather-like in appearance and have an almost cosmopolitan distribution. About 14 species are considered to be valid, with *Pennatula fimbriata* (known from Japan and the Phillipines), *P. indica* (known from the Indian Ocean), *P. murrayi* and *P. pearceyi* (known from the Indo-West Pacific) and *P. phosphorea* (a cosmopolitan species) known from tropical areas. The polyp leaves are usually large and conspicious.

In *Ptiloscarus*, the colonies are stout and feather-like. The polyp leaves are kidney-shaped, often with sinuous margins. The genus is distributed in the eastern Pacific, with *Ptilosarcus gurneyi* as a common species found from Alaska to southern California. *P. undulatus* is distributed from the Gulf of California to Peru.

Family Pteroeididae

While members of Virgulariidae possess thin polyp leaves, these are thick in the Pteroeididae, a family that otherwise shares the characters of Virgulariidae.

In *Gyrophyllum*, the colonies are stout and clavate, with a pe-

duncle longer than the rachis, and thick, fleshy, fan-like polyp leaves. *Gyrophyllum sibogae* is the only tropical species. In *Sarcoptilus*, the colonies are stout and feather-like, but the six described species are all from southern temperate waters. The genus *Crassophyllum* contains two species, one of them from tropical West Africa, but none are likely to appear in the trade.

In *Pteroides*, the colonies are, mostly, stout and feather-like, with an axis present throughout the colony. The polyp leaves are well developed and rigid due to the presence of one to many supporting rays composed of needle-like sclerites. Accessory leaves may be present between the main leaves. The siphonozooids are minute, but numerous and crowded in the proximate zone of each polyp leaf (i.e. in the area nearest to the point from which each leaf arises). The genus contains about 25 valid species, but as many as 87 species have been described (WILLIAMS, 1995). Two common tropical species are: *Pteroides caledonicum* from New Caledonia and the Malay Archipelago, and *P. esperi* from the Indo-West Pacific.

Virgularia sp. (KA4-PEN-02)
Photo from Indonesia: Scott W. Michael

Virgularia sp. (KA4-PEN-03) with a symbiotic crab
Photo from Indonesia: Scott W. Michael

Virgularia sp. (KA4-PEN-04)
Photo from Indonesia: Scott W. Michael

Pteroeides sp. (KA4-PEN-05)
Photo from Indonesia: Scott W. Michael

Virgularia sp. (KA4-PEN-06) from Madang, Papua-New Guinea   Photo: L. Newman and A. Flowers

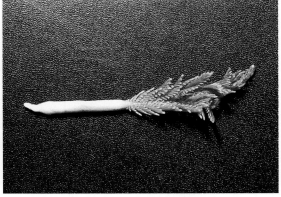

Pennatula phosphorea is a cosmopolitan sea pen. This specimen was dredged from 30 m depth off Bergen, Norway.

Chapter 13:

Actiniaria

Sea anemones constitute the order Actiniaria (see page 237 for a systematic overview) of the subclass Zoantharia or Hexacorallia. They have been popular animals among marine aquarists for many years and were among the first invertebrates ever to be kept in tropical reef aquaria. Anemones are very simple animals. The order contains cnidarians which lack any sort of skeleton and live attached to the bottom or with the column buried in the sediment. Some species may reach very large sizes, with a diameter of up to 1 m, but the most remain smaller.

Anemones can change their shape considerably and from time to time contract heavily. The body contains mesenteries, which are of two types: complete and incomplete, consisting of diaphragms that are arranged transversely to the longitudinal musculature and to which the muscles

A very unusual type of symbiosis between the anemone *Triactis producta* and other animals is characteristic of this small crab of the genus *Lybia*. The tiny crab carries the anemones in special modified claws and uses the anemones like a mop and sweeps them through detritus. The detritus gathering on the anemones is then picked off and eaten by the crab. If the crab is attacked, it uses the stinging anemones as defence weapons.   Photo: Scott W. Michael

On the left: The largest of all anemones, *Stichodactyla mertensii*, on the Myrmidon Reef (Great Barrier Reef)
Photo: E. Svensen

are attached.

Basically, an anemone consists of three main body parts. At the bottom we find the pedal disc, **base**, which fastens the anemone to the substratum. The boundary between the base and the column, **stem**, above, is often distinct and is called **limbus**. On the top of the column is the **oral disc**, with the mouth and tentacles, from the ground. The mouth is situated in the centre of the oral disc.

It is generally assumed today that the largest part of the nutrients that are required by the large "host" sea anemones, i.e. those that accommodate other creatures, found on the reefs is provided by their zooxanthellae. In addition, these anemones also capture plankton and other food. Anemones without zooxanthellae are totally dependent on their catch of food and can utilise plankton, as well as much larger food, such as crustaceans and smaller fish. We have observed that seahorses, gobies and shrimps of the genus *Saron* are eaten by large symbiotic anemones and have seen, in the wild, anemones no bigger than 10 cm in diameter consuming crabs nearly as large as themselves. In addition, some tropical species are able to take in dissolved nutrients directly from the water.

When anemones attach themselves to the substratum with their pedal disc, it is virtually impossible to move them to another spot without hurting the animal severely. In aquaria one should never try to loosen anemones by force. Yet, the anemones are able to move slowly around, which is sometimes a nuisance in an aquarium. If the aquarium water does not contain sufficient oxygen, or if the water motion is not strong enough, anemones attach themselves in a place near to the surface of the water close to a water inflow, i.e. where the oxygen concentration is most favourable.

The sea anemones have nematocysts, which contain stinging poison. In some species (like *Alicia* spp., see page 246-250) the sting is so severe, that it can even

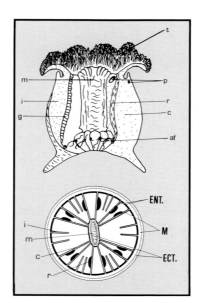

Longitudinal section (above) and cross-section (below) through an anemone (after BARNES, 1980):
p = canals in the mesentery; t = tentacles; c = complete mesenteries; af = acontial (sticky) filaments, which are ejected if stimulated; g = gonads; i = incomplete mesenteries; m = mouth opening; ECT = ectoderm; M = mesogloea.

hurt humans and these should be handle with care. The majority of anemones are, however, not harmful to humans, but if you buy anemones for your aquarium, you should keep their severe stinging qualities in mind.

Anemones are identified on the basis of a variety of characters including their colours. In some cases the colours alone give sufficient information for a proper identification of the species. The most reliable criteria for their distinction are, however, anatomical details, such as the position of the mesenteries and the types and distribution of the stinging cells - characters not really assessable to aquarists.

Most coral reef aquarists have come across sea anemones in one way or another, mostly the large "symbiotic anemones". The term "symbiotic anemones" is used with some justification, as these animals act as hosts for

anemonefishes of the genera *Amphiprion* and *Premnas*, although they also house other animals, like e.g. shrimps or crabs. There are also anemones that are inhabited by fish and other animals, but which are not referred to as symbiotic anemones in common usage. Even though these species are much smaller, they are as interesting for the coral reef aquarium as their symbiotic counterparts.

When large "symbiotic anemones" are introduced into a coral reef aquarium, the consequences can often be unpleasant. Most anemones have a big potential for stinging and in a small aquarium it is almost impossible to prevent them from sooner or later damaging other animals. Moreover, the size that these symbiotic anemones can attain must be kept in mind. If the conditions are favourable, the symbiotic anemones may easily double their size. Even if a specimen has already attained 20 to 30 cm when bought, it may later grow and expand to much more than this. Many other sessile animals, like stony- and soft corals, loose the competition for space in the reef aquarium if they have to fight with a big anemone.

Sometimes, we can observe host anemones opening their mouth widely and almost turning their insides out. This can be either a reaction to lack of oxygen (such as following transportation, or after some hours in a plastic bag) or it can be a reaction to a bacterial infection. In any case, the anemone should be subjected to good water circulation and given excellent water quality. See SPRUNG & DELBEEK (1997) for further details on this subject.

We think that the best we can do for these symbiotic anemones is to keep them in a special aquarium, which need not be very large: 150 to 200 litres will be adequate and will still allow the extremely interesting relationships to be easily observed at close quarters.

In this volume, we would like to deal with the larger symbiotic or host sea anemones more thoroughly. To do justice to their systematic position, we will describe them in turn as we come to the families to which they belong.

At present ten species are recognised as symbiotic anemones. They are accommodated in the following three families:

❶ Actiniidae, members of which are found worldwide, includes 43 genera; two species in the genera *Entacmaea* and *Macrodactyla* are symbiotic anemones.

❷ Thalassianthidae, with the monotypic genus *Cryptodendrum* being a symbiotic anemone (in addition to an unknown number of smaller anemones from other genera, some of which can be troublesome in reef aquaria).

❸ Stichodactylidae, with the genera *Heteractis* and *Stichodactyla*. Nearly all of the species in these two genera are symbiotic anemones.

The symbiosis of fish and sea anemones was discovered by COLLINGWOOD (1868). Since then, it has always fascinated biologists, visitors to the reef and aquarists. While very much is known about the fishes and their biology, this is note the case with the anemones. FISHELSON (1970 and 1971) holds the opinion that symbiotic anemones probably play an important role in the ecology of shallow reef areas. We also know that certain anemones contain substances of pharmaceutical potential.

Our descriptions of host sea anemones are adapted from the revision of the symbiotic anemones by DUNN (1981) (who now publishes under the family name, FAUTIN). A more useful book for the aquarists, dealing with both the host sea anemones and their fish partners, is provided by FAUTIN & ALLEN (1992).

Systematic overview of the order Actiniaria

Order **Actinaria**

Family **Gonactiniidae***

Family **Boloceroididae** *Boloceroides, Bunodeopsis*

Family **Aliciidae** *Alicia, Triactis, Lebrunia, Phyllodiscus*

Family **Edwardsiidae** *Edwardsia*

Family **Halcampidae***

Family **Halcampoididae***

Family **Ilyanthidae*** *Ilyanthus*

Family **Andresiidae*** *Andresia*

Family **Actiniidae** *Actinia, Anemonia, Anthopleura, Actiniogeton, Bunodactis, Bunodosoma, Condylactis, Cribrinopsis, Entacmaea, Macrodactyla, Urticina* (= *Tealia*)

Family **Aliciidae** *Alicia, Triactis, Lebrunia, Phyllodiscus*

Family **Stichodactylidae** *Heteractis, Stichodactyla*

Family **Minyadidae***

Family **Aurelianidae***

Family **Phymanthidae** *Heteranthus, Phymanthus, Epicyctis*

Family **Actinodendridae** *Actinodendron, Actinostephanus, Megalactis*

Family **Thalassianthidae** *Heterodactyla, Cryptodendrum, Thalassianthus*

Family **Actinostolidae***

Family **Isophellidae*** *Telmatactis*

Family **Paractidae***

Family **Metrididae*** *Metridium*

Family **Diadumenidae*** *Diadumene*

Family **Aiptasiidae** *Aiptasia, Bartholomea, Capnea, Viatrix*

Family **Sagartiidae*** *Actinothoe, Cereus, Sagartia, Sagartiogeton*

Family **Hormatiidae*** *Adamsia, Calliactis*

Family **Nemanthidae** *Nemanthus*

The families marked with an asterisk (*) are not dealt with in this book.

Boloceroides mcmurrichi photographed at Sulawesi, Indonesia. Photo: J. Cairns-Michael

Family Boloceroididae

This family contains the peculiar "swimming anemone" *Boloceroides mcmurrichi*. The anemone is somewhat unusual as it is capable of swimming by beating the tentacles. The body is small compared to the large crown of tentacles surrounding the mouth. Although the total size seldom increases 5 cm, specimens as big as 15 cm has been observed. The base is weakly adherent. The short column is smooth, thin-walled and translucent and coloured pale raw sienna. The oral disc is pale violet or bluish grey except for the colourless section between the tentacles. The tentacles themselves vary in colour from white to pale raw sienna to reddish brown and may be unmarked or posses transverse band of pale bluish grey (DEVANY & ELDEREDGE, 1977).

B. mcmurrichi is hermaphroditic and reproduces both sexually and asexually. According to VINE, (1986) it reproduces asexually by budding and can therefore often be found in small aggregations. DEVANY & ELDEREDGE (1977) report that specimens at Hawaii reproduce sexually in spring and asexually in fall when the asexually young arise as buds on the outer tentacles and are shed when they have developed 10 to 30 tentacles and become capable of swimming. *B. mcmurrichi* is often found among sea grass attached to the leaves of the plants. It does also occur in mangrove areas, on sandy and muddy bottoms, on the under side of table shaped corals, among sponges and even among the spines of sea urchins. The species is known from the Red Sea eastwards to Hawaii, but is rare in the trade. *B. mcmurrichi* can, however, be introduced to the reef aquarium together with other animals or with live rocks. The large nudibranch *Baeolidia major* closely mimics and preys on *B. mcmurrichi* (DEVANY & ELDEREDGE, 1977).

Another genus in the family is *Bundeopsis* with *Bundeopsis medusoides* as the most common species. This species is small and has a height of only 2 cm and a diameter of 1 cm. The about 30 tentacles are long and adhesive. The species is found among rubble in shallow water and is widely distributed in the Indo-Pacific. In the western Atlantic we meet the species *Bundeopsis antilliensis*. This maximum 15 mm big species has zooxanthellae and is commonly found among dead corals, live sponges, mangrove roots and sea grasses (STERRER, 1986). It has a strong sting and reproduces asexual by pedal laceration.

Family Edwardsidae

Edwardsia spp. are often found on sandy bottoms near shore where

Edwardsia sp. on a sandy bottom at Sulawesi, Indonesia

Photo: J. Cairns-Michael

they dig themselves deeply into the substratum with only the disc possessing tapering tentacles exposed. The genus is poorly known. According to COLIN & ARNESON (1995) *Edwardsia pudica* is found at the Marshall Islands, while DEVANY & ELDEREDGE (1977) mention two species from Hawaii.

Family Actiniidae

The two genera *Actinia* and *Urticina* (= *Tealia*), which are very common along European coasts and the temperate coasts of America, belong to the family Actiniidae, as do a large number of other interesting tropical species for the coral reef aquarium.

A species commonly on sale is the Anemone, *Condylactis gigantea*, from the Caribbean, Bermuda and tropical Brazil. It is the largest of the Caribbean anemones and is very frequently found in shallow water. Its colouration varies according to its habitat. Generally, the tentacles and body are brown, green or purple often with contrasting colours in the tips of the tentacles. Juvenile, *C. gigantea* has knobby tentacles. Bright yellow specimens, which sometimes are on offer in aquarium shops, have been artificially enhanced. We would recommend aquarists never to buy artificially coloured anemones, but to regard the natural colours as "beautiful enough".

Condylactis gigantea prefers sandy ground between rocks, where it can dig itself in, so that, normally, the body is partly or totally hidden in crevices. Because of its powerful nematocysts, it is a species for the special aquarium.

The Giant Anemone is host for many symbionts. Shrimps of the species *Thor amboniensis*, *Periclimenis pedersoni* and *Periclimenes yucatanicus*, as well as the Banded Anemone Crab (*Mithrax cinctimanus*) and the Diamond Blenny (*Malacoctenus boehlkei*), have all been reported to associate with the anemone (HUMANN, 1993). A special aquarium housing a few anemones and a number of symbionts would constitute a "magical" tank from the Caribbean. In addition, one could keep Caribbean live rock and let the macro-algae develop and introduce other anemones or carpet anemones. See fact page 242 for more information on the species.

The genus *Condylactys* also occurs in the Indo-Pacific, and a beautiful, bluish species is observed in Indonesia and in Palau (COLIN & ARNESON, 1995).

In the family Actiniidae, we also find two beautiful symbiotic anemones, *Entacmaea quadricolor* and *Macrodactyla doreensis*. The Bubble Tip Anemone, *Entacmaea quadricolor*, which was originally described by RUPPELL & LEUCKART in 1828 as *Actinia quadricolor*, is, by far, the most common species of the two, although both species are frequently seen in the trade. Usually, this species has clearly visible bulbs at the very tips, or

Anemones of the same species may display very different colours, depending on the region or the type of habitat they occupy. *Urticina* (= *Tealia*) *felina* may be a good example of this (photo on the right: T. Luther).

near the tips, of its tentacles, which makes it easy to identify. These bulbs may be totally missing, being replaced, in some cases, by a light band where the bulb would have appeared, or being reduced to an elongated swelling. In such instances, there are usually blue or purple pigments in the tips of the tentacles. According to FAUTIN & ALLEN (1992) the presence of bulbs seems to be related to the presence of anemonefishes. The tips of the tentacles are usually red and blunt-ended in those specimens lacking bulbs, but both types of tips may be present on the same individual. The columns is smooth and without any warts (verrucae), a character which di-

stinguishes this species from all other large symbiotic anemones. The colour of the stalk varies from green-brown to brown, to violet, red and purple. The disc is, mostly, of a fainter colour, often with brown or green nuances.

Entacmaea quadricolor is distributed from Samoa in the east, to East Africa and the Red Sea in the west from the surface down to 40 metres. Often, several specimens live together in clusters, with their pedal discs deeply embedded in crevices or in between the branches of stony corals.

Interestingly, there are two ecotypes of *Entacmaea quadricolor*, a fact which has occasionally caused confusion in the classification. The two types look quite dif-

ferent, depending on the habitat they come from. In shallow water the specimens live in large groups which have been produced asexually from the female parent. Usually, these individuals are smaller than those that live solitary and may reach a size of 40 cm across. The two ecotypes have sometimes been regarded as separate species. ALLEN (1972) describes the solitary *E. quadricolor*, which lives in deeper water as "*Radianthus gelam*", and the other type that occurs as a group of smaller individuals as "*Physobranchia douglasi*".

We observed this species in abundance in the Coral Sea and on the Great Barrier Reef. In these regions, the most common fish partner of the species are *Premnas biaculeatus* and *Amphiprion melanopus*. This sea anemone is also accepted as partner by most of the anemone fishes of the *Amphiprion clarkii* and the *A. ephippium* complex.

E. quadricolor is perhaps the most easily kept host anemone. It may live for many years and quite frequently reproduces asexually in aquaria by longitudinal fission.

The genus *Macrodactyla* contains only one species, *Macrodactyla doreensis*. Very little is known about this species, whose geographical distribution is rather remarkable. It is found within a broad belt, which runs in a north-south direction, from Japan in the north, to Moreton Bay on the east coast of Australia as the southernmost point. To the west and

A beautiful and unknown species of *Condylactis* from Sulawesi, Indonesia
Photo: Scott W. Michael

the east, its distribution is very limited. *Amphiprion chrysogaster, A. clarkii* and *A. perideraion*, as well as *Dascyllus trimaculatus*, are fishes known to associate with this species.

Macrodactyla doreensis is attached very firmly with its pedal disc to pits in coral rocks at depths of 1 to 15 m. If it is disturbed, it sometimes withdraws completely into its hiding place. In the sea, *Macrodactyla doreensis* only rarely becomes the symbiotic partner for anemone fishes, but it is found in most areas where many aquarium fish are caught and is often collected. This species can be easily identified by the numerous white warts on the upper part of the stalk (column) and the few, regular tentacles, which have the same mauve-grey or brownish colour as the disc. Now and then, the disc may have light stripes, a pattern which is then also found on the tentacles. See fact page 243 for detailed information on this species, which, despite its limited distribution is common in the trade.

For many years, a small species of sea anemone, which is imported on live rock, but which has remained unknown for a long time, has been quite a frequent occupant of German coral reef aquaria (see vol. 1, page 176). This species was described by CARLGREN (1900) as *A. majano*. It's accommodation in *Anemonia*, however, is incorrect (J.C. den Hartog; pers. com.). The anemone can reproduce very rapidly asexually to become a plague by completely overgrowing an aquarium. See fact page 244 for details.

Another species incorrectly included in the genus *Anemonia* is *A. mutabilis* from the shores of Hawaii. This species is sticky to the touch and has a crown diameter of about 40 mm and a height of 25 mm. The column is smooth, except for a ring of prominent bright orange-brown, marginal spherules (which may be missing in small specimens). There are 96 non-retractile smooth and tapering tentacles.

Bubble Tip Anemone, *Entacmaea quadricolor*

Amphiprion melanopus in association with *Entacmaea quadricolor* in Anemone Garden on Flinders Reef, in the Coral Sea. This reef contained a large population of the Bubble Tip Anemone without the typical bubble-tip tentacles.

Typical habitat appearance of a Bubble Tip Anemone which has anchored itself deep in between the branches of a large stony coral. Photograph from Harrier Reef, on the Great Barrier Reef.

Close-up of tentacles with bubbles.

Condylactis gigantea

Caribbean Giant Anemone, Condy Anemone, Atlantic Anemone or Haitian Anemone
(Referred to by many authors under the synonym *Condylactis passiflora*.)

Distribution: In the Caribbean Sea and the western Atlantic, from Bermuda, the Bahamas and South Florida, to Brazil.

Size and growth form: Diameter of the expanded oral disc and tentacles up to 30 cm; base 8 cm. The tentacles are up to more than 15 cm long, sometimes even longer. Common in shallow water, but may occur as deep as 30 metres. Usually on coral reefs, rubble flats and in sea grass beds.

Food: This anemone probably feeds mainly on the products of its zooxanthellae, but also takes in plankton and other small animals as food.

Description: This is the largest and most spectacular anemone from the Caribbean. Column smooth, short cylindrical to trumpet-shaped; colour bluish grey, yellowish or brick-red. The large number of very long tentacles display beautiful colours. Tentacles tapering, greenish or brownish. The tips of the tentacles are usually purple and slightly swollen; the rest of the tentacles, whitish to greenish. Juveniles with knobbly tentacles. The colour of bright yellow specimens, which sometimes are on offer in aquarium shops, has been artificially enhanced.

Symbionts: *Periclimenes pedersoni, Thor amboinensis* and other crustaceans.

Aquarium maintenance:

– **General conditions:** Very well suited for a lagoon aquarium, in which sandy and rocky zones alternate, and in which fish from the Caribbean and hardy crustaceans are kept together with algae.
– **Lighting:** Strong.
– **Water circulation:** Medium.
– **Reproduction:** Unknown.

GA: + ; TO: - ; SE: +

Photos:

Top: Underwater photograph; Dr. A. Spreinat
Centre: Underwater photograph; O. Gremblewski-Strate
Bottom: Underwater photo from Bonaire
Photo: J. Cairns-Michael

Macrodactyla doreensis

Corkscrew Anemone, Sebae Anemone, Sand Anemone, Long Tentacle Anemone (L.T.A.), Red Base Anemone, Long Tentacle Red Based Anemone, Purple Long Tentacle Anemone.

Distribution: Central Indo-Pacific; found in a narrow N-S range, from southern Japan, through the Philippines, Indonesia and Papua-New Guinea, to the Great Barrier Reef.

Size and growth form: The oral disc grows to a maximum of 50 cm in diameter, but is usually smaller; typical: 10-20 cm. Tentacles usually 5-10 cm long; maximum 17.5 cm. The oral disc is spread at the surface and the column and base buried in muddy, sandy or gravelly bottom where it can retract completely if disturbed. In depths of 1-15 metres in pockets of sediments on coral platforms or in sediment bordering coral reefs (DUNN, 1981).

Food: This anemone probably feeds mainly on the products of its zooxanthellae, but also takes in plankton and other small animals as food.

Description: (Modified from DUNN, 1981). Base well developed, circular and smaller than the oral disc. Column is thin and easily damaged during collection. Lower portion equal in diameter to the pedal disc. Colour dull orange to brilliant red. Central part typically creamy green. Upper part broadly flared in large specimens, grey-brown or brownish violet with non-adherent white verrucae in longitudinal rows. The oral disc is flat, purplish grey to brown, sometimes with a red cast; some individuals with paired white, radial lines extending from the mouth onto each tentacle or around it. Others with single white radial lines only around the mouth. Few long tentacles, all alike, sinuous, tapering to a point and sometimes corkscrew in shape, having the same colour as the oral disc.

Symbionts: The following clownfishes have been occasionally found associated with this anemone: *Amphiprion chrysogaster*, *A. clarkii*, *A. perideraion* and *Dascyllus trimaculatus*.

Aquarium maintenance:
- **General conditions:** Often imported, mostly from the Philippines, where it appears to be very common. Easily kept and a good choice for the beginner setting up a small tank with anemones and their fish partners. Excellent in a sand zone aquarium with thick gravel or sand.
- **Lighting:** Strong to medium.
- **Water circulation:** Medium.
- **Reproduction:** Unknown.

GA: + ; TO: - ; SE: +

Photos:
Above: Top view of *M. doreensis*   Photo: R. Heijboer
Below: *M. doreensis* on a rubble bottom at Sulawesi, Indonesia   Photo: J. Cairns-Michael

"Anemonia" cf. *majano*

Distribution: Indo-Pacific. Few details are known, but the species seems to be widespread in Indonesia. The original description from material collected in Zanzibar, while specimens have also been collected from the Seychelles (J.C. den Hartog; pers. com.).

Size and growth form: Grows to a height of 2 to 4 cm in aquaria. The diameter of the oral disc is about 1-3 cm.

Food: This anemone feeds on the products of its zooxanthellae, but may also catch plankton. There is no need to provide it with additional food in aquaria.

Description: In the sea, it lives between the branches of stony corals. We often find it growing on live rock imported from Indonesia. The colour is usually light brown, with green fluorescent pigments, especially in the tips of the tentacles. The tentacles are long, sometimes with swollen tips. They are arranged in two or three rows on the rim of the disc. There are no tentacles in the centre of the disc.

Aquarium maintenance:

– **General conditions:** This anemone grows very well in most coral reef aquaria; in fact, it does not only thrive, but, provided with enough light, will easily overgrow the complete aquarium decor. For this reason, this species must be regarded as unsuitable for the coral reef aquarium. Because of its high reproduction rate, we must also take care that it does not overgrow other animals. Juvenile anemones commonly settle in tiny holes in a rock, with only the tentacles visible. In order to prevent overgrowth in an aquarium, the very first animals that appear should be removed, either by taking out the rock they are attached to, or by injecting the anemones with 5% HCl.

– **Lighting:** Strong.
– **Water circulation:** Medium to strong.
– **Reproduction:** This species reproduces very quickly. Nothing is known about the exact mode of reproduction, but it probably reproduces longitudinal fission in aquaria. However, sexual reproduction also seems to occur.

GA: - ; TO: +/- ; SE: +

Photos:

– Top: Collected individual specimen measuring about 2 cm in diameter.
– Bottom: Dense population of somewhat larger individuals in an aquarium.

The colours of the column vary from olive-green to sepia, to orange-brown, while the oral disc is sepia, with a triangle running from the tentacles about halfway to the mouth, which is surrounded by an reddish brown area.

The genus *Anthopleura* is widespread in the Indo-Pacific, but is only occasionally seen in the trade. *Anthopleura nigrescens* is common in Hawaii, where it is found intertidally in holes in basaltic rocks, but is also found throughout the Indo-Pacific; we have also spotted the species ourselves in the Maldives. Fully grown individuals have a disc diameter of 30 mm and a column height of 15 mm. The column has about 50 rows of adhesive verrucae which have a white central spot. The colours of the disc and upper column are generally dark violet sepia, but, occasionally, brick-red specimens are also found. The base and the lower column are a shade paler than the disc. The tentacles often exhibit the same general colours, but may be whitish, or may have white spots along the margin of the disc. This species, like the others in the genus, often reproduces asexually by longitudinal fission. See CUTRESS (in DEWANY & ELREDGE, 1977) for more information on this and other species of Actiniidae from Hawaii.

Anthopleura elatensis is found in shallow, sandy habitats in the Red Sea, where it is partly covered by sand. The colour is pale brown with darker patches on the upper column (VINE, 1986).

Along the west coast of America and in the Gulf of California, three beautiful species of *Anthopleura* occur. The brilliant green *A. xanthogrammica*, which contains symbiotic algae, is found attached to rocks in the tidal zone down to 30 metres. The elegant *A. elegantissima* is found in the intertidal zone down to 18 metres, while the extraordinary, bright purple or pink *A. artemisia* occurs attached to rocks or buried in sand from the tidal zone down to 30 metres.

Anthopleura nigrescens photographed in the Maldives

Family Aliciidae

The Caribbean genus *Lebrunia*, species of which are only rarely imported, belongs to the family Aliciidae. The best known species is *L. danae*, commonly referred to as the Branch or Antler Anemone, but also known as the Brown or Gill-bearing Anemone. In the nature, it lives attached in deep crevices in coral rocks at depths of 2 to 60 m. Only their tentacles, which protrude from the hole, are visible. The column is smooth and has 4-8 highly expandable, dendritic pseudotentacles that bear conspicious, semi-globular, white to bluish nematocyst batteries. The oral disc has an oval shape and 96 tentacles with white and brown spots and knots, which contain nematocysts (CAIRNS et al. in STERRER, 1986). The sting from *L. danae* is extremely painful. The pseudotentacles are expanded during the day to capture light for the symbiotic algae, while the feeding tentacles are expanded during the night. These characteristics easily distinguish this genus from all others. The anemone shrimp *Periclimenes pedersoni* is often found between the

Anthopleura elegantissima from the Gulf of California

Lebrunia danae Photo: Scott W. Michael

pseudotentacles, especially in specimens from deeper water.

A second species, *Lebrunia coralligens*, lives at depths of up to 10 m and has, like the previous species, long pseudotentacles with enlarged tips. The colours are brown to dark grey or bluish-green, with shaded line and ring markings. This anemone inhabits narrow fissures in coral heads and cannot be collected without removing the coral and the anemone simultaneously. The feeding tentacles, which are extended during the night, are long and unbranched. In general, *Lebrunia* species do very well in aquaria,

provided they are given sufficient light. Both species should, however, be kept in a special aquarium.

One of the strangest, most dangerous and most interesting of all reef anemones is the "Hells Fire Anemone" *Phyllodiscus semoni*. The species shows a variety of camouflage patterns and mimics several other organisms including algae and corals. The significance of the camouflage and mimicry may at least serve two functions; it may be used to deceive potential prey or to destracts potential predators (den HARTOG, 1997).

We found this extremely varia-

ble species in the muddy sea grass beds of Bunaken, North Sulawesi, by almost stepping on it. It was living in only a foot of water, obviously thriving in the burning sunlight and being used as host by numerous symbiotic shrimps.

P. semoni is the worst stinger of all anemones! Its powerful sting gave it its English popular name "Hells Fire Anemone". During the Vietnam War, beaches that were used by American soldiers for bathing were closed, because the soldiers were stung so badly that they could not return to duty. The story is presented and discussed by HANSEN & HALSTEAD (1971). The authors did, however, misidentify the anemone to be *Actinodendron plumosum*, while the "Hells Fire Anemone" in fact was *Phyllodiscus semoni*, (J.C. den Hartog; pers. com.). The same authors report that the local fishermen of Vietnam regard the anemone as a food delicacy. The anemones are taken in nets and dried in the sun until they are completely dehydrated. They are then cut open and the inside of the animal is eaten with great relish.

We have not yet seen it in the trade, but it should do very well if given enough light, and must appear spectacular in a small, special aquarium, where it could be used as a host anemone for numerous symbiotic shrimps and crabs. See fact-pages 248-249 for more details.

Another member of In the Aliciidae is *Triactis producta*. This species is known by the popular name of Boxer Crab Anemone, because it sometimes lives associated with the claws of the boxer crab *Lybia leptochelis*, which uses the anemones and their very powerful batteries of nematocysts for defence, being totally dependent on the anemones for its survival. The anemone can, however, also live freely and has a much wider habitat tolerance than the boxer crabs which are restricted to the very shallow waters of the reef flats. *T. producta* is found in shaded crevices, as well as among the branches of the hy-

Triactis producta photographed at Sulawesi, Indonesia.
Photo: J. Cairns-Michael

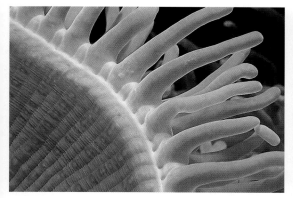

Heractis magnifica, on the left, a close-up of the rim of the oral disc and of the rows of verrucae; on the right, atypical colours in the tips of the tentacles.   Photos: Scott W. Michael

drocoral *Millepora dichotoma* (VINE, 1986). According to GOSLINER et al. (1996), it can be observed as deep as 30 metres. Many slender tentacles surround the smooth oral disc and several pseudotentacles occur near the top of the upright column just below the tentacles. The colour is brownish-red, with pinkish vesicles around the oral disc. *T. producta* in distributed in the Indo-Pacific, from the Red Sea, to Ryukyu Islands.

The family also contains the genus *Alicia*, with *Alicia pretiosa* as a common species of the Indo-Pacific. GOSLINER et al. (1996) mention *A.* cf. *sansibariensis*, with a distribution from East Africa to the Philippines, and ALLEN & STEENE (1994) illustrate *A. rhadina* (?) from the Indo-Pacific, while VINE (1986) mentions *A. mirabilis* and *A. sansibariensis* from the Red Sea. According to BAENSCH & DEBELIUS (1992), *A. mirabilis* is also distributed in the Mediterranean. HUMANN (1992) uses this name for an anemone from the Western Atlantic (with the popular name of Berried Anemone), a species that does, however, have a totally different appearance from that mentioned by VINE (1986). All of the species in *Alicia* are night-feeders that extend their long tentacles during the hours of darkness. During the day, the column is withdrawn, but becomes fully expanded during night-time. According to COLIN & ARNESON (1995), *Alicia*

spp. look like tiny clumps during the day, but can expand to a height of two feet (ca. 60 cm) during the night. These anemones have prominent vesicles on the column (brightly coloured in some species), containing extremely powerful nematocysts that sting so badly that they can seriously hurt humans. We have not yet seen *Alicia* spp. in the trade, but they certainly have the potential to show up on pieces of live rock; great care should be taken with these dangerous stingers.

Family Stichodactylidae

The family Stichodactylidae contains the well-known genera *Heteractis* and *Stichodactyla* which, for decades, have been the most popular host sea anemone species seen in the hobby.

The genus **Heteractis** includes the best known four species of symbiotic anemones. They are sometimes still referred to by the older synonym, *Radianthus*. *Heteractis* species are found in shallow reef areas all over the Indo-Pacific. According to DUNN (1981), three of the species have relatively few, moderately long and sinuous to digitiform tentacles, while the last species has swellings along the tentacles. All the species share a common charac-

teristic in that they possess only a few, but rather long, and sometimes thin, tentacles. The base is usually a little wider than the column and both are well developed, with the latter being equal to the diameter of the oral disc, or equal to the diameter of the base. At the top of the smooth stalk, we find inconspicuous to prominent verrucaee (warts), which occasionally gather detritus from the substratum. The disc is almost flat and barely retractile. The four species are not difficult to distinguish from each other.

The Magnificent Sea Anemone, *Heteractis magnifica,* is easy to identify (although it may sometimes be confused with *Entacmaea*), it is beautiful and probably the most popular of all the host sea anemones. In spite of this, several older synonyms are still used in publications. Some authors use e.g. *Radianthus ritteri,* while FRIESE (1972) and ALLEN (1975) use *Radianthus paumotensis*, and Vine (1986) and Schmid & Paschke (1990) use *Gyrostoma helianthus.* This anemone is widely distributed, being found in the Indo-Pacific, from East Africa and the Red Sea, east to French Polynesia, and from the Great Barrier Reef, to the Ryukyu Islands. It is very common in the trade and hobby and is found in most import shipments.

Heteractis magnifica usually reaches a diameter of 30 to 50 cm, although some specimens may

Phyllodiscus semoni
"Hells Fire Anemone"

Distribution: Indo-West Pacific; Vietnam, Indonesia, the Philippines, further details are unknown. Usually found in shallow water, less than 10 m deep, and often as shallow as 1 or 2 metres, as a rule in quiet water such as shallow protected lagoons, inlets and bays, among dead or living hard corals, among soft corals or in sea-grass beds. According to HANSEN & HALSTEAD (1971) the anemone (which by the auhors was mistaken for *Actinodendron plumosum*) showed a scattered distribution in Vietnam.

Size and growth form: Occasionally found in larger groups, but most commonly occuring as individuals or in small groups with equal sized individuals (den HARTOG, pers. com.). May exceed 25 cm across the column with expanded vesicles. *P. semoni* is a master of camouflage and mimicry, which affects its colour pattern and shape. One form resembles variegated patches of algae-covered substratum. In another form the columnar vesicles are long and ramified, and the animal looks like a bunch of algae. In a

Photo: *Phyllodiscus semoni* is one of the strangest-looking, but also one of the most beautiful, of all anemones. We found this specimen on muddy bottom among sea grass near the beach at Bunaken, north Sulawesi. Here it mimics a bunch of algae.

third, and most striking form, the anemone mimics almost to perfection a colony of branching coral (den HARTOG, 1997). See the photos by Bert Hoeksema and J. Cairns-Michael (page 249), which clearly illustrate the camouflage potential of this species.

Food: Utilise the nutrients translocated from its zooxanthellae during the day when the anemone exposes only pseudotentacles. The true tentacles open fully only during night when it probably capture small planktonic organisms only. *P. semoni* has never been observed to capture fish and allows juvenile damsel fish like *Dascyllus albicella* to move among its pseudotentacles without being harmed.

Description: *P. semoni* is the largest member of the order Boloceroidaria. The column is completely covered with compound vesicles (pseudotentacles). The vesicles are provided with many, globular, extremely powerful nematocysts and the species is the worst stinger among all anemones. The stinging power is most probably used for protection (den HARTOG, pers. com.). Whether *P. semoni* is the only, extremely variable species of the genus or a number of specialists, each of which mimics another organism, is being studied by den HARTOG & HOEKSEMA (in prep.).

Symbionts: Associated with numerous commensal shrimps, including the genus *Periclimenes* and often host small commensal brittle stars on its column. Juvenile fish like *Dascyllus albicella* are frequently associated with the anemone.

Aquarium maintenance:
– **General conditions:** Must be kept in a special aquarium. In a special aquarium parts of the biology of this unique animal can be studied in detail. A sea-grass aquarium with *P. semoni* and its associated animals would indeed be an impressive display. A shallow and rather wide aquarium designed to be viewed from above and housing a number of *P. semoni* and their symbionts would also be a most interesting although it could not be designed as a "touch tank".
– **Lighting:** Very strong to strong.
– **Water circulation:** Medium.
– **Reproduction:** Details are not known, but the fact that *P. semoni* often occurs in small aggregations with individuals of the same size indicates that it reproduces asexually, probably by longitudinal fission (den HARTOG, pers. com.).

GA: +/- ; TO: - ; SE: 0

A specimen that mimics a branching stony coral.
Photo: B. Hoeksema

A specimen that mimics a knobby and colourful stony coral.
Photo: B. Hoeksema

A specimen camouflaged as algae in shallow water in Sulawesi, Indonesia.
Photo: J. Cairns-Michael

A specimen growing among algae and small branching stony corals, which it mimics.
Photo: B. Hoeksema

A specimen that mimics a branching soft coral. Note the true soft coral on the right.
Photo: B. Hoeksema

P. semoni with associated shrimps.
Photo from Indonesia: J. Cairns-Michael

We found two different colour morphs of the Magnificent Sea Anemone in the Maldives; both contained the endemic clownfish *Amphiprion nigripes*.

grow as large as 1 m - a size usually found among specimens that live a solitary existence and not in aggregations. The colour is often very intense and the base, which is light in colour, circular, with irregular lobes and wider that the lower column, firmly attaches itself to the substratum (usually, to a coral boulder), but also very rarely, among branching corals, just as *Heteractis crispa* so commonly does. The column is colourful and uniformly purple, orange, blue or green, but it may also be intensely red. The disc and lower portions of the tentacles are usually brownish. The terminal ends of the tentacles, are yellow, green or white, but, mostly, avocado green. The tentacles do not taper to a point, but are more or less blunt and may end in a sort of knob. Occasionally, branched tentacles are also found. Along the outer margin of the disc we find numerous verrucae, (blister-like outgrowths of the body wall) which continue in longitudinal rows arranged downwards along the column. *H. magnifica* is able to retract almost completely, leaving only a few tentacles visible, but rarely does so and when it happens, it happens very slowly.

In the Maldives, we nearly always saw this sea anemone at depths of 1 to 10 m on the reef edge, where the motion of the water was strong and the light intensity high. The clown fish *Amphiprion nigripes* was always associated with the anemone. However, it is also accepted as a symbiosis partner by at least 11 other species of clown fishes, among them the well known *A. clarkii* and *A. ocellaris*, as well as *Amphiprion* spp., and by the damsel fish *Dascyllus trimaculatus*.

We have kept *Heteractis magnifica* in our aquaria more than once and our experiences have always been positive. Like all symbiotic anemones, *H. magnifica* accepts different kinds of food, such as ground shrimps, bits of fish, mussels and Mysis shrimps. It also utilizes nutrients translocated from the photosynthesis of the zooxanthellae, and

The Magnificent Anemone, *Heteractis magnifica* in an aquarium.

under optimal light conditions can do well in a reef tank with little additional food.

On the reef, *H. magnifica* is found solitary or in aggregations. Specimens living in groups tend to be smaller than those living a solitary existence (DUNN, 1981). Solitary individuals are usually large and exhibit a regular anatomy, implying that they result from sexual reproduction, while the smaller specimens found in aggregations are smaller, have uniform colours and exhibit an irregular anatomy, indicating that they result from asexual reproduction through longitudinal fission.

In a special aquarium for host sea anemones, we can imitate such aggregations. This is the only way in which we can really do justice to this beautiful anemone and its symbionts. In a coral reef aquarium where various corals dominate, *H. magnifica* will be a nuisance, to say the least, and may even do harm to other inhabitants because of its strong sting and its tendency to wander around, causing burns to the other sessile organisms in the tank.

The Leathery Sea Anemone, *Heteractis crispa*, usually remains smaller than *H. magnifica*. It may reach a diameter of 50 cm, but is

usually about half this size. In the literature it is often referred to under other names, e.g. *Anthopsis koseirensis* and *Heteractis malu* by HAYWOOD & WELLS (1989), *Bartholomea* sp. in BAUMEISTER (1990), *Radianthus kuekenthali* by WILKENS (1980), and *Radianthus malu* by various other authors. The Leathery Sea Anemone is a widely distributed native of the Indo-Pacific and is found from the Red Sea, east to French Polynesia, and from Japan, south to southeast Australia.

The base is flat and regular and does not normally exceed the diameter of the lower column. It fastens itself to the substratum, but this attachment is not too strong. The column of *Heteractis crispa* feels thick and leathery. While the upper part of the column, which is pale grey or purple-brown, has longitudinal rows of verrucae, there are none in the lower part, which is white or beige. Particles of detritus are often adhere to these warts.

The disc of *Heteractis crispa* is brownish-purple, or grey, or sometimes even green. The diameter of the disc is, typically, about 20 cm, but it can occasionally reach as much as 50 cm or more and exhibit a faint striped pattern. The tentacles are all of the same shape, tapering from the base to

A colour variant of *H. crispa* on the Great Barrier Reef.　A colour variant of *H. crispa* from the Maldives.

the top and ending in a pointed tip. They have the same colour as the disc. DUNN (1981) estimates that a moderately large specimen has about 800 tentacles. The pointed tips of the tentacles are purple, violet or blue.

Specimens from the western part of the Indian Ocean, e.g. the Maldives, have a distinct colour pattern that differs markedly from that of specimens from the Central and Eastern Indo-Pacific (see photograph above). Today specimens with this pattern are regarded as belonging to a geographical type of *H. crispa*. They have, however, not surprisingly, been mistaken for a separate species and may perhaps be so?

Typical habitats of *Heteractis crispa* are shallow reef flats and reef slopes, where it often settles among branching corals. This anemone prefers strong light intensity and is rarely seen at depths exceeding 15 m. Occasionally, it lives among the branches of stony corals of the genus *Acropora*. FAUTIN & ALLEN (1992) list 14 anemone fishes as *H. crispa* symbionts: *Amphiprion* species and *Dascyllus trimaculatus*. We have found this to be a very hardy anemone that, however, requires strong light conditions in aquaria.

The Beaded Sea Anemone, *Heteractis aurora*, has distinct tentacles and can hardly be confused with the other species in the genus. It is, however, not so often found on offer in the aquarium trade. It is distributed in the Indo-Pacific, from East Africa, the Red Sea and the Persian Gulf, eastwards to Micronesia and Melanesia, and from the Ryukyu Islands, southward to the Great Barrier Reef. This species too has been known under different names in aquarium literature. ALLEN (1975) and FRIESE (1972) refer to it as *Radianthus simplex*, and SCHMIDT & PASCHKE (1990) as *Radianthus koseirensis*.

The base is thin, almost circular in outline, and weakly adherent, i.e. weakly attached to the substratum. The lower part of the column of *Heteractis aurora* is often orange or red, but pales towards the top, while the top is similar in colour to the disc, which is grey, brownish or green. The upper part of the column has light-coloured adhesive verrucae.

A colour variant of *H. crispa* from Papua-New Guinea.
Photo: Scott W. Michael

A colour variant of *H. crispa* from Indonesia.
Photo: J. Olsen

The Beaded Sea Anemone, *Heteractis aurora* in the Maldives

The disc is not very large, usually 5 to 15 cm in diameter, occasionally 25 cm, and it is coloured brownish-violet (due to zooxanthellae) and possesses light brown or white stripes. Much of the disc is visible, as the tentacles are sparse. The peculiar tentacles, which are up to 40 mm long, have distinct swellings and taper to a point from a basal diameter of 2-3 mm. They are highly contractile and may be very sticky to the touch (DUNN, 1981). The colour of the tentacles is brownish-violet, like the disc, but some marginal ones might be whitish. These may have a lot of verrucae of the same colour as the disc, but, mostly, they have small protrusions of a white or other light colour. This is the most reliable character of the species. The tentacles can be contracted considerably and have strong stinging cells, which cause a burning sensation when they are touched.

In the sea, *Heteractis aurora* is usually buried in the sand or gravel so deeply, that only the disc and the tentacles stick out. It is most common in the shallowest part of the reef, down to a depth of about 20 m. Symbionts are some of the species of the *Amphiprion clarkii* complex and the damsel *Dascyllus trimaculatus*.

The Delicate Sea Anemone or Hawaii Anemone, *Heteractis malu*, is very similar in colour to *Heteractis crispa*, but, in contrast to it, has very thin and delicate tissue. When *Heteractis malu* is fully unfolded, it is nearly transparent and can easily be damaged. *H. malu* has a scattered geographi-

A group of the Delicate Sea Anemone, *Heteractis malu* in an exhibition at the Waikiki Aquarium, Honolulu.   Photo: Dr. B. Carlson, Waikiki-Aquarium

cal distribution in the central Indo-Pacific and is much more restricted than the other *Heteractis* species. It is found in certain locations from Hawaii (where the species is particularly frequent), west to Japan, east Australia and Java. Thus, *Heteractis malu* is also known from Indonesian areas and is occasionally imported from there into the aquarium trade.

The base is thin, almost colourless, and has a diameter of 5-7 cm. The lower part of the stalk is light creamy-coloured; the upper part is brownish or light purple and has length-wise rows of verrucae. The disc has the same colour as the upper part of the stalk, is flat, and has a maximum diameter of 20 cm when fully unfolded. At 10 to 40 mm, the tentacles are rather short. They are of unequal length and are arranged in rows on the disc. The tips are pointed, and their colour is brownish to light purple.

Heteractis malu is found in shallow, quiet water, as e.g. in docks or quiet lagoons, where it buries its foot and stalk in the sand or between fragments of corals. Its only known symbiotic fish partners are juvenile *Amphiprion clarkii*.

It is probable that most sea anemones which are sold under the name *Radianthus malu*, (which was the most frequent name given to almost every imported host sea anemone in Europe in the early days of the marine hobby), or which are referred to by this name in aquarium publications, are really *Heteractis crispa*. As *Heteractis malu* comes from very shallow water, it requires high light intensity in aquaria. On the other hand, it does not need as strong a water current as the other *Heteractis* species.

In the genus **Stichodactyla**, we find the real giant anemones. Most of the species in the genus can easily be recognized by their folded structure, their considerable size and the numerous short globose, clavate or bluntly pointed small tentacles which cover most of the main area of the disc. On the reef, these anemones

The Sun Anemone, *Stichodactyla helianthus*, off St. John, Virgin Island
Photo: Dr. N. Furman

spread over the substratum, with the largest species covering areas of more than a square metre. The members of this genus are often sold under their popular name "carpet anemones". The genus *Stichodactyla* is distributed throughout the Indo-West Pacific and in the Carribbean Sea and were formerly known under the generic name *Stoichactis*.

Stichodactyla tapetum is undoubtedly, the least known member of the genus and differs from the other species by its small size and lack of symbiotic fishes. The base is 10-30 mm in diameter and has the same colour as the column. The column is about half as long as the diameter of the pedal disc, although some specimens can be taller, and is mostly red with white flecks. It is smooth with a firm texture due to a thick mesogloea. The oral disc is flat with a diameter of 12-40 mm and has green colour with brown stripes and (sometimes) yellow spots. The tentacles that nearly cover the whole disc, are very densely arranged and very small, almost bulbous, with a diameter of no more than 0.25 to 0.5 mm and a length of about 1 mm. They are, in fact, so numerous and densely packed, that the single tentacles have a square shape,

as they clamp each other sideways-on.

Little is known about the biology of *Stichodactyla tapetum* and, so far, there have not been any reports about a symbiotic relationship between this anemone and fish or invertebrates. In its natural habitat, *Stichodactyla tapetum* lives in holes in corallive rock. It has been found in the Red Sea, in Zanzibar, Indonesia, West-Australia and Tahiti and is therefore widespread in the Indo-Pacific, but easily overlooked, especially since it lacks anemonefishes which would attract attention. DUNN (1981) reports about numerous finds of this species off the Moluccas Islands (Indonesia). *S. tapetum* lives especially in very shallow water, often intertidally in habitats that are dried out during low tide. We often failed to spot this species on the reef, in comparison to its larger relatives. As it occasionally dries out, it is rarely associated with symbiotic animals although shrimps of the genus *Periclimenes* sometimes occupy the species.

So far, we have not yet heard about any imports and we totally lack experience regarding the maintenance of this anemone in the reef aquarium. We would, however, not be surprised at all if, one day, *S. tapetum* appears on offer, together with live rock.

The Sun Anemone, *Stichodactyla helianthus*, is a symbiotic anemone that is very common in the eastern and southern Caribbean, as well as in the Bahamas, but more rarely seen in the northwestern Caribbean (HUMANN, 1993). Its geographical distribution reaches as far north as the Florida Keys. Although it does not have a symbiotic relationship with any fish, the beautiful Squat Anemone Shrimp, *Thor amboniensis*, and the Banded Clinging Crab, *Mithrax cinctimanus*, are among many symbiotic crustaceans that use this sea anemone as host.

The base (pedal disc) is round or irregular and about 50mm in diameter, with the same colour as the lower part of the column. The column, itself, is very short. Small verrucae are found in longitudinal rows on the upper part of the column, but, unlike the verrucae of many other host sea anemones, these do not hold debris. The disc may reach up to 12 cm in diameter with the margin slightly undulating. It is mostly covered with tentacles, but, these cannot be contracted. The disc and tentacles, are variable in colour: whitish, or brown, or grey, or even green, with the brownish and greenish colours always present owing to the possession of endodermal symbiotic algae. The tentacles are only 8 to 10 mm long, blunt or finger-shaped, and cover the whole disc, except for a small area around the mouth. Their lower portion bears the same colours as the disc, while the upper part may be bright green or yellow and, as they exhibit different colours in one and the same individual, this can produce an exciting colour pattern.

Stichodactyla helianthus lives on sandy bottoms in shallow water down to about 3 metres, where it can form dense clusters, but solitary specimens can also be found. The base and column are, typically, buried in the sand, with the disc spread at the surface.

The geographical distribution of this species reaches as far north as the Florida Keys. Symbionts are crustaceans, like *Periclimenes* spp., *Thor amboinensis* and *Mitrax cinctimanus*. We have, to date, had no opportunity of personally gathering data on the Sun Anemone.

Stichodactyla haddoni, the Saddle Anemone, is the most frequently imported species of the genus. It should - like the majority of the host sea anemones - be given a special aquarium. Our experience has taught us that this species is more difficult to adapt to aquarium conditions than the other species of host sea anemones. Careful acclimatization is therefore absolutely necessary, and should be carried out over a period of hours. *S. haddoni* is a magnificent beauty, once it has established itself in an aquarium.

The light-coloured base is generally round, but irregularly lobed, and about half as wide as the disc when fully expanded. The column is of variable length, translucent-white, yellow or light green in colour and widens towards the oral disc, where it becomes yellowish to pinkish. *Stichodactyla haddoni* has a folded disc that may lie flat over the substratum in fully expanded specimens, which usually attain a diameter of 30 to 50 cm and, rarely, up to 80 cm. The fluorescent colours of the disc show brown nuances, which are the result of possessing symbiotic algae. This species has a distinct area around the mouth, measuring 10-20 mm in diameter, which is free of tentacles and brightly coloured yellow, orange or red. The tentacles are arranged very densely along the rim and are, typically, 3-8 mm long and 1 mm in diameter at their base. Their pigmentation varies, which gives this anemone a very particular colour pattern that is the most reliable method of identifying it. The tentacles contain powerful nematocysts that can cause severe stings. It is therefore really important to be very careful with *Stichodactyla haddoni*, which is not suitable company for other cnidarians, like soft- and hard corals, possessing less powerful nettling poison. It should, consequently, be kept in a special aquarium, where it may develop its stinging power to the full - perhaps, in the presence of other anemones.

Stichodactyla haddoni is not dependent on the coral substratum, but lives, mostly, on sandy bottoms, or among coral rubble on reef flats. It may also occasionaly be found sitting on coral rocks. It is distributed widely in the Indo-Pacific, from the Red Sea and East Africa, east to Australia, Japan and the Fiji Islands. However, it is really abundant in only a few places, e.g. in the northern part of the Great Barrier Reef. According to FAUTIN & ALLEN (1992), *S. haddoni* is host to six species of clownfishes, including the commonly imported *Amphiprion clarkii* and the much rarer *A. polymnus*.

The Giant Carpet Anemone, *Stichodactyla gigantea*, formerly generally called *Stoichactis giganteum* by some authors, is, despite its scientific or popular names, not the largest species in the genus. The majority of specimens only measure 15 to 20 cm in diameter, which means that this giant is, in fact, among the smaller of the host sea anemones. Some individuals may grow to 50 cm or more, i.e. about the same size as the previous species, *S. haddoni*. *S. gigantea*, however, lacks the shades of colours that are typical of *S. haddoni* and, thus, the two species are easy to tell apart. The colours in *S. gigantea* vary from yellow to brown, and from purple to greenish. Some forms exhibit extremely bright colours and, occasionally, unimaginably deep purple specimens are found. Its symbiosis partners are seven species of clown fishes, *Amphiprion* spp. and shrimps of the genus *Periclimenes*, as well as *Thor amboinensis*.

The base, which is firmly attached to the substratum, is irregular, with its colour the same as the lower column and a diameter that is always less than half that of the oral disc. The column is usually

The Saddle-Anemone, *Stichodactyla haddoni* at the Löbbecke Museum and Aqua-Zoo, Düsseldorf, Germany

short and ranges in colour from yellowish or pinkish, through greenish or greenish blue, to orange-brown. The upper part has non-adhesive verrucae, which are blue to maroon in colour. The disc is undulating, with colours like those of the terminal parts of the tentacles, i.e. most often, pinkish brown to maroon. In *Stichodactyla gigantea*, most of the tentacles, which are about 1 cm long and taper slightly from the base to the bluntly pointed tip, are found on the outer halfrim of the disc, where they are quite numerous; towards the centre, there are fewer. The tentacles are very sticky and adhere to human skin on contact, detaching from the disc in clumps. The outer 1-3 mm of the tentacles may often have the same colours as the disc, but, sometimes, they have extraordinarily bright colours like green, yellow, blue, pink or purple. In addition, they contain powerful nematocysts, so we should always handle this symbiotic anemone with care.

Stichodactyla gigantea is very common all over in the Indo-West Pacific, from the Red Sea and Zanzibar, to Australia, Micronesia and the Ryukyu Islands. It is one of the most common anemones of the coral reefs. Usually, it is restricted to very shallow water in calm surroundings, e.g. on sandy or muddy bottoms, or on platform reefs with sea grass beds near the beach, or in shallow lagoons

The Saddle Anemone, *Stichodactyla haddoni*: on the left, off the Fiji Islands; on the right, (photo: G. Spies) close-up of the tentacles with a symbiotic shrimp, *Periclimenes* sp.

Green specimen at the zoo in Bochum, Germany (above) and a purple-coloured specimen (below, photo: Scott W. Michael).

at depths of only one metre or less. In some places, e.g. in Jakarta Bay (Indonesia), *S. gigantea* may attain such a high population density, that it has been used as a source of food for the local people who regard it as a special delicacy. "Symbiotic anemones à la carte" are served there under the name of "kalamonat".

Stichodactyla mertensii, (the Carpet Anemone), listed by some authors as *Stoichactis giganteum*, is the real giant among the host sea anemones. The largest specimens may reach a diameter of more than 1 metre and MARISCAL (1970 and 1972) found a specimen with the disc measuring 1.24 metres across. Most specimens are smaller, though, measuring 25-50 cm across. *S. mertensii* is very widespread in the Indo-Pacific and is found from East Africa, northwards to the Gulf of Aden, and eastwards to Micronesia and Melanesia, and from the Ryukyu Islands, southwards to the Great Barrier Reef. Its fish partners are 12 species of *Amphiprion* spp., including *Amphiprion clarkii* and *A. ocellaris*, as well as *Dascyllus trimaculatus*. We have also spotted symbiotic crabs associated with this anemone.

The base in *Stichodactyla mertensii* is very irregular and whitish, while the column can be greatly extended and is white with irregularly distributed orange or purple spots. The upper part of the tan-coloured to white column is greatly flared, greying towards the margin, due to symbiotic algae, and possesses lengthwise rows of red or orange warts. The disc is usually brownish, sometimes slightly lighter, and spreads against the substratum, tracing its contour. The finger-shaped, non-adhesive tentacles, which are 1 to 2 cm long, are densely arranged and usually uniformly brown. The central tentacles are longer, up to 5 cm, and their lengths are characteristic of the species.

In the sea, this anemone is nearly always found firmly attached in crevices and holes in rocks or corals, or in natural pits between corals, where it can re-

Stichodactyla mertensii off Papua-New Guinea. Photo: Scott W. Michael

Close-up of the orange verrucae of *Stichodactyla mertensii*, which are typical of this species.

treat into its hiding place if disturbed. This species is very often seen on the reef, but, because of its size, it is frequently mistaken for *S. gigantea*.

Family Phymanthidae

The anemones of the family Phymanthidae are usually sold in Europe as "sand anemones" and are frequently imported. Strangely, sand anemones are known by the somewhat misleading popular name of rock anemones in the States. In any case, they are, perhaps, the most commonly seen anemones from Singapore. The European popular name points to their habitat, in which

they bury themselves, or where they cling to the underside of a rock, so that only the tentacles protrude. Sand anemones belong to the genera *Heteranthus*, *Phymanthus* and *Epicystis*.

The oral disc is wide and divided into a distinct, peripheral, tentaculate region and a central one with radial rows of wart-like protuberances (STERRER, 1986). Several species or forms are imported from the Indo-Pacific, among which *Phymanthus buitendijki* is perhaps the most common. VINE (1986) mentions *P. loligo*, a species from the Red Sea, that lives in shallow waters, embedded among coral rubble. *Heteranthus verruculatus* is widespread in the Indo-Pacific and is reported from the Red Sea, eastern Australia and Hawaii (CUTRESS (in DEWANY & ELREDGE),

Phymanthus spp.
Rock Anemone, Sand Anemone

Distribution: Indo-West Pacific; details unknown. Very common and widespread in tropical and subtropical seas.
Size and growth form: As a rule, 10 to 15 cm in diameter; some species remain smaller, however. Height about 10 cm. These species prefer sandy habitats and commonly settle under a rock lying on a sandy substratum.
Food: These anemones probably feed mainly on the products of their zooxanthellae, but also take in plankton and other small animals.
Description: The genus probably contains around 6 true species although 10 species have so far been described (J. C. den HARTOG; pers. com.). Column whitish or pale yellowish, with tiny, crystal- white warts. Oral disc olive green or brownish. The colour and the shape of the tentacles are very varied. Each tentacle has a series of lateral tree-like outgrowths. The tentacles are found in the periphery of the disc; the central disc itself is without tentacles. These species prefer sandy habitats. Their stinging power is not as strong as that of other anemones.
Symbionts: Partners in their natural surroundings are not known. In aquaria, they are accepted by many crustaceans, including *Periclimenes* spp., *Thor amboinensis* and *Neopetrolisthes* spp.

Aquarium maintenance:
– **General conditions:** These anemones are hardy and do not cause many problems in aquaria. Their nematocysts are not as powerful as those of many other anemones associated with reef aquaria. We have never seen other cnidarians harmed by these anemones. Nevertheless, we must take care, especially if these sand anemones are associated with delicate animals. They do not wander around in the aquarium and are very well suited for a sand zone aquarium.
– **Lighting:** Strong.
– **Water circulation:** Medium.
– **Reproduction:** Nothing is known about their reproduction in aquaria.
GA: + ; TO: +/- ; SE: +

Photos:
– Above: *Phymanthus* sp. (KA4-ACT-01)
– Centre: *Phymanthus buitendijki* with the column easily visible
– Bottom: Close-up of the tentacles of *Phymanthus buitendijki*.

Phymanthus sp.   Photo: Scott W. Michael

Phymanthus sp. from Sulawesi, Indonesia   Photo: J. Cairns-Michael

Phymanthus sp. from Sulawesi, Indonesia   Photo: J. Cairns-Michael

1977). This last named species is rather small, with a maximum height and disc diameter of only a couple of cm. The oral disc is dark greenish brown to sepia, overlayed with varying amounts of opaque white that can be distributed as numerous fine flecks and spots. The upper column has longitudinal rows of conspicuous warts, which are tentacle-like at their margins.

Only one species of the family, *Epicystis crucifer,* comes from the Caribbean. The column is short and trumpet-shaped, with a flamed pattern of cream and red. There are numerous longitudinal rows of 3-6 conspicuous verrucae, each row ending in a conical marginal region. The tentacles are short and up to 384 in number. The oral disc is up to 15 cm across, while the base is about half this size. Two varieties occur in Bermuda: one form with elevated crossbars on the tentacles, and another with a brown oral disc and smooth tentacles with yellow to faint orange, radial-longitudinal stripes. Intermediate forms also occur (STERRER, 1986). Their tentacles are about 5 cm long and, in several species, have small protuberances arranged in three or four circles along the rim of the disc.

Phymanthus and *Epicystis* species are very suitable for a coral reef aquarium especially as symbiotic anemones for crustaceans. Porcelain crabs (anemone crabs) of the genus *Neopetrolisthes* do particularly well between their tentacles. For instance, some *N. ohshimai*, which we had in our reef aquarium, lived in their host sand anemones all the five years that we kept them. If a little gorge is constructed from larger pieces of live rock and five or six sand anemones are introduced, a beautiful arrangement is achieved, which, at the same time creates surroundings in which the anemones and their symbiotic partners may well thrive. See fact page 259 for additional information.

Anemone of the genus *Actinodendron*, perhaps *Actinodendron plumosum* (on the left: in its typical habitat; on the right: close-up of a branch). This anemone is very common off Indonesia, New Guinea and in south east Asia. Yet, only little is known about it; it lives in the sand zone, which is rarely ever visited by divers. It has very strong nematocysts and its sting can severely hurt humans.   **Photos: Scott W. Michael**

Family Actinodendridae

Typical habitats for the species of this family of anemones are silt and sand bottoms in relatively shallow water. The rather long tentacles often branch like bushes, so, at first sight, these anemones may be easily mistaken for soft corals. If threatened, they retract into the sand very rapidly. The three genera *Actinodendron*, *Actinostephanus* and *Megalactis* are the only one in the family.

On one of our expeditions to the Maldives, we observed, close to the beach on the island of Kuredu, a number of circular holes with a diameter of 5 to 7 cm, which went right down into the sandy bottom at a depth of 2 m. The borders of these holes were completely smooth. We were curious to discover what kind of organism occupied these strange holes and, late one afternoon, we finally got our answer, when a specimen of *Actinodendron arboreum*, appeared from one of the holes and started to unfold just above the sandy bottom. Between its tentacles, we saw two *Periclimenes brevicarpalis* anemone shrimps. When the anemone retracted into the hole, because it

was disturbed, the shrimps were left sitting on the bottom.

The oral disc of *Actinodendron arboreum* has large tentacles that are covered with knobbly pyramid-like vesicles. This anemone may reach a diameter of up to 50

cm if it unfolds fully. Its sting is very painful and great care must be taken not to touch the animal. We have never heard of it being imported for the aquarium hobby. If you should ever get hold of it, however, it is important to know

Actinodendron arboreum also lives in the sand zone, seen here in the Maldives. It has very powerful nematocysts and retracts quickly into the sand if it is disturbed.

Megalactis hemprichii photographed at Sulawesi, Indonesia.

Photo: J. Cairns-Michael

that it needs sandy ground which must be deep enough to allow it to dig itself in. We would also like to draw aquarists' attention once more to the very strong stinging poison of this anemone. Despite its painful sting, *Actinodendron arboreum* may be very interesting as a special organism for a sand zone aquarium.

We have occasionally seen the Tree Anemone, *Actinodendron plumosum*, on offer in aquarium shops. It reminds us somewhat of a *Phymanthus* species, but has longer, large, tree-like tentacles with clusters of finger-like vesicles and possesses extremely powerful nematocysts that can cause severe and very painful stings if touched. It may reach diameters of up to 20 cm and, just as *A. arboreum*, it requires a special aquarium with plenty of sand into which it can dig itself. Both *Actinodendron* species are widely distributed in the tropical Indo-West Pacific.

Megalactis hemprichii closely resembles *A. plumosum*, but the tentacles are thinner and the vesicles smaller and more elongated.

The genus *Actinostephanus* includes only one species, *Actinostephanus haechkeli* commonly called "Octopus anemone". It has lone, unbranched arm-like tentacles with short protuberan-

ches and with colours that resemble an octopus. It was originally described from Ambon and according to den HARTOG (1997), this is the only place where it so far has been collected from. However, the species obviously has a wider distribution in the central Indo-Pacific.

Family Thalassianthidae

The most important species in the family Thalassianthidae, from the aquarists' point of view, is the Pizza Anemone, *Cryptodendrum adhaesivum*, the only species in its genus. *C. adhaesivum* is found widely in the Indo-West Pacific, but it is most common in the Red Sea and Indonesia. According to FAUTIN & ALLEN (1992), *Amphiprion clarkii* is the only fish species, which lives in symbiosis with *Cryptodendron adhaesivum*. We have, however, observed (while in the Maldives in 1980) that the damsel fish *Dascyllus trimaculatus* also lives in close contact with this anemone. DUNN (1981) mentions that this species is only found in shallow water, which accounts for its invariably rather intense pigmentation that varies from yellow-orange to brownish purple. *C.*

adhaesivum has a very strong nematocyst poison that stings painfully and "burns" the skin on contact. Great care should therefore be taken when handling this anemone. We have only very rarely seen it kept in aquaria in Europe, most probably because it is only imported sporadically. In the States it appears to be more common, though. See fact page 263 for more information on this species.

In the same family, we find *Thalassianthus aster*, a rather small species that grows in clone colonies in shallow water. It does very well in aquaria and its nematocysts do not seem to be particularly powerful. We have kept it together with many other cnidarians in a coral reef aquarium without any negative consequences resulting.

Thalassianthus aster reproduces very easily in aquaria, and this may develop into a severe problem as the tiny anemone will soon overgrow all the available space. The animals can, however, be loosened and removed if the oral disc is injected with 5% HCl. A few minutes after the injection, the base detaches from the substratum and the complete anemone can be picked up with forceps. In order to prevent a disaster, though, one should remove the anemone as soon as the first specimens are observed. We neglected the presence of these small animals, which, when introduced, looked interesting, especially since at the time, the species was rare in European reef aquaria. However, after a year or so, the upper parts of our aquarium were densely covered with *T. aster* and a great deal of injecting had to be done in order to remove the little creatures!

The family Thalassianthidae also contains *Heterodactyla hemprichii*, which is a rather large and beautiful anemone that may resemble the host sea anemones of the genus *Stichodactyla*, but does not carry any symbiotic fishes. The shrimp *Periclimenis brevicarpalis* is, however, often associated with this anemone. *H. hemprichii*

The usual colour variant of *C. adhaesivum*, seen here off Indonesia.

Cryptodendrum adhaesivum
Pizza Anemone

Distribution: In the Indo-West Pacific, from the Red Sea, the Maldives and the Seychelles eastwards to Polynesia, Melanesia and Micronesia, and from Japan, southwards to northern Australia.

Size and growth form: Up to 30 cm in diameter. Tentacles short, only 5 mm high. Found from the intertidal zone, down to a depth of about 3 metres in protected areas of coral reefs and in littoral boulder fields (DUNN, 1981).

Food: This anemone probably feeds mainly on the products of its zooxanthellae, but also takes in plankton and other small animals.

Description: (Modified from DUNN, 1981). Base wider than lower column. Column short; very sticky verrucae in longitudinal rows on upper flared portion. Colour of column variable. Oral disc lies flat when expanded and is, typically, but not always, round. Colour variable, from yellow-orange to brownish purple, occasionally bright green. Disc densely covered with tentacles, except near the mouth. Tentacles small; some tentacles with 3-4 digitiform branchlets, each less than 1 mm long. Tentacles along the rim of the disc are short bulbs about 1 mm in diameter. Very sticky to the touch. This species is often very beautifully coloured. It is easy to identify because of its flat disc and short tentacles, which have a maximum length of 5 mm and are extremely sticky. Towards the rim of the disc the tentacles show burly structures and are not branched, so that the rim looks as if it is of a different colour.

Symbionts: *Amphiprion clarkii*, occasionally *Dascyllus trimaculatus* (personal observation), *Periclimenes brevicarpalis*, *Neopetrolisthes maculatus*.

Aquarium maintenance:
– **General conditions:** This species needs a special aquarium, in which it should be kept on its own, or in the company of other very robust anemones. If kept in a mixed reef aquarium, ensure that an adequate distance is allowed between this species and other sessile animals.
– **Lighting:** Very strong.
– **Water circulation:** Medium.
– **Reproduction:** Unknown.
GA: +/- ; TO: - ; SE: +

lives attached in crevices and under coral boulders on the upper reef slopes or in sea grass beds of reefs in the Indo-Pacific. The oral disc is flat and contains small multi-branched tentacles, surrounded by longer and thicker, marginal tentacles that contain globular violet nematophors between them (VINE, 1986). The colours of the oral disc may be green, yellow, red, purple or brownish, while the column is whitish with many purple verrucae. The species is, asccording to SPRUNG & DELBEEK (1997) not frequently imported. Other species of this family are never, or only very rarely, imported.

Family Aiptasiidae

Thalassianthus aster comes from the tropical Indo-West Pacific. In the west, it is found as far as East Africa and the Red Sea, while nothing is known about the limits of its geographical distribution to the east. In aquaria, it may reach a diameter of about 5 cm. In its natural surroundings, it grows in colonies, which develop into large mats in shallow water right under the surface. Its colours vary from light pink, to brown or bluish-green. This anemone feeds on the translocated products of its symbiotic zooxanthellae, but probably also takes in plankton organisms as food. As it does not have much stinging power, it may be safely kept in a coral reef aquarium, even with delicate stony corals. This species can multiply so rapidly that it can overgrow large areas in the reef aquarium and really become a plague. The photograph below shows details of the tentacles with bubble-like nematophors.

The Glassrose Anemones off the genus *Aiptasia* are well-known and much feared by reef aquarists. Glassrose Anemones are the most troublesome of all organisms in the reef aquarium. They have an enormous potential for asexual reproduction by pedal laceration and, if not controlled, can completely overgrow an aquarium within a relative short time. It is strange, however, that, in some aquaria, *Aiptasia* neither grow nor reproduce. In such aquaria, even if a few specimens are present, they never multiply into a troublesome population, while, in other tanks, they explode. We have observed this in our studies of European aquaria, but cannot explain the reasons for this phenomenon. It could be that Glassrose Anemones compete with other organisms in the aquarium or, perhaps, they are dependent on a certain amount of planktonic food before they can develop into a dense population - we just don't know.

Various techniques have been utilised in dealing with an already established population of *Aiptasia*. For example, mechanically, the population can be reduced to some degree by injecting the

anemones with 5% HCl, a weak solution of KCl, hot water, copper sulphate, potassium hydroxide or calcium hydroxide. Such injections take a great deal of time and patience and, if many injections are carried out over a short period of time, there is always a danger than one can severely disrupt the ionic balance of the aquarium. Biologically, a population of *Aiptasia* be controlled by introducing the butterflyfishes *Chelmon rostratus* and/or *Chaetodon kleinii*. Other fishes and some invertebrates have also been tried in the fight against Glassrose Anemones, (see SPRUNG & DELBEEK, 1997). However, any fish that eats *Aiptasia* will also eat other coral animals, such as hydrozoans, small polyp stony corals and many other invertebrates that we want to keep in our aquaria. In general, fish will decimate, not only the anemones, but also the valuable flora and fauna that develop from live rock. In other words, they will kill the Glassroses, but will simultaneously ruin other types of life in the aquarium.

During the last few years, enormous progress in controlling *Aiptasia* has, however, been made by CARROLL & KEMPF (1990), who have managed to cultivate the tiny nudibranch *Berghia verrucicornis* that feeds exclusively on *Aiptasia* spp. In the next volume of this book series, we will deal with the cultivation of *B. verrucicornis* in detail. In the meantime, see CARROLL & KEMPF (1990 a, b), KEMPF & BRITTSAN (1996) and KEMPF (1991) for further information. There is no doubt that the research done by these authors represents a major break through for the marine reef aquarium hobby.

Another species of the Aiptasidae is occasionally imported from the Caribbean and is quite suitable for an anemone aquarium. It is the Curley-Cue Anemone, i.e. *Bartholomea annulata*, which is one of the most common anemones in the Caribbean. It occurs in bays, inlets, on coral reefs, among rocks or stones, and is so-

A nudibranch of the species *Berghia verrucicornis* approaches a couple of *Aiptasia* to feed on them.

Bartholomea annulata in an aquarium. This common anemone has a powerful sting.

Aiptasia spp.
Glassrose

Distribution: Very common in tropical and subtropical seas.

Size and growth form: Very variable. The specimens we usually find in aquaria are 2 to 6 cm high and have a diameter of 1 to 3 cm.

Food: These anemones probably feed mainly on the products of their zooxanthellae, but they also take in plankton and other small animals, as well as aquarium fish food.

Description: Usually, these anemones are transparent and brownish (hence, the popular name), less often white. The tentacles are, alternately, long and very short, with the long ones having the same length as the stalk. They live individually, or in dense colonies on dead corals, rocks or mangrove roots. Numerous specific names are used in publications, such as *Aiptasia tagetes* from the Caribbean, *A. pallida* from the Gulf of Mexico to North Carolina and *A. californica* from the Gulf of California (Sea of Cortez). The systematics of these species are, however, highly confusing, so a genus determination may only be considered as somewhat reliable, if it is carried out by a specialist.

Aquarium maintenance:

– **General conditions:** Glassroses are usually introduced into our aquaria with live rock. Because of their extremely high reproduction potential, these anemones are regarded as a "pest". If there are too many, they harm other animals quite badly. The nudibranch *Berghia verrucicornis* preys exclusively on *Aiptasia* and is now cultivated to be used as a predator on uncontrollable *Aiptasia* populations in aquaria. See CARROLL & KEMPF (1990 a, b), KEMPF & BRITTSAN (1996) and KEMPF (1991). The cultivation of the nudibranch will be dealt with in the next volume of this book series. Further instructions on how to control or eradicate *Aiptasia* are given in the text on pages 264-265. Keeping these species on purpose should always, and only, take place in a special aquarium.

– **Lighting:** Medium to strong.

– **Water circulation:** Medium.

– **Reproduction:** The reproductive capacity of *Aiptasia* is extremely high. It takes place sexually or asexually, although sexual reproduction has never been observed in captivity. Asexual reproduction by pedal laceration is possible and common, so these anemones should never be removed from the aquarium by cutting or crushing.

GA: - ; TO: - ; SE: +

Photos:

– Top: Solitary *Aiptasia* sp. may look very impressive.

– Bottom: A colony of *Aiptasia* sp.

Nemanthus **sp. photographed at Jervis Bay, south eastern Australia.**   **Photo: Scott W. Michael**

metimes abundant in sea grass beds and in mangrove areas (but does not attach itself to the mangrove roots themselves). Occasionally, it is also found on sandy patches on the reef. This species resembles a large *Aiptasia* sp., but can easily be separated from the Glassrose Anemones by its long, knotty and nearly transparent tentacles. Like many other anemones, *B. annulata* has very powerful nematocysts and is therefore best kept in a special aquarium. Several symbiotic crustaceans live associated with this anemone, including *Thor amboniensis, Periclimenes pedersoni* and even pistol shrimps from the genus *Alpheus*. In a special aquarium, that need not to be very large, these creatures can be kept very successfully together with the Curley-Cue Anemone. We have even observed that live rock arranged around a small specimen of this anemone, has not been able to survive in its vicinity. *Bartholomea annulata* grows

rather large and may reach a diameter of up to 30 cm in its natural surroundings.

Another Aiptasid anemone that inhabits Caribbean reefs and areas of sand and rubble in habitats with clear water, is the Knobbly or Knobby Anemone, *Bartholomea (= Heteractis) lucida*. It hides in small holes or crevices and rapidly retracts into its burrow when disturbed. Several shrimps, Thor *amboniensis* and *Periclimenes* spp. as well as a red mysid shrimp that lives in shoals among the tentacles (SPRUNG & DELBEEK, 1997), are associated with this species. A special aquarium is needed to keep *B. lucida*. However, specimens are difficult to collect, as their pedal disc is usually very well anchored to hard substratum deeply hidden in a hole. This anemone has long, thin and pointed translucent tentacles with whitish vesicular outgrowths. The tentacles, oral disc and column are all coloured in shades of grey, brown or green (HUMANN, 1993).

Family Nemanthidae

The most common genus in this family is *Nemanthus* where the species settle on dead sea whips. The anemones multiply asexually and can build large populations that can cover the entire skeleton of the once living sea whip. *Nemanthus annamensis* is a common species of the Indo-Pacific that has a variable colour. It is generally yellowish to orange, variegated with dark specks or blots. This species is often found in considerable numbers on gorgonians in water deeper than 10 metres. Thus it has been given it the popular name "Gorgonian Wrapper" (den HARTOG, 1997). There are also many species of *Nemanthus* found in colder seas. We have no experiences with this genus in the reef aquarium and have not heard that it has ever been imported.

Chapter 14:

Zoanthid Anemones

The order Zoanthiniaria or Zoanthidea, as they are also often called, contains the popular aquarium animals known as zoanthid or colonial anemones, also referred to, rather meaninglessly within the trade, as "polyp colonies". They are abundant in both shallow and deep waters of the tropical seas, yet some species are also found in colder ocean regions, including the Mediterranean Sea and the North Sea. On the reef, they are, typically, found in distinct zones, such as backreef flats, lagoon floors, reef crests and the shallow sublittoral zone.

Many zoanthid anemones are fast-growing, hardy and highly beautiful aquarium animals, which have been popular among aquarists for a long time; they were actually among the first invertebrates to be kept with considerable success. Quite a large number of species are now commonly available in the aquatic trade, but, unfortunately, the systematics of the Zoanthiniaria - being based on the morphology and anatomy of both colonies and individual polyps - is extremely

Zoanthid anemones are rarely the dominant animals in reef habitats, but are frequently encountered by divers. The photograph on the left shows "KA4-ZOA-01", a *Parazoanthus* species, growing on a sponge on a reef off Indonesia. The top photograph shows "KA4-ZOA-02", a *Palythoa* species, on a reef wall in the Maldives. This species incorporates sand particles into its tissue which stabilize it.

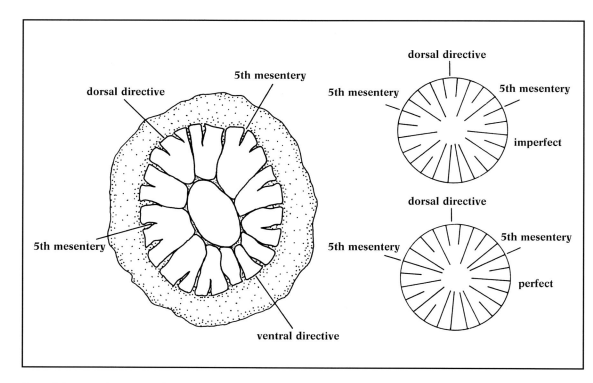

One of the most important characters in the systematics of zoanthid anemones at higher levels is the state of the mesenteries, or, rather, the distribution of perfect mesenteries (reaching the pharynx) and imperfect mesenteries (not reaching the pharynx). The retractor muscles of the zoanthids are placed bilaterally of the ventral and dorsal directives. The ventral directive mesenteries are always perfect, the dorsal ones always imperfect. Counting on either side from the dorsal directive, the fifth mesenteries will either be perfect or imperfect. In the first case, the animal will have what is known as a macrocnemic condition (i.e. members of the suborder Macrocnemina - with a long "splint") and, in the second, as having a brachycnemic one (i.e. members of the suborder Brachycnemina - with a short "splint"). The remaining mesenteries, with the exception of the dorsal and ventral directives, are all alternately imperfect and perfect. The diagrams, based on HERBERTS (1987), show a cross-section of a zoanthid with a brachycnemic mesentery arrangement (left) and schematic sketches of both varieties (right).

poorly known. It is, thus, very difficult even to get a fair review of the genera, let alone the species.

Important reasons for the current chaos in their taxonomy are:

- The variety of shape in polyps and colonies that exists from population to population.

- The absence of skeletal structures.

- Failure by taxonomists, in general, to evaluate the criteria used.

- Reliance on preserved, rather than live, material as the basis of most published accounts.

All these are reasons why (especially) the early publications on zoanthid anemones are highly unsatisfactory from our present point of view, and why the species described therein are only very rarely recognizable to later workers (MUIRHEAD & RYLAND, 1985). The number of nominal species (at least 300) is immense, but many of these will eventually turn out to be synonyms. Nevertheless, there are still probably many species yet to be recognized and formally described. Moreover, it is unlikely that specific names used up to the present were always attributed to the correct species.

Basically, zoanthid anemones have many characters in common with the sea anemones of the order Actiniaria. The general appearance of the individual polyp is very similar - with foot, stem, disc and tentacles. The internal anatomy also shows many similarities. As in sea anemones, but in contrast to most other colonial cnidarians, most zoanthids do not secrete a skeleton. The only exception to this rule, is the rare and little-known genus Gerardia. However, many other species incorporate sediments into the mesogloea during growth, which gives support and protection to the polyps. Alternatively, the mesogloea is sometimes significantly thickned.

The characters that have proven to be most valuable in sorting out the taxonomy above species level (i.e. genus and family) are mainly anatomical details that can be seen only by thorough dissection. The most important feature is the state of the fifth mesenteries, counted either way from what is known as the dorsal directive mesenteries (see explanation in drawing on page 270). The fifth mesenteries may either be perfect (reaching the pharynx) or imperfect (not reaching the pharynx). Zoanthid anemones of the suborder Brachycnemina have imperfect fifth mesenteries, while those in the suborder Macrocnemina have perfect ones. The other mesenteries, apart from the paired dorsal and ventral directives, are alternately perfect or imperfect in both suborders.

The formation of the sphincter muscle at the mouth opening also provides another important systematic character. The relevant questions here are whether it is situated in the mesogloea or in the endoderm, and whether it is single or divided into two parts. HERBERTS (1972a; 1987) extensively discusses all the characters used in Zoanthiniarian systematics. A briefer summary is given by RYLAND & MUIRHEAD in MATHER & BENNETT (1993).

Zoanthid anemones are either solitary or colonial. In colonial species, there are three basic forms of growth, defined by whether or not, and how, the polyps are connected to each other (see drawing on page 272):

A: Solitary growth, without any contact between the adult polyps.

B: Connected growth, where the polyps are connected through a common creeping coenenchyme (stolon or lamella).

C: Massive growth, where the polyps are completely embedded in a mutual, well-developed coenenchyme.

Many species, probably the majority which live in shallow water, have zooxanthellae in their endoderm and/or their ectoderm. These symbiotic algae are partly

The general appearance of zoanthid anemone polyp is very similar to that of a sea anemone, with a foot, stem, disc and tentacles. This photograph shows a colony of "KA4-ZOA-03", a *Protopalythoa* species.   Photo: T. Luther

responsible for the colours of the animals. It is not quite clear, however, how crucial they are - as compared to the food ingested - for the energy balance of their hosts. Obviously, this also varies a great deal between the different members of the order. Several zoanthid anemones, e.g. *Palythoa*, *Protopalythoa* and *Zoanthus* spp. open in response to light, a rather typical behaviour of cnidarians which depend on the zooxanthellae for energy. Others, however, such as *Isaurus* and *Sphenopus*,

are known to open only at night, when active feeding on planktonic organisms may be observed as well. A number of diurnal species, including *Protopalythoa* spp., are also known to feed heavily on zooplankton, particularly crustaceans.

REIMER (1971a) reports that, in laboratory experiments, the polyps of *Protopalythoa psammophilia* capture live prey with their tentacles. They close only partially while they use the tentacles to hold the prey against the mouth.

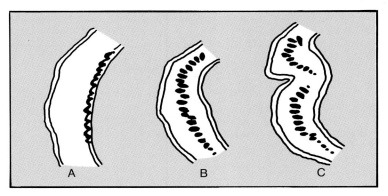

The shape and position of the sphincter muscle at the mouth opening is another important systematic character in zoanthid anemones. The diagrams show longitudinal sections of the three arrangements: A - endodermic sphincter; B - simple mesogloean sphincter; C - double mesogloean sphincter.   After HERBERTS (1987)

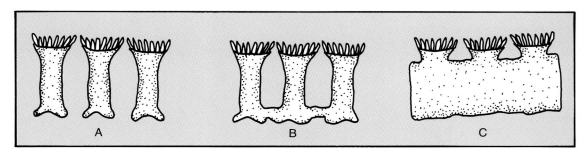

There are three basic growth forms in zoanthid anemones: A - solitary growth, without any contact between the adult polyps; B - connected growth, where the polyps are in contact through a common creeping coenenchyme (stolon or lamella); C - massive growth, in which the polyps are completely embedded in a mutual, well developed coenenchyme.

Zoanthid anemones often grow in immensely large colonies containing thousands of genetically identical individuals, which have been produced through asexual reproduction. The picture shows such a colony of *Zoanthus sociatus* off Miami, Florida.

Systematics of the order Zoanthiniaria

Suborder Brachycnemina

Family Zoanthidae
Zoanthus, Acrozoanthus, Isaurus, Palythoa, Protopalythoa, Sphenopus

Family Neozoanthidae
Neozoanthus

Suborder Macrocnemina

Family Epizoanthidae
Epizoanthus, Thoracactis

Family Parazoanthidae
Parazoanthus, Gerardia, Isozoanthus

Very few nematocysts (stinging cells) are discharged, and they do not paralyse the prey. While the food is being ingested, other tentacles protrude above the rim of the contracted disc. This behavioral response, called "tentacle protrusion", enables the polyp to capture additional prey, while ingesting the one previously caught. This is quite contrary to what we see in most other cnidarians, in which the polyps close completely while they ingest food.

Protopalythoa psammophilia showed clear feeding responses, both to live and dead *Artemia*, to live worms (syllid polychaetes: family Syllidae, Nemerteans and *Tubifex*) and to pieces of various types of fish meat (all cut to 1 x 2 mm in size). Ingestion of the food particles was rapid, taking no longer than one to three minutes, and the polyps were fully expanded again after eight to ten minutes. Ten to twelve hours later, the indigestible remains of the food were extruded through the mouth.

In the same series of experiments, REIMER also carried out tests on *Zoanthus pacificus*. This species did not show any disposition to prey actively on any kind of live food. Dead *Artemia* elicited a small response in terms of contraction, but apparently no food was ingested. However, all polyps tested showed a definite positive reaction to offerings of fish meat (cut into 0.5 to 1 mm pieces). Their response consisted of curling down the tentacles, raising the mouth, exposing the pharynx and ingesting the food. The process of ingestion took approximately 30 minutes. The undigested remains were extruded after 12 to 24 hours.

In another study (REIMER, 1971b) a *Zoanthus* sp. was exposed to high temperatures (30 °C), as a result of which the polyps lost their zooxanthellae. Although the temperature was corrected within two days, the polyps continued to extrude zooxanthellae until, at the end of three months, they were completely bleached. The zooxanthellae were extruded in uniform, polyp-like pellets, with a largest diameter of approximately 0.25 mm. The bleached aposymbiotic colonies, which were held in the same aquarium as normal control groups, regressed rapidly in size. The tentacles disappeared, the polyps remained permanently contracted and they lost the ability to rid themselves of extraneous materials, such as sand grains and algae. Eventually, they became smothered with filamentous algae and sediments. This is interpreted as indirect evidence that, at least, this *Zoanthus* sp. may be nutritionally dependent on the photosynthetic products of its zooxanthellae.

In most coral reef-dwelling zoanthid anemones, asexual reproduction is common and also very rapid. Frequently, this results in large colonies with a diameter of up to 1 m, and large areas being dominated by genetically identical individuals. Many such colonies may consist of several thousand polyps.

Zoanthid anemones also reproduce sexually, but, so far, we have only limited knowledge about this. Some species have separate sexes, while others are hermaphroditic. There are simultaneous hermaphrodites, in which the mesenteries bear testes, as well as ovaries, at one and the same time, and sequential hermaphrodites, where testes and ovaries appear at different times. One species, *Protopalythoa* sp., found at Orpheus Island on the Great Barrier Reef, has been reported to spawn simultaneously with the

Protopalythoa species (this is "KA4-ZOA-04") are among the most frequently seen zoanthid anemones in aquaria. In aquarium literature, they are often referred to as *Palythoa* spp. We follow MUIRHEAD & RYLAND (1985), however, who distinguish between the two genera. The connected growth form of *Protopalythoa* spp. distinguishes them clearly from *Palythoa* spp., with their massive growth.

mass-spawning stony corals, on the fourth to sixth nights after full moon in November (RYLAND & BABCOCK, 1991). The fact that RYLAND & BABCOCK found only very few sexually mature polyps when collecting zoanthid anemones in Fiji and the Great Barrier Reef during the cooler months (April to September) suggests that strong seasonality of spawning is common in many species. Further, the time that the gametes take to mature (the cycle of gametogenesis) is probably short. This is, at least, partly, supported by earlier studies on e.g. *Zoanthus sociatus* and *Palythoa caribaeorum* in Panama (FADLALLAH et al., 1984). Nevertheless, RYLAND (pers. com., 1998) has found from experience in Fiji, GBR, Bermuda and Florida, that intertidal zoanthids only rarely breed sexually. He suggests that RYLAND & BABCOCK (1991) were lucky to hit on an exception. Still, he found several breeding *Proto-*

palythoa and *Zoanthus* on shores along the coast north and south of Durban, South Africa, during November 1997.

It is reasonable to draw the conclusion that the spawning of zoanthid anemones may be induced by the same factors as the spawning of stony corals (see chapter 2, pages 42-52 for more details about this). More information on reproduction of zoanthid anemones can also be found in HERBERTS (1972b).

Suborder Brachycnemina

As the name indicates (brachys, Greek = short; and knemis, Greek = splint), all members of this suborder show the imperfect condition of the fifth mesenteries; i.e. they are short and do not reach the pharynx. The family Neozoanthidae is defined by the presence of an endodermal sphincter muscle. The only genus of this family is *Neozanthus*, which is monotypic, with *N. tulearensis*, originally described by HERBERTS (1972a), as its only species. The polyps of this species are up to 12 mm long and have a diameter of 5 mm. They are joined in small clusters of three to ten specimens, connected at the base by a 1-2 mm thick stolon. The colour is described as brownish green on the stem, and green to yellow on the disc. *N. tulearensis* possesses zooxanthellae. The holotype was collected in the Tulear region off Madagascar. There are reasons to assume that they are also found in other regions, but relevant faunistic studies are few and far between. It is highly improbable that it has ever been imported for the aquarium trade.

The Zoanthidae is the second family in the suborder. All members of this family have a mesogloeal sphincter muscle, which is either divided into two parts (as in *Zoanthus*), or remains single (as in all other genera). Except for the genus *Sphenopus*, they all pos-

The brown *Protopalythoa* sp. "KA4-ZOA-05" is shown here growing in a mixed colony with a *Zoanthus* species, "KA4-ZOA-06". This phenomenon of intermingled *Protopalythoa* and *Zoanthus* colonies is seen quite often in the sea, as well as in imports for the aquarium hobby.

sess zooxanthellae.

The principal genera of the tropical zoanthid anemones are *Palythoa*, *Protopalythoa* and *Zoanthus*, all belonging to the family Zoanthidae. They are the most common zoanthid anemones on the reef, as well as in the aquarium trade. More irregularly, one may also encounter *Isaurus* species on offer, while the last recognized genus, *Sphenopus*, is not yet known to have been imported.

The key on page 275 will provide some help in identifying these five genera of the family Zoanthidae.

Acrozoanthus is a most peculiar genus. It has long been thought to belong in the family Parazoanthidae, but its true systematic position, as a close relative of *Zoanthus*, has been decided by RYLAND (1997). Its extremely long tentacles clearly separate it from the other known species of Zoanthidae. *Acrozoanthus* species

are obligate commensals on tubeworms of the species *Eunice tubifex* (Polychaeta: Eunicidae). The zoanthid grows on the upper part of the parchment-like polysaccharide tube of the worm. The worm retracts to a deeper section of the tube, 10-15 cm below the substratum, except while feeding, and is therefore not included when collectors cut off the tube with the zoanthids. Thus, for a long time, aquarists did not recognise the worm tube as such, but, rather, thought that it was the dead remains of a sponge. It is highly unlikely that the worm itself will occur in regular trade, as it is too difficult to collect and grows very large (up to 1.5 metres).

Acrozoanthus spp. possess zooxanthellae and require strong lighting in addition to regular feedings to do well in aquaria. However, although they must be considered as among the more difficult zoanthids for the aquarium, it seems that *Acrozoanthus* species are capable of living independently of a host, as the polyps occasionally encrust rocks and aquarium walls, provided conditions are appropriate.

It is important to point out that several of the common aquarium species referred to as *Palythoa* spp. in earlier publications, are here placed in the genus *Protopalythoa*, in accordance with

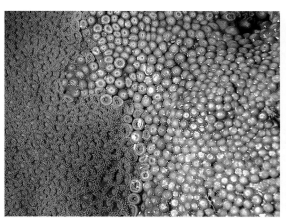 

The Caribbean *Zoanthus sociatus* is one of the few readily identifiable species of *Zoanthus*. It grows in large, mat-like, mono-specific colonies, covering huge shallow-water areas at depths down to some five metres (left). Its polyps (on the right, photo: Scott W. Michael) are connected by branching stolons and grow 2 - 5 cm high. In aquaria, *Z. sociatus* may also develop into an extensive colony within a short time.

This very beautiful yellow, long-tentacled Indo-Pacific zoanthid is one of the most frequently seen in reef aquaria. It is also hardy and fast-growing and reproduces rapidly by budding, provided it is offered regular feedings of plankton or of plankton substitutes. In most aquarium literature, it has been referred to as a *Parazoanthus* species, often as *P. axinellae* or *P. gracilis*. The first alternative is definitely wrong, as the true *P. axinellae* is a readily identifiable species from the Mediterranean Sea that lives commensally on sponges of the genus *Axinella*. The second name is likely to be wrong as well, as *P. gracilis*, although actually found in the Indo-Pacific, is known in the wild only as a commensal on the nettle fern *Plumularia habereri* (Hydroidea; Plumulariidae). None of the imported colonies of the illustrated species have been known to be attached to hydroids, or any other living animals for that matter. Apparently, the true *P. gracilis* also reaches a maximum height of some 5 mm; while "our" species frequently attains 3 cm or more. This is a typical example of the difficulties involved in making correct identifications of zoanthid anemones. Until detailed studies on this species can be carried out, we choose to refer to it as "KA4-ZOA-07". Generic placement may be either within *Parazoanthus*, *Protopalythoa*, or some quite different genus. Sources: HERBERTS (1972a) and RYLAND (pers. com.).

MUIRHEAD & RYLAND (1985). Only those species whose polyps are deeply embedded in the coenenchyme remain in the genus *Palythoa*. As with all Zoanthiniaria, species identification, or even de-fining what actually constitutes a species, is extremely difficult. Without substantial further research it is impossible to put a specific name to most of the zoanthid anemones of the Indo-Pacific.

The situation is far better for the Caribbean species, with valid names available and recognisable for most of the (rather few) species.

The genus *Palythoa* is of parti-

Key to the family Zoanthidae

Adapted from RYLAND & MUIRHEAD in MATHER & BENNETT (1993)

1. Living as solitary animals on sandy bottoms .... *Sphenopus*
   Living in colonies, colony form A*, B* or C* 2

2. With sand particles embedded in the coenenchyme 3
   Without sand particles in the coenenchyme 4

3. Colony form C* .... *Palythoa*
   Colony form A* or B* .... *Protopalythoa*

4. Polyps erect, expanded during the day .... *Zoanthus*
   Polyps recumbent, never expanded during the day .... *Isaurus*

(* for colony forms see drawing on page 272)

Acrozoanthus sp "KA4-ZOA-08" is found quite regularly in the trade. Despite its general appearance, reminiscent of a parazoanthid, it has been found to be a close relative of *Zoanthus*, belonging to the Zoanthidae (RYLAND, 1997). It grows on the parchment-like tubes of the worm *Eunice tubifex*. It seems that *Acrozoanthus* is capable of living without its host in aquaria, as the polyps occasionally encrust rocks and aquarium walls, provided aquarium conditions are appropriate. This species requires strong light and regular feedings of plankton or plankton substitutes, and must be considered as one of the more demanding aquarium organisms.

All the members of the family Zoanthidae are rather small animals. The discs of the polyps are, typically, 1 to 2 cm in diameter and the tentacles are usually some 3 - 5 mm long, but they can also reach 2 - 3 cm in a few species. The colouration is highly variable, with the more colourful forms being beautifully bright red, orange, yellow, turquoise or green. More commonly, however, one sees animals with some shade of brown or brownish colours. The stem, disc and/or the tentacles, frequently exhibit varying colouration.

In general, all anemones of the family Zoanthidae do very well in aquaria, provided there are relatively algae-free conditions and sufficient light. Either fluorescent tubes or metal halides will suffice for most species, but placement directly beneath a metal halide lamp is not recommended.

Suborder Macrocnemina

In the suborder Macrocnemina, we find zoanthid anemones with perfect, long (i.e. reaching the pharynx) fifth mesenteries (makros, Greek = large, long). Several genera have been described, but only two are sufficiently well known to warrant their inclusion in this book. These are the genera *Epizoanthus*, of the family Epizoanthidae, and *Parazoanthus*, of the family Parazoanthidae. Both genera are normally found living epizootically on other animals, primarily sponges, hydroids or gorgonians.

Some *Epizoanthus* species may also live on bare rock, without any commensals, while a few deep-water species live in symbiosis with hermit crabs. Some commensal species grow completely embedded in the tissue of their hosts, while others, like the Caribbean species *Parazoanthus swiftii*, have their complete coenenchyme on the outside of the

cular interest, as its members are widely known to contain the toxic substance palytoxin. Palytoxin is a highly complex chemical compound, which destroys cell membranes, resulting in a breakdown of normal osmotic pressure control in the cells. More recently, palytoxin has also been recorded from *Zoanthus* spp. (GLEIBS et al., 1995).

Palytoxin is said to be one of the strongest naturally-occurring poisons, along with tetanus and botulinum. Both of these latter to-

xins are produced by bacteria and, interestingly enough, this most probably holds true for palytoxin as well. Certain bacteria that live as symbionts in *Palythoa* species have been shown to produce palytoxin when isolated in laboratory cultures. Strangely, however, this production stops after some time in isolation. We do not know what factors induce the production of toxins in zoanthid anemones. More information on palytoxin may be found in MEBS (1989).

sponge which serves as their host.

There are no easily observable characters to separate the genera. Only careful dissection will reveal that the sphincter muscle of *Epizoanthus* spp. is found in the mesogloea, while that of *Parazoanthus* spp. is endodermal (see page 271).

Neither genus is common in the aquatic trade, but they do show up occasionally. Aquarists that dive on reefs will certainly be able to find them, however. The present state of knowledge regarding the systematics of the genera is not exactly what we might wish it to be. There are, at least, 53 nominal species of *Epizoanthus* and 25 of *Parazoanthus* (HERBERTS, 1972a), but most of them are only poorly known. Except for the very few Caribbean species, identifications can barely be made with the little information we have at present.

Most of the species in *Epizoanthus* and *Parazoanthus* lack zooxanthellae. Thus, it is absolutely necessary to feed them with plankton or some plankton substitute when they are kept in an aquarium. Light does not seem to be important, but algae-free conditions are essential. Many species have proven to be hardy, but, unfortunately, their host animals are often much more difficult to keep alive for any length of time. Some species, however, appear to be able to live in aquaria without their natural hosts.

Left: *Parazoanthus swiftii* from the Caribbean lives epizoitically on sponges of several species, in this case probably a *Ptilocaulis* sp. It is easy to identify, provided one knows that the colony was imported from the Caribbean. Right: "KA4-ZOA-09", another *Parazoanthus* species, growing on a holaxonian coral on an Indonesian reef.

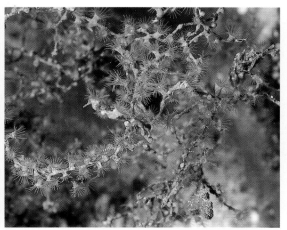

Left: "KA4-ZOA-10", a *Parazoanthus* species, growing on black corals in the Maldives. Right: "KA4-ZOA-11", an *Epizoanthus* species on a sponge in the Gulf of California (photo: Scott W. Michael).

Isaurus spp.

Distribution: Widespread in all tropical seas.

Size and growth form: The polyps are elongate and recumbent. They live in loosely connected colonies, with or without connecting stolons (A or B according to the diagram on page 272). Their height varies considerably: 15 - 160 mm. Colonies of more than 50 individuals are quite rare.

Food: May obtain some nutrition from the zooxanthellae which are present both in ectoderm and endoderm, but is also known to feed actively on plankton during the night. Polyps never open during the day and, in aquaria, only rarely during the night. Proper feeding in aquaria therefore constitutes a problem.

Description: Systematically, this is probably the best known genus of zoanthid anemones. According to a revision by MUIRHEAD & RYLAND (1985) there are three valid species: *Isaurus cliftoni*, *I. maculatus* and *I. tuberculatus*. The first two are known only from the Fiji Islands and Western Australia, respectively. *I. tuberculatus* is found in all tropical seas and is the species most likely to occur in the trade. The shape and colour of the polyps is highly variable. The stem is normally covered with large tubercles, which are often arranged in longitudinal series. It is usually green to grey, with cream/white tubercles. The tentacles are reported to be white in Caribbean specimens (LARSON & LARSON, 1982), while the Indo-Pacific colony shown above has red tentacles. We do not yet know for certain, if the red tentacles are typical of all populations from the Indo-Pacific. The stem of *I. cliftoni* is emerald green with mauve blotches; that of *I. maculatus* is pale grey with many darkly pigmented small tubercles, which are arranged in regular rows.

Aquarium maintenance:

– **General conditions:** For unknown reasons, these anemones often refuse to open their polyps and feed. In the long term, their zooxanthellae do not seem to provide sufficient energy. Therefore, for the time being, these animals must be regarded as difficult to keep.

– **Lighting:** As these are animals from shallow-water regions, we can assume that they need medium to high light intensities.

– **Water circulation:** Moderate to strong.

– **Reproduction:** Unknown.

GA: +/- ; TO: + ; SE: -

Photos:
Two colour variants of *Isaurus tuberculatus* with retracted polyps

Palythoa spp.

Distribution: Common in all tropical seas of the world.

Size and growth form: These anemones grow in massive colonies (C, according to the diagram on page 272). Sand particles are encrusted into the coenenchyme. The colonies are, typically, convex and (seldom) reach 30 cm in diameter.

Food: Probably obtain much of their nutrition from the zooxanthellae, but seem to do best with additional feedings of plankton substitutes.

Description: *Palythoa* colonies often grow in large numbers on reef flats immediately behind the reef crest, but they are also found on lagoon floors and in the spur-and-groove channels of reef slopes. Their coenenchyme is, typically, light brown to yellow; the polyps are often darker. The systematics of the genus is extremely confused. The most common species of the Indo-Pacific is *P. caesia*, which may, however, be a synonym of *P. tuberculosa* (RYLAND, pers. com. and in MATHER & BENNETT, 1993). There are other names mentioned in publications, but their validity is highly uncertain. Caribbean species are often referred to as *P. caribaeorum* and *P. mammillosa*, both names also being of uncertain validity.

Aquarium maintenance:

– **General conditions:** These are rather hardy aquarium animals, which are, however, only rarely seen on offer in the aquarium trade. If algae grow too abundantly in the aquarium, the colonies are quickly overgrown and destroyed.

– **Lighting:** Medium light intensity. They tend to "burn" easily under metal halide light.

– **Water circulation:** Moderate to strong.

– **Reproduction:** These zoanthids readily reproduce asexually, but sexual reproduction has not yet been reported in aquaria. YAMAZOTO et al. (1973) report on studies of the reproductive cycle of *Palythoa tuberculosa* off Okinawa. The oocytes grow from March/April, to a peak in the middle of the year, which is followed by a second peak in October. This leads to the assumption that there may be two spawnings per year. Mature eggs are rather large, with a length of 300 - 500 μm.

GA: + ; TO: + ; SE: +/-

Photos:

– Top: Habitat in a shallow sand zone in the Maldives
– Centre: A colony of "KA4-ZOA-12" off the Fiji-Islands
                                                Photo: Scott W. Michael
– Bottom: "KA4-ZOA-13" - typical pieces of colonies as offered in in shops.

Protopalythoa spp.
(Referred to by most authors as *Palythoa* spp.)

Distribution: Common in all tropical seas of the world.
Size and growth form: Typically found in loosely connected colonies; either without any contact between the polyps, or with contact at the base through a stolon (A or B according to the diagram on page 272). The polyps are 15 - 25 mm high and 7 - 11 mm in diameter. Fully expanded discs may attain a diameter of 2 - 3 cm.
Food: Probably obtains much of its nutrition from the zooxanthellae, but seems to do best with additional feedings of plankton substitutes, which are readily accepted.

Protopalythoa sp., "KA4-ZOA-14" (green), and *Zoanthus* sp., "KA4-ZOA-15" (brown), in an aquarium

Description: These zoanthids are mostly found in small to medium-sized colonies in shallow fore reefs, reef crests or outer reef flat areas. Shallow reef zones may sometimes be dominated by this genus, and cover may exceed 90% (RYLAND in MATHER & BENNETT, 1993). Some species only occur as small assemblages of polyps, or even as separate individuals. The polyps are encrusted with sand particles. Sometimes, the polyps are unable to retract completely because of the size of their disc. The colour is usually uniform on the stem and oral disc, often brown or dark green. A few forms have distinct, brightly coloured discs. Colours may vary considerably, depending on the light conditions. The systematics of these species is thoroughly confused. Apparently, the total number of nominal species is higher than 100, yet, with the exception of a few Caribbean ones, hardly any species can be positively named at present. See, however, BURNETT et al. (1997) for species on the GBR. (continued on next page).

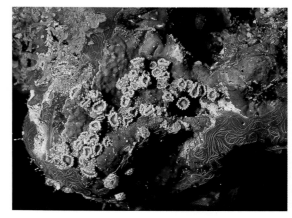

Photos:
– Top: "KA4-ZOA-16" in the Maldives
– Centre: "KA4-ZOA-17" in the Maldives
– Bottom right: "KA4-ZOA-18" off Indonesia
– Bottom left: "KA4-ZOA-19" in an aquarium

Photo: T. Luther

Aquarium maintenance:
- **General conditions:** Reasonably hardy inhabitants of the reef aquarium, but excessive algal growth can quickly overgrow and damage the colony. Large amounts of sediment will also constitute a problem.
- **Lighting:** Medium to high light intensity. Some species or colonies may "burn" easily under metal halide lamps.
- **Water circulation:** Moderate to strong.
- **Reproduction:** They readily reproduce asexually. Sexual reproduction has not yet been reported in aquaria. BABCOCK & RYLAND (1990) and RYLAND & BABCOCK (1991) have described reproduction and larval development in Nature.

GA: + ; TO: + ; SE: +/-

Photos:
- Top: "KA4-ZOA-20" in an aquarium
  Photo: Scott W. Michael
- Centre: "KA4-ZOA-21" in an aquarium
  Photo: Scott W. Michael
- Bottom left: "KA4-ZOA-22" in an aquarium
- Bottom right: "KA4-ZOA-23" in an aquarium

***Zoanthus* spp.**

Distribution: Common in all tropical seas of the world.

Size and growth form: Typically, these zoanthid anemones form more or less crowded colonies, which may become very large (1.5 m^2 or more). The polyps are 7 - 15 mm high and have a diameter of 3 - 7 mm. Fully expanded discs are 4 - 15 mm in diameter, only rarely larger.

Food: Probably obtain most, or all, of their essential nutrients from their zooxanthellae. Show little response to feeding.

Description: They are found mostly in back reef areas and the shallow sub-littoral zone. No sediments are incorporated in their tissues, but many species are highly tolerant of sediments in the surroundings. *Z. mantoni*, from the Great Barrier Reef, is capable of growing up through 1 cm or more of accumulated silt (RYLAND in MATHER & BENNETT, 1993). Most of the species have very bright colours, with disc and tentacles often contrasting strongly. Several colour morphs are often found in close proximity, where clonal patches - distinguished by colour - often intermingle with species of *Protopalythoa*. Several species are recognized, both from the Caribbean and the Indo-Pacific, but due to the high degree of variability, positive identifications often present a problem.

Aquarium maintenance:
– **General conditions:** Hardy inhabitants of the reef aquarium. Less susceptible to algae growth and sediments than most other zoanthid anemones.
– **Lighting:** Strong.
– **Water circulation:** Moderate to strong.
– **Reproduction:** They readily reproduce asexually. Sexual reproduction has not yet been reported in aquaria. Information about reproduction in Nature is given by COOKE (1976) for *Z. pacificus*, and by FADLALLAH et al. (1989) for *Z. solanderi* and *Z. sociatus*.

GA: + ; TO: + ; SE: +

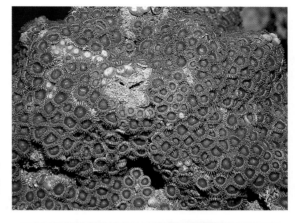

Photos:
– Top: "KA4–ZOA-24" Photo: Scott W. Michael
– Centre: "KA4–ZOA-25" Photo: T. Luther
– Bottom: "KA4–ZOA-26" on the left and "KA4–ZOA-27" in an aquarium owned by D. Stüber, Berlin.

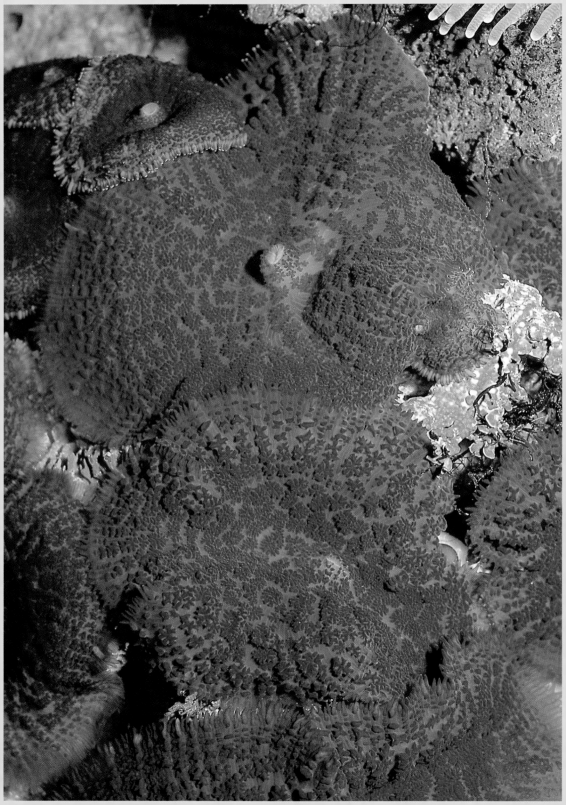

Chapter 15

Corallimorpharia
Disc- or Mushroom Anemones

In the preceding chapters, we have pointed out more than once how insufficient our knowledge regarding the systematics of the animals dealt with still is. The order Corallimorpharia is no exception. In fact, it is probably the group of cnidarians we know least about, at least, as far as the species from the Indo-Pacific are concerned. On the other hand, mushroom anemones are very popular as inhabitants of reef aquaria and have been so since they first appeared in the hobby in the middle of the seventies. They were among the first invertebrates ever kept in marine aquaria and were then, in the early days, just as they are today, found in almost every reef tank. The group is, however, poorly known generally and little has been published on their systematics and ecology during the past few decades, particularly with regard to Indo-Pacific species. There is no doubt that in some aspects aquarists know more about mushroom anemones than scientists do.

The popular names "Disc- or Mushroom Anemones" commonly used by aquarists are somewhat misleading, and should actually only be used for the members of the family Discoso-

Top: "KA4-COR-01", a *Discosoma* species, often regarded as belonging to the genus *Actinodiscus*. The Indo-Pacific species in this genus remain relatively unknown.   Photo: Scott W. Michael

Left: The small elephant ear, *Rhodactis inchoata*, has very variable colours and can be very beautiful (see fact page 301).   Photo: Scott W. Michael

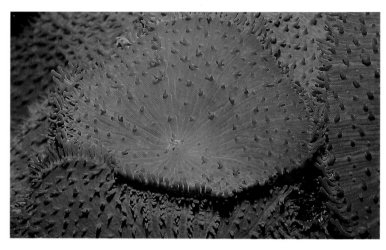

The tentacles on the discs appear very different from species to species, and are sometimes being only rudimentary. The picture above shows the unknown species "KA4-COR-02" in an aquarium.   Photo: Scott W. Michael

Close-up of the marginal tentacles of the mushroom anemone "KA4-COR-6".

matidae. "False Corals" or "Coral Anemones" would indeed be more appropriate popular names.

Corallimorpharians are found worldwide. FAUTIN & LOWENSTEIN (1992) include about 50 known species in the order Corallimorpharia, while den HARTOG (1980) mentions about 30. The true number of species, however, remains unknown. CARLGREN (1949) divides the species into three families, while den HARTOG (1980) recognizes four families and suggests that three (Sideractidae, Corallimorphidae and Ricordeidae) might be placed in the suborder Scleractinia, while the last (Discosomatidae) should be placed in a separate suborder. As with many other invertebrate groups, there are controversies within corallimorpharian systematics.

Although many species live in the shallow areas of tropical waters, there are only few publications about this group of animals. A detailed description of the species of the Caribbean Sea was given by den HARTOG (1980), in a paper which forms the basis for the description of the Caribbean species given in this book. In addition, den HARTOG et al. (1993) describe a number of Atlantic species, which are of less importance for the coral reef aquarium. CARLGREN (1943 and 1949) dealt with species of the central Indo-Pacific and species distributed world wide, but these publications are outdated by now; at least, many of the systematic details given by CARLGREN are now regarded as dubious. DUNN (1982) gives a brief survey of mushroom anemones from a general perspective, while CHEN (pers. com.) is working on a review of the most common species of the Great Barrier Reef. The most recent papers on the group are those by CHEN et al. (1995a, b, c, 1996), FAUTIN & LOWENSTEIN (1992), who assume that there are about 50 species in the order Corallimorpharia, and CHEN & MILLER (1996), who, among other matters, discuss new aspects and present new views on the systematic relationships within the group.

There are large numbers of names mentioned in aquarium publications, but it is highly probable that only very few of these are used correctly. It seems as if the generic name *Actinodiscus* has come to be used by aquarists more or less accidentally for most of the disc anemones of the Indo-Pacific. Most of the species commonly seen in the aquarium trade have probably not yet been described scientifically, and it is unclear if the many colour forms represent valid species, or are just colour morphs of one, or a few, species.

Corallimorpharians are, morphologically, very similar to the stony corals as the two groups have many features in common, such as the range and distribution details of the cnidae and other anatomical details of the tentacles and the possession of a single lobe of ciliated tract (den HARTOG, 1980). However, there are also many differences between the two groups. For example, mushroom anemones have no kind of skeleton, which is the most typical feature of the stony corals. These were the main reasons for the confusing classification of the group in the early days, when authors like HADDON & SHACKLETON (1893), HADDON (1898), CARLGREN (1900) and GRAVIER (1918), all grouped the mushroom anemones among the sea anemones (order Actiniaria). Other authors, like KREMPF (1904), STEPHENSON (1921 and 1922), MIGOT (1922) and WEILL (1934), became aware that the characters linking the group to the sea anemones were heterogeneous and, as they noticed a striking resemblance with the stony corals, they concluded that the corallimorpharians were actually stony corals lacking a skeleton. Even authors like GOSSE (1860) and MOSELEY (1877) assumed a close relationship between Corallimorpharia and Scleractinia. SCHMIDT (1972 and 1974) discusses the systematic position of Corallimorpharia and concludes that the group is fundamentally like the Scleractinia and that both groups

Large colony of disc anemones on a shallow reef flat close to shore off the Maldives.

"KA4-COR-03" with a disc diameter of about 10 cm photographed at a depth of 10 m off Indonesia.

should be united in a taxon of higher rank called Madreporaria (den HARTOG 1980). Today, the group is generally regarded and treated as an order class within the Anthozoa, equivalent in rank to the Actiniaria and Scleractinia.

An important systematic character of the disc anemones is the structure of the cnidae. These can only be examined in detail using a good microscope equipment. Examinations of this type are very difficult to undertake and this is one of the reasons why so little is known about the group. There is a

detailed review of the cnidae of mushroom anemones in den HARTOG (1980).

Mushroom anemones are distributed worldwide, and many species are found in tropical waters, but several also occur in colder seas. Tropical mushroom anemones are found from the tidal zone to deep water. The members of Ricordeidae and Discosomatidae possess zooxanthellae and often form colonies in shallow water in which every single individual is attached to the substrate. The rest of the mushroom

Some disc anemones, like this *Amplexidiscus* sp., eat fish and other moving animals. They trap their prey by changing to a balloon-like shape, from which it (the prey) cannot escape.   Photo: Scott W. Michael

anemones lack zooxanthellae, and the deep-sea species always live solitary and do not contain symbiotic algae. Only the shallow-water species are of interest for the coral reef aquarium; therefore, the deep-sea species are not dealt with here.

The disc of corallimorpharians is usually rather thin and may have a diameter measuring from one centimetre, to several decimetres. Sometimes, the discs possess strong tentacles, which can be seen easily with the naked eye. The tentacles can be cylindrical or have small branches. In other species, there are only rudiments of tentacles around the margin of the disc. In yet other cases, the discs are completely devoid of tentacles.

The colours of disc anemones are very varied, often being conspicuous and bright. However, this feature cannot generally be used as a specific characteristic, since one and the same species may occur in markedly different colour forms.

There is considerable confusion among scientists regarding the systematics of the order Corallimorpharia. Occasionally, the genus *Ricordea* is placed in the family Corallimorphidae, but we follow den HARTOG (1980), who places *Ricordea* in its own family, the Ricordeidae. In addition, the family name Actinodiscidae, which is sometimes used, is a junior synonym of Discosomatidae, in which the genera *Rhodactis*, *Metarhodactis* and *Discosoma* are included. The genus *Actinodiscus*, which is often used in aquarium publications, is, objectively, a synonym of *Discosoma* and should therefore no longer be used (den HARTOG, 1980 and pers. com.).

The morphological and anatomical details that the various genera are based upon, are confused and unreliable. *Rhodactis*, for example, is distinguished from *Discosoma* and *Paradiscosoma* by having a "bald" area between the

tentacles of the margin of the disc and those situated further inwards.

According to den HARTOG (1990), although the cnidae in the family Discosomatidae exhibit significant similarities, there are, at the same time, considerable variations within one and the same species. Den HARTOG holds the opinion that there are many more species in this family than assumed and that more genera should be established. In this volume, however, we follow CHEN (pers. com.) and older publications by CARLGREN on the species from the Indo-Pacific, i.e. we stick to the traditional subdivision and place four genera within the family Discosomatidae.

We have found disc anemones several times when diving various coral reefs, but we have only rarely found large colonies or monospecific populations. To date, we have found the majority of corallimorpharians interspersed exclusively between other corals

Corynactis californica photographed in Monterey Bay Aquarium, Monterey, California.

in shallow water where the light intensity has been high, or deeper on the reef slope where the light intensity is much lower.

The way in which some disc anemones take in food is very interesting. One would assume that, like other cnidarians of the shallow waters of tropical seas, these anemones would take advantage of their symbiosis with zooxanthellae, feeding on the organic compounds which are produced by the algae during photosynthesis and which are partly translocated to the host animals. This is true for many species, but not for all. Some mushroom anemones are actually voracious predators, which may even catch and consume fish (HAMNER & DUNN, 1980). *Amplexidiscus fenestrafer* traps its prey by closing their mouth so that the water pressure is maintained within the body tissue. Water is then pressed by muscle movement to the margin of the disc, so that this margin is pushed upwards, forming a funnel. Next, the anemone contracts to the extent

that the mouth is pressed onto the foot. The process of closing takes only a few seconds. Nematocysts in the marginal disc tentacles presumably prevent the prey from escaping though the rapidly closing opening. However, mucus was excreted from the gastrovascular cavity into the sac and it is likely that it contains poison that paralyzes the prey. Fish kept in the mucus for ten minutes do in general not recover even if transferred to fresh seawater (HAMNER & DUNN, 1980). When the disc is completely closed and has almost the shape of a balloon, the mouth can be opened. This whole mechanism is triggered off when a fish or other organism brushes the top of the disc.

HAMNER & DUNN (1980) describe this action in detail and have also observed similar feeding habits in two other species of the family Discosomatidae. One of these was "*Actinodiscus fungiformis*", which was first described by VERRILL (1870) and is said to have a maximum disc diameter of only 2.5

cm. The other is *Rhodactis howesi*, with a maximum disc diameter of 8 - 10 cm. In these species the closing occurred more slowly than in *A. fenestrafer* and mesenterial filaments were extruded into the cavity and the large number of nematocysts that these filaments contain were thought to subdue the prey. Extruding of mesenterial filaments does not occur in *A. fenestrafer*.

Family Corallimorphidae

The family Corallimorphidae contains the genera *Corallimorphus*, *Corynactis* and *Pseudocorynactis*, none of which have zooxanthellae. *Corallimorphus* species are found in deep-sea regions and are not dealt with any further here. However, the two other genera include species that live in relatively shallow water.

Pseudocorynactis caribbeorum off Playa Paraiso, Tenerife

Photo: Prof. Dr. P. Wirtz

Genus *Corynactis*

The genus *Corynactis* is mainly restricted to temperate, waters and occurs from subtidal shallow water, down to about 200 metres. Individuals live solitary lives and, as a rule, are very small, with a disc diameter no larger than 1 cm. Their colour is often light red, light brown or white. Around the mouth, there are well-developed, transparent tentacles, which become thinner towards their tips, with the tip itself ending in a little knob. The tentacles are of two types: some that are arranged in radial rows of 2-7 tentacles each, and other longer tentacles that occur singly (den HARTOG, 1980).

Corynactis viridis is very well known from the temperate regions of the East Atlantic. In the Caribbean Sea, there is only one species, *Corynactis parvula* (syn.: *C. myrcia*), which occurs in shallow water, even up to the surf zone. It lives on the underside of rocks and often reproduces asexually by pedal laceration, which results in colonies of genetically identical individuals. These "clone" colonies of *C. parvula* are generally made up of only a small number of individuals, as opposed to the colonies of *Corynactis viridis*, which may consist of several hundreds. *C. parvula* has been found in several places off Florida and in the Caribbean Sea, but it is often overlooked.

We have not heard of anyone who has kept *C. parvula* in a reef aquarium, but as the species lacks zooxanthellae, we expect it to be difficult to keep alive for any length of time if it is not fed regularly.

In the Eastern Pacific, occuring from Northern California to Baja California, and in the Gulf of California, we find *Corynactis californica*, which, according to BAENSCH & DEBELIUS (1992), should be kept in aquaria at temperatures a little below 20 °C. Under these conditions, it is said to be not too difficult to keep and even to get it to reproduce asexually. We have observed this beautiful species ourselves in the Monterey Aquarium, where it did very well in an open system tank. *C. californica* contains large stinging capsules, but its sting is not harmful to humans. In the wild, this species is found on rocks, ledges and pilings, and on open shores and in bays, from the low tide line, down to depths of about 30 metres (McCONNAUGHEY & McCONNAUGHEY, 1994).

CARLGREN (1943) mentions *Corynactis globulifera* from Thailand and from the Red Sea, and CUTRESS (1977) assert that there is an undescribed species of *Corynactis* off Hawaii. It is quite probable that there are several undescribed species of this genus in the Indo-Pacific.

Genus *Pseudocorynactis*

The genus *Pseudocorynactis* includes only one described species, *Pseudocorynactis. caribbeorum*. SPRUNG & DELBEEK (1997) mention a second, undescribed species from Fiji, a species which is now being described by den HARTOG (pers. com.) and which shows a superficial similarity to *Corallimorphus profundus*, but which probably is identical to *Pseudocorynactis caribbeorum*. COLIN & ARNESON (1995) also mention the genus from the Indo-Pacific. *P. caribbeorum* grows much larger than *Corynactis parvula*. The base has a diameter of up to 4 cm, is irregular in outline, adapts to the substrate, and often exhibits a spreading habit, with or without short, rounded basal expansions. The column is smooth and distinctly divided into two regions, a large scapus (lower, thick-walled and rigid part) and a narrow marginal scapulus (upper, thin-walled part). The two parts may have the same colour, but, most often, the scapus is pale to vivid orange or lilac, or contains different shades of brown, with or without opaque, whitish, greenish or blackish streaks or specks, while the scapulus is less intensely coloured. The oral disc is circular, with a maximum diameter of 4 cm and is semi-transparent, usually with opaque patches or streaks of cream, white, or faint green (den HARTOG, 1980). The well-developed tentacles taper towards the tip and end in little knobs (acrosphere), which are always orange. Otherwise the colours are quite variable colouration - which often including nuances of white, green or black markings. The acrospheres contain very strong nematocysts with a powerful sting, enabling *P. caribbeorum* to catch rather large prey. Aquarists are familiar with the fact that this disc anemone can be fed pieces of fish, oysters and small live crabs. There have also been observations that it can make waving movements with its tentacles to trap prey (den HARTOG, 1980).

P. caribbeorum is found in the Caribbean and in the tropical Atlantic, at depths of 4 to 20 m, sit-

Pseudocorynactis sp. (KA4-COR-16) from Sulawesi, Indonesia
Photo: J. Cairns-Michael

ting on rocks between corals and is therefore definitely a reef species. It is fairly common in the southern and eastern Caribbean. This mushroom anemone is nocturnal and can only be seen fully unfolded after dusk. Den HARTOG (pers. com. and 1980) also reports the species from a tide pool in the Canary Islands and from about 35 fms off the coast of Venezuela.

This false coral has great regenerative powers and will heal quickly if it is damaged. Although *P. caribbeorum* is capable of reproducing asexually (den HARTOG et al., 1993) it is almost always found as solitary specimens. *Pseudocorynactis* species are very popular with aquarists and is also probably imported with live rock. We have seen *P. caribbeorum* in reef tanks and have tried to keep the species ourselves. It appeared to do well, as long as enough food was provided at the appropriate time, i.e. during the night, when it expands its tentacles.

Family Ricordeidae

The family Ricordeidae contains only one genus, *Ricordea*, which, as mentioned earlier, is placed in

the family Discosomatidae by some authors. Den HARTOG (1980) considers the family to occupy an intermediary position between the families Corallimorphidae and Discosomatidae. He points out several anatomical details to support his opinion, among others, the structure of the nematocysts and the shape of the tentacles, which we do not, however, wish to elaborate upon.

A flat disc with numerous simple, short, cylindrical tentacles covering the whole disc, but which cannot be retracted, is characteristic of *Ricordea*. So far, two (perhaps three) species are known in this genus: *Ricordea florida* from the Caribbean Sea and *Ricordea yuma* from the Indo-Pacific. Both species contain zooxanthellae and prefer shallow reef flat water with a high light intensity; they are also, however, found at moderate depths. Specimens from deeper water generally do not seem to form colonies which are as dense as those produced by specimens living in shallow water. Both species are known in the aquarium hobby and do very well in reef aquaria. See fact pages 292 and 293 for more information on the two species. A third species, mentioned as *Discosoma fungiforme* in older publications (like VERRILL, 1869, and HADDON, 1898), may actually

Ricordea yuma
Hairy mushroom anemone or Yuma disc anemone

Distribution: Indo-Pacific; further details are not known. It has been observed in different shallow water areas (3-12 m depth) on the Great Barrier Reef (CHEN, pers. com.), and off Zanzibar (CARLGREN, 1900). Common in Indonesia often in very shallow waters (den HARTOG, pers. com.).

Size and growth form: Disc diameter up to around 8 cm, but 5 cm on average. This species lives as solitary individuals or in clone colonies.

Food: Feeds mainly on the products of its zooxanthellae, but also traps plankton and smaller invertebrates like crustaceans.

Description: Irregular basal disc measuring about 2-3 cm in diameter, pale or colourless, spreading and firmly attached to the substratum. A short, rather rigid column measuring a maximum length of 3 cm. There is usualy only one oblong mouth opening. The tentacles are densely arranged and cover the whole disc, they have rounded or clavate (club-shaped) tips. Two types of tentacles: one short, about 3 mm long and purplish, the other longer, at about 6 mm, and greenish. The marginal tentacles are well developed and longer than the central ones and often posseses distinct acrospheres. The colour of the disc is variable, usually brownish to greenish.

Aquarium maintenance:
- **General conditions:** Easy to keep and hardy. It often grows in dense populations which can be difficult to control. Very well suited to aquarium life.
- **Lighting:** High light intensity. Can tolerate and adapt to high light intensity, but generally does better in indirect light and in semi-shade, probably as a result of its response to "reactive" oxygen produced under high light intensities containing UV (see page 305).
- **Water circulation:** Medium.
- **Reproduction:** This species reproduces very rapidly asexually by longitudinal fission and pedal laceration or budding.

GA: + ; TO: +/- ; SE: +

Photos:
- Top: Dense population in an aquarium
- Centre: Specimens in an aquarium, displaying beautiful colours.   Photo: Scott W. Michael
- Bottom: Specimens off the Fiji Islands
                                      Photo: Scott W. Michael

Ricordea florida
Florida false coral

Distribution: Caribbean Sea, including Florida and the Bahamas.

Size and growth form: Solitary individuals reach a maximum disc diameter of 8 cm, but usually less than that. Found on coral reefs, where it usually settles on dead hermatypic corals or on rocky bottoms at depths from less than 1, to more than 50 metres. According to SPRUNG & DELBEEK (1997), this species prefers slightly turbid water, but is also found in clear waters. It often forms dense clone colonies resulting from asexual reproduction, primarily by longitudinal fission, but also, more rarely, by pedal laceration. The deeper they are found, the more often they occur as solitary specimens. Most of the specimens found in shallow waters are orientated with their oral disc perpendicular to the surface, resulting in reduced exposure to very high light intensities. More colourful pink and orange specimens growing in very shallow waters, do not show this kind of orientation, and can tolerate extreme light intensities.

Food: This species feeds on the products of its zooxanthellae, as well as on plankton and smaller invertebrates like small crustaceans.

Description: (Based on den HARTOG, 1980) The basal disc is irregular and very variable in outline: in solitary individuals, it is usually round, while in individuals living in colonies, it is oblong and wavy. There are usually one or two mouth openings for each individual, but up to seven have been found of the oblong and wavy type. The column is smooth and short and spreads over the substratum. Its colour is usually brown or brownish-purple, especially on top, while the lower portion looks paler. The oral disc is more or less circular and has hundreds of short tentacles which cannot be retracted, look more or less knob-like and have varying colours. The marginal tentacles are usually slimmer with rounded tips. The tentacles have varying colours, but are mostly green or light green at their tips, while their stems are usually the same colours as the oral disc. The periphery of the disc is often bright blue, while the central part is dull bluish, purplish or brownish, often with a bright green hypostome (conical projection containing the mouth).

Associated animals: Shrimps: *Periclimenes* spp.; Copepods: *Asteropontius longipalpus* and *Paramolgus antillianus*.

Aquarium maintenance:
– **General conditions:** Easy to keep. This species is very well suited to the Caribbean aquarium. Grows and reproduces asexually, especially if fed.
– **Lighting:** In the aquarium colonies can tolerate and ad-

apt to high light intensity, but, in general, this species does better in indirect light and in semi-shade. This is probably a response to "reactive" oxygen produced at high light intensities (see page 305). Solitary individuals require less UV-containing light.

– **Water circulation:** Medium.
– **Reproduction:** This species reproduces very rapidly by longitudinal fission and, occasionally, by pedal laceration or budding. There are no reports regarding their sexual reproduction, either in aquaria, or in nature.

GA: + ; TO: +/- ; SE: +

Photos:
– Top: Specimens in an aquarium
– Bottom: Small colony off the Bahamas

Photo: Scott W. Michael

represent a valid species of *Ricordea* (den HARTOG, 1980).

Family Discosomatidae

Den HARTOG (1980) uses the family name Discosomatidae according to DUCHASSAING & MICHELOTTI (1864), who were the first to describe these disc anemones, at that time, under the name Discosomae. CARLGREN (1949) introduced the name Actinodiscidae, but, according to the rules of zoological nomenclature, Discosomatidae is the valid family name and Actinodiscidae must be regarded as a synonym (see also pages 286 and 287).

The body of the members of Discosomatidae is, according to den HARTOG (1980), soft to very rigid and wide calyciform (cup-shaped) or flat saucer-shaped. The oral disc is more or less circular to elliptical in outline and discal and marginal tentacles may be present or absent. The marginal tentacles are often reduced in size, but when present, they are tiny, acute or finger-shaped, often with well developed small bulbs (acrospheres) on the tips. The mesogloea is very well developed and there is no ectodermal musculature present. Anatomical peculiarities which distinguish the members of the family Discosomatidae from those of other families in the order are, for example, the lack of sphincters (ring muscles), or their considerably reduced size, and the different structures of the cnidae. All the species in the family possess zooxanthellae and occupy shallow waters. The disc is usually round or oval, with more or less well-developed tentacles. The central tentacles may vary from very large and strong, which are easily seen, to minute ones others that are hardly visible at all.

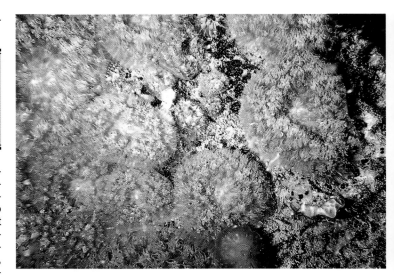

Discosoma sanctithomae　　　　　　　　　　　　Photo: Dr. J.C. den Hartog

The marginal tentacles are often reduced.

Genus *Amplexidiscus*

These giants among the mushroom anemones are often referred to by their popular name "elephant ears" or "giant mushrooms". They belong to the genus "*Amplexidiscus*", with only one species, *Amplexidiscus fenestrafer*, which occurs in the Indo-Pacific. This species is more thoroughly portrayed on page 295. It grows to a very large size and can hardly be mistaken for any other species. *Amplexidiscus* can resemble a host sea anemone. As described on page 289, it traps fish and crustaceans and, in a coral reef aquarium, is able to reduce the number of fish considerably.

Genus *Discosoma*

The generic name, *Actinodiscus*, is well known to aquarists and is a generic name that has been used for almost all mushroom anemones in the trade in Europe since the beginning of the modern aquaristic in the middle or late seventies. Some information on the nomenclature situation here are therefore interesting to notice. BLAINVILLE described this

genus in 1830 and used *Discosoma nummiforme* as the type species (RUPPEL & LEUCKART, 1828). However, *Actinodiscus* is, according to the international rules of nomenclature, a junior synonym of *Discosoma* and the correct name of this species, which is also the type species, is *Discosoma nummiforme*.

The three Caribbean species of the genus *Discosoma* (*D. sanctithomae*, *D. carlgreni* and *D. neglecta*) are all quite well known, (den HARTOG, 1980). The Indo-Pacific species are, however, rather poorly known, and a revision of these is badly needed. CARLGREN (1949) listed 18 species of *Discosoma*, but several of these are compecific.

In general, the species from the Indo-Pacific have rudimentary tentacles, which (often) can only be seen as dots on the surface of the disc. Only *Discosoma nummiforme*, from the Great Barrier Reef, has been examined thoroughly (CHEN, pers. com.). The original description of *D. nummiforme* was, however, based on material from the Red Sea. Specimens from the Great Barrier Reef material are very varied and further extensive research must be carried out on a basic revision of the species from the Indo-Pacific. This is absolutely necessary

Amplexidiscus fenestrafer
Large elephant ear

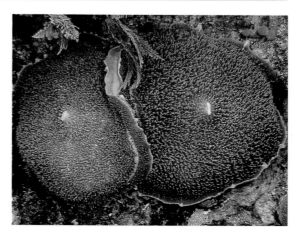

Distribution: Indo-Pacific; further details are not known. It has been seen on the Great Barrier Reef and off Indonesia. According to BAENSCH & DEBELIUS (1992), it is quite common in the Indo-Pacific. Often found in shallow, calm and slightly turbid water, but also occurs on reef slopes, vertical walls and protected caves on fringing reefs. Like most other mushroom anemones, *A. fenestrafer* prefers indirect light.

Size and growth form: Disc diameter up to around 45 cm, but 20-25 cm on average, and exceeding the base. Often occurs as solitary specimens, or in smaller groups of 3-4 individuals.

Food: Mainly feeds on the translocated products of its zooxanthellae, but also takes in fish, shrimps and other organisms and has developed a rather peculiar technique for capturing prey (see page 289).

Description: The base is colourless, irregular in outline and firmly attached to the substratum. The column is short, about 50 mm high, thin and smooth, with the marginal region often folded downwards and overhanging the base. This species has no sphincter, but possesses strong endodermal muscles in the upper part of the column. The oral disc is dull grey-greenish to brown, becoming lighter towards the rim. The disc tentacles are short and conical, arranged in radial rows. There are only a few marginal tentacles, which look like short lobe-like protrusions if the disc is expanded. There is no "bald" zone between the mouth and central tentacles, but there may be a circular zone without tentacles in the area of the disc tentacles. There is only one mouth opening. It may grow in small clone colonies as the result of asexual budding.

Aquarium maintenance:

– General conditions: This species is easy to keep. Its feeding requirements must, however, be observed. To keep it from consuming aquarium fish, it is best kept on its own in a special aquarium, preferably a sand zone one containing boulders and several individuals of the species. It should also be perfect for an aquarium containing sea grass and a muddy bottom. If kept in a "normal" coral reef aquarium, it should be given ample space and should be abundantly fed with *Artemia* and other plankton substitute foods.

– Lighting: Tolerates and adapts to high light intensity, but generally does better in indirect light and in semi-shade, probably as a response to "reactive" oxygen produced under high light intensities containing UV (see page 305).

– Water circulation: Medium.

– Reproduction: This species reproduces asexually, usually by pedal laceration or longitudinal fission. There – are no reports of sexual reproduction, neither in reef aquaria, nor in Nature.

GA: + ; TO: +/- ; SE: +

Photos:
– Top: Fully expanded animals in a deep reef at Sulawesi, Indonesia   Photo: J. Cairns-Michael
– Bottom: The balloon-shape that is formed when feeding.

Discosoma spp.
(Nearly always referred to as *Actinodiscus* in aquarium publications.)

Distribution: The genus is widespread in the Indo-Pacific, but details of the distribution of individual species are lacking. Little research has been carried out and little is known scientifically about those species which are widespread in the Indo-Pacific. Opposite is the case for the Caribbean species, which have been surveyed in some detail by den HARTOG, 1980.

Size and growth form: The disc diameter of most species is less than 10 cm, but this may vary strongly in aquaria, depending on lighting conditions. Individuals kept in shady places or under weak light, grow larger. When the light intensity increases, this species has occasionally been observed shrinking or contracting.

Food: Unknown; it probably feeds mainly on the translocated products of its zooxanthellae, but may also take in planktonic food and smaller invertebrates.

Description: Not very much taxonomic research has been done on the genus *Discosoma*. A revision therefore seems urgently needed and may lead to the genus being split into several new genera. Most of the species from the Indo-Pacific have a short column and smooth disc surface, with small or only rudimentary tentacles. The disc may exhibit all sorts of colours: bright blue, bright red, orange, blue-striped, green, red with blue spots - there seems to be no limit to the possible variations. It is unclear whether the colours represent variations within one single species, or are characters belonging to separate species, but we expect the former to be the case. Only a revision of the genus will tell us for certain.

(continued on next page)

Photos:
– Top: "KA4-COR-04" photographed off the Fiji Islands
Photo: Scott W. Michael
– Bottom: *Discosoma* sp. (KA4-COR-17) in a reef at Sulawesi, Indonesia
Photo: J. Cairns-Michael

Discosomatidae · Disc- or Mushroom Anemones

Aquarium maintenance:

– **General conditions:** *Discosoma* spp. are aquarium animals that are, in general, very easy to keep and that are suitable for beginners, as well as experienced aquarists. Many of the species can be kept together with other cnidarians without any problems, e.g. with stony corals or soft corals without any problems. However, their different requirements regarding light have to be taken into account.

– **Lighting:** Can tolerate and adapt to high light intensity, but generally do better in indirect light and in the semi-shade, probably as a result of their response to "reactive" oxygen produced under high light intensities containing UV (see page 305). Requirements differ from species to species and from colony to colony.

– **Water circulation:** Requirements differ from species to species and from colony to colony. Our experience is that medium to slow water movement suits these animals best.

– **Reproduction:** These anemones reproduce asexually, usually by pedal laceration and, occasionally, by longitudinal fission. Budding of daughter colonies from the column also occurs frequently among some species, and these sometimes grow to form large populations. This asexual reproduction potential can lead to the formation of large clone colonies.

GA: + ; TO: + ; SE: +

(continued on next page)

Photos:

– Top: "KA4-COR-07" in an aquarium
– Centre: "KA4-COR-08" in an aquarium
– Bottom right: "KA4-COR-10" in an aquarium
– Bottom left: "KA4-COR-09" in an aquarium

Continuation *Discosoma* spp.

Photos: Scott W. Michael

Two colour variants of "KA4-COR-11" in an aquarium

"KA4-COR-12" in an aquarium

"KA4-COR-13" in an aquarium

"KA4-COR-14" in an aquarium

"KA4-COR-15" in an aquarium

and will probably lead to the establishment of new genera. Since such a revision has not been carried out yet, we follow den HARTOG (1980) and think that the most sensible solution is to use the generic name *Discosoma*.

Red, blue and striped forms of *Discosoma* have been kept in aquaria since the beginning of the reef aquarium hobby, and have also been dealt with in many popular books and articles worldwide, where they are often still referred to as *Actinodiscus* spp. They are easy to keep, are beautiful and reproduce quickly by pedal laceration. We have often wondered whether all these beautiful colour variants are really separate species, or whether they are merely colour morphs of just one or a few species, but this question cannot be answered at present. In any case, *Discosoma* spp. are hardy and very interesting animals for the reef aquarium, where we can study aspects of their biology at our leisure.

Discosoma sanctithomae can be placed either in the genus *Discosoma*, or in *Rhodactis* (see page 288), given the ambiguity of some of its taxonomic characters. This species is widespread in the Caribbean, including the Bermudas, the Bahamas and Florida. It is a typical coral reef species which lives in shallow waters, in semi-darkness, or under full light. It appears in large clone colonies and reproduces asexually by pedal laceration, as well as by longitudinal fission.

The body is smooth and very lubricous (slippery) and, almost always, soft. The base reaches a diameter of 4.5 cm, is irregular in outline, spreads over the substratum and is able to secrete a chitinous membrane. The column is fully expanded and calyciformous (cup-shaped), with the marginal region often folded downwards, overhanging the base. The oral disc may reach 6 cm in diameter and has an elliptical or circular shape. Three distinct zones are normally found on the oral disc: a narrow, delicate, naked, peripheral zone, a subsequent

The disc tentacles of *Discosoma* species are often rudimentary and only visible as "rows of knobs", which make the anemones look quite attractive.

tentacle zone and a central area with the distinct raised hypostome and few reduced tentacles (den HARTOG, 1980). The disc margin always bears clearly discernible tentacles, which often have ball-like protrusions on their tips. There is always an empty, "bald" space between the central tentacles on the disc and those on the rim. Altogether, the tentacles may number 300, with the disc tentacles having characteristic excrescences and protrusions. The disc and the tentacles are usually light yellow to pale violet, brown or green, but may also be whitish, bluish, or beautifully iridescent.

Discosoma carlgreni is almost

Discosoma carlgreni   Photo: J. Sprung

Discosoma neglecta in an aquarium   Photo: J. Sprung

exclusively found in very shallow water, i.e. under very high light intensity. According to den HARTOG (1980), *D. carlgreni* has only been recorded from the north-eastern Caribbean, including South Florida, from the Bahamas and the Bermudas. It usually occurs in small groups of 5-20 specimens in coral reef habitats, and must be regarded as rather uncommon. This species reproduces asexually by pedal laceration and transverse fission and, possibly, also by longitudinal fission.

The body is rigid, owing to a well developed mesogloea, and the base is up to 3 cm in diameter in large specimens. *D. carlgreni* has a very wide column, which often spreads over the substratum. The oral disc is circular, with a maximum diameter of 5 cm, and lacks a naked peripheral zone. In *D. carlgreni*, there is no "bald" zone between the numerous outer and the central disc tentacles, which are very small and, in some cases, may be reduced to wart-like protrusions. The colour of this species is very varied; the disc, as well as the tentacles, may be green to brown, or even dark purple.

D. carlgreni is, according to SPRUNG & DELBEEK (1997), very easy to keep in reef aquaria, where it, despite its natural occurrence in high light intensity, adapts to nearly all light and current conditions.

Discosoma neglecta is found all over the Caribbean Sea, but not in the Bermudas or Brazil (den HARTOG, 1980). It is a typical coral reef species found at depths of 5 to about 30 m. In contrast to the two species mentioned previously, it seems to prefer more shady places. *D. neglecta* usually lives solitarily or in small groups, which are created by asexual reproduction through pedal laceration, a feature which proceeds less prolifically than in the other species. Longitudinal fission has not been observed in this species (den HARTOG, 1980). The body is, in general, fairly large and very rigid. The base is up to 5 cm across, while the column is long or widely calyciform in expansion and often spreads over the substratum. It is usually chocolate-brown in colouration, but can occasionally be greenish on the upper part. Dark brown spots loosely arranged in rows may be present. The oral disc is wide and concave and larger than in the preceding two species, sometimes attaining a disc diameter of 8 cm. In fully grown specimens, distinct marginal lobes are well developed, while juvenile specimens are almost circular and without marginal lobes. The colours of the disc are variegated, with white, cream and different shades of green and brown. Occasionally, it can also be streaked

with faint purple or blue and usually possesses a number of continuous or discontinuous white to yellow radial stripes. *D. neglecta* is very sturdy and appears firm and stiff to touch. This species neither has marginal tentacles, nor a "bald" zone in front of the rim, which has strongly writhing lobes. The disc tentacles are small, but numerous, and are arranged in rows, totaling up to 200 in large specimens.

According to SPRUNG & DELBEEK (1997), *D. neglecta* is, like most species in the genus, easy to keep in reef aquaria. This species prefers moderate illumination, which is logical, since it often occurs in more shady locations on the reef, and does best in calm water. It can be fed and will capture prey, such as shrimps, blackworms or chopped earthworms, but can also live exclusively from the nutrients translocated from its zooxanthellae. The tentacles are numerous but very small and often reduced to a fine pattern of spots which are arranged in radial rows. Disc and tentacles may have different colours; generally they are brown, green, white or cream-coloured.

Genus *Rhodactis*

The genus *Rhodactis*, is characterised by having clearly visible, branched disc tentacles; the marginal tentacles are mostly small and not branched. *Rhodactis rhodostoma*, which was first described by EHRENBERG (1834), is the type species of the genus. If we keep to the more traditional views of systematics and disregard the general problems in this family, it turns out to be easier to determine a species in this genus than in *Discosoma*. CHEN & MILLER (1996) have found that *Discosoma* (= *Rhodactis*) *sanctithomae* is generally more distinct from the two most common Indo-Pacific species of *Rhodactis* (*Rhodactis indosinensis* and *R. rhodostoma*) than the latter two species are from each other. The causes of

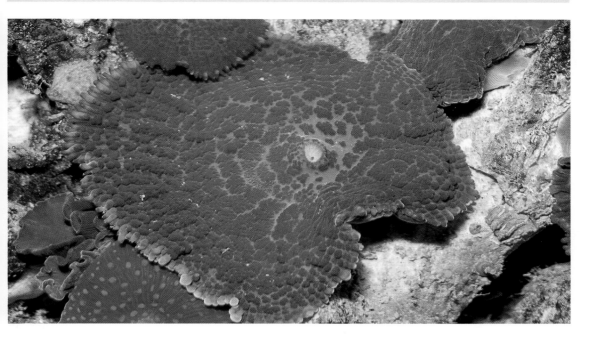

Rhodactis cf. *inchoata*
Small elephant ear, hairy mushroom anemone, Tonga blue mushroom

Distribution: Tropical Indo-Pacific; further details are not known. This species was originally described from shallow water areas in East Asia (CARLGREN, 1943), but has also been observed on the Great Barrier Reef at depths of 2-6 m.
Size and growth form: The disc diameter is usually not more than 3 cm. This species usually lives in small groups of 3 to 7, but sometimes up to 20 individuals.
Food: Unknown, this species probably feeds mainly on the products of its zooxanthellae, but may also take in plankton and small invertebrates.
Description: (Based on CHEN, 1993). The base is colourless, irregular in outline, spreading and firmly attached to the substratum. The column stalk is small, about 1 cm high, and rather firm. The oral disc is ovoid in outline, exceeding the base, with a small central mouth. The marginal tentacles are mostly short, only rarely longer. The disc tentacles are short and star-shaped, with the central ones being branched and arranged in circles, the outward ones being only rudimentary and arranged in rows. The colour of the disc is very variable; it is often quite brightly coloured, e.g. blue or green. The disc and column have identical colours. The tentacles are brownish or greenish.

Aquarium maintenance:
– **General conditions:** This is a hardy species which is very well suited for a coral reef aquarium, but is not on offer in aquarium shops as often as the other species of the genus.
– **Lighting:** Can tolerate and adapt to high light intensity, but generally does better in indirect light and in semi-shade, probably as a response to "reactive" oxygen produced in high light intensities containing UV (see page 305).
– **Water circulation:** Medium.
– **Reproduction:** It reproduces asexually, primarily through longitudinal fission, but probably also by pedal laceration (SPRUNG & DELBEEK, 1997).
GA: + ; TO: 0 ; SE: +

Photo:
Rhodactis cf. *inchoata* in an aquarium
Photo: Scott W. Michael

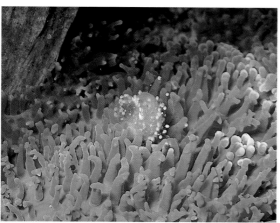

Rhodactis cf. indonsinensis
Hairy mushroom anemone, Indonesian elephant ear

Distribution: Indo-West Pacific; further details are not known. This species was originally described from shallow water areas in East Asia (Indochina) at depths of 2 - 10 m (CARLGREN, 1943), but has also been observed on the Great Barrier Reef.

Size and growth form: Maximum disc diameter 11 cm, but 5 cm on average. This species usually forms large clone colonies.

Food: Unknown. It probably feeds on prey, which consists of plankton, as well as larger animal organisms, but may also utilise the translocated products from its zooxanthellae.

Description: (Based on CHEN, 1993). The base has an irregular shape and is pale to colourless, spreading and firmly attached to the substratum. The column is small, thin and soft and has the same colour as the disc, but is paler towards the base. The colour of the oral disc is liver-brown, becomiing lighter towards the rim. There are well-developed marginal tentacles up to 5.5 cm length. The disc tentacles are arranged in radial rows and are somewhat shorter than the marginal ones. They possess 4 to 10 branchlets per tentacle that make *D. indosinensis* look bushy and hairy. The tentacles are fluorescent brownish or greenish, while their tips are white. The usually single mouth is white or pink. *R.* cf. *indosinensis* tends to live in large groups.

Aquarium maintenance:
- **General conditions:** A hardy aquarium animal regularly on sale in aquarium shops and a very good choice for the beginner. One has to keep in mind, however, that larger aggregations may harm other sessile animals and are difficult to remove from the aquarium.
- **Lighting:** Seems to love high light intensities, but will adapt to indirect and weaker light also.
- **Water circulation:** Medium to strong water motion is preferred.
- **Reproduction:** This species reproduces asexually by budding. If conditions are appropriate, there is a risk of over-population, resulting in damage to other sessile animals.

GA: + ; TO: +/- ; SE: +

Photos:
- Top: A colony with green fluorescent tentacles photographed in an aquarium.   Photo: Scott W. Michael
- Centre: The usual aquarium variant
- Bottom: The sexual reproduction of disc anemones can sometimes be observed in aquaria. In this photograph, *Rhodactis* cf. *indonsinensis* is seen ejecting egg-sperm bundles.   Photo: Scott W. Michael

Rhodactis cf. *mussoides*
Elephant ear, metallic mushroom, leaf mushroom

Distribution: Indo-West Pacific; Great Barrier Reef and Indonesia; further details are yet not known.

Size and growth form: Often with oblong and wavy discs; longest disc diameter usually up to 6 cm, but sometimes up to 16 cm. Often found on reef walls and in deeper reef habitats attached to a solid substrate or, occasionally, attached to coral rubble in shallower waters. Usually forms clone colonies of 10 to 30 specimens.

Food: Utilises the translocated products from the zooxanthellae, but may also be able to feed on bacteria captured by a film of mucus. Does not take larger food particles or smaller organisms.

Description: (Based on Chen, 1993). Originally described under the name *Platyzoanthus*. The basal disc is colourless, irregular in shape, spreading and attached firmly to the substratum; it also anchors loosely on coral ruble. The column is small, usually 2 cm high, and rather rigid. The oral disc has an irregular shape and is covered with numerous rudimentary tentacles. There are more than two mouth openings; sometimes as many as 19. No marginal tentacles are present. The disc and tentacles have the same colour, usually greenish-brown, sometimes light brown. The inside of the mouth is white or pink. This anemone usually lives in groups of 10 to 30 individuals.

Aquarium maintenance:
– **General conditions:** Easy to keep. It requires lots of light and ample space.
– **Lighting:** Tolerates and adapts to high light intensities, but generally does better in indirect or weaker light, probably as a response to "reactive" oxygen produced in high light intensities containing UV (see page 305). Some specimens fluoresce beautifully under weak blue light.
– **Water circulation:** Medium.
– **Reproduction:** Reproduces asexually by longitudinal fission. Budding and pedal laceration also occur, but only occasionally. We have observed an individual which split in two halves.

GA: + ; TO: +/- ; SE: +

Photo:
A colour variant photographed in an aquarium.
Photo: Scott W. Michael

Rhodactis cf. *rhodostoma*
Red mouth elephant ear

Distribution: Tropical Indo-West Pacific, but details are not known. Originally described from shallow water areas of the Red Sea, but was also reported from the Great Barrier Reef. As it is also found in imports from Singapore and Jakarta, it may be found there as well.

Size and growth form: Disc diameter 3-4 cm; but sometimes up to 8 cm. The species lives in small to medium-sized groups of 5 to 20 individuals.

Food: Unknown, but most probably feeds on planktonic prey, as well as larger animals, but may also utilise the translocated products from its zooxanthellae.

Description: (Based on CHEN, 1993). The base is irregular in outline, thin, colourless to pale, and firmly attached to the substratum. The column is short (up to 2 cm), thin and soft, with a colour similar to that of the oral disc. The oral disc is ovoid in outline, with an irregular shape and is liver-brown, pale or colourless, lightening towards the margins. There is only one oval mouth opening, which is placed in a central position on the disc and is white or pink-coloured on the inside. The disc has sturdy-looking, short, 3-5 mm long tentacles, or just rudiments, arranged in radial rows. These are not very numerous and are sometimes arranged in groups. The marginal tentacles are unbranched and well-developed, about 50 mm in length, possessing a white acrosphere. The internal disc tentacles are usually branched, with as many as 4-20 closely arranged branchlets per tentacle. Tentacles around the actinopharynx (oral opening) are usually unbranched. The colour of the disc is greenish-yellow, red-brown or purple. The tentacles are always brown. R. cf. *rhodostoma* lives in small to medium-sized groups of 5 to 20 individuals.

Aquarium maintenance:
– **General conditions:** Hardy and easy to keep. Very suitable for beginners. If an extensive population develops in an aquarium, it is very difficult to remove.
– **Lighting:** Tolerates and adapts to high light intensities, but generally does better in weaker or indirect light, probably as a response to "reactive" oxygen produced in high light intensities containing UV (see page 305). Some specimens fluoresce beautifully under weak blue light.
– **Water circulation:** Medium.
– **Reproduction:** This species reproduces by longitudinal fission or pedal laceration. There is a risk of over-population, resulting in damage to other sessile animals.

GA: + ; TO: +/- ; SE: +

Photos:
– Top: A colony in a reef at Sulawesi, Indonesia
Photo: J. Cairns-Michael
– Bottom: This view from above shows the typical arrangement of the tentacles.

this probably go back to ancient times when the Atlantic and the Pacific oceans separated. We present the four species, *Rhodactis* cf. *mussoides*, *Rhodactis* cf. *indonsinensis*, *Rhodactis* cf. *rhodostoma* and *Rhodactis* cf. *inchoata* in separate fact pages (see pages 301-304). There are, however, most likely to exist many other species which are not yet easy to identify.

Some *Rhodactis* species will grow excellently in aquaria. In our experimental aquarium *Rhodactis* sp. grew vigorously, a large colony of which developed from a few individuals introduced on live rock. The individual disc diameter reached 7 cm. The individual anemones had very powerful nematocysts with a sting that damaged corals in their vicinity. After we had scraped off some individuals, it only took a few weeks for the residues left behind to develop into new anemones. Even the tiniest overlooked fragments developed into new individuals. Their unlimited growth did more harm in our aquarium than the glass anemones referred to earlier, ever managed.

Genus *Metarhodactis*

The genus *Metarhodactis* was first described by CARLGREN (1943), with *M. boninensis* as the only species mentioned. According to CARLGREN, this species can only be distinguished from *Rhodactis* by structural details of the cnidae of the type known as "p-mastigophores", while BAENSCH & DEBELIUS (1992) write that *Metarhodactis* may be distinguished by the fact that it has several mouth openings. We have not found any other reference to this last feature in either scientific or aquarium publications. The only disc anemone that is reported as having several mouth openings, is *Rhodactis mussoides*, which was formerly regarded as a colonial anemone (Zoanthiniaria). However, *Metarhodactis* is such a little known and uncertain taxon, that we will not go into further details regarding this genus.

Keeping disc- or mushroom anemones in aquaria

Some, but not all, disc or mushroom anemones are suitable for coral reef aquaria. They are very common in the trade and many aquarists now have a great deal of experience with them, having observed aspects of their biology (such as behaviour, asexual reproduction and growth) in detail for years. The reproductive potential of mushroom anemones is enormous and most species will develop large colonies through asexual reproduction, i.e. by pedal laceration and by longitudinal fission or budding, from a small colony of just two or three individuals. Some species also divide intra-tentacularly, i.e. their oral disc splits in the middle to create two individuals. Asexual reproduction may, in fact, occur so rapidly that these anemones become a nuisance. TYREE (1993) reports of an isolated occasion in which the sexual reproduction of a disc anemone was observed. The picture on page 302 shows the ejection of egg and sperm cells from a *Rhodactis* cf. *indonsinensis*. In general, though, sexual reproduction in coral animals is only rarely observed in aquaria.

Some species do, however, have rather strong nematocysts and are therefore able to spread so vigorously that they eventually overgrow other coral animals or damage them in other ways.

Whether disc or mushroom anemones do well in an aquarium depends, on the species that is kept and on the general conditions in the aquarium. Some species do well only if kept under strong light and will shrink if they are placed in shady areas. Others, like the blue and red *Discosoma* species seem to do best under moderate light intensities. However, in our experience, they expand to a considerably lesser extent if they are subjected to strong light from metal halide lamps. The reason for this is in our view the production of toxic levels of "reactive" oxygen in their tissues. When symbiotic algae in the endoderm are exposed to high light intensities containing high levels of UV (see vol. 1, pp. 196), this high-energy radiation (in the presence of photosynthetic agents, such as chlorophyll), reacts to produce singleton oxygen atoms and super oxide ions, which combine very readily to form hydrogen peroxide (H_2O_2). The zooxanthellae attempt to resist the formation of hydrogen peroxide by using an enzymatic defence (superoxide dismutase) that reduces the concentration of hydrogen peroxide, while other enzymes, catalase and peroxidase, convert hydrogen peroxide into water and oxygen (TAPLEY et al., 1988; DYKENS, 1984). Similar reactions can also be observed among anemones and corals, but mushroom anemones seem to be more sensitive to hydrogen peroxide, perhaps because of their thin, flat disc which, when expanded, acts as a very efficient "solar" panel.

We have also noticed on several occasions that many disc anemones shrink and cease to multiply asexually when a strong protein skimmer and intensive filtration with activated carbon are installed, as they reduce the concentration of organic nutrients to a minimum and keep the aquarium extremely clean. We therefore assume that the combined growth and health of these anemones depends on the presence of organic compounds dissolved in the aquarium water. Disc anemones belong to the most common animals of the reef aquarium. They have been around for decades and will probably hold their popularity for decades to come. Their beautiful colours attract the enthusiasts, but they are not only colourful, they are also in general hardy and easily kept and can multiply so well that once introduced they are hard to remove. We still have remains of a 15 year old colony in our aquarium.

Chapter 16

Stony Corals

Stony corals are the major builders of coral reefs. Reef-building stony corals always possess symbiotic algae known as zooxanthellae. The common opinion is that, without the partnership between coral polyps and algae, imposing reef structures would not have been possible. It is also believed that symbiotic algae favour calcification. Although new theories on this subject have been put forward (MARSHALL, 1996), symbiotic algae are still regarded as being a major cause of the extraordinary ability of stony corals to build reefs. The symbiosis between the zooxanthellae and the coral reef polyps is explained in detail on pages 30-32, as well as in volume 1, pages 319-323.

Calcification in tropical coral reefs is so extensive and efficient that the reef can built up more quickly than it can be broken down through natural decomposition. The result is net growth of the reef, or, more correctly stated, a net growth of the bound calcium carbonates fixed as the crystal form "aragonite". In the Great Barrier Reef, which covers a good 200000 km^2, about 50 million tons of calcium carbonate become fixed each year. The surface area

Above: View from above into the authors' stony coral experimental aquarium, spring 1993. At this time, more than 75 stony coral colonies (mother and daughter colonies) were growing in the aquarium, which has been in use since 1987, but has contained mainly hermatypic stony corals only since 1990.

Left: Thick growth of *Porites cylindrica* and other stony corals on the reef flat of Bunaken Reef, Indonesia.

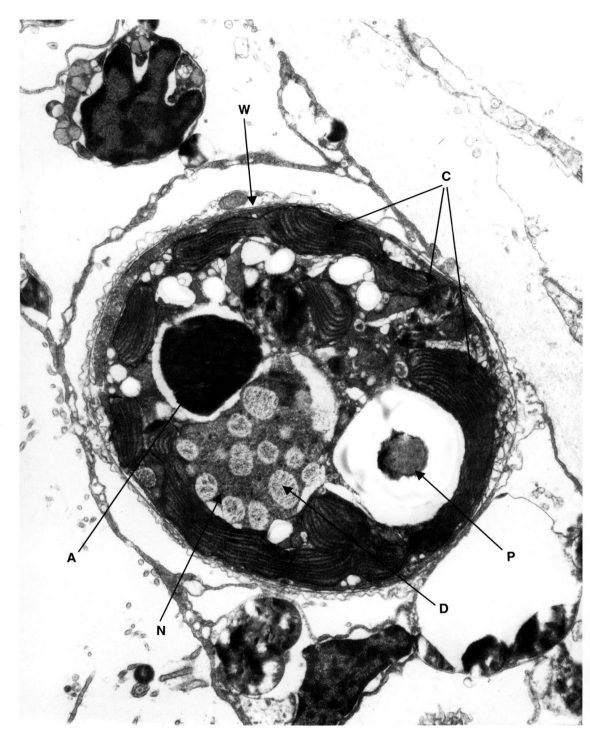

Electron micrograph of a zooxanthella from the stony coral *Acropora formosa*. The alga has a circumference of approximately 4 μm (magnification: 27,500 X). Key to the symbols: W = Cell wall; P = Pyrenoid (small protein-rich grains in which storage of nutrients takes place); N = Cell nucleus; D = DNA (deoxyribonucleic acid); C = Chloroplasts; A = Accumulation bodies (for the storage of metabolic products). Photo: Dr. P. Harrison, Southern Cross University

Right: Reef-building stony corals bind millions of tons of calcium carbonate a year. Throughout the earth's history, reefs have been lifted out of the water, as shown here in the Animal Flower Bay north of Barbados. The picture shows a 85,000-year old reef terrace that was laid down on top of a 125,000-year-old reef. **Photo: Prof. D. Hopley**

of all coral reefs in the world is calculated to be about 617000 km^2. The total production of calcium carbonate amounts to approximately 900 million tons per year!

Stony corals can be split into reef-building (hermatypic), non-reef-building (ahermatypic), solitary and colonial types. Solitary corals have only one single coral polyp. Good examples are *Heliofungia actiniformis*, normally found among colonial reef-building corals, and *Cycloseris* spp., normally found among sea grasses and on sandy bottoms. Although *Cycloseris* contains zooxanthellae, it is definitely not a reef builder. The majority of stony corals, however, form colonies. These can be composed of just a few individuals, as in *Trachyphyllia geoffroyi*, or of thousands of individuals, as in *Porites* spp. or *Montipora* spp.

In general, it must be stated that stony corals belong to a group of animals which are difficult to keep in aquaria. Although the modern coral reef aquarium has developed into a functioning

system in which many species of stony corals will grow and breed, and even though commercial farms for stony corals are being established, this group of invertebrates must be viewed as more challenging than, for example, soft corals or star polyps. However, they are by no means impossible to keep!

Beware that all **stony corals** are listed on **CITES Appendix II**. CITES, the Convention on International Trade in Endangered Species of Wild Flora and Fauna, regulates transboundary trade in live and dead specimens, as well as products made from threatened or potentially threatened species. This is accomplished through a system of licenses applied to international trade in the

listed species. Imports and exports of any species listed on Appendix II requires a license which is issued by the responsible authorities of the export country. In these permits, the country of origin confirms that the specimens in question have been legally obtained and are free to be exported. This, of course, implies that the export of the particular specimens is considered to be of no danger to the continuous survival of the species. Besides the internationally applied regulations, some of the countries which have signed CITES have also chosen to enforce extended and stricter rules on trade in and/or the keeping of CITES-listed species within their own country. With this scrutiny of stony coral imports, it

Front view of the authors' stony coral experimental aquarium in 1992.

goes without saying that we, as aquarists, are obligated to acquire good knowledge of the appropriate aquarium technology, as well as the biology, of stony corals before we acquire any colonies for our aquaria.

In order to provide appropriate living conditions for stony corals, the following eight points should, in our opinion, be fulfilled (these conditions are described in detail in Volume 1):

❶ completed break-in period;

❷ stable algae conditions, through which the growth of green filamentous and other filamentous algae should be kept absolutely minimal;

❸ optimal lighting, including both the light intensity, as well as the spectral quality;

❹ optimal availability of calcium ions (Ca^{2+}): around 420 ppm;

❺ stable and natural carbonate hardness about 5-9 °KH, pH in the range of 8.00-8.50, temperature in the range of 22-28 °C and salinity in the range of 32-35 ‰;

❻ nutrient-poor water where the concentrations of nitrate and phosphate are kept to an absolute minimum;

❼ very good water flow;

❽ availability of important trace elements, although in minimal concentrations.

Bleaching

Since first observed in Nature as early as in 1931, bleaching has been the subject of many studies throughout the last century. Between 1982 to 1983, this phenomenon occurred at dramatic levels near the Thousand Islands in Indonesia, with more than 80% of

This colony of *Acropora* sp. on a reef flat near Bunaken, North Sulawesi, Indonesia, clearly shows signs of bleaching.

the corals dying (BROWN & SUHARSONI, 1990). Bleaching can even occur in aquaria. In general, it appears that corals lose their colours (see photo in Volume 1, page 212) as a result of a diminishing number of symbiotic algae and/or a diminishing concentration of pigments in the algal cells (BROWN, 1990). During a study of bleaching carried out in the Caribbean from November 1987 to May 1988, it was observed that bleaching occurred in populations of *Montastrea annularis* in colonies with either a low number of zooxanthellae, but normal pigment content, or in colonies with a high number of zooxanthellae, but very low pigment content (SZMANT & GASSMANN, 1990).

Bleaching is not solely limited to stony corals, although these usually react first in an aquarium. All organisms with symbiotic algae can bleach, for example,

A colony of *Acropora microphthalma* bleached when the temperature of the aquarium water rose above 30 °C for a period of only a few days.

some sponges, many soft corals, some gorgonians and mussels.

There are many theories regarding the reasons for bleaching. It must be noted, however, that the causes of bleaching in aquaria are not necessarily the same as those in the sea, where bleaching is a reaction to temperature stress, or, more specifically, to anormally high temperatures over a short or long period of time. JOKIEL & COLES (1990) studied how corals reacted to high temperatures in Hawaii and other locations in the Indo-Pacific and found that bleaching occurred as soon as corals were exposed to temperatures 3 to 4 °C higher than the normal maximum summer (September to October) temperature. In Hawaii, this temperature was on average 26.2 °C. Corals also lost their colouring when the temperature rose, over a period of several weeks, by only 1 to 2 °C over the normal maximum summer temperature. We would like to add that bleaching occurs in connection with respiratory rate. Under conditions which increase coral respiration, i.e. additional amounts of light, corals at high temperatures will also bleach more quickly. In aquaria, we can observe strong bleaching in *Acropora* spp. during our warmest summer months (July to August) at temperatures from 28 to 30 °C (morning to evening). When the temperature is brought back to its normal level (through the insertion, into the tank, of cooling hoses with running cold freshwater), the corals, once more, regain their normal colouring.

Another direct cause of bleaching is an increase in ultraviolet radiation. In Nature, this can occur through the thinning of the ozone layer, or through the loss of normal suspended articles which, thus, make the water unusually clear. In aquaria, a change in the pigmentation of corals can often be observed when the lighting is changed, for example through the replacement of fluorescent bulbs with HQI-bulbs, or when replacing very old HQI-bulbs with new ones. This can, in the worst ca-

ses, even kill the corals if they cannot adapt quickly enough to the new light regime.

LESSER et al. (1990) have proven that there is an increase in enzymes that neutralize the active form of oxygen as soon as radiant energy, UV radiation and temperature rise. This can be seen as indirect evidence that changes in these physical parameters lead to a change in the concentration of active forms of oxygen. We have also observed a clear bleaching of stony corals under intense filtering conditions over activated carbon. One such filtering operation which was sustained over a long period of time, led to the impoverishment of trace elements in the water. In addition, the water became extremely clear, thus allowing UV light to penetrate deeper than normal, resulting in an increase in the amount of UV radiation hitting the corals.

Many stony corals appear to react decidedly negatively to such conditions, resulting in loss of colouration and death of the body tissue. This affects, first and foremost, the corals that are closest to the light source and, thus, receive the highest intensity of UV. It is difficult to say, though, whether it is the UV radiation itself, or the lack of trace elements, that leads to this reaction. It is possible that carbon filtering removes elements that are vital in protecting coral tissue against UV radiation. In some cases, we have observed that bleached corals redevelop their normal pigmentation after trace elements are added to the water if, at the same time, carbon filtering is turned off. Similarly, corals also regain their colouring if potassium iodide is added to the water (for dosage, see Volume 1, page 237). We have a suspicion that, when bleaching occurs in an aquarium, iodide is often the deciding element which is lacking. This, however, needs further research before it can be verified.

The conclusion we have come to as a result of our observations is that filtering over activated carbon must be carried out very carefully. Our experience, and that of many other aquarists, tells us that carbon filtration should only be carried out over short periods of time, for example, two to three days a month. Additionally, this filtering should only be done in order to remove dye compounds or other organic materials which cannot be removed using a protein skimmer.

Symbiotics and Parasites

It would be incomplete to discuss stony corals without, at the same time, discussing the many associated animals that live among their branches. Here, we find a complete world of tiny organisms, only a small number of which damage their hosts.

Symbiotic animals

During an Indonesia expedition in 1994, we had the opportunity of studying symbionts found in association with stony corals. We chose a colony of *Seriatopora hystrix* which had a 25 cm circumference (see picture on next page). This colony grew near a beach where other coral colonies, growing on boulders lying on sand or mud, could also be found. As we pulled the coral colony out of the water and shook it in a water-filled container, a large number of various organisms appeared. Among them were three different types of fish, specifically, five very small white-tailed damselfish *Dascyllus aruanus*, two pairs of gobies of the species *Gobiodon albofasciatus* and one yellow-speckled dottyback *Pseudochromis marshallensis*.

Numerous small crustaceans were also found living between the extremely sharp-edged branches of the coral. Eventually, we could have collected more than 20 crustaceans, including six 2 cm-large crabs of the family Xanthidae. Further, we could identify two different types of shrimp: se-

A closer look at a colony of *Seriatopora hystrix* reveals many small symbiotic crabs and other animals associated with the coral.

coral gall crab, *Hapalocarcinus marsupialis* from the family Cryptocharidae.

Juvenile females of this species of crab settle onto coral branches, as a result of which, the coral becomes irritated and reacts by developing the so-called coral "gall", an outgrowth from its tissue. The outgrowth encloses each female crab completely, except for a small opening through which she catches plankton with the help of her bristle-bearing chelae. The male crab can enter through the opening for mating, but, otherwise, lives permanently free, unlike the female, which must live imprisoned her entire life. It is not usually difficult to find a tiny male crab on a branch near a female's burrow. Without a doubt, it would be very interesting to observe this symbiosis between corals and crabs optimally in a small special aquarium. For those aquarists who would like to know more about this symbiosis, we recommend the work of BRUCE

veral red pistol shrimp which appeared to be living in pairs, and several *Periclimenes* sp. In addition, we discovered various burrowing organisms living inside the coral skeleton, including mussels and snails. One burrowing animal was particularly interesting: the

Some of the animals that we found in a colony of *Seriatopora hystrix* shown above during our expedition to Indonesia in 1994. These shots were taken in a photographic tank.

Right - *Pseudochromis marshallensis*

Bottom left - Coral crab from the family Xanthidae

Bottom right - Pair of pistol shrimps, *Alpheus* sp. (?)

(1976). In other corals, we found various crabs, mostly small species from the family Xanthidae.

We should, in principle, work to maintain natural living arrangements within our aquaria, provided that they do not damage the corals.

Parasites

Parasites conduct themselves in a very different way to symbionts, through their obvious damaging and, in the end, destroying of the coral tissue. There are innumerable examples of this, only a few of which can be discussed here. In volume 1 (page 186) we report on a parasitic ocean spider (Pycnogonida) which was imported with an *Acropora* sp. from the Fiji Islands. The attacked *Acropora* colonies subsequently regenerated the damaged tissues and grew into beautiful colonies.

The most troublesome parasites are single-celled organisms. This is especially true of the protozoan *Helicostoma nonatum* from the family Philasteridae (BEUL, 1987). This protozoan feeds on zooxanthellae and attacks stony corals, especially those of the genus *Acropora*, but even star polyps, soft corals and colonial anemones can be attacked. Even though the parasite's attack is not always fatal, it usually causes heavy damage to colonies. *H. nonatum* has sometimes been found on individual colonies of cnidarians in aquaria, but it is, however, still unclear how widely distributed this parasite is in the aquarium world. An attack appears as a brown, gelatinous mass on the corals. Treatment can be attempted through sucking off the damaged tissue and then submerging the coral for one to five minutes in freshwater. Next, the coral must be placed in a special aquarium with very effective water circulation, where it will emit a massive amount of mucus and will regenerate, if the treatment was effective, or die, if it was too weak to withstand the exposure to freshwater.

Helicostoma nonatum is, itself, devoured by predatory ciliates,

Above: This small coral crab from the family Xanthidae hides itself among the branches of an *Acropora* sp. Many coral crabs have specialized on feeding on coral slime. We have not found these to be harmful to their hosts at all, and we recommend them to be left in the corals.

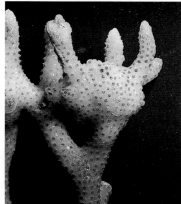

To the right: The small gall crab, *Hapalocarcinus marsupialis*, lives in a special symbiotic relationship with stony corals from the family Pocilloporidae, especially with *Seriatopora hystrix*. The juvenile female settles on the coral branch and irritates the coral polyps so that they modify their growth and form a gall in which the female becomes imprisoned for life. Only a small opening for contact with the outside world remains open and, through this, the female obtains the necessary food, as well as sperm cells when the time comes for reproduction. By opening the coral gall carefully, the female becomes visible (lower photo). The male lives outside and his colouring perfectly matches that of the corals. For comparison purposes, we have placed a white male near the female (below and to the right of the female) in this photo.

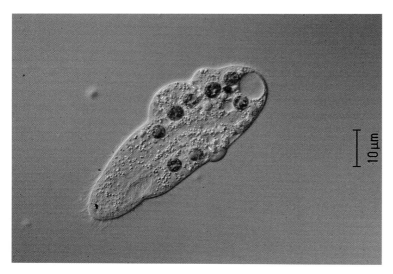

Montipora that originated from the Fiji Islands. The white, less than 3 mm large, sea slugs ate the coral tissue, causing the branches of the coral to die, starting at the base and moving towards the top. The slugs attacked at least two species: the branching *Montipora digitata* was badly decimated, while another encrusting *Montipora* was less damaged. Although many *Acropora* types were found in the same aquarium, we could not observe these being attacked. Later on, we have had other reports that this nudibranch seems to attack *Montipora* sp. only. This is a distinctive feature of many parasites, i.e. they are specific in their choice of host animals. An attempt to use freshwater cleaning (see previous page) proved unsuccessful. After about one year, of which the last six months of the attack could be described as "very extensive", the parasites disappeared as suddenly as they had appeared, without any visible cause. The corals survived and regained their vitality.

Commensal flatworms from the order Acoela in the phylum Platyhelminthes, are commonly associated with cnidarians. They occupy the surface of stony corals, soft corals and gorgoni-

The ciliate *Helicostoma nonatum* is one of the most persistent parasites. It can severely damage the coral tissue and completely destroy a coral colony if not removed. Photo: J. Yaiullo

such as *Euplotes* spp. and *Aspidisca* spp. The number of parasitic ciliates in an aquarium is, to a large extent, dependent on how many parasite-feeding predators there are; it is a balancing act between hunter and prey. In the ocean, this balance is perfectly maintained, but in an aquarium, the balance can shift. It is certainly likely that an aquarium with live rock is better protected against an attack by *Helicostoma nonatum* than an aquarium with a "dead decoration" and a "non-biological" set-up.

Other parasites that can be particularly burdensome are small nudibranchs that feed on the body tissue of corals. We experienced such a parasitic plague on stony corals of the genus

Small nudibranchs are often problematic coral parasites. This small, only 1-2 mm long species (left) lives exclusively on *Montipora digitata* and feeds on the coral's tissue. Nudibranchs lay their eggs at the base of the branches (right). About one year after its appearance in one of our aquaria, this harmful parasite suddenly disappeared without us being able to determine "why".

ans and several are photosynthetic, a subject that we shall return to in detail in the next volume. So far, it is uncertain whether or not they disturb the host, or if they feed on the mucus secreted by the host.

The majority of aquarists will experience an attack of parasites or observe commensalism among their corals. In such cases, it is important to keep notes of developments and to document the attack with photos, if possible. It is just as important, though, to publish your records of the attack and its treatment, so that other aquarists can make use of your experience. But do remember: not all animals that live associated with corals are harmful; most are, in fact, just an expression of the natural reef diversity and, most often, there is little or no reason for removing the "parasite" and thereby ruining a beautiful and perfectly natural partnership.

Tiny acoelomate flatworms on a *Tubastraea* sp. on an Indonesian reef. The flatworms grow to about 5 mm long and contain symbiotic algae. They were also found on other stony corals at this location.

The structure of polyps and their growth form

Stony corals are normally divided into, at least, 16 families, with more than 400 species, this classification being based on numerous morphological characteristics. In addition, stony corals are often grouped according to their growth form, although a variety of different forms can often be found in a single family. This occurs, both in colony-building species, as well as in solitary ones.

Colonies grow by separating into polyps and this can occur in two different ways. In intra-tentacular budding, the polyps divide into two or more polyps, while in extra-tentacular budding, a daughter polyp develops on the outside (side) of the mother polyp. The budding of new polyps can exert an influence on the colony form, but this is not invariably the case. The skeleton of a single

polyp is called the "corallite" and is a tube that contains vertical plates radiating from the tube's centre. The plates are known as "septo-costae" and are joined together by horizontal plates and other structures called the "coenosteum". As long as the corallite has its own distinct corallite walls, the colony structure is defined either as "plocoid", as in the genus *Favia*, or as "phaceloid", as in *Caulastrea* sp., depending on the

length of the separation troughs between the polyps.

If the polyps have common corallite walls, and if the colony builds long, stretched-out structures (so-called "valleys"), the colony structure is "meandroid", as in *Symphyllia* spp., and *Leptoria* spp. If the polyps have common corallite walls, and the colony has no valleys, then it is "cerioid", as in *Favites* spp. Finally, there are polyps with long, stretched-out

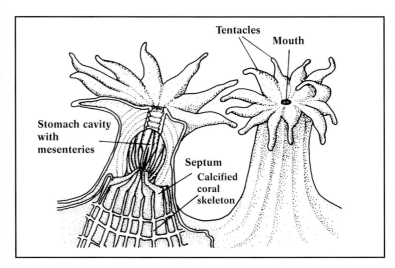

The structure of a stony coral polyp

Labels on figure: Tentacles, Mouth, Stomach cavity with mesenteries, Septum, Calcified coral skeleton

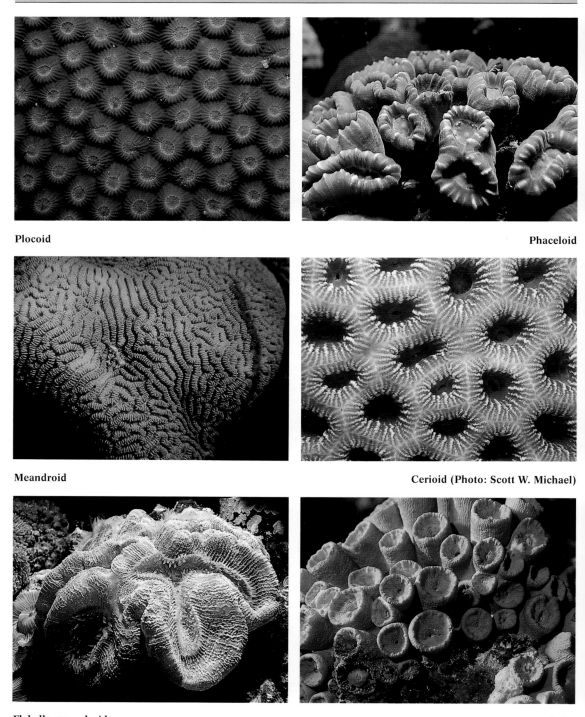

Plocoid

Phaceloid

Meandroid

Cerioid (Photo: Scott W. Michael)

Flabello-meandroid

Tubular

Sometimes, the entire spectrum of coral colony growth forms can be found in one reef section, as here on Agincourt Reef, GBR (the drawing is a reproduction of the photo).

1. *Acropora* spp. - table-shaped; 2. *Pavona clavus* (?) - column-shaped; 3. *Montipora* sp. - encrusting; 4. *Symphyllia* sp. - massive with meandroid corallite structures; 5. *Goniastrea* sp. - massive with cerioid corallite structures; 6. *Acropora danai* - branching; 7. *Acropora humilis* - corymbose with thick branches; 8. *Platygyra* sp. - massive with meandroid corallite structures; 9. *Heteractis magnifica* (giant anemone); 10. *Palythoa* sp. (colonial anemone); 11. *Lobophytum* (?) sp. (soft coral).

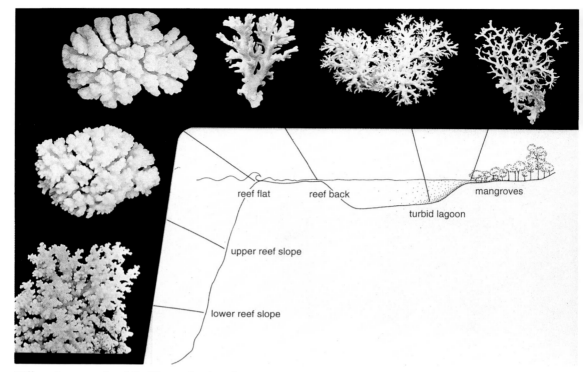

Different ecomorphs of *Pocillopora damicornis*.

From VERON (1995)

structures with separate corallite walls. These are said to have a "flabello-meandroid" growth form. *Trachyphyllia geoffroyi* is a good example of such a coral. If the corallites are tube-shaped, then the colony structure is referred to as "tubular", as we know from the ahermatypic genus *Tubastraea*.

Corallites are, however, very variable, not only within a species, but even within one single colony. Almost all corals show variation in skeletal structure between different corallites of the same colony, a variation that reaches an extreme in the genus *Acropora* (see page 319; VERON, 1995). Often, growth in a reef aquarium is faster and occurs under conditions that are very different to those found in the wild. One must therefore expect, both the shape of the colony, as well as the structure of its corallites, to differ gradually from that found in the same species growing under natural conditions. This makes species identification of many of corals growing in aquaria difficult

and sometimes nearly - if not totally - impossible. This is especially true of the family Acroporidae.

Because, additionally, polyps have a genetically determined structure, colonies exhibit varying growth forms. For polyps with a phaceloid or flabello-meandroid structure, the same name is usually used when describing the growth form of the colony. For the remaining polyps, colonial growth forms are divided into massive, irregular, encrusting, laminar, or free-living.

Growth form is not always clear and colonies with the same basic growth form can appear very differently, depending on where the species is growing on the reef. These different forms are known as ecomorphs. Biotic and abiotic factors, such as currents, tides, wave impact, predation, composition of neighbouring and associated fauna and - last, but not least - light, all have a strong impact on the growth form of a colony. An extreme example is the wide-

spread *Pocillopora damicornis* (see fact page 326 and above) which shows four different ecomorphs and a wide range of growth forms. This species is a very common coral in the trade; it is very durable and is the most studied of all the stony corals. On the reef edge and reef flat, where waves break and where water motion is strong, colonies are often robust, with short, stout branches. Near shore in protected, but perhaps turbid, habitats, colonies might be thin and branching, while colonies from the lower reef slope might show a wide, branching structure composed of rather thick branches. The figure above shows this clearly. The different ecomorphs shown are all linked by intermediate growth forms (VERON, 1995).

Variation between colonies within the same biotope, where corals grow under the same physical conditions, also commonly occurs. Then there are variations from biotope to biotope, and from region to region. Colonies might

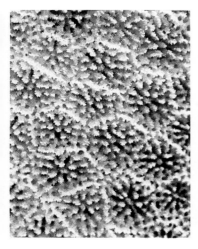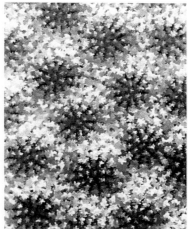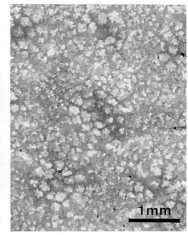

Corallite variation within a colony of *Porites lutea*. The corallites occur within 300 mm of each other, around the lip of base of a helmet-shaped colony.

From Veron (1995)

also show variations in growth form within different parts of the same colony; such variations can, most often, be linked to the age of the colony.

To identify species of corals, their polyp structure, detailed structure of the corallites and their growth form must all be taken into consideration. Fundamentally, species identification of corals is a job that only few specialists are capable of doing properly. With the exception of some easily recognizable species, only a minimum of stony corals can be identified down to species level by aquarists. Frequently, even the identification of the genus can be difficult.

For all those who would like to learn more about stony corals, the book by Veron (1986) "Corals of Australia and the Indo-Pacific" is indispensable, as well as Veron (1995) dealing with the biogeography and evolution of the Scleractinia. Veron is also the source of a very valuable biography of the stony corals (1993) and a monograph of the hermatypic corals of Japan (1992). In addition to these books, valuable information can be found about many genera in Wood (1983) and Ditlev (1980), who has written an interesting field guide to the stony corals of the Indo-Pacific. Randall & Myers (1983) concern themselves with the stony corals around Guam, while Humann (1993) has compiled an unusually complete overview of stony corals of the Caribbean. Based on these works, we would next like to discuss the families that are most interesting from an aquarist's point of view.

Environmental conditions exert considerable influence on the growth form of a coral colony. In exposed habitats, species can form ecomorphs with a shape that can withstand the forces of the waves - growth forms that may be atypical for their species and very different from the shape of the same species found in protected areas. On the right is the rare *Acropora indiana* growing near the reef edge.

This picture shows a corallite (coral goblet) from *Favites flexuosa*, photographed from above. The drawing (after VERON, 1986), shows the same structure in a simplified form. The corallite, whose shell is a single polyp, is shown as a tube which contains vertical plates radiating from the centre. The tube itself becomes the corallite wall and the plates are described as septo-costae. This double name stems from the plates' names: when the plates are inside the tube, they are called septa (singular: septum = dividing wall); when they are outside the tube, they are called costae (singular: costa = rib). The individual corallites are connected with one another through horizontal plates and other structures. This construction is called the coenosteum. It can be said, in a somewhat simplified way, that the septo-costae correspond to the mesenteries and the coenosteum corresponds to the coenenchyme of the polyp tissue.

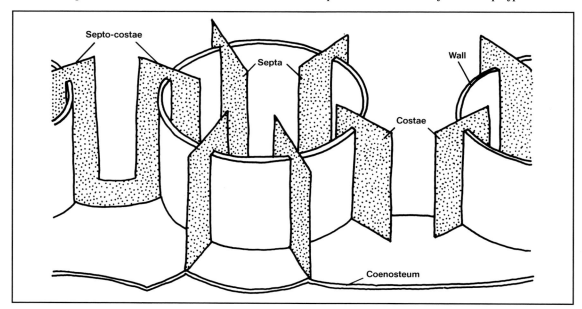

Family Astrocoeniidae

This small family is of little significance to aquarists, but with regard to evolution, it is interesting, especially since its systematic position has been changed several times (VERON, 1995).

The two rather inconspicuous species of the genus *Stylocoeniella*, *S. guentheri* and *S. armata*, belong to the oldest evolutionary group of stony corals, whose fossil record goes back to the Eocene. Both species are very similar to *Porites* spp. in their growth form, and can create large, metre-high colonies on the developing edge of a coral reef. They are widely distributed in the Indo-Pacific and are found from the Red Sea to east Africa and Mauritius, eastwards over west Australia to the Lord Howe Islands and Sydney and as far as Japan. In the central Pacific, the genus spreads all the way to the Tuamotu Islands (VERON, 1986). The colonies are small and encrusting and often found in crevices. Some colonies of *S. guentheri* can be massive with knob-like or column-like vertical expansioins up to 7 cm high which are sometimes fused, and most colonies of *S. guentheri* are deformed by infestations of the serpulid worm *Spirobranchus* spp. (VERON & PICHON, 1976). We know nothing about the aquarium care of *Stylocoeniella*.

The genus *Stephanocoenia* can be found in the Caribbean. The only species is *S. michelinii*. The distribution area stretches from south Florida and the Bahamas, over the entire Caribbean Sea. The colonies, which grow in almost all reef zones, create smooth domes on the substratum or, sometimes, encrusting structures which therefore resemble the growth form of *Siderastrea* spp. Small red tube worms often

To the right: *Stephanocoenia michelinii* is endemic to the Caribbean.
Photo: Scott W. Michael

Systematic overview of the stony corals, Scleractinia

Astrocoeniidae
 Stylocoeniella, Stephanocoenia
Pocilloporidae
 Pocillopora, Seriatopora, Stylophora, Madracis
Acroporidae
 Montipora, Acropora, Astreopora, Anacropora
Poritidae
 Porites, Goniopora, Alveopora
Siderastreidae
 Siderastrea, Psammocora, Coscinaraea
Agariciidae
 Pavona, Leptoseris, Pachyseris, Agaricia, Coeloseris
Fungiidae
 Diaseris, Cycloseris, Heliofungia, Fungia, Herpolitha, Polyphyllia, Sandalolithia, Halomitra, Lithophyllon, Podabacia
Oculinidae
 Galaxea, Acrhelia, Oculina
Pectiniidae
 Echinophyllia, Oxypora, Mycedium, Pectinia, Physophyllia
Mussidae
 Cynarina, Scolymia, Acanthastrea, Blastomussa, Lobophyllia, Symphyllia, Mussa, Mycetophyllia, Isophyllia, Isophyllastre
Merulinidae
 Hydnophora, Merulina, Scapophyllia
Meandrinidae
 Dendrogyra, Dichocoenia, Meandrina
Faviidae
 Caulastrea, Echinopora, Platygyra, Oulophyllia, Goniastrea, Montastrea, Favia, Favites, Leptoria, Colpophyllia, Manicinia, Diploria, Solenastrea
Trachyphylliidae
 Trachyphyllia
Caryophylliidae
 Cataláphyllia, Euphyllia, Plerogyra, Physogyra, Nemenzophyllia, Eusmilia
Dendrophyllidae
 Turbinaria, Dendrophyllia, Tubastraea

Ecomorphs of *Pocillopora verrucosa*: The picture on the left shows a colony in the shallow water and intense illumination of a coral sea, while the one on the right, shows the same species on a reef wall at 20 m depth in the Maldives.

live in the colonies (HUMANN, 1993) and if they stretch out their tentacles, the surface of the corals becomes red. This then looks as though the corals are beginning to "blush". For this reason, *Stephanocoenia michelinii* is popularly known as the "blushing star coral".

Family Pocilloporidae

In the family Pocilloporidae, the bush corals, we find beautiful, fast-growing stony corals. They are very numerous on the reef and often even more so in the trade. The family has five genera, of which the closely related *Pocillopora*, *Seriatopora* and *Stylophora* belong to the most common stony corals found in shallow reef areas. The remaining two genera, *Palauastrea* and *Madracis*, differ in many ways from the other three and are far more rarely found.

Genus *Pocillopora*

Pocillopora is a common genus with a world wide tropical and warm-temperate distribution (VERON & PICHON, 1976). The bush corals of the genus *Pocillopora* shows a great deal of poly-

morphism, which means that the species can appear in highly variable growth forms - forming many ecomorphs -, depending on where they grow on the reef (see page 318). The great variability in growth has caused a complexity of nomenclature within the genus to be used by early taxonomists. We have ourselves also experienced a colony which we collected from the shallow reef flat on Suva Reef in the Fiji Islands, rapidly changing its colour and growth form when we placed it in an aquarium. It can therefore be difficult to separate the 10 or so living species of *Pocillopora* from one another. In general, the genera can be identified by the cup-shaped warts, small cups and/or pores that cover the skeleton.

The three most common species are *Pocillopora damicornis*, *P. verrucosa* and *P. eydouxi*. *P. damicornis* has been especially well studied, with particular reference to its genetics and reproductive biology, and been found to produce sexual as well as asexual larvae (see pages 40 and 63). This species is very widespread and belongs to the stony corals that are among the easiest to keep in aquaria (see fact page 326). However, one should be aware that stout colonies of *P. damicornis* growing on exposed reef flats, can easily resemble *P. verru-*

cosa, but *P. damicornis* lack true verruca.

Pocillopora verrucosa is also very common on the reef and can appear, among others, in intensely purple-coloured populations. The branches have very distinct warts (verruca, Latin = wart) and are normally thicker than those of *P. damicornis*. In areas of strong wave action the two species can look very similar. *P. verrucosa* thrives in aquaria and grows vigorously. It is sometimes available in the trade (see fact page 328).

The species of the genus *Pocillopora* are very sensitive to transportation. If colonies are packed too tightly in little water, losses can be high. The highest possible care is therefore required when packing and transporting.

Coral crabs from the family Xanthidae live almost exclusively between the branches of *Pocillopora damicornis* and *P. verrucosa*. They are harmless "tenants" which, in our experience, do not damage the corals. The crabs have special mouth bristles which they use to brush off mucus from the surface of the coral. This mucus serves as the crab's food. We recommend that these crabs be tolerated, so that the relationship found in Nature can be allowed to continue in the aquarium, and also that the partnership can be observed.

Unlike the two previous spe-

Pocillopora eydouxi: The picture on the left shows a bright yellow colony on a shallow reef flat, while the one on the right, shows a colony in a sandy lagoon. Both photos were taken in the Maldives. *Dascyllus aruanus* often lives associated with *Pocillopora* sp.

cies mentioned above, *Pocillopora eydouxi* is seldom found in stores. However, it is certainly one of the most beautiful species of the genus. It is widely distributed in the Indo-Pacific, from the Red Sea and south-east Africa, to Hawaii where it almost always occur in clear water. The colonies have stout, upright flattened branches which can be compactly arranged in habitats that are exposed to strong currents. The branches are generally much larger in all dimensions than those of the other species in the genus. The branches vary greatly in size and shape within the same colony, major branches being cylindrical with a diameter of 2-4 cm, or broad-ended up to 15 cm wide. Colonies up to 95 cm high have

Close-up photo showing the branches of *Pocillopora eydouxi*.

been recorded at the Palm Islands (VERON & PICHON, 1976). The colours are usually brown or green. This species is abundant in the entire Indo-Pacific and is often seen in starkly exposed habitats where colonies can occasionally be found in large aggregations. The branches can then be compactly arranged. We have only very little experience with this species in aquaria, but it seems as if *P. eydouxi* is more difficult to transport and keep than other species of *Pocillopora*.

Pocillopora woodjonesi is similar to *P. eydouxi*, but has bigger branches that tends to be more dwarfed and become fan-shaped instead of elongated as in *P. eydouxi* (VERON & PICHON, 1976). The species is only found in the central Indo-Pacific: in the Coral Sea, around Australia: the Great Barrier Reef in the east, and south to the Dampier Archipelago on the west coast, and further west to the Cocos-Keeling Islands in the Indian Ocean. Compared with the three previously-named species, *Pocillopora woodjonesi* is rare and is only found in habitats with strong currents and heavy wave action.

Pocillopora meandrina is very similar to *P. verrucosa*, but the colonies have uniform sprawling

branches and small uniform verrucae (VERON, 1986). For the amateur, it is quite impossible to distinguish between the two species. The species is common along the Great Barrier reef and in the Coral Sea reefs exposed to strong wave action. However, *P. meandrina* is recorded from south Papua-New Guinea, GBR, the Coral Sea, western Australia, the Cocos Keeling Atoll, the Philippines and Japan as well as from locations in central Indo-Pacific only found from Australia to the Samoa Islands and Hawaii.

Pocillopora elegans (see page 329) is limited in its distribution to the east Pacific, where it is one of only a few reef-building stony corals. The species is found in the shallow subtidal zone in depths from 1 to 17 metres. In the Sea of Cortez it forms the only true reefs near Cabo Pulmo and Los Frailes (KERSTITCH, 1989). The colonies can reach a height of 75 to 100 cm which range in colour from pale to dark brown or green and are found at depths from 1 to 17 m. Many symbionts normally inhabit the colonies, including the coral shrimp *Harpiliopsis depressa*, the striped porcelain crab *Petrolisthes marginatus* and the falcon fish *Cirrhitichthys oxycephalus*.

"Occupied Water Volume"
one out of many ways to the measure growth among stony corals in the reef aquarium

In 1991, we were presented with the opportunity to collect tiny colonies of stony corals legally from Suva Reef, off Suva in Fiji, and to use these for experiments on the growth of stony corals in closed reef aquaria systems. Most of the colonies collected belonged to the family Acroporidae, and the tests began in the autumn of 1991.

The diagrams (shown here, as well as in some of the fact pages in this chapter) and the table, all use the term "volume" - a term that may, perhaps, appear somewhat meaningless. We have, nevertheless, chosen to use it, as we are linking the word "volume" with what can be called "occupied water volume", which we define as "the space or volume of water which a colony controls at any one time".

Very few other sessile cnidarian animals can grow in this space, as the colony defends the area by secreting protective chemicals. By estimating the volume (i.e. multiplying length by width by height) on different days during the growth period and calculating the volumetric increase, we can indicate how colonies grow in aquaria.

All in all, we grew and measured about 20 different colonies, which had been found growing in different forms on the reef. *Acropora cytherea* (fact page 364) is table-shaped, *Acropora latistella* (fact page 365) is corymbose, caespitose or table-shaped, while colonies, such as *A. selago* (fact page 363) and *A. formosa* (to the right and fact page 354), grow in arborescent form. In other words, an individual colony can exhibit very different growth forms and can therefore occupy different water volumes. However, this volume is always well defined and gradually increases by rapid growth.

The most commonly em-ployed way of measuring growth is by weighing a colony at certain intervals, but as colonies grow attached to decorations, this is not always practical in a private reef tank. Measuring occupied water volume might therefore be a better alternative. One should, however, be aware that two colonies having the same mass (weighing the same) can occupy very different volumes (see drawing below). It must also be noted that the growth diagrams only show the occupied water volume on specific days and that the intervals between the days on which the volumes were measured vary.

We believe that, so far, our tests show that several species of Acroporidae can exhibit very good growth and can thrive in an aquarium if this is run correctly.

The table on page 325, measured and estimated the growth of five colonies of *Acropora*. The numbers refer to our catalogue numbers. Colony "80" and "64" are the same species, but grow in different light intensities. Colony "80" in app. 8000 lux and colony "64" in app. 16000 lux with an average daily light period of about 13 hours. Colonies "51" and "64" are shown in the photo-series below and the increasing in "occupied water volume" for colony "64" is also shown in the diagram below.

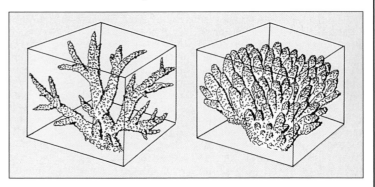

Examples of two *Acropora* sp. with about the same "occupied volume", but with very different mass.

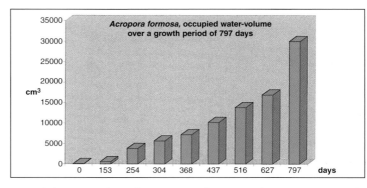

Occupied water volume for *Acropora formosa* (colony "64") grown in strong illumination near the surface.

Growth of five colonies of *Acropora* in our aquarium

Identification	A. microphthalma (#51)		A. cytherea (#61)		A. formosa (#80)		A. latistella (#89A)		A. formosa (#64)	
Growth Form	arborescent		tabular		arborescent		corymbose plate		arborescent	
Growth Period days	339		1302		345		967		304	
months	11,3		43,4		11,5		32,2		10,1	
Measures Day 0										
Length (cm)	9		8		6		7,6		8	
Width (cm)	3		4		4		7,6		2	
Height (cm)	2		2,5		5,5		11		6	
Square (cm²)	27		32		24		58		16	
Volume (cm³)	54		80		132		635		96	
Mesuares Last day										
Length (cm)	10		23		10,5		30		18	
Width (cm)	10,4		12,8		13,5		45		2	
Height (cm)	6,5		10		11		23		17,5	
Square (cm²)	104		194,4		142		1350		324	
Volume (cm³)	676		2944		1427		31050		5670	
Growth %	Total	Average Growth per month	Total	Average Growth per month	Total	Average Growth per month	Total	Average Growth per month	Total	Average Growth per month
Length (cm)	11	1	188	4,3	75	6,5	295	9,2	125	12,4
Width (cm)	247	22,3	220	5,1	238	20,7	492	15,3	800	78,4
Height (cm)	225	19,9	300	6,9	100	8,7	109	3,4	192	19,2
Square (cm²)	285	25,2	820	18,9	492	42,8	2227	69,1	1925	190,6
Volume (cm³)	1152	101,9	3580	82,5	1081	94	4790	148,8	5806	563

Series of growth pictures showing *Acropora microphthalma* (colony "51") and *Acropora formosa* (colony "64") at two different times: 24 November 1991 and 8 January 1993.

Series of growth pictures showing *Acropora formosa* (colony "80"; 8000 lux) at three different times: 24 November 1991, 22 January 1992 and 30 June 1992.

Pocillopora damicornis

Distribution: Distributed in the Indo-Pacific, from the African east coast to the Central American west coast, north to Japan and Hawaii, south to Durban, to Lord Howe Island and to Easter Island. It occupies a variety of habitats, from outer exposed reef flats to protected lagoons and mangrove areas. Although this species is most common on shallow to moderate depths, it has been trawled from 38 metres depth outside Townsville, Australia and also recorded from 42 metres depth (VERON & PICHON, 1976).

Size: Small to medium-sized colonies normally imported. Can rapidly grow into large colonies.

Food: Lives primarily from the products of the zooxanthellae; does not require extra feeding in aquaria if provided with high light intensity.

Description: Branching, but verrucae and branches integrate. Forms four main intergrading ecomorphs (see illustration on page 318); Short description of the ecomorphs based on VERON & PICHON, (1976). ① P. damicornis ecomorph brevicornis from exposed biotopes where colonies may be so stunted that outer branches are reduced to simple ridges a few millimetres high and the main branches are set close together and are as thick or thicker than they are high. ② P. damicornis from semi-protected biotopes, the form that occurs in most reefs which are not exposed to fully wave action and covers a wide range of growth forms. The outermost branches are usually 2-4mm in diameter, of irregular length and do not form distinct heads to main branches as occurs in P. verrucosa. ③ P. damicornis ecomorph bulbosa from turbid deep or very protected water that differs from the above ecomorphs by having thinner, elongated branches. ④ P. damicornis from temperate biotopes often have long thick branches which divide relatively frequently. thick and compact in zones with strong waves, delicate in deeper or protected areas. Colouring can be brown, green, or pink. The most studied of all corals.

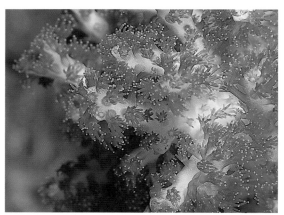

Photos:
Top: Colony in the aquarium owned by D. Stüber, Berlin.
Centre: Close-up photo of branches
Bottom: Typical growth forms in shallow water near a reef flat, shown here near Green Island, Australia.

Pocillopora damicornis

Aquarium maintenance:

- **General conditions:** Not a very sensitive species; often found in trade. Can grow into thick populations in aquaria. Filamentous algae must be kept under control because, left unchecked, they will lodge in the delicate branches and overrun the colony. Caution must be taken with strong carbon filtration because bleaching can appear very quickly.
- **Lighting:** High light intensity.
- **Water circulation:** Weak, medium or strong.
- **Reproduction:** Extraordinarily good and simple. Reports are available from reef aquaria regarding spawning, production of asexual planula larvae and polyp bail-out.

GA: + ; TO: + ; SE: +

Photos:

Growth of a colony in an aquarium.
- Top: June 30, 1992;
- Centre: September 1, 1993;
- Bottom: January 1, 1994.
We collected this colony from a reef flat of the Suva Reef near the Fiji Islands. After a short time in the aquarium, it changed its colouring and growth form dramatically.

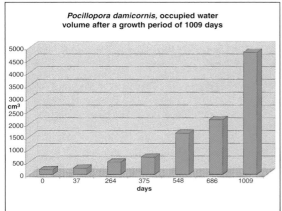

Pocillopora damicornis, occupied water volume after a growth period of 1009 days

(cm³ vs. days; values at 0, 37, 264, 375, 548, 686, 1009 days)

Pocillopora verrucosa
Warty bush coral

Distribution: Indo-Pacific; from east Africa to Hawaii. Most common in exposed areas such as outer reef fronts, more uncommon elsewhere.

Size: Usually, medium-sized colonies.

Food: Lives primarily from the products of the zooxanthellae and does not therefore require extra feeding.

Description: Grows in branching colonies with numerous thick, upright branches with verrucae easily visible in this species. The branches are clearly distinct from the verrucae. The minimum diameter of all main branches within a single colony varies less than approximately twice the diameter of the smallest branch (VERON & PICHON, 1976). Colouring can be green, brown, or purple.

Aquarium maintenance:

- **General:** Easy to care for; however, requires very good water quality. Sensitive to filamentous algae. It is not easy to keep the fluorescent colours often found in colonies collected in shallow waters intact. Without very strong light intensity with natural UV, the colour changes from purple or green to brown.
- **Lighting:** High to moderate light intensity.
- **Water circulation:** Weak, medium or strong.
- **Reproduction:** Little is known of the potential for sexual reproduction in aquaria, but this species is easily fragmented.

GA: + ; **TO:** + ; **SE:** +/-

Photos:
- Top: Colony of *Pocillopora verrucosa* with strong pigmentation in the shallow and protected habitat of a reef flat near Indonesia   Photo: J. Olsen
- Centre: Close-up photo of a *Pocillopora verrucosa* in the Red Sea   Photo: Dr. N. Chadwick-Furman
- Bottom: Close-up photo of a dark orange colony near the Fiji Islands (photo: Scott W. Michael). In both photos, the many verrucae for which this species is named, are easily visible.

Genus *Seriatopora*

The genus *Seriatopora* contains around five species, at least one of which has proven to be very durable in reef aquaria. All species are characterized by polyps that are arranged in longitudinal series clear rows along the branches. This separates the genus *Seriatopora* from the other genera in the family. The species of *Seriatopora* also exhibit variations in growth depending on the habitat they occupy, and form ecomorphs and growth forms similar to those of *Pocillopora damicornis* (see page 318). "Polyp bail-out" (see chapter 2, page 61) has been observed in *Seriatopora* spp. on several occasions.

In the *Seriatopora* species, we come across one of the oddest animal associations found among stony corals - the small gall-forming crab *Hapalocarcinus marsupialis*, which is also known to live associated with *Pocillopora* spp. and *Stylophora pistillata*. The juvenile female gall crab settles on a

Pocillopora elegans, photographed in the Galapagos Islands.

Photo: Dr. D. Brockmann

coral branch and this leads to the body tissue of the coral growing around the crab which is, thus, imprisoned for life (see page 313). We do not know if this type of living arrangement can be obser-

ved in aquaria, but even if this particular relationship does not occur in captivity, we believe that coral reef aquaria are especially suitable for the closer study of the biology of coral associations. In

In this strongly pigmented colony of *Seriatopora hystrix*, we can easily see how the polyps are arranged in the straight rows which are typical for the genus. This photo was taken at about 15 metres depth at Bunaken, Indonesia on a reef that was protected from heavy wave action.

Seriatopora hystrix
Thorny bush coral

Distribution: Indo-Pacific; from east Africa and the Red Sea, east to Samoa and the Phoenix Islands, north to the Ryukyu Islands, and south to Lord Howe Island.
Size: Small to middle-large colonies.
Food: Depends on the habitat; can live from the products of the zooxanthellae, but also from dissolved organic compounds and small planktonic organisms.
Description: Colonies are composed of masses of anastomosing branches of very variable shape, size and appearance. Usually the branches taper to a point. Forms several growth forms. According to VERON & PICHON, (1976) the growth forms of this species varies enormously according to the many micro-environments in which it grows. In deeper zones, with less light or in turbid water thin branches that divide infrequently develop. In exposed habitats, the colonies become very compact, being composed of masses of frequently dividing, anastomosing branches. In semi-protected biotopes - biotopes protected from strong wave action, but exposed to a current and light of different strength - the variation in growth may be extraordinary high. The colouring is normally white-yellow, occasionally pink. The polyps are lined up in straight rows. Gall crabs can cause atypical branch structures (see page 313).

Photos:
Left: Growth of a colony in an aquarium
- Top: August 26, 1992;
- Centre: October 20, 1993;
- Bottom: May 1, 1994.

Aquarium maintenance:

- **General:** Very well suited for the aquarium, although it must be carefully handled because the branches are very thin and delicate. Very sensitive to filamentous algae which easily infiltrate the thin branches. Excellent species for studying coral associations.
- **Lighting:** Strong to medium light intensity, depending on the ecomorph; colonies with thicker branches can also, based on their growth in shallow water, be illuminated somewhat more strongly. Nevertheless, caution must be taken that the lighting does not become too strong; our experience is that the delicate tissue is then easily damaged.
- **Water circulation:** Medium.
- **Reproduction:** Spawning should be possible in aquaria. Polyp bail-out is known in Nature. This species is very easily fragmented.

GA: + ; TO: + ; SE: +/-

Photos:

Top: Colony in the shallow water of a reef flat near Indonesia. Photo: J. Olsen

Centre: Pink-coloured colony on a reef flat on the Great Barrier Reef. Photo: E. Lovell

Bottom left: Colony with thick branches in an aquarium owned by D. Stüber, Berlin, Germany.

Bottom right: Colony with thick branches near Papua-New Guinea. Photo: Scott W. Michael

Stylophora pistillata

Distribution: Very widespread in the Indo-Pacific: from east Africa and the Red Sea, to the Tuamotu and Pitcairn Islands, around Australia; from Houtman Abrolhos Island to the Great Barrier Reef and south to Lord Howe Island and north to Japan. The species is spread by larvae which can attach themselves to floating objects, where they can grow into small colonies which might even produce new larvae as they are carried over the oceans.

Size: Medium-sized colonies.

Food: Lives primarily from the products of the zooxanthellae; does not require extra feeding in aquaria if kept under high light intensity.

Description: Forms a wide range of growth forms. Branched growing colonies with blunt-ended branches becoming thick and submassive. The corallites are immersed, conical or hooded. The colony surface appears smooth. Colouring is often yellow, white, pink, red and, rarely, green fluorescent. S. pistillata is often found on exposed places of the reef front and reef edge where strong water movement takes place.

Aquarium maintenance:
- **General:** Easily kept and grows very well if given general good conditions. Often contains associated animals, such as coral crabs from the family Xanthidae.
- **Lighting:** Very high light intensity.
- **Water circulation:** Strong to medium recommended.
- **Reproduction:** Hermaphrodites. Therefore, spawning in aquaria should be possible. Can easily be propagated from fragments.

GA: + ; TO: + ; SE: +/-

Photos:
Top: Close-up of the branches of a colony kept for years in a reef aquarium. Note the coral crab from the family Xanthidae.
Centre: Night photo of a light-red colony near Papua-New Guinea　　　　　　　Photo: Scott W. Michael
Bottom: Close-up of the polyps

Madracis kirbyi is rarely seen in the trade. On the left is a colony in an aquarium at Aqua Design, Oldenburg, Germany, and on the right, the polyps in close-up.

addition to the gall crab, there are many other crabs associated with *Seriatopora* spp (see photo page 312).

The best known species, *Seriatopora hystrix*, has striking, thorn-topped branches which are coloured yellow-white or pink. This species is, in our opinion, one of the most attractive stony corals. It thrives in a coral reef aquarium, although the thin branches are easily broken and must be handled with utmost care. *S. hystrix* is, however, extremely polymorphic forming a number of growth forms and VERON & PICHON (1976) illustrate at least 19 different colony-shapes. These growth-forms are often formed by the differences in the micro-habitats where the colonies grow. During the taxonomic history the different growth forms of *S. hystrix* have many times been described as separate species. See fact page 330 for more information.

Seriatopora caliendrum is found from east Africa and the Red Sea, east to the Coral Sea and New Caledonia. Its growth form is similar to that of *S. hystrix*, although *S. caliendrum* has stubby branch tips. but the branches are thicker than those of *S. hystrix* from the same biotope. The diameter of all sub-branches within the same colony is relatively constant and the average angle of branching is approximately 60-80 °. The ends of the branches are blunt, rarely bulbous and do not

taper (VERON & PICHON, 1976). Although the species is widely distributed in the Indo-Pacific it is relatively rare. In addition, it is relatively rare in Nature. The colouring is normally brown to yellow-green.

A further species from the Red Sea and the Gulf of Suez is *Seriatopora octoptera*. It has eight to ten wing-shaped outgrowths on the tips of the branches.

Genus *Stylophora*

The genus *Stylophora* contains at least five species. By far the most common is *S. pistillata*, which is, as Professor Veron puts it: "one of the tramp species of the coral world". Larvae of these corals can attach themselves to floating pumice or even to wood and are, in this way, carried across the oceans (VERON, 1986). This results in a very wide distribution stretching from the Red Sea, south to South Africa, across the Indian Ocean and central Indo-Pacific, around western, northern and eastern Australia and into the Pacific, north to southern Japan and as far east as the Pitcairn and Tuamotu Islands. During the taxonomic history there is a long list of synonyms for this species which reflects the many growth forms of the species.

S. pistillata is one of the hardiest of all stony corals. It can grow on mangrove roots, flooded tree stumps and the shallowest

places on the reef, in clear, nutrient-poor water, as well as in relatively nutrient-rich places. Its colours vary from white to yellow, pink and red, all the way to fluorescent green. This species is, in general, easy to keep in a reef aquarium, as long as the set-up fulfils the general conditions required for stony corals (see fact page 332).

Genus *Palauastrea*

The genus *Palauastrea* is monotypic and its single species, *P. ramosa*, is found in the central Indo-Pacific, from the Andaman Islands in the west, north to the Ryukyu Islands, as well as east to the Great Barrier Reef where it occurs down to depth of about 10 metres.

Palauastrea ramosa resembles *Porites cylindrica*, but the corallites appear star-like are arranged in star-shaped branches. In fact, the genus was discovered from the Great Barrier Reef by Professor Veron when he took a closer look at what was believed to be *Porites cylindrica* growing on a sandy substrate. In the ocean, this species is often found in muddy water or on sandy ground. We do not know if *Palauastrea ramosa* has ever been imported.

Genus *Madracis*

The genus *Madracis* contains only four hermatypic species, but many ahermatypic ones found in tropical and sub-tropical oceans,

Madracis decactis: colony in an aquarium (left) and close-up of the polyps (right)   Photos: J. Yaiullo

most of which are deep-water corals. In general, the species form ramose, encrusting or sub-massive, plocoid or plococerioid colonies, knobby or branching colonies with club-shaped branches. The polyps have rings of tiny tentacles which are partially, or even completely, expanded during the day. In the central Indo-Pacific, the only hermatypic species is *Madracis kirbyi*, which is relatively rare. This species generally forms encrusting colonies. In comparison, hermatypic species of the genus can be found abundantly in the Western Atlantic, where *Madracis decactis* has the widest range. It can be found throughout the Caribbean Ocean and normally grows in massive or encrusting forms, but can sometimes develop rounded colonies which can resemble the shape of some *Porites* species. *Madracis decactis* appears mostly in lagoons behind the reef flats, or in deeper reef areas. In shallow water, it is most frequently found in spots that are shaded from the strongest sunlight.

Madracis mirabilis can build colonies with a diameter of several metres and thick branches. Living polyps are usually only found a few centimetres along the outermost sections of the branches. The colours vary from pale cream-yellow to robust yellow. Normally, this species grows in depths of more than ten metres, although it can also be sporadically found in shallow water.

Madracis pharensis has two very different growth forms. Either it grows in an encrusted form in deep water and open areas, or it builds small columns or ball-shaped colonies. The latter only appear where they have been established in weakly lit areas. The colouring is usually red.

Madracis formosa is rare and grows in depths of over 35 metres. At these depths, it grows into large, clump-shaped colonies with a diameter of over one metre.

Madracis species appear to do well in reef aquaria, although they do not grow particularly quickly.

Madracis mirabilis in its natural environment in the U.S. Virgin Islands
Photo: Scott W. Michael

"The successful staghorns": *Acropora* species and their relatives can occupy large areas in a short time. No other group of stony corals can grow with such rapidity. Their success is total. As a result, we can find, on some reef flats - as here in the Great Barrier Reef at low tide - a most stupendous growth of *Acropora* showing the genus' full range of shapes and colours. Great care must be taken when walking in such a "coral garden".

Photo: Prof. J. E. N. Veron

Family Acroporidae

The Acroporidae constitutes the most species-rich family of stony corals. The majority of species are found in the genus *Acropora*, which represents the "essence" of stony corals, and the "symbol" for reef-building corals. In addition, the family also contains the genera *Montipora*, *Anacropora* and *Astreopora*. This family contains all growth forms known for hermatypic stony corals. Many of the species are characterized by their rapid growth and can colonize new areas within a short period of time. They are therefore usually victorious in the fight for living space on the reef. In the seventies, early and mid-eighties, the general opinion was that it was not possible to keep *Acropora* and other species of Acroporidae in aquaria. This is by no means true. On the contrary, many of the species in the Acro-

poridae belong to the toughest and easiest-to-keep corals and most can be very easily cultivated and grown from tiny fragments.

Growth and development in aquaria

The fast-growing corals of the family Acroporidae have provided us with new perspectives on coral reef aquatics and, today, it is possible to imitate small living reefs in our aquaria. From a few small fragments of *Acropora*, one can, within a couple of years, grow a beautiful crop. Therefore, instead of such corals being problematic to cultivate, the opposite is true, with excessive growth becoming more of a problem as the colonies grow too large and fight with other corals for the available space. The result is that the aquarist has to harvest fragments and cut the colonies to size in order to create space.

During 1990/91, we began to remodel our test aquarium which, until then, had been predominantly stocked with soft corals.

The intention was to create an aquarium to house fast-growing stony corals, mainly from the family Acroporidae. The picture on page 307 and the series of pictures on page 336 show how the growth of various branching stony corals and other corals developed during a period of two years (from the beginning of 1992 to New Year 1993/94). At the beginning of 1994, the colonies had grown so much that the population had to be cut back and new fragments had to be planted. In this way, the various species were, at the same time, distributed to other aquarists, as well as to other spots in our test aquarium.

There is no longer any doubt that our attempt to create an aquarium system for stony corals, especially those from the family Acroporidae, was a success. The general development of technical equipment available to aquarists, in combination with both an increasing knowledge of the biology of corals and the tremendous amount of effort applied to

The Growth of *Acropora* and other Stony Corals in Aquaria

Top photo: Our experimental aquarium on September 1, 1993 (for March 1993, see page 307): The *Platygyra* sp., right of the blue giant clam, is still thriving, the colony of *Acropora selago* to its right (a colony collected at Suva Reef in the Fiji Islands) is growing quickly and is beginning to shade the brain coral. On the left edge of the photograph is a *Montipora* sp., which also originated from the Fiji Islands. The yellow colony in the centre of the photo is a *Porites* sp. collected in the Maldives. Two ecomorphs of *Pocillopora damicornis* have established themselves well in the foreground and are both growing rapidly. The thin-branched form originates from D. Stüber in Berlin, Germany, while the thick-branched form was collected in Fiji in 1991.

Centre photo: 4 months later, on January 1, 1994: All corals have grown well and have started to touch each other. The beautiful *Platygyra* sp. is showing the first signs of degeneration from being shaded by *Acropora selago* and from the table-shaped *A. latistella* growing very rapidly (back right). Note that the "Stüber" *Acropora* (*A. formosa* ?) at centre left has been fragmented. Behind this coral, is another *Acropora* from the Fiji Islands, which has developed beautifully from a tiny fragment. In the lower right corner of the photo is another *A. selago* from Fiji, growing on the bottom of the aquarium. The big, beautiful brain coral to the left is *Montastrea* sp., possibly *M. curta*.

Bottom photo: approximately 5 months later, on May 25, 1994: The branching *Acropora* spp. have overgrown the area and demonstrate their ability to compete for space. Several fragments need to be cut in order to make space for the other corals. The *Platygyra* sp., is clearly dying off and the yellow *Porites* from the Maldives is struggling for its existence. The fight for living space (space competition) is in full force.

the hobby by thousands of hobbyists all over the world, has resulted in the fact that, in today's closed aquarium systems, we are not only capable of keeping and growing corals, but perhaps even propagating them. In the same vein, there is also no doubt that stony corals can be effectively maintained in relatively small aquarium systems; nowadays, an aquarium does not have to contain thousands of litres of water to maintain stony corals, including the formerly "impossible" *Acropora* spp.

Identification of species, however, remains a problem. It would, obviously, be desirable to know exactly which species grow best under aquarium conditions, but the systematics of the family Acroporidae are so complex and difficult that, in many cases, it is very hard, if not impossible, for an amateur to identify corals down to species level. In addition comes the fact that the corallite and colony-shapes that develop from growth in a closed aquarium differ a lot from those found in the nature, factors that further complicate the identification of our *Acropora* species in aquarium.

With the increased success in growing stony corals in captivity, reef research has acquired an entirely new dimension and new possibilities in that it is now feasible to use aquaria as observation laboratories to study the biology of these creatures. There is therefore no reason why we could not, for example, set up aquaria with populations of only a few species of corals being grown under different lighting and/or water current conditions, or why we could not study how fluctuations in different natural seawater elements influence coral growth. In addition, there is no doubt that the possibility exists for us to study sexual reproduction of corals in aquaria (see chapter 2).

Today, stony corals are actually being grown and artificially propagated through fragmentation for commercial and scientific purposes. Facilities such as the Monaco Aquarium (Monaco) and the Waikiki Aquarium (Honolulu, Ha-

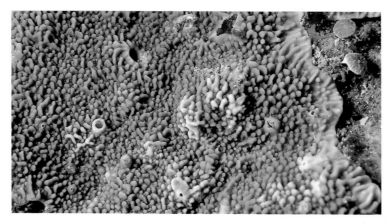

The surface of *Montipora* species is often covered with "papillae" and/or "tuberculae", which can be seen here as small "hills" in between the tiny red polyps.

waii), both grow fragments for scientific purposes while "Tropicorium Inc." situated in Romulus, outside of Detroit, Michigan, produce juvenile colonies for commercial purposes. Indeed, this aspect of the aquarium industry is increasing quite rapidly; only a few years ago, though, this was utopia. As we begin to benefit from coral farming, it is our hope and prophesy that, in the future, most of the corals kept in captivity will come from farms, rather than from natural reefs. See chapter 2 for further treatment of this subject.

Genus *Montipora*

The genus *Montipora* contains a huge number of species, so it seems almost hopeless to try and achieve an overview here. VERON (1986, 1995) estimates, at least, 80 species world-wide and about 38 from Australia alone. The same author lists 57 species from the central Indo-Pacific (VERON, 1993) and VERON & HODGSON (1989) list many more species from the Philippines. VERON & WALLACE (1984) give an excellent overview of the taxonomic history of the genus and deal with all the described species known from Eastern Australia.

The genus is distributed throughout the entire Indo-Pacific and must be regarded as extremely common. Although *Montipora* is the second most species-rich genus of all the stony coral genera, it is, nevertheless, little studied.

One problem relating to species identification in *Montipora* is, again, polymorphism. Colonies belonging to one and the same species can appear very different, depending on the area in which they grow. Most species of *Montipora* develop encrusting or plate-like colonies, but a few species, such as *Montipora digitata*, grow into branching forms. At first sight, *Montipora* can look like *Porites* (see page 378), but it is easy to separate the two genera if one examines the corallites; those of *Montipora* are mostly empty, with the septa consisting of rows of inwardly projecting spines, while *Porites* species possess corallites that are filled with septa and associated structures. In addition, all species of *Montipora* have tiny polyps and the structure of the coenosteum (unlike in other stony coral genera) differs among the species, a factor which is important for species identification in this genus. Some species develop ornaments from the coenosteum; these are known as "tuberculae" (if they are larger than the corallites) or "papillae" (if they are smaller). Different species of *Montipora* have different combinations of these structures (VERON, 1986).

Montipora spp.

Distribution: Widely distributed in the Indo-Pacific, from the Red Sea and East Africa, as far south as northern South-Africa, east to Hawaii and Marquesas Island, north to southern Japan and south to Pitcairn and Lord Howe Island.

Size: Normally small to medium-sized colonies; only a few species can grow into large colonies.

Food: In shallow water areas, mainly, the products of the zooxanthellae. Extra feeding in aquaria is not necessary.

Description: The second largest genus in terms of species, but the number of valid species is not known and *Montipora* is, in general, little studied. Normally, the colonies grow slowly and in an encrusting manner, but branched, laminar, foliaceous and submassive colonies also occur. Lack axial corallites. Difficult to identify the individual species; the structure of the coenosteum, and combination of structures associated with the coenosteum, are important characters for species identification, but characters that can only be used by specialists. The corallites and the polyps, which, in some species, are found in between numerous papillae and tuberculae formed from the coenosteum, are very small, between 0.5 and 1.0 mm in diameter. The corallites are "open" and do not contain dominant septa and associated structures; the septa consist only of vertical rows of inward-projecting spines. Colony colouring is brown, green, or yellow, sometimes purple. *Montipora* spp. can sometimes be confused with *Porites* spp., but can be separated from this genus by the structure of the corallites. In *Montipora* the corallites are almost "empty" while in *Porites* the corallites are filled with septa and associated structures.

Photos:

Top: On *Montipora venosa*, the *papillae* and *tuberculae* are absent.

Centre and bottom: This *Montipora* sp., "KA4-MON-01", shows different growth forms in the same habitat, photographed near Bunaken, Indonesia.

Montipora spp.

Aquarium maintenance:
- **General:** Easy to keep. Encrusting colonies common in the trade, as well as the branching *M. digitata*, which is, possibly, the most common *Montipora* kept in aquaria.
- **Lighting:** Medium to high.
- **Water circulation:** Weak, medium or strong, depending on the colonies' natural habitat.
- **Reproduction:** Easy to propagate from fragments. There are no reports of spawning in aquaria; it could be possible, though.

GA: + ; TO: + ; SE: +

Photos:
Top right: Delicate *Montipora* sp., "KA4-MON-03", with tiny polyps near Rangiroa, Polynesia   Photo: Scott W. Michael
Centre right: Several years old *Montipora* sp., "KA4-MON-04", in the Waikiki Aquarium, Hawaii.
Bottom right: *Montipora* sp. (*M. spongodes* or *M. mollis*). This colony doubled its volume in May 1992.
Bottom left: *Montipora* sp., "KA4-MON-02", near the Hawaii Islands   Photo: Dr. D. Brockmann

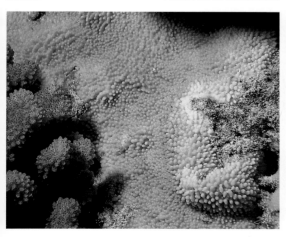

Montipora digitata is one of the few branching species in the genus.

Photo: Scott W. Michael

Right: At extreme low tide on Wheeler Reef, GBR, the corals are exposed to the open air for a few hours. This is a "field of dreams" for biologists and aquarists.   Photo: T. Done

Genus *Anacropora*

The genus *Anacropora* is closely related to *Montipora*. The colonies are branched, although they lack axial corallites (in contrast to *Acropora*, where axial corallites are typical) and branch growth thus grow from undifferentiated coenosteum in which corallites later develop. This is a fundamental difference between *Anacropora* and *Acropora*. While *Acropora* have specialised corallites for budding, such corallites lack in *Anacropora* which consequently lack the highly deterministic growth strategies, and shows mainly one single type of growth form (VERON & WALLACE, 1984). When competing for space on the reef, *Anacropora* always loses out to the faster-growing *Acropora* species. *Anacropora* is most often found in muddy habitats, or in areas with polluted water where many other corals cannot grow. It is seldom found among growth of *Acropora*, but can occur on fringing reefs where the water is moderately turbid.

Bruce Carlson, the director of the Waikiki Aquarium, reports of a colony of *Montipora digitata* - a species that can be very common in some locations - which, in the course of two years, took over a quarter of a show aquarium. We have seen this species on shallow reef flats, where the water was crystal clear, as well as in muddy areas of inshore reefs. *M. digitata* also seems to be very common in the trade and is easily kept. Do,

however, note that this coral sometimes carries a predatory nudibranch that feeds on the body tissue of the coral (see page 314). Even other *Montipora* spp. like *M. monasteriata* (?), which we brought back from the Fiji Islands, grew well in our aquarium. Therefore, in general, *Montipora* species can be counted among the easy-to-care-for stony corals (see fact pages 338 and 339).

The genus contains six species, of which *Anacropora forbesi* has the widest distribution. It is found from the Seychelles in the west, to the Marshall and Fiji Islands in the east. Although it is the most common species of its genus, *A. forbesi* must, in general, be regarded as rare. *A. puertogalerae* is even rarer and has compact branches, which are somewhat thicker than those of *A. forbesi*, while *A. reticulata*, which is even rarer still, possesses wide spaces between the tapering, blunt-tipped branches. *A. matthai*, on the other hand, has thin, but not pointed, branches. We saw *Anacropora* at the Waikiki Aquarium in Hawaii, where it grew beautifully outdoors in a basin in direct sunlight and with constant running water. This genus is rare in the trade, but should, in general, be easy to keep.

Anacropora forbesi   Photo: Dr. B. Carlson, Waikiki Aquarium

Genus *Acropora*

WELLS (1955) described a particular group of corals in the following way: "The protean scleractinian genus, with bewildering speciation, and reef-former par excellence." This is a very good characterization of the most species-rich genus of the stony corals - *Acropora*, which is found on all coral reefs and is by far the most important genus of living Scleractinia and also the genus with the highest number of living species.

Almost every shallow reef area of the Indo-Pacific is dominated by *Acropora* species, which occur in large populations. Why are *Acropora* spp. so successful? The answer is probably based on three morphological characteristics: 1) small corallites that can build fine, detailed structures in the skeleton, 2) division of the roles of axial and radial corallites that makes it possible for highly deterministic growth forms to develop, and 3) a porous skeletal micro-structure that gives maximum strength for weight (VERON, 1995). In addition, many species contain UV-absorbing substances, which protects them against strong ultra-violet radiation. This allows *Acropora* species to grow in the most shallow areas of the reef where only a few other species can survive (DUNLAP & CHALKER, 1986). The UV-absorbing pigments are visible as the typical purple or pink colouration that makes many *Acropora* species some of the most colourful of corals.

The number of species in the genus is not known. VERON (1986, 1995) named 73 species just for east Australia alone, and at least 150 world-wide. *Acropora* spp. can be divided into specific growth-forms as shown in the figure on page 344. On the reef edge, for instance, large table or plate-shaped colonies can be found, such as those of *A. cytherea* and *A. hyacinthus*, which contain hundreds of thousands of individual polyps in each colony. They offer entire schools of fish hiding places and house many other asso-

The individual animals, the polyps, live in the corallites. In *Acropora* spp., there are two types of corallites: those on the end of the branches, running down the centre of a branch and which are purple-coloured in the photo, are called "axial corallites", while those on the side of the branches are called "radial corallites". Note how a new ring of radial corallites bud off from the axial corallite near the top of the branch.

In most cases it is not possible to identify *Acropora* spp. and other stony corals from their colouring alone. This *Acropora*, possibly *A. humilis*, has developed two different colours in one and the same colony.
Photo: E. Enzmann

ciated animals, such as tiny crabs and shrimps. Branched colonies, like those of the very common *A. formosa*, can stretch hundreds of metres across the reef, while some finger-shaped colonies, such as those of *A. humilis* and *A. valida*, survive in the surf of the reef edge or grow in the quieter water of the lagoon. On the outermost reef flat, we can find a beautiful variety of species.

The colonies found on the reef edge and on the reef flat can sometimes dry out during low tide when they are exposed to open air and burning UV-radiation for hours, conditions that are obviously stressful to corals. However, such is the almost unending variability of the genus, that we find species even in these harsh environments.

To get into species identifications, or a detailed description of the *Acropora* species would overstep the boundaries of this book. For readers who are especially interested in this genus, we would like, once more, to refer to VERON (1986). This author gives an excellent overview with sketches and colour photographs of the most common species from Australia and the Indo-Pacific. For a scientific reference to Acroporidae, please see VERON & WALLACE (1984).

Keeping *Acropora* species in aquaria was the dream of many aquarists in the seventies and early eighties. Most, however, regarded their upkeep impossible, as they did for the majority of other stony corals. The only *Acropora* most aquarists had experience of at that time was in the form of dead skeletons, which were commonly offered as aquarium decorations. A large number of *Acropora* species have, for decades, been "harvested" by the ton, dried in the sun, and their chalk-white skeletons - which look more like graveyard decorations - offered to the aquarium trade. Unfortunately, even today, we still see large (though lesser) amounts of such dead corals in trade. CITES regulations cover trade in all stony corals, living or

"Stüber's *Acropora*" (*A. formosa* ?) is probably the first *Acropora* species to be successfully kept in a closed reef aquarium. Fragments and tiny branches were generously given to numerous aquarists by Dietrich Stüber, Berlin, Germany, probably the first aquarist who grew stony corals successfully in a closed aquarium system. The pictures illustrate the growth of fragments of the "Stüber *Acropora*".

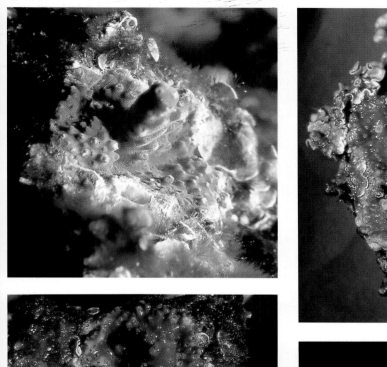

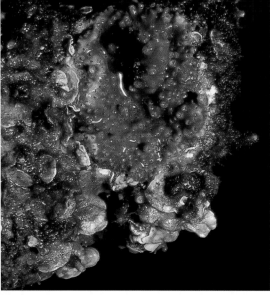

- Top left photo: The 2 cm long fragment is mounted on live rock on May 10, 1992, and has begun to grow an encrusting base.
- Bottom left photo: 50 days later (June 30), the fragment is still producing only encrusting growth.
- Top right photo: In this picture taken on November 1, 1992 (about 170 days after mounting the fragment), the colony has formed the first axial corallites and begins to develop about 15 branches from the encrusting base.
- Bottom right photo: After about ten months, on March 20, 1993, the colony shows clear branching and had grown to a size of 6 x 5 x 4 cm (length x width x height).

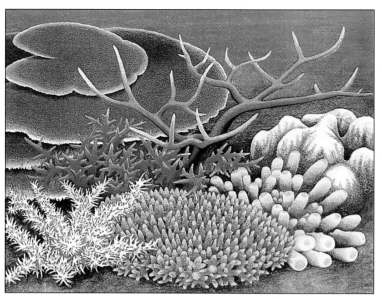

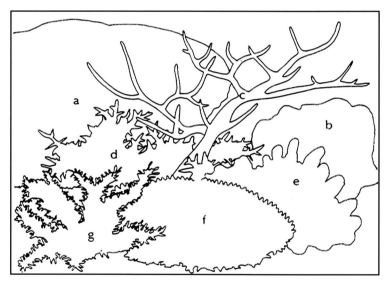

Acropora growth forms. a: tables and plates, b: massive, c: arborescent, d: caespitose, e: digitate, f: corymbose, g: bottlebrush. Drawings: G. Kelly

coral reef aquarium. At the same time, it was also a sign of the deep seriousness which many reef aquarists applied to their hobby and, in particular. how clever the marine aquarists of Berlin in the mid-eighties were; indeed, they have, up to the present time, continued to be leaders in the field of reef aquatics. Within the course of three years, Stüber's original colony grew to a height of 30 cm and from this colony, hundreds, if not thousands, of fragments have been distributed to other aquarists. The genes of this small polyp have therefore spread from an aquarium in a flat in Berlin, to thousands of homes all over the world. This is direct evidence that, today, we can practise our hobby without straining natural resources (see also STÜBER 1987, 1988, and 1990a). A fact page about the "Stüber *Acropora*" is presented on page 359, but do also see volume 1, page 178.

Nowadays, *Acropora* spp. are common in the trade. As time has passed, it has also become apparent that the majority of species are very easy to look after in a well maintained coral reef aquarium, where colonies can be propagated simply by breaking off tiny branches and mounting these loosely but securely, e.g. using dental wax, on pieces of live rock or on an artificial substratum.

Bruce Carlson from the Waikiki Aquarium uses a special epoxy glue, the American brand "Z-Spar Splash Zone Compound A-788™". Uwe Richter, director of the aquarium in Hagenbecks Tierpark, Hamburg, Germany, has had good results using the French brand "Devcon Epoxy 11808 UW™". Personally, we have used "Aquastick™" (see volume 1, page 121) with good results, but we find the material best to use with smaller fragments or small branches. Larger pieces need extra support. After a while, it can be observed how the coral tissue distributes itself on the chosen rock and, with this step, how a new colony takes up the fight for space in the aquarium. Given a

dead, but, for some strange reason, it almost appears, at least, in some cases, to be easier to obtain an import license if you kill the coral first (?!). Marine hobbyists are often blamed for the importation of live stony corals, but one may wonder what is worse: carefully collecting small living coral colonies for growing and propagating in captivity, or harvesting large, magnificent corals, which are killed, bleached and sometimes even artificially coloured, for decorative purposes only!

At the beginning of the 1980s, a small primary polyp appeared in an aquarium owned by marine aquarist Dietrich Stüber in Berlin, Germany. This was the first *Acropora* species which was successfully kept in an aquarium in Europe. This tiny polyp marked the birth of the era of the modern

little bit of patience, plus a bunch of *Acropora* fragments, it is no longer impossible to grow a miniature reef in captivity. The dream of yesterday has become today's reality!

Acropora species are not only fast-growing, they also secrete terpenes, which drive away other corals. Terpenes are organic compounds, which are built out of isoprene units (C_5H_8). When you smell an *Acropora* colony, you can clearly detect the terpene aroma. This is possibly why it can be difficult to achieve good soft coral growth in an aquarium in which *Acropora* and other stony corals predominate (for more on this, see STÜBER, 1989b).

Acropora species are numerous and, as many other stony corals, show considerable variability and a high degree of polymorphism. The different colonies vary within biotopes, and especially varying over environmental as well as geographic ranges which they occupy. In the Caribbean Ocean, only three species can be found and these are all easy to identify. Yet, in the Indo-Pacific, there are at least 150 different species and all - with few exceptions - are very difficult to identify. For those who would like to study the nomenclature of the groups more closely, we refer you to WALLACE (1978) and VERON & WALLACE (1984), both of whom have revised the genus. In the following lines, we would like to provide you with some principles to help you with species identification; these are, essentially, based on VERON (1986) and VERON & WALLACE (1984), and are valid for Indo-Pacific species. VERON & WALLACE (1984) divide the genus *Acropora* into 14 non-taxonomic species groups based on their shared characters. We use these groups as the basis for the treatment of the genus and would like to point out those features which are especially typical of these groups.

The type and placement of the corallites is an important characteristic and appears in two main forms: axial and radial. The axial polyps bud off radial corallites in

Acropora sp. on a reef flat near Madang, Papua-New Guinea.
Photo: Dr. D. Brockmann

a regular fashion during growth and become distributed around the branches of the colony. The structure of the coenosteum is also important for species identification in *Acropora*.

Finally, certain terms are used for the many colony forms found in species of the genus Acropora (see the drawing on page 344 - from VERON, 1986):

- **arborescent**: Colonies composed of tree-like branches;

- **bottle brush**: Colonies have short side branchlets;

- **caespitose**: Colonies grow "bushy", being composed of anastomosing branches (i.e. branches that ramify into a mesh-like pattern) inclined at varying angles;

- **corymbose**: Colonies have horizontal, anastomosing branches and short vertical branchlets;

- **digitate**: Colonies are composed of short, non-dividing, non-anastomosing branches like the fingers of a hand;

- **encrusting**: Colonies adhere to the substrate - most species have an encrusting base;

- **massive**: Colonies are similar in all dimensions;

- **pillow-like**: Colonies are composed of fine branches and grow in thick, pillow-like clumps;

- **prostrate**: Colonies sprawl over the substrate;

- **ridges and columns**: Colonies create ridges and columns without branches;

- **tables and plates**: Colonies are flat, either with one central leg, or attached to the substrate on one side.

As mentioned earlier environmental conditions can exert a very strong influence on the colony form of *Acropora* species. In starkly exposed places, for example, some colonies can develop thick branches, or grow as columns, while the same species can create a completely different colony form in quieter water. In aquaria, conditions are different from those found in Nature and we must therefore expect that, at least for some species, the colony form and/or the corallite structure, will change over time when compared to those typically found in wild colonies.

Mass Spawning of Stony Corals in Aquaria

Partial view of F. Jørgensen's aquarium (mid-1993)   **Photo: K. Nagy**

During the work on this volume, the first documented mass spawning of stony corals in a closed aquarium system occurred. This event took place on July 5, 1994, in an aquarium owned by Flemming Jørgensen of Stavern, Norway. The corals which were involved in the spawning were all placed in the aquarium and grown from small offshoots, the majority of which were taken from other aquarium colonies. The largest colony had been in the aquarium for about three years.

The spawning corals were two colonies of *Acropora* sp.: 17 x 20 x 9.5 cm and 14.5 x 12.5 x 10 cm; two colonies of *Acropora microphthalma*: 23.5 x 24 x 20 cm and 23 x 16.5 x 14 cm, originating from Fiji and introduced to Scandinavian aquarists from 2-3 tiny fragments from the Waikiki Aquarium; a colony of *Acropora* sp. ("Stüber's *Acropora*"): 36 x 25 x 24 cm, originally brought to Scandinavia from Dietrich Stüber's aquarium in Berlin in the late seventies; a colony of *Acropora formosa*: 34 x 28 x 25 cm, plus several smaller colonies which had been produced from fragments of

larger colonies; average occupied water volume: 5 x 5 x 5 cm (for the definition of occupied water volume, see page 324).

Spawning took place two days before the artificial full moon, with the first activities being observed at 7:15 a.m., although the process had probably already begun an hour earlier. At 2:00 p.m., spawning reached its peak; it ended at 5:30 p.m. (the pictures of page 347 were taken at 4:30 p.m.). The reproductive cells (gametes) were released from the corals as mucous egg-sperm bundles. The eggs were decidedly small; only one species from the family Faviidae released several larger, pink-coloured eggs. The actual spawning was so vigorous that the aquarium water became milky and the back pane (wall) disappeared from view. On the next day, as we examined water samples taken from the aquarium, we could still identify the gametes clearly.

At the same time as the above-named corals spawned, a 40 cm long *Tridacna squamosa* also began to spawn and this lasted for two further days. The huge mus-

sel had spawned before, although never prior to the installation of the artificial moonlight. On the day after the mass spawning of the corals, various snails of the genus *Turbo* also spawned, although they had spawned several times previously.

Except for the Redox potential, the measured water values were at normal aquarium levels. The Redox potential dropped during the spawning activities to 330 mV, but stabilized at normal values after several days. No corals or fish were damaged due to the spawning.

It can be concluded that the event was a truly synchronized spawning in a closed aquarium system. We feel that the artificial moonlight contributed to the release, but we would not like to state this as a firm assertion. It can, nevertheless, be stated with certainty, that stony corals, even when they have grown from fragments, can mature in an aquarium.

The eggs were, without doubt, very small and did not look normal, but the size of stony coral eggs varies greatly. We do not know for certain if the eggs were fertile or infertile, but we have reason to believe that they were not fully developed, although research to verify this could not be carried out. Further investigations in this area are still necessary.

Description of the aquarium

- Basic data: 630 l and 65 l in the reservoir; artificial seawater with HW-sea salt; established October 1991; 175 kg living rock as decoration material; minimal water change; 20,000 l/h water circulation, powered with automatically controlled interval, aquarium computer with pH and temperature control, Redox and density measurement.
- Filtration: External skimmer with 119 mm diameter; mechanical filtration through an internal power filter; activated charcoal (200 g) used irregularly, and only when necessary.
- Lighting: 3 x Osram HQI 250 W TS/D 12-14 hours daily); 1 x Philips 40 W TL 03 and 1 x Philips 40 W TL 05 (15 hours per day each); 1 x 15 W UV-Light. Artificial moonlight with a blue 15 watt incandescent lamp was installed in February 1994. It was set up as shown in the diagram on page 50, and was turned on from 12:30 a.m. to 9:00 a.m.
- Water additives: Calcareous limewater, which was produced from calcium oxide (110 g CaO per week) in a lime reactor (see volume 1, page 230) – the water in the lime reactor was osmosis-produced water; 10 ml Combi-San per week; 25 ml Sera Marinvit per week; 8 ml Strontium chloride per week (see volume 1, pages 235); 2 ml potassium iodide per week (see volume 1, page 237); several crystals of calcium chloride per month (see Volume 1, page 229).
- Water values: pH 8.2-8.45 (top reading of 8.45 is regulated by the addition of carbon dioxide); 7 °KH; 25-27.5 °C (latter value in summer); Redox potential 370-400 mV; density 1.022 at 25 °C.
- Animal occupants: approxima-

tely 60 stony coral colonies, a few soft corals, one *Tridacna squamosa*, 17 smaller fish, 15 to 20 brittle stars and three sea cucumbers as detritus feeders.

Another spawning took place in the 300-litre aquarium owned by Mr. Marko Haaga of Tampere, Finland, late on the evening of August 28, 1997. The species that spawned was a large *Acropora* sp. (possibly *A. latistella*) that was ori-

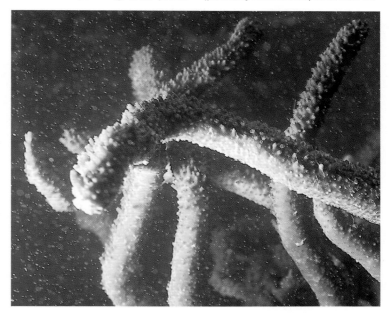

The spawning was so vigorous, that the aquarium water, because of the eggs seen in the photo as small white points, became milky.   Photo: T. Karlsen

In this close-up, it can be seen how the polyps discharge the mucous and probably not fully developed egg-sperm bundles. Some polyps, especially those of *Acropora* sp. ("Stüber's *Acropora*") and *A. formosa*, became white during spawning, but regained their normal colouring within several weeks.

Photo: T. Karlsen

ginally imported from Indonesia 28 months prior to the spawning. The colony had grown considerably in the aquarium and must have reached maturity during its time in captivity. Although the gametes were not viewed under a binocular microscope, it was pretty obvious that the colony had produced egg/sperm bundles.

The gametes were light brown in colour, nearly round and had a diameter of about 1 mm. The spawning occurred at a temperature of 26 °C, a few days after the temperature had reached its maximum of about 29 °C as a result of a very hot Finland summer. The spawning also occurred 10 days after the natural full moon and, as

the aquarium was facing windows to the south, it received both natural sunlight and moonlight. Other parameters in the aquarium during the spawning event were: pH: 8.2-8.5, KH: 5-7 °, Ca^{2+} : 350 mg/l, salinity: about 35 ‰, phosphate and nitrate: not detectable with aquarium test kits (NILSEN, 1998).

Acropora species are very successful in colonizing living space. From this, huge monospecific stands can grow, as shown here in *A. microphthalma* found in a shallow water reef near the Fiji Islands.

Photo: Dr. B. Carlson, Waikiki Aquarium, Honolulu, Hawaii

Acropora species of the Indo-Pacific

Acropora is the largest genus of scleractinian corals; it also has the largest number of the very common species on most Indo-Pacific reefs. However, the species are also highly polymorphic, establishing a large number of growth forms in the many biotopes and environments that they occupy. VERON & WALLACE (1984) list 364 nominal species of *Acro-*

pora, which illustrates that, historically, many of the growth forms have been described as valid species. Complex zoogeography and the high diversity of species in one and the same location, are other factors complicating the identification of *Acropora* species. The fact that many *Acropora* species form their own "aquarium growth forms" further complica-

tes the identification of *Acropora* grown in reef aquaria. As mentioned earlier, the genus *Acropora* was divided by VERON & WALLACE (1984) into 14 non-taxonomic groups, with each group usually containing species that resemble each other. In the following treatment of the most interesting species from an aquatic point of view, we follow this grouping. The description of colony shape and corallite structure, as well as information given on habitat preferences and species distribution, are mainly based on Veron & Wallace (1984). For those who want to study the Indo-Pacific species of *Acropora* in detail, we strongly advise them to study this monograph. A fifteenth group was established by Wallace (1994) and we also base our descriptions on this source, as well as on Wallace (1997) and Veron (1986).

Acropora (Isopora) palifera group

The species in this group differ clearly in their construction from the other species of the genus. The three species *Acropora palifera*, *A. cuneata* and *A. brueggmanni*, were grouped in the subgenus *Isopora*, while all other species were placed in the subgenus *Acropora*.

The colonies of the subgenus *Isopora* have thick, often flattened, branches and can build ridges and columns. They are distinguished by having more than one axial corallite per branch. Additionally, the branches show an atypical placement of the corallites, which gives them (the branches) a variable cross-section, depending on how the corallites are grouped. The coenosteum has a smooth and fine structure and bears uniformly distributed spinules with very elaborate tips.

Aropora palifera is widely distributed in the Indo-Pacific and appears in the majority of habitats, from lagoons with turbid water, to ocean reefs with crystal-clear water. Colonies occur as thick encrusting plates, or plates bearing domes, ridges or columns, or as thick cylindrical, irregular or plate-like branches. The branches may be horizontal or vertical and are sometimes irregulary anastomosed, i.e. they possess an irregular net-like pattern. The growth form varies depending, on the degree of exposure to wave impact. In starkly exposed places, *A. palifera* grows almost without branches and with flattened ends,

Acropora palifera in a shallow reef flat near Bunaken, Indonesia. Growing in the background are *Stylophora pistillata* and *Porites cylindrica*.

but in calm water, it can create large colonies with thick, branching and flattened ends. In eastern Australia, it is the most common reef builder of most outer slopes exposed to heavy wave action. We have not yet seen this species in aquaria.

While *A. palifera* belongs to the most common *Acropora* species, the similar species *A. cuneata* is nowhere near as common and, although it is distributed throughout the tropical Indo-Pacific, from Madagascar in the west, to the Marshall Islands in the east, it is seldom found in great abundance. Colonies are partly encrusting plates and ridges which develop varying combinations of free horizontal plates and upward-projecting, flattened branches or plates. Since it possesses finer plates that divide much

A large colony of *Acropora* sp. (*A. brueggemanni* ?), at Green Island, Great Barrier Reef

more frequently than those of *A. palifera*, it can usually be distinguished from this species; it also has a tendency to form horizontal plates.

A. brueggemanni forms colonies that are arborescent, with an irregular, weakly branching pattern. Its branches are thinner and more pointed than those of the two previous species. It occurs in shallow water, including exposed outer reef slopes and protected reef flats. This species is only found in the central Indo-Malayan region, the Philippines and the Great Barrier Reef.

Acropora humilis group

The members of the *Acropora humilis* group are species with limited branching, this giving them a sturdy, corymbose (raceme-like) growth form. They also possess radial corallites which are dimidiate (having only one side developed) or nearly so, and the coenosteum with a dense arrangement of fine spinules, but without elaborated tips (WALLACE, 1994). This group contains three closely related species: *A. humilis*, *A. gemmifera* and *A. monticulosa*. They all grow in the surf of the reef edge, where they can become dry during low tide. In addition, three relatively rare species also belong to this group: *A. samoensis*,

Acropora monticulosa
Photo: Prof. J. E. N. Veron/E. Lovell

A. digitifera, and *A. multiacuta*, as well as the recently described *A. pocilloporina* (WALLACE, 1994) from Society, Cook Islands, Rarotonga, Tuamotu Archipelago and the Pitcairn Islands.

Acropora humilis is one of the most common species in the Indo-Pacific. Its colonies have a typical corymbose growth form and, as with all species of this group, corallites are found in two sizes, with the axial corallites being hemispherical in shape and very large, attaining a diameter of

8 mm. In shallow reef plateau, or on the upper reef ridge, *A. humilis* can dominate. Together with *A. gemmifera* and *A. monticulosa*, *A. humilis* can create large colonies on ocean reefs in very nutrient-poor water and strong current. The colouring varies widely; it can be red, purple, beige, or brown. In general, *A. humilis* is a very polymorphic species and, especially in exposed biotopes, it can be difficult to distinguish between this species and *A. gemmifera* and *A. monticulosa*, all of which have similar growth forms. It is not known to us how this species behaves in aquaria, but considering its manner of living in starkly exposed places, and based on experiences with the closely related *A. gemmifera*, it is not certain if *A. humilis* can be counted among the easy-to-care-for corals.

Acropora gemmifera can be similar to *A. humilis*, especially in exposed biotopes, although it usually has somewhat thicker or more cone-shaped branches. This species also likes strongly exposed places and can dominate in such environments (see fact page 351).

A small colony of *Acropora gemmifera* in the aquarium owned by J. Olsen; the polyps are easily recognizable.

Acropora monticulosa is nowhere near as common as the previous species and is only distributed in the central Indo-Pacific. It may form large colonies on upper reef slopes. Colonies are

Acropora humilis on a reef flat in Indonesia

Colony on a protected reef flat

Large colonies on the edge of an exposed reef flat

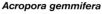

Acropora gemmifera
Pearled Staghorn Coral

Distribution: Indo-Pacific; from the Red Sea, to New Caledonia and the Fiji Islands. Commonly found on exposed upper reef slopes.

Growth form and size: Colonies are thick, laterally attached, corymbose plates, or are digitate with broad bases, or are groups of corymbose plates arranged in tiers. The branches are thick and tapering. The branches become shorter and thicker with increasing wave action, but otherwise, the species shows little variation in growth form (VERON & WALLACE, 1984). Normally creates small to mid-sized colonies, but can grow in large populations, together with other species of the *A. humilis* group.

Food: Feeds upon the translocated products of the zooxanthellae, but also captures plankton and probably utilizes dissolved organic compounds.

Description: (Based on VERON & WALLACE, 1984). The colonies grow in corymbose to digitate forms. Branches are thick and conical, with clear axial corallites, < 2mm exserted

and 2.8 - 4.2 mm in diameter, with calices 1.0-1.3 mm in diameter. Radial corallites can be found in two intermixed types. The first are immersed (i.e. embedded within the tissues), while the second are up to 5 mm at the base of the branches and gradually decrease in size towards the branch tip. The larger-sized radial corallites are 2.0-3.4 mm in diameter, tubular with rounded to dimidiate openings and calices 0.8-1.0 mm in diameter. There are various colour forms, the most common ones being light brown and pink. Normally grows on the reef edge or in places on shallow reef flats where they are exposed to turbulent water.

Aquarium maintenance:
- **General:** According to our experience, *A. gemmifera* is the most difficult-to-care-for *Acropora* species. A possible reason for this could be inadequate water movement.
- **Lighting:** Very high light intensity.
- **Water circulation:** Very strong and alternating. A wave generator should be tried.
- **Reproduction:** Unknown.
GA: +/- ; TO: + ; SE: +/-

Photos:
Bottom left: Small, beautifully coloured colony, typical of a shallow, exposed reef flat   Photo: J. Olsen

Bottom right: Close-up of the radial corallites (polyps)

thick, with plates attached laterally to each other, or have corymbose plates arranged in tiers. Branches are very thick and tapering, producing a conical shape. *A. monticulosa* resembles *A. gemmifera*, but has smaller axial corallites, and the radial corallites are uniform in size and are usually arranged in rows.

Acropora lovelli group

This group comprises four species: *A. bushyensis*, *A. verweyi*, *A. loveli* and *A. glauca*. Except for *A. verweyi*, which can also be found in the Coral Sea, the others are only known in Australia and, even there, are rare. We will not go further into this group, as it is somewhat improbable that these corals will ever appear in the trade.

Green-brown colonies of *Acropora lovelli* on the Great Barrier Reef, mixed with colonies of a purple-coloured *Acropora*, possibly *A. formosa*.

Photo: T. Done

Acropora robusta group

The species of this group: *A. robusta*, *A. danai*, *A.palmerae*, *A. nobilis*, *A. polysoma*, *A. listeri* and *A. sukarnoi*, all have very similar radial corallites that are a mixture of tall and short individuals, the tall ones having dimidiate; the coenosteum - which is coarsely developed - is costate (ridged) on radial corallites and reticulate (net-like) with simple spinules between the radial corallites (WALLACE, 1997). In general, these species thrive best on the reef edge and on the reef plateau, where they are exposed to strong wave impact.

Acropora robusta is a strong and coarsely structured species with anastomosing horizontal branches possessing a side or central attachment and upturned

Occasionally, *Acropora danai* can extend itself to cover a surface, as shown here on an outer reef slope in the Maldives.

Acropora danai: colonies on a reef flat in the Maldives (left) and a typical growth form in the background on the Great Barrier Reef, shown here with other *Acropora* spp. (right; photo: T. Done).

ends, the latter forming thick cones or bosses near the colony centre, a characteristic which distinguishes it from *A. danai*. The radial corallites can be of different sizes and shapes, but are generally appear as a coarse file or rasp. Major growth variations occur within a single colony, in colonies growing in the same biotope and in colonies growing in different habitats. The colour of live colonies is bright green with deep pink branch tips or pink-brown, yellow-brown or cream all over. *A. robusta* is found from Chagos Achipellago, east to Tahiti, and appears only in shallow water, most often on the reef edge.

Acropora danai is similar to *A. robusta* and has irregular colony forms. However, the colonies lack the very thick, central branches, which are typical for *A. robusta*. The thick, sprawling horizontal branches proliferate distally into short, oblique branchlets, or short, thick, upward-projecting branches, or a mixture of both. The horizontal branches may be free or encrusting, are usually flattened and divide frequently. The corallites and the coeno-steum are very much like those of *A. robusta*. *A. danai* is more widely distributed in the Indo-Pacific

than the previous species, and can be found from Madagascar in the west, to Tahiti in the east. We have not, to date, heard of *A. robusta* or *A. danai* being kept in aquaria. Both species, though, appear to be well qualified.

The very rare *Acropora palmerae* is one of the few species of this genus which corresponds to

the encrusting growth form, either with or without short, irregular branches.

Appreciably more common, but with a limited geographical distribution of Australia and the west Pacific, is *Acropora nobilis* whose colonies are arborescent, usually large and open, with robust, occasionally anastomosed,

Acropora nobilis is usually cream-coloured, shown here on a back-reef margin on the Great Barrier Reef (behind it is a purple-coloured *A. formosa* and a high diversity of other corals).

Acropora formosa
(Shown as *A. microphthalma* by FOSSÅ & NILSEN, 1992, 1994)

Distribution: In the Indo-Pacific; from Madagascar, east to the Marshall and Phoenix Islands.

Growth form and size: Arborescent; can create powerful, monospecific populations in the ocean. One of the most widespread and abundant of the Indo-Pacific staghorns. Frequently the dominant species of large areas of lagoons and fringing reefs.

Food: Probably feeds mainly upon the products of the zooxanthellae, captures plankton and probably utilizes dissolved organic compounds as well.

Description: (Based on VERON & WALLACE, 1984). A typical arborescent growing staghorn coral. The branches are relatively straight, usually < 2 cm thick. Branching is irregular and indeterminate. Radial corallites are tubular to immersed, sometimes appressed, with circular or oval openings. They may be of similar size and evenly distributed in rows, or else have an erratic orientation with adjacent corallites of different sizes facing in different directions. They may protrude up to 5 mm, but are always small with an internal diameter of 0.6-1.2 mm. The colouring is cream, brown or light brown; the branch tips are pink or white, sometimes even blue.

Aquarium maintenance:
- **General:** Grows very quickly and can create large populations within a short period of time.
- **Lighting:** High lighting intensity.
- **Water circulation:** Weak to strong.
- **Reproduction:** Easy to propagate through fragmentation.
GA: + ; TO: + ; SE: +
Photos:
Growth in the aquarium:
Top: May 1992; centre: January 1993; bottom: January 1994

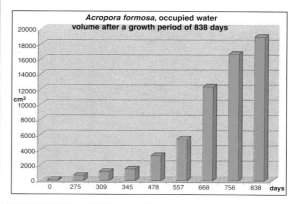

Acropora formosa, occupied water volume after a growth period of 838 days

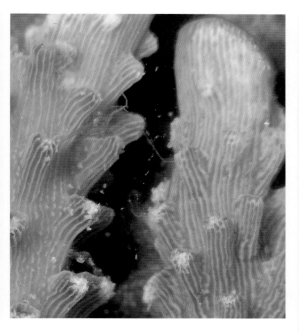

Photos:
- Top left: Close-up of the radial corallites.
- Top right: Vigorous monospecific population on the Great Barrier Reef.   Photo: Prof. J. E. N. Veron/E. Lovell
- Bottom: Colony on a reef flat (left) and in a shallow lagoon (right), both from the Maldives.

branches. The radial corallites are of mixed sizes and shapes and are similar to those of *A. danai* and *A. robusta*. This is one out of several "staghorns" or horned corals of the genus found in the Indo-Pacific. Two similar species: *A. grandis* and *A. formosa*, may have similar growth forms to *A. nobilis*, and can only be distinguished from this species by the shape or form of the radial coral-lites. These are file-shaped in *A. nobilis* and can be found in two sizes in one and the same colony. Veron (1986) reported that the species can very often be found on sandy ground, especially in la-goons, where it can often create single-species (monospecific) populations; it can often occur mixed with *A. formosa*. Based on experience with similar staghor-ned species, *A. nobilis* should be easy to care for, although we are not aware of any reports of it being kept in aquaria.

Acropora polystoma and *A. li-steri* are also rare. *A. polystoma* is distributed from the Red Sea and Mauritius in the west, east to the Great Barrier Reef and Samoa. Both species develop corymbose colonies with very irregular radial corallites, which give the colonies a thorny appearance.

 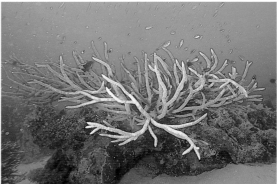

Normally, *Acropora grandis* develops thick branches, especially in nutrient-poor water, as in the picture on the left ta-ken in the Coral Sea. In turbid water, as in the picture on the right (photo: E. Svensen) taken on the Great Barrier Reef, it develops thinner branches.

Acropora formosa group

In this group, we meet five spe-cies, all of which have an arbore-scent branched, or modified ar-borescent branched, colony form. Some can be counted among the most commonly found species, namely: *A. grandis*, *A. formosa*, *A. abrolhosensis*, *A. acuminata* and *A. valenciennesi*. Some of the species in this group are very much like those in the *A. robusta* group. *Acropora formosa* can create enormous single-species (monospecific) populations and colony development is related to age, with large colonies forming a compact mass of thick branches. Daughter colonies of old colonies can sometimes grow extensively after an old growth of *A. formosa* has been decimated by a storm; such colonies have thinner bran-ches and are "open", colonies re-sembling older colonies from deeper waters (Veron & Wallace,

Acropora formosa can vary widely in its colouring; shown here: a purple-coloured colony in sand on the Great Barrier Reef.

Acropora valenciennesi (?) in its typical corymbose growth form on the Great Barrier Reef (left) and in a close-up of the branches (right).

1984). This species is distributed from Madagascar, east to the Marshall and Phoenix Islands. Its colouring varies, but is normally brown, creamy-coloured, or blue. The growth points are usually coloured white or red-pink. We collected *A. formosa* near the Fiji Islands and, in our aquarium, it grew very quickly, but developed an atypical branching structure (see fact pagees 354-355).

Acropora grandis also has an arborescent colony form, although the branches are usually spread horizontally, which gives this species an unique growth form. The branches can be up to 12 cm thick and over 2 metres long, thus forming enormous colonies. Additionally, the colonies can become very large and can reach diameters of several metres. *A. grandis* is distributed in the central Pacific, from Australia's Great Barrier Reef, the Coral Sea, to Samoa and the Philippines, but is seldom common. As far as we know, it has not yet been kept in aquaria.

Acropora abrolhosensis is only known from Australia, where it can often be found in lagoons and reefs which are protected from strong wave impact. *A. acuminata* is distributed in the central Pacific, appearing as far east as the Gilbert and Marshall Islands, in the Coral Sea, and along the Great Barrier Reef. It is, however, very rare. These two species are hardly known in the marine aquarium hobby.

Certainly more interesting and more common is *Acropora valenciennesi*, which is distributed from Sri Lanka in the west, to the Palau and Fiji Islands in the east. The species forms open corymbose tabular colonies, up to 4 metres in diameter. Smaller colonies are composed of radiating, anastomosing branches with upturned ends, or are caespito-corymbose (i.e. having a densely tufted, raceme-like growth form). The branches of large colonies can be up to 4 cm thick and, where lateral growth is not restricted, the colonies are often table-shaped, although with clear, divided horizontal branches, which grow almost singly, with their branch tips clearly pointing upwards. This growth form can be described as consisting of corymbose tables, which makes the species easily identifiable and, at the same time, unbelievably decorative. The colours are mixtures of brown, blue and green.

Acropora horrida group

The species in this group, *A. microphthalma*, *A. horrida*, *A. kirstyae*, *A. tortuosa*, *A. vaughani*, *A. austera* and *A. derawanensis*, show arborescent to hispidose branching (i.e. bearing strong spines or bristles) and simple appressed (i.e. pressed close together, but without uniting) tubular corallites with round openings; the coenosteum is reticulate throughout, with scattered

simple spinules. More simply, the colonies all have a distinct staghorn or bush-shaped growth form and the species are very difficult to distinguish from one another. Only three are interesting for us, of which *A. microphthalma* has proven itself as the most easily kept in aquaria.

Acropora horrida has widely and irregularly spaced corallites which are irregular in orientation and prominence, making the surface look rough. The colonies are, most often, compact bushy with the polyps extended during the day. The colouring often shows blue nuances, from light to dark blue, while the polyps are mostly coloured light blue or white. Occasionally, brown or yellow colonies can also be found. *A. horrida* is distributed widely throughout the Indo-Pacific, from the Red Sea in the west, to the Marshall Islands, but is not common. It occupies biotopes ranging from exposed reef slopes, to deep waters surrounding fringing reefs and, compared to other species of *Acropora*, prefers turbid conditions.

A. microphthalma is the smallest of the arborescent *Acropora* species, and can develop thick, monospecific growth over a limited area. Normally, it forms thickets with slender and straight branches which grow strongly infiltrating each other. We have kept *A. microphthalma* for years in a reef aquarium and it is a very hardy species that can grow ex-

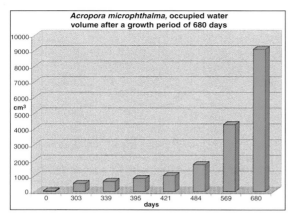

Acropora microphthalma, occupied water volume after a growth period of 680 days

cm³ / days

Acropora microphthalma
(Shown as *A. elseyi* by Fossà & Nilsen, 1992, 1994)

Distribution: In the Indo-Pacific; from Madagascar, east to Australia and the Marshall Islands and north to the Ryukyu Islands, to Australia.

Growth form and size: (Based on Veron & Wallace, 1984). Colonies are arborescent, with slender, straight, tapering branches. This is the smallest of the arborescent *Acropora*. The branching may be open, with branches spaced or compact and with sub-branches forming at acute angles, but the colonies always have a regular, uniform appearance. The basal branches of most colonies are dead, less than 2 cm in diameter and easily broken. Normally small and numerous to mid-sized arborescent colonies. Occupies most reef biotopes protected from strong wave action, and can be very abundant in turbid waters with low *Acropora* diversity, or on sandy substrate in lagoons.

Food: Feeds upon the translocated products from the zooxanthellae, captures plankton and probably utilizes dissolved organic compounds as well.

Description: (Based on Veron & Wallace, 1984). The radial corallites are short, tubular appressed, frequently with tubo-nariform openings. They have a calyx diameter of 0.4-0.6 mm. Axial corallites are up to 2.3 mm in diameter with a calyx diameter of 0.6-1.0 mm. Living colonies are uniform pale grey or pale brown or cream. The branches are thick and straight; radial corallites are small.

Aquarium maintenance:
- **General:** Very robust species; grows to large colonies in sufficient light. Can take over large areas and suppresses other corals, so that a trimming is necessary. Belongs to the easy-to-care-for corals, although it tends to bleach at high temperatures.
- **Lighting:** High lighting intensity.
- **Water circulation:** Weak to strong.
- **Reproduction:** Easy to propagate through fragmentation. Belongs to the species that should be included in experiments, since it can attain sexual maturity in the aquarium and can spawn under the right conditions.

GA: + ; TO: + ; SE: +

Photos:
Above: Close-up of the branches of a colony near the Fiji Islands.   Photo: Scott W. Michael
Below: Series of pictures showing growth in an aquarium Left: June 1992; centre: November 1992; right: January 1994

Acropora sp.
"Stüber's *Acropora*"

Notes on identification: Stüber's *Acropora* was the very first *Acropora* sp. to be kept in a private aquarium in Europe and probably one of the first *Acropora* colonies ever to be kept successfully for a longer period of time in captivity in a closed reef tank. We dare say that, in a sense, this single event revolutionized attitudes towards keeping the fast-growing reefbuilders from the family Acroporidae in reef aquaria. Since it appeared from live rock in the early eighties, several attempts have been made to identify this coral to species level. Peter Wilkens identified the young colony (obviously wrongly) as *A. humilis*. Due to a misunderstanding, the species was identified as the rare *A. cardenae* by Prof. Veron in 1992 and, later, as *A. pulchra* by Julian Sprung. This last identification is doubtful. Although many aquarists now agree that the species resembles *A. formosa*, it is most likely that, after more than 15 years in captivity, being distributed to hundreds of aquarists worldwide and grown successfully under a variety of conditions, the original structure of the corallites and the natural colony shape have changed so much that a species identification is no longer possible. In other words, this species is perhaps the first truly domesticated coral that cannot be named anything but "Stüber's *Acropora*".

Distribution: The first polyps grew out of a piece of live rock imported from the Singapore/Indonesia area.

Growth form and size: Arborescent and staghorn-like, but "Stüber's *Acropora*" forms many different colony shapes under differing aquarium conditions, most of them, however, being like those shown in the photos on this page.

Food: Probably feeds mainly upon the products of the zooxanthellae, captures plankton and probably utilizes dissolved organic compounds as well.

Description: A typical staghorn coral with equal-sized axial corallites. The radial corallites resembles those of *A. formosa* (see page 354/355), are of varying sizes, stand far apart from one another and have a fantastic lower lip. Their colouring is normally brown, with pink-coloured branch tips.

Aquarium maintenance:
- **General:** Grows very well and can create large populations within a short period of time. Came into the coral reef aquarium of D. Stüber, Berlin, with live rock in the 1980's.
- **Lighting:** Prefers strong illumination.
- **Water circulation:** Medium to strong.
- **Reproduction:** Easy to propagate through fragmentation and has, in this way, been distributed to aquarists in many countries.

  GA: + ; TO: + ; SE: +

Photos:
Top: The approximately three-year-old mother colony in D. Stüber's aquarium, Berlin, photographed in July 1985.
Centre: Aquarium colonies seen from above.
Bottom: Close-up photo of the branches.

Acropora austera is a common coral near the Maldives, where it grows on reef edges, as well as in shallow lagoons.

tremely quickly (see fact page 358).

Acropora austera is distributed in the Indo-Pacific, from Madagascar, around Australia, and further east to the Marshall Islands; we have even found it often near the Maldives. Its growth form varies greatly, from open arborescent, to caespitose, and is therefore very difficult for a layperson to distinguish. It is most abundant in biotopes exposed to some wave action, particularly on open ocean reefs. We experimented with a colony from the Maldives, where we legally collected two different pieces of the species. One had branchlets that had broken off naturally from a large colony growing in a sandy habitat under very high light intensity. The other was a smaller (about 3 cm long) fragment that we broke off at a branch point along the largest branch. It was difficult to establish the pieces in our aquarium, and the large piece gradually died. However, the small fragment that we broke off ourselves, suddenly thrived excellently and continued to grow for years. Indeed, it is still growing well today, and is in the same aquarium in which the mother colony died out.

Acropora aspera group

The species *Acropora aspera*, *A. pulchra*, *A. millepora* and *A. indiana* have polymorphic growth forms which complicate the identification of the species in this group. Primarily, the species have radial corallites with no upper wall and a lower wall with a round or flared lip, characters which are most abundant in *A. millepora*. The coenosteum is costate (ridged) on radial corallites and reticulated (net-like) between corallites. A good characteristic is, however, that the corallites have no lime walls above, and barely a lip below.

Acropora aspera is a highly polymorphic species, where different colonies, or even parts of the same colony, can have long, slender spreading branches with

Acropora horrida (?) in turbid water near the beach in Bunaken, Indonesia. This is the usual habitat of this staghorn coral.

scattered radial corallites, or shorter, thicker branches with crowded corallites. It normally exhibits branched growth and can develop thick colonies with relatively straight-standing main branches and shorter side branches. The corallites are large and scale-shaped. This species is most common in shallow, protected biotopes, where it can form micro-atolls, or in slightly deeper waters, where it can form arborescent colonies with sturdy branches. Three different ecomorphs are known: from exposed reef fronts, from shallow protected biotopes and from protected biotopes with reduced light intensity (see VERON & WALLACE, 1984, for details). According to VERON (1986), this species is distributed from the Cocos Islands, eastwards to the Fiji Islands. The growth form is similar to that of *A. pulchra*, although the *A. aspera* corallites are thicker. The colonies are normally pale bluegreen, green, or cream-coloured. *A. aspera* thrives best in quiet surroundings, in lagoons and behind the reef edge; it is seldom seen in exposed places.

Even *Acropora pulchra* produces colonies with growth forms ranging from open arborescent to compact corymbose. Most often, this species exhibits a growth form that lies somewhere between thickly branched and bushy, and can be designated as caespito-corymbose. The radial corallites have protruding under-

Acropora millepora in the Coral Sea

lips and are smaller than in the above-named species; otherwise they are similar. This species has the same distribution as *A. aspera* and often appears together with it. *A. pulchra* also shuns strongly exposed zones and living colonies are pale to dark brown, often with blue branch tips.

Acropora millepora has a corymbose to tabular growth form with short, thick branches. The colonies are commonly about one metre in diameter and almost circular in shape. It is very beautiful and has strong colouring in green, orange, or red. Its distribution spans from Sri Lanka and Thailand in the west, to the Marshall and Tonga Islands, although it

is relatively rare. We have tried to keep this species, collected at Suva Reef, Fiji, in aquaria, but with no luck. Even when placed under various light intensities, we have not been able to grow *A. millepora*.

A. indiana was described by WALLACE (1994) and has only been found in shallow reef flat situations, where it occurs as semi-encrusting, limited branching colonies with sub-horizontal growth. We found the species ourselves on the reef flat of the coral island of Siladen, near Manado, North Sulawesi, where we mistook it for *A. monticulosa*.

Acropora indiana on an exposed reef plateau near Indonesia (below) and a close-up of its typical corallite structure (right)

Acropora selago group

It is difficult to find common characteristics for the six species in
this group, but all, *Acropora
tenuis*, *A. selago*, *A. donei*, *A. dendrum*, *A. yongei* and *A. loisetteae*
have similar radial corallites with
strongly developed lower walls
and flared or pointed lower lips.
At least one species has shown
an ability to grow in coral reef
aquaria.

**Right: Colony of *Acropora selago* in
an aquarium**

Acropora selago produces caespito-corymbose growth with
thin branches and scaly corallites. It is distributed from the central west Pacific, to the Marshall
and Solomon Islands. We were
able to collect it near the Fiji Islands in 1991 and, since then,
have been able to care for it with
great success in our aquarium
(see fact page 363).

**Right: *Acropora tenuis* grows in some-
what unevenly formed plate-shaped
colonies, like this colony, photographed on a reef flat in Indonesia.**

Acropora tenuis has a wide distribution in the Indo-Pacific, from
Mauritius in the south west, to the
Marshall Islands in the east. It is
one of the most common species
of the reef edge and grows everywhere where the diversity of
Acropora spp. is high. It is also,
however, difficult to identify. Normally, it forms thick corymbose
plates which are primarily characterized by the regular arrangement of up to 9 cm long and 7-10
mm thick branchlets having a
neat arrangement of radial corallites, which have wide lower lips,
giving them a rosette-like appearance when viewed from above.

Acropora donei and *Acropora
dendrum* are both rare and therefore not significant for us at the
moment. *A. yongei* produces arborescent colonies with straight
branches, usually dividing at fre-

**Right: *Acropora yongei* on a reef flat
near Bunaken, Indonesia**

Acropora selago

Distribution: From the central west Pacific, east to the Marshall Islands.

Growth form and size: Colonies are caespito-corymbose or plate-like with lateral attachment. The branches are relatively thin. Sub-branches at irregular intervals and sometimes anastomosing. Occurs in a wide variety of habitats, from exposed outer reef slopes, to turbid lagoons and fringing reefs (VERON & WALLACE, 1984). Small to mid-sized colonies.

Food: Probably feeds mainly upon the products of the zooxanthellae, but captures plankton and probably utilizes dissolved organic compounds as well.

Description: (Based on VERON & WALLACE, 1984). Caespitocorymbose colonies with somewhat thin branches. The radial corallites are strongly appressed and cochleariform, having a scale-like-, but not rosette-like, appearance. The radial corallites are < 1.9 mm wide with a calyx diameter of 0.7-0.8 mm. The axial corallites are < 3 mm exserted and 1.5-2.4 mm in diameter. Polyps often expand during the day. Colouring normally cream to brown.

Aquarium maintenance:
- **General:** Grows very well. Our experience is that the polyps are always expanded, which gives the colonies a bushy appearance. Growth points are normally blue.
- **Lighting:** High light intensity.
- **Water circulation:** Medium to strong.
- **Reproduction:** Easy to propagate through fragmentation.

GA: + ; TO: + ; SE: +

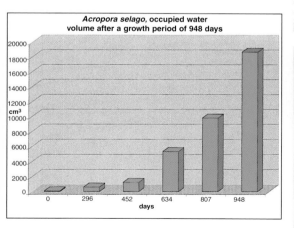

Acropora selago, occupied water volume after a growth period of 948 days

Photos:
Growth in an aquarium; Top: 1.4.1993; centre: 1.1.1994; Bottom: close-up of the bushy branches.

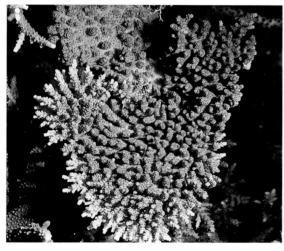

Acropora cytherea

Distribution: In the Indo-Pacific; from Mascarene Archipelago of Madagascar, east to Tahiti and Hawaii.

Growth form and size: Young colonies are initially caespito-corymbose, then become vasiform (vase-shaped) and later tabular. Mature colonies consist of thin, flat plates reaching more than 3 metres in diameter. The colonies are composed of radiating branches, usually highly anastomosed, 4-15 mm in diameter, with supporting short branchlets, or bundles of branchlets, each with one or more protuberant axial corallites. Occupies a wide range of habitats and forms many skeletal variations. Common on upper reef slopes exposed to heavy wave action, but not common on reef flats, see VERON & WALLACE (1984) for details on skeletal variations.

Food: Feeds upon the translocated products from the zooxanthellae, captures plankton and probably utilizes dissolved organic compounds as well.

Description: (Based on VERON & WALLACE, 1984). The branches are thin, grow upright, and are not arranged in a rose-shaped fashion. The radial coralites are appressed, tubular with nariform to dimidiate openings and, frequently, with slightly flaring lips. Axial corallites are 1-5 mm exserted, 1.3-2.5 mm in diameter, with calices 0.7-1.0 mm in diameter. Colouring is brown, cream, or blue-green. Often found on reef flats. Can become dry during low tide.

Aquarium maintenance:
- **General:** Grows very well, and can create large plate-shaped colonies when the water and lighting strengths are correct. Needs a great deal of a space.
- **Lighting:** High ligh intensity.
- **Water circulation:** Strong.
- **Reproduction:** Easy to propagate through fragmentation; has the potential to spawn in aquaria.

GA: + ; TO: + ; SE: +

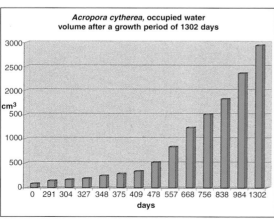

Acropora cytherea, occupied water volume after a growth period of 1302 days

cm³

0   291 304 327 348 375 409 478 557 668 756 838 984 1302
days

Photos:
Growth in an aquarium; top: 25.08.1992; centre: 07.10.1993 (picture taken from above)

Acropora latistella

Distribution: Indo-Pacific; known from Australia, the Philippines and Samoa.

Growth form and size: Corymbose, corymbose plates or caespitose, sometimes growing into very large colonies. The branches are 5-9 mm thick and relatively straight in corymbose and caespitose colonies, or curved in corymbose plate-shaped colonies. Sub-branches form at acute angles, but do not anastomose. Occurs in a wide range of habitats, from exposed outer reef slopes, to bays and protected lagoons.

Food: Feeds upon the translocated products from the zooxanthellae, captures plankton and probably utilizes dissolved organic compounds as well.

Description: (Based on VERON & WALLACE, 1984). The radial corallites are regulary arranged, usually in rows along the branches, and are tubular appressed, with open rounded to slightly dimidiate calices. Those towards the proximate end of the branches become immersed. Axial corallites are 2-3 mm in diameter and < 2 mm exserted. Living colonies are usually uniform pale cream, grey or brown.

Aquarium maintenance:

- **General:** Grows very well. Can develop very large colonies, even in aquaria, if given enough light and good water conditions. Needs a large amount of space.
- **Lighting:** High ligh intensity.
- **Water circulation:** Medium to strong.
- **Reproduction:** Easy to propagate through fragmentation.

GA: + ; TO: + ; SE: +

Photos:
Right: Growth in an aquarium; top: 30.06.1992; centre: 01.01.1994
Bottom right: Close-up photo of the corallites (magnified 17 times)

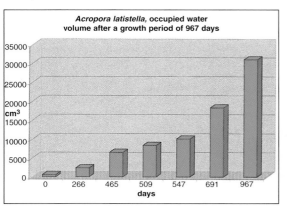

Acropora latistella, occupied water volume after a growth period of 967 days

The *Acropora hyacinthus* group consists of species which can grow to impressive levels, like this *Acropora spicifera* in Papua-New Guinea.
                                                                                            Photo: Scott W. Michael

quent intervals, or forming cae-spito-corymbose growth forms. This species is common and is found in many different habitats, from exposed reef fronts, to shallow, protected lagoons, and can sometimes form monospecific stands. It is distributed from the Philippines to Australia, where it can be found in the Great Barrier Reef and along the northern coast to the Houtman Abrolhos Atoll.

Acropora hyacinthus group

In this group, all the species (except *A. anthocercis*) form table- or plate-shaped colonies, with thick horizontal branches that grow together and terminate in small end branches that point upwards. The corallites are small, the radial corallites having an extended outer wall or lip; the coenosteum is costate on the radial corallites and reticulate with simple spinules between the radial corallites. The following species are found in this group: *Acropora cytherea*,

A. microclados, *A. paniculata*, *A. hyacinthus*, *A. spicifera*, *A. anthocercis* and *A. indonesia*. All species can be found almost exclusively in shallow water, often completely open on the reef plateau, where they can become dry in extremely low water. If found in deeper water, the shape tends to be more open and arborescent.

Acropora paniculata, with a distribution from Australia, through the Pacific Ocean to Hawaii, and *A. microclados*, with a distribution from Indonesia and around Australia, are counted among the relatively rare species that are still significant for aquarists. Both species are only found in shallow water. *A. spicifera* dominates the upper reef slopes of many reefs in the Houtman Abrolhos Islands in west Australia, although it can be found even farther east to the Fiji Islands. *Acropora anthocercis* has a wide distribution in the Indo-Pacific, from Madagascar and the Red Sea (?), east to Australia and the Great Barrier Reef. Unlike the other species in the genus, *A. ant-*

hocercis has relatively thick branches which point upwards in the colonies. The numerous axial corallites are strongly developed and marked.

Acropora hyacinthus and *A. cytherea* are far more common. We have had good experience with the latter in aquaria and have given it its own fact page 364. *A. hyacinthus* forms wide, flat tables which are thin and finely structured. The fine, upward projecting branchlets have a rosette-like arrangement of radial corallites. The axial corallites are not exsert (do not protrude; VERON, 1986). It is a very abundant species of shallow reef flats and is an early coloniser after a reef has been destroyed, where it can become a dominant species of regenerating reefs. Like many other *Acropora*, *A. hyacinthus* forms different ecomorphs in exposed, shallow or turbid habitats (VERON & WALLACE, 1984). *A. hyacinthus* is found from the Mascarene Archipelago in the west, east to Tahiti.

A. Indonesia was described

from North Sulawesi by WALLACE (1997) and is widely distributed throughout Indonesia. This species produces arborescent colonies, where slender, upward-curving branches form a table top up to 10 cm thick. The branches are loosely interlocking, with some of the lower ones forming an anastomosing pattern, and all, taken together, forming a generally very fragile structure. The radial corallites do not, generally, touch each other and are nariform (nostril-shaped), with only the outer wall being extended upwards to a greater or lesser extent, sometimes to a fine point. The coenosteum has open costae (ridges) on radial corallites, and is reticulate and flaky, with very few spinules between the radial corallites. This species occurs as flat tables, ranging from one to several metres in diameter. Many tables can form layers. *A. indonesia* is commonly found on horizontal surfaces, such as submerged reef flats or ledges, or on gentle slopes. The colours are cream, pale brown, or pinkish brown. An unusual feature of this species is a mineral deposit within the skeleton which gives the dried skeleton a yellow appearance.

The table-shaped *Acropora* spp. are, in general, easily kept in reef tanks. It should, however, be noted at this point that table-shaped *Acropora* species grow very quickly, soon requiring a lot of space, and that everything that grows underneath the colony can become completely shaded. At the same time, they are some of the most decorative and interesting stony corals for the reef aquarium.

Acropora latistella group

The species in this group all form small, bushy colonies with slender branchlets and appressed corallites, but some of the species can also form large plates. *A. latistlla*, *A. subulata*, *A. aculeus*, *A. nana* and *A. azurea* are assigned to this group, but according to VERON & WALLACE (1984), these species are grouped together

Acropora indonesia was described by Prof. Carden WALLACE (1997) and belongs to the *Acropora hyacinthus*-group. It is recorded from various locations in Indonesia like this colony photographed at Sangihe Island.

Photo: R. Aiello

more on the basis of superficial similarities, than on a consideration of affinities. The corallites are small and pressed together, and the branches are thin.

Acropora latistella (see fact page 365) is common within its distribution area and creates large, table-shaped or corymbose colonies, with thin (5-9 mm), straight, horizontal branches.

Acropora subulata also grows in large table-shaped, circular colonies, which can often reach a diameter of several metres. Even this species has a network of straight, thin, horizontal branches. Out of these grow small, thin, vertical equidistant branches of the same height, so that the colony appears to be pillow-shaped. This fantastic growth form gives *A. subulata* a special appearance and structure which is beautiful, but extremely fragile. The colouring shows nuances of grey or brown. This species is distributed from Australia and the Philippines, to the Fiji Islands, and can be found almost exclusively in shallow reef inclines (where the diversity is great) and in areas which are protected from strong wave impact.

Acropora nana and *A. azurea* are both very rare. *Acropora acu-*

leus is, on the other hand, extremely common and distributed throughout a large area in the Indo-Pacific, from Sri Lanka in the west, to the Marshall Islands and Samoa in the east. Even this species develops corymbose colonies which are often pillow-shaped. It is most often found in biotopes protected from strong wave action and is often abundant in lagoons. The colouring is often grey, blue-green, or yellow, normally with very colourful branch tips.

Acropora nasuta group

All the species in this group have similar corallites and coenosteum and, with one exception (*A. lutkeni*), they all form corymbose or caespito-corymbose colonies. The species also have the same habitat preferences and show the same modifications in growth as a response to environmental conditions (VERON, 1986). In this group, we meet some of the most common species of the genus. They thrive, especially, on the upper reef slope, where they build round, plate-shaped colonies. All have similar corallites and a similar coenosteum. Their growth is corymbose or caespito-corym-

Acropora cerealis, shown here is a colony in Indonesia, grows into beautiful, compact, almost-circular shapes.

Photo: J. Olsen

The radial corallites of *Acropora nasuta*, shown here in a colony in the Maldives, look like small noses. The growth tips of the horned branches are often wonderfully coloured.

Acropora valida has highly variable growth forms and can, like this colony on the Great Barrier Reef, be purple-coloured.

bose. The group is comprised of the species *Acropra nasuta*, *A. cerealis*, *A. valida*, *A. secale* and *A. lutkeni*.

Acropora lutkeni is restricted to Australia and the Coral Sea. In specific places, it can be very numerous and exhibit a variety of growth forms, from bottle-brushed to corymbose. *Acropora cerealis* is distributed from Indonesia and the Philippines, eastwards to the Marshall and Tonga Islands, where it is very common on reef slopes. The colonies are caespito-corymbose or corymbose plates with short, highly anastomosing branchlets. The branches appear thick, although it is the corallites that produce this effect; the branches themselves are actually very thin.

Acropora nasuta got its name from the radial corallites which look like small noses standing up-side down in neat rows. This species characteristic makes it very easy to recognize. The colonies are corymbose, or form small corymbose tables. The colouring is generally light, with purple-coloured growth points on the branch ends. This colouring can, however, as in many *Acropora* species, change into browner shades. *A. nasuta* is found in large areas of the Indo-Pacific, from east Africa in the west, to Tahiti in the east, but it avoids very turbid habitats and lagoon floors. We found *A. nasuta* frequently in the Maldives, most often on the upper reef slopes.

We also often found *Acropora valida* in the Maldives. It is the species with the largest distribution of all *Acropora* species and can be found in the entire Indo-Pacific, from the Red Sea and east Africa, to the American west coast. It belongs to the small group of stony corals which also grow on subtropical reefs. *A. valida* can be distinguished from the other species in the group because of the radial corallites, which are of different sizes, and are strongly appressed (pressed closely together, but without fusing) and possess small openings. We have not been able to confirm the existence of *A. valida* in aquaria, but feel certain that it is being grown in some aquaria and is, most likely, a very good aquarium species.

Acropora secale can be confused with *A. gemmifera* because the branch tips have the same conical form and can be up to 25 mm in diameter. However, the axial corallites are smaller on *A. secale* and the radial corallites project farther out from the branches. Furthermore, the corallites are of different sizes. This species is distributed from Mauritius in the west, to the Marshall Islands in the east, and commonly grows in shallow water.

Acropora divaricata group

This group contains two species that are of interest for the aquarist: *Acropora clathrata* and *A. divaricata*. Three other species: *A. solitaryensis*, *A. stoddarti* and *A. hoeksemai*, will probably only be rarely, if ever, encountered by aquarists. All species have similar nariform (nostril-shaped) to tubonariform radial corallites and a similar coenosteum, with spinules having barely elaborated or forked tips, between the small and thin corallites.

Acropora divaricata is probably the species with the most variable growth form in the genus. It can develop large, platform-shaped, or thick, bush-shaped colonies. Nevertheless, *A. divaricata* can be recognized by the vertical branches which are interconnected in a manner similar to the horizontal branches of corymbose colonies (VERON, 1986). Living colonies are usually dark brown or greenish-brown, sometimes with colourful branch tips. This species is very common and is usually very abundant on reef slopes, where the diversity of the genus is high, but it also occurs on patch reefs in lagoons and on fringing reefs. It is distributed from the Seychelles in the west, to the Fiji Islands in the east.

Acropora clathrata is, easy to recognize. It creates large, plate-shaped colonies and is the only

Acropora divaricata (above) can be found very often in the sea, especially in lagoons. The axial corallites are often separated by many radial corallites. On the picture below, the polyps are expanded. This photo was taken on a night dive.

Typical growth form of an *Acropora clathrata* colony, photographed in the Maldives.

The bottle-brush staghorn coral, *Acropora echinata* (purple-coloured colony), is difficult to confuse with other *Acropora* species.

Acropora subglabra growing on a deeper reef slope at Bunaken, Indonesia.

Acropora carduus (?) growing together with brown algae of the genus *Padina*.
Photo: Scott W. Michael

shallow-water species of the genus with horizontal primary, as well as secondary, branching. The horizontal, interlocking branches do not have upright branchlets as those which normally develop in colonies with this growth form. The colouring is often decorative yellow-green. Essentially, this species cannot be confused with any other. *A. clathrata* is common on upper reef slopes, on reef back margins and on fringing reefs, and is distributed from the Seychelles in the west, to Fiji in the east. We brought back a tiny fragment from the Maldives, which, within two years, grew into a colony measuring 6 x 6 cm. Unfortunately. the colony died accidentally, so we cannot currently provide any growth rates for this wonderful staghorn coral.

A. hoeksemai was described from North Sulawesi, Indonesia, by WALLACE (1997). According to Wallace's description, the species forms arborescent tables that may be more or less stalked and usually measure around 1-2 metres in diameter, with tapering and broadly separated branches up to 15 mm in diameter. This species is easily confused with *A. valenciennesi*.

Acropora echinata group

In this group, we find the bottle-brushed (hispidose) *Acropora* species which create this peculiar colony form due to evenly distributed secondary branchlets, each consisting of an axial corallite and just a few radial corallites. Because of their growth form, species can be easily distinguished from those of the other groups. Within this group, however, individual species are difficult to identify. The axial corallites are numerous and clearly cylinder-shaped. On the other hand, the radial corallites resemble small pockets with an edge curving inwards. Typical places to find this group are the lowest reef slope, or on sandy ground in lagoons. The group includes *Acropora echinata, A. subglabra, A. carduus, A. elseyi, A. longicyathus, A. turaki*

Acropora elseyi

Distribution: Indo-Pacific; from the Maldives, to the Great Barrier Reef and the Coral Sea, although not in West Australia.

Growth form and size: Colonies are composed of subdividing branches surrounded by branchlets. Some colonies which are composed mostly of branchlets are small and bushy; others are arborescent with hispidose branchlets. Found in lagoons and on reef slopes not exposed to strong wave action. Can create large, monospecific stands at certain locations. Little variation in growth within one biotope, but variations from biotope to biotope occur.

Food: Feeds upon the translocated products from the zooxanthellae, captures plankton and probably utilizes dissolved organic compounds as well.

Description: (Based on VERON & WALLACE, 1984). Both radial and axial corallites are of very variable length. Radial corallites are tubular with round openings, becoming round tubular distally. They are usually evenly distributed on the branches and can be touching each other. Sometimes, the upper surface of small branchlets lack corallites. Axial corallites are < 2 mm exserted, 1.6-2.3 mm in diameter, with calices 0.5-1.0 mm in diameter. The colouring is typically yellow or light brown, with white branch tips.

Aquarium maintenance:
- **General:** Grows very well and can be used to create monospecific populations.
- **Lighting:** High light intensity.
- **Water circulation:** Weak to medium.
- **Reproduction:** Easy to propagate through fragmentation.

GA: + ; TO: + ; SE: +

Photos:
Top: Monospecific population near the Fiji Islands
Photo: Dr. B. Carlson
Middle: Colony in the Waikiki Aquarium, Honolulu
Photo: Dr. B. Carlson
Bottom: Close-up photo of the branches
Photo: Scott W. Michael

Acropora loripes   Photo: Scott W. Michael   *Acropora florida*, close-up of the corallites

and *A. batunai*, the two last being described by WALLACE (1994, 1997).

Acropora echinata is, perhaps, the most beautiful of all the species in the genus. It has the typical growth form of the group, with colonies composed of sprawling, irregularly dividing branches evenly covered on all sides by secondary branchlets. It almost always has a strong purple colouring, so it can hardly ever be confused with other species. It is distributed from the Maldives east to the Marshall Islands and Samoa, although it is not abundant on some reefs. It is usually restricted to clear water on protected reef backs, deeper than 8 metres, and is most often found mixed with dominant growth of other *A. echinata*-group species.

Acropora subglabra is similar to *A. echinata*, although it is rarer and only has a limited distribution, from the central Indo-Pacific, to the Fiji Islands. It is normally coloured brown or green-brown and usually grows in deeper water, where it can be quite numerous. *Acropora subglabra* grows quite differently to *A. elseyi*, which is distributed very abundantly from the Maldives in the west, to the Coral Sea in the east.

Acropora longicyathus can, like *A. elseyi*, appear dominating in some places, but it is difficult to distinguish from the previous species.

Acropora loripes group

This group consists of clearly re-lated species with a very wide gradation of growth forms. All possess a very fine coenosteum which gives them a smooth appearance. Out of this group, only two species are actually relevant for us: *Acropora loripes* and *A. granulosa*. The remaining species: *A. chesterfiedensis*, *A. caroliniana*, *A. willisae*, *A. jacquelineae*, *A. desalwii*, *A. suharsonoi* and *A. lokani* (the four last species being described by WALLACE, 1994), are rare and have limited distributions. In general, these species show a wide range of growth forms, but can, nevertheless, be grouped according to shared individual features. For example, they all possess a smooth coenosteum. In addition, the species of this group seem to prefer clear water with good circulation, but protected from strong wave action, and often grow on the lower outer reef slopes, or in shallow reef back margins.

Acropora loripes is definitely the most abundant species of the group and is also its most polymorphic one. The colonies are hispidose, corymbose or plate-like, with central lateral attachment, and vary in such a way that they can be easily confused with those of many other species, especially *A. granulosa* and *A. longicyathus*. One characteristic can be that the tubular axial corallites of *A. loripes* may have no radial corallites on one side. This species is distributed in the central Indo-Pacific, from the Philippines in the north, to the Great Barrier Reef in the south, and is especially abundant on outer reef slopes.

The long cylinder-shaped axial corallites, which can be a characteristic of *Acropora longicyathus*, are even more clearly limited in distribution than *A. granulosa*. *A. granulosa* is rare and can be found in the deeper sections of the reef. It is nevertheless widely distributed in the Indo-Pacific, from Madagascar to Tahiti.

Acropora florida group

This group consists of only two species: *Acropora florida* and *A. sarmentosa*. Both species can be clearly distinguished in growth form and build from the remaining *Acropora* species, in that short, club-shaped, vertical branches grow out of the thick main branches. The short vertical branches are dotted evenly and possess similar-looking corallites.

Acropora florida is the more common of the two species and the more widely distributed one. It is found from the Maldives in the west, to the Marshall Islands in the east, and can create extremely large colonies, especially in shallow, protected water, where colonies with a diameter of ten metres are not a rarity. The main branches are up to 25 cm (!) thick. It can be confused with *A. grandis* and is similar in appearance to *A. sarmentosa*. The latter has, however, a more branched appearance, and the smaller secondary branches are thick. As a result, *A. sarmentosa* does not have as gnarled an appearance as *A. florida*.

Acropora palmata photographed in the U.S. Virgin Islands.

Photo: Scott W. Michael

Acropora species of the Caribbean

While it is almost impossible to get an overview of the *Acropora* species of the Indo-Pacific, the opposite is true in the Caribbean, where there are only three species: *A. cervicornis*, *A. palmata*, and *A. prolifera*. All three are extremely rare in aquaria because all stony corals are protected by law in the Caribbean and cannot be exported legally. Sporadically, fragments appear on live rocks or on stones containing other cnidarians. In general, we believe that it is somewhat difficult to keep Caribbean species together with species from the Indo-Pacific. When they are kept to themselves in a special aquarium, they seem to do better, although experiences among aquarists differ in this matter.

Acropora cervicornis grows in a branching manner and is always coloured light brown. This species is treated in detail on fact page 374 (see also BATES, 1997).

Acropora palmata is generally known as an elk stony coral, because the branches are flattened and look like the horns of an elk. The surface is covered with small, protruding, tubular corallites and

the colour is brown to yellow-brown, with a white lining of the branches caused by the colour of the terminal corallites. *A. palmata* is restricted to the shallowest part of the reef exposed to wave action. This rapidly growing species of *Acropora* is, according to Hu-MANN (1993), most common between 0-10 metres, where it can sometimes cover large areas of the bottom (it is rarely found deeper than 15 m). It thrives in areas with strong water current or breaking waves, for which it is well adapted as a result of its broad

Limestone layer in the Florida Keys. This limestone is 125,000 years old and was mainly built by *Acropora palmata*.

Photo: Prof. D. Hopley

Acropora cervicornis

Distribution: Caribbean Sea, including the Bahamas and Florida. Found at shallow to moderate depths, on reefs and on sandy bottoms, from 3 to about 20 metres in clear water.

Size and growth form: Can grow into large, branching colonies. Normally forms antler-like racks of cylindrical branches that grow in great tangles. The lower branches can die out in older colonies and be taken over by algae and other organisms. According to HUMANN (1993) *A. cervicornis* can grow as much as 5-6 inches per year.

Food: Probably feeds primarily on products translocated from its zooxanthellae, but also on plankton.

Description: The colouring is light brown with white branch tips. The surface of the branches is covered with small, protruding corallites. The polyps are normally retracted during the day.

Aquarium maintenance:

– **General:** Grows very well, although it is somewhat more sensitive than species of the Indo-Pacific. Our experience is that a dying out of the lower branches cannot be avoided. It is best taken care of in a special Caribbean aquarium. Please note that this species is protected by law in the States (BATES, 1997).

– **Lighting:** High light intensity.

– **Water circulation:** Moderate to strong.

– **Propagation possibilities:** Propagation can only be accomplished through fragmentation, but seems to be more difficult than in Indo-Pacific branching *Acropora* species. Broken-off branches and fragments often die off, especially when in contact with other *Acropora* species.

GA: +/- ; TO: + ; SE: +/-

Photos:
– Top left: A typical colony photographed in the Cayman Islands   Photo: Scott W. Michael
– Centre: A three-year-old colony in an aquarium
– Bottom: Close-up of the expanded polyps

Astreopora myriophthalma on the Ribbon Reef, Great Barrier Reef   Photo: J. E. N. Veron

Colony of *Astreopora* sp. in a reef tank. This colony was collected legally in the Maldives.

branches. We have no experience with this species in reef aquaria.

Acropora prolifera is not as common as the other two species and usually grows best in depths of 5-10 metres. This species has a branching habit, forming antlerlike racks of cylindrical branches. Several shorter branches often fuse and spread to form a fanshaped, flattened structure at the ends of the branches - a good identification character for *A. prolifera*. Single branches can also grow together, a characteristic never found in *A. cervicornis*, which, in many other respects, resembles *A. prolifera*. The colour is brown to yellow-brown, with white axial corallites. As far as we know, *A. prolifera* has never been kept in captivity.

Genus *Astreopora*

BERNARD (1896) assimilated the genus *Turbinaria* within *Astreopora*, causing confusion among early authors. The growth form

A reef edge on the leeward side of the Island of Bunaken, North Sulawesi, Indonesia: the diversity of stony corals is very extensive here. Although *Acropora* species dominate the scene in this photograph, the reef flat is home to an enormous abundance of species. Between the *Acropora* colonies, the pink-coloured *Porites* species and many soft corals from the genus *Sinularia* are easily recognizable. From the reef edge on the upper left, the reef slope falls off steeply to a depth of 200 m.

and polyp structure exhibited by *Turbinaria* species is similar in many ways to that found in *Astreopora*, but the 15 species of the genus *Astreopora* clearly belong to the Acroporidae, even when their growth form clearly differs from other species in the family. The encrusting colonies are massive, foliaceous or laminar and lack axial corallites. Veron & Wallace (1984) list seven species of *Astreopora* and report that few reefs in the GBR complex possess any great abundance of the genus; it is, however, more abundant in the Coral Sea. Only one of the species is common, namely *Astreopora myriophthalma*, which is distributed from the Red Sea in the west, to the Tuamoto Islands in the east, and can be found on the majority of coral reefs. The growth form is massive, hemispherical or flattened, with an even surface. The small, conical corallites are evenly spaced out.

We have collected *Astreopora myriophthalma* ourselves in the Maldives, and kept it in an aquarium for years. It thrives quite well, although it grows rather slowly.

Astreopora listeri is, according to VERON & WALLACE (1984), frequently found in intertidal pools, where its growth can sometimes form micro-atolls. Although occurring in many habitats, tide pools are the only places where the species is common. Growth forms are the same as those listed for the previous species, but have immersed corallites. This species is widely distributed in the Indo-Pacific, from the Nicobars, to the Marshall Islands.

We found this huge *Porites* colony in a habitat with shallow, crystal-clear water near Rock Arch on Flinders Reef in the Coral Sea. The colony is inhabited by many calcareous tubeworms belonging to the genus *Spirobranchus*.

Family Poritidae

The family Poritidae contains the genera *Porites*, *Goniopora* and *Alveopora*, all having several species and being morphologically and ecologically distinct. The Poritidae also contains the monos-

pecific and very rare genus *Stylaraea*, which is clearly related to *Porites*. *Porites* and *Goniopora* are very different, but show their relationship in the patterns of their septal fusion, while *Alveopora* has tenuous affinities with *Goniopora* (VERON, 1986). According to the same author, the three genera must be regarded as heterogeneous and only distantly related. All three are also well known to aquarists and *Goniopora* spp. were among the first stony corals to be kept in captivity, being frequently imported from Singapore in the early days. The species in this genus are, however, not easy to keep over a long period of time. The genera *Porites* and *Alveopora* contain many interesting species for aquarists.

Genus *Porites*

The best known corals of the family Poritidae belong to the genus *Porites*, which has a circum-tropi-

cal distribution: from the Red Sea in the north, to South Africa in the south, and from the Persian Gulf, Indonesia, Malaysia and West-Australia, along the Great Barrier Reef to Japan. From there, it stretches all over the entire Pacific to the west coast of Mexico and from the Caribbean to the Gulf of Guinea in west Africa. Only very few other coral genera have spread in such a manner.

All *Porites* spp. have very small corallites and, in this respect, resemble *Montipora*. The corallites of *Porites* are, however, filled with septa and other structures, while those of *Montipora* are almost empty. The various species of *Porites* can only be distinguished by minor differences in the shape of the corallites. There are also differences in growth forms, even within a single population growing in the same habitat. According to VERON (1986), it is necessary to study and learn such differences before it is possible to separate many of the *Porites* species. The

Porites lobata is the most common hermatypic stony coral in the reefs of Hawaii. This colony was found near Kailua-Kona.   **Photo: Dr. D. Brockmann**

Many *Porites* spp. form micro-atolls in shallow waters. The upper part of the colony dies as a result of strong UV radiation during low tides, but the colony, itself, continues to grow outwards, forming small atolls on the shallow reef flats. Photograph taken at Green Island, Australia, in 1991.

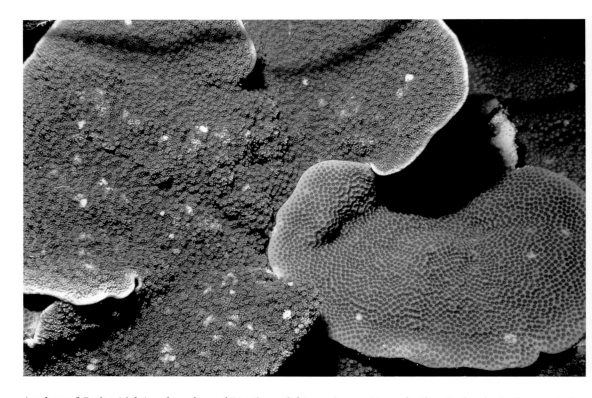

A colony of *Porites* (right) and a colony of *Montipora* (left) growing next to each other. Both colonies have a similar growth form. However, the two genera can easily separated. *Porites* calices are filled with septae, while *Montipora* calices are almost empty and are usually surrounded by elaborate skeletal structures.   Photo: E. Lovell

identification of the species of this genus therefore remains a task for the few existing specialists, with the result that, to date, the number of true species still remains unknown.

The growth of *Porites* is very slow, often less than 1 cm per year. However, some of the species can grow into gigantic, spherical colonies with a diameter of several metres, giving them an age of almost 1000 years! The species have separate sexes, internal fertilization and brooding of the planula larvae in their body cavities.

Many *Porites* species live in lagoons or on reef flats, where they can experience difficulties in surviving because of water levels at low tide exposing them to extreme radiation. This often causes the upper part of the colony to die away, but still allows the colony to continue growing sideways. This creates a colony structure with a pit of dead coral tissue in the middle surrounded by living tissue: a micro-atoll (see page 377). A massive or crust-like form of growth is the most common colony shape, although there are species that branch out, such as the common *Porites cylindrica*.

This *Porites* species, "KA4-POR-01", photographed in an aquarium owned by Kjell Nagy, originates from a shallow-water area in the Maldives, where it was legally collected in 1992.

VERON (1986) proposed dividing the species of the Indo-Pacific into five groups, which do not necessarily reflect their relationships to one another.

❶ Species that grow in **large, massive round** or **helmet-shaped colonies**, often with a rim or edge around their centre: Out of this group, three species are more frequently seen than the others: *Porites lobata*, *P. australiensis*, and *P. lutea*. *Porites lobata* is very common and widespread in the Indo-Pacific, from the Nicobar Islands in the west, to Hawaii in the east, where it is numerous. This species is usually pale brown, but may develop brighter colours in shallow waters. It can form huge colonies measuring several metres in diameter or form micro-atolls in shallow waters. *Porites australiensis* is also very common in the Indo-Pacific, where it is found from Chagos Archipelago in the east, to the Marshall Islands in the west, often occurring together with the two other species in the group. *Porites lutea* is perhaps the best known species in this group, forming massive colonies that can reach several metres across. The surface is usually smooth, but the colonies often develop irregular humps of variable size, or develop columniform lobes (VERON & PICHON, 1982). It is distributed from the Red Sea to the Tuamoto Archipelago.

Smaller *Porites* colonies are often introduced into aquaria with pieces of live rock. Although many of these rocks are taken from shallow-water areas, far away from any coral reefs, it is still possible that *Porites* colonies growing on them belong to this group. We have observed that these colonies do amazingly well in aquaria, although, as in all *Porites*, the growth rate is rather slow and restricted to a few mm per year.

Porites cylindrica is one of the branching species of the genus. It can be frequently found in shallow-water areas on reef flats, as here at Bunaken, Indonesia.

❷ Species that grow in **small, massive round** or **helmet-shaped colonies**. Among this group, the species that stands out is *Porites murrayensis* which can be found from the Maldives and the Nicobars, to Samoa and the Marshall Islands, and which grows in helmet-shaped colonies with a circumference of up to 20 cm. We collected a *Porites* species near the Maldives that is probably *P. murrayensis*. It grew on the reef flat exposed to the most intense sunlight and showed a deep and most beautiful blue colour. However, this rapidly turned to light beige in an aquarium illuminated with a 1000 Watt-HQI 6500 °K bulb. The colony prospered and grew significantly; it still continues to do so today, five years on from the date of collection.

❸ Species that form **branching colonies**: *Porites cylindrica* and *P. nigrescens* are two commonly found members of this group. *P. cylindrica* lives in shallow water on reef flats and is a splendid yellow, violet, or green colour. The colonies can be very large, reaching a diameter of more than 10 metres. Although the growth form is clearly branching, the bases of the colonies may be encrusting in habit. The branches are usually less than 30 cm long and less than 4 cm across near their bases. In general, they are cylindrical and taper towards the tips, which are blunt, conical or flattened at the points where branch division occurs. These branches may also anastomose (VERON & PICHON, 1982). *P. cylindrica* is one of the most widely distributed of stony corals, being found from Madagascar and east Africa, to the Marshall and Tonga Islands.

The growth of *Porites nigrescens* is very similar to that of *P. cylindrica* and the two are difficult to distinguish, but *P. nigrescens* looks more knotty. *P. cylindrica* has very flat corallites, while those of *P. nigrescens* grow twice as deep and have a concave form. The branches of *P. nigrescens* arise from a base that may, as in *P. cylindrica*, be encrusting,

Porites rus

Distribution: Indo-Pacific; from the Red Sea, to Hawaii and as far east as Costa Rica.

Size and growth form: Can create huge colonies that are laminar or consist of contorted anastomosing branches and columns. Can cover large areas of reef flats, and is found in many habitats, but is usually uncommon.

Food: Probably feeds primarily on products translocated from its zooxanthellae, but probably also utilizes minute plankton and possibly dissolved organic nutrients.

Description: The branches are fragile and the corallites are very small. Colouring is normally pale cream or yellow, or dark bluish-brown, often with pale branch tips.

Aquarium maintenance:
– **General:** Grows very well. It is a tenacious species which grows excellently in strong light near the surface. Easily stung by other corals, however, so its location in an aquarium must be chosen carefully.
– **Lighting:** Strong.
– **Water circulation:** Moderate to strong.
– **Propagation possibilities:** Easily propagated through fragmentation.

GA: + ; TO: + ; SE: +

Photos:
– Top left: Population in the Maldives
– Bottom left: Aquarium colony
– Bottom right: Close-up of the small corallites

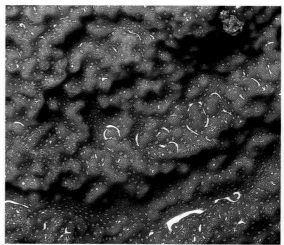

but is not more than 2.5 cm thick. These branches taper gradually from the base to the tips which are usually acute (VERON & PICHON, 1982). *P. nigrescens* can be found from east Africa, to the Fiji and Tonga Islands.

❹ Species that grow in **shallow, irregular** or **column-shaped colonies**. *Porites lichen* stands out in this group. It has a variety of growth forms and may exhibit an encrusting habit that develops laminae (thick plates) or can be sub-massive with columns and branches. It can be found from the Red Sea, to Samoa and French Polynesia, and is of a strong yellow colour.

❺ One species, *Porites rus*, with significantly smaller corallites than the members of the other groups. This species is not like the other *Porites* spp. and can easily be confused with *Montipora* spp. As *P. rus* clearly differs from the other *Porites* species it is grouped in the subgenus *Synaraea* (see fact page 380).

Porites species of the Caribbean

There are at least four Porites species in the Caribbean (Colin, 1978). *Porites divaricata, P. porites* and *P. furcata* form branching colonies, while *P. asteroides* forms massive, encrusting growths.

Porites furcata has thin branches, forms dense populations and grows in regions with shallow water, where it can cover large areas. At low water, many parts of the colony die off; thus *P. furcata* contributes to the "coral rubble" in considerable amounts. In some locations, *P. furcata* even grows on deeper reef inclines. The colouring is usually yellow or brown.

Porites divaricata has very thin branches measuring a maximum of 6 mm in thickness (COLIN, 1978). It normally grows in calm, shallow water areas which are seldom deeper than 15 m and is well distributed in the Caribbean Sea, including south Florida. Some authors consider *P. divaricata* as a sub-species of *P. porites*.

Porites porites has branches which can be up to 2.5 cm thick, although they are very short. Because of these characteristics, the growth form appears more massive than branched. *P. porites* is well distributed in the Caribbean Sea, including south Florida. Its colouring varies from pale beige to purple, often with bleached branch tips.

Porites asteroides is variable in its growth form. In strongly exposed, shallow water areas, it grows as encrusted, creeping colonies.

At 8-10 m deep, it grows as round, massive colonies, while at greater depths - it has been found at depths of up to 50m - it forms flat colonies which maximize the intake of light (COLIN, 1978). *P. asteroides* has the widest distribution of the Caribbean species: it can be found in the entire Caribbean Sea,

near the Bermudas and even along the Texas coast.

HUMANN (1993) considers the various *Porites* species of the Caribbean as only growth forms of *P. porites*. At the same time, he names *P. branneri*, which develops encrusted growths on coral rubble and stones.

Porites porites (above) and *Porites asteroides* (below) Photos: Scott W. Michael

The long and delicate polyps of a *Goniopora* sp., "KA4-GON-01", photographed in an aquarium.

Beautiful *Goniopora* sp., "KA4-GON-02", on the Great Barrier Reef

Aquarium care of *Porites* species

When caring for *Porites* species in aquaria, it must be remembered, as a general principle, that the majority of species live in shallow-water areas subjected to high light intensities which are often fully exposed to wave action and tidal currents. Their slow growth can cause difficulties when attempting to get tiny fragments to attach, making it necessary to anchor such pieces well to the substratum, so that they will not be moved by the current. Many colonies of *Porites* contain christmas tree worms from the genus *Spirobranchus*. These tiny tubeworms settle as larvae on the surface of the colonies, often where there is a weakened or slightly damaged spot. Subsequently, the corals slowly overgrow the worms' calcareous tubes. The result is a colony of *Porites* covered with the most beautiful feather duster crowns in all imaginable colours.

There are several species of *Spirobranchus*, a group that we will return to in the next volume of this book series. In the early days of the hobby, corals housing these worms were frequently imported, but the corals themselves were, nearly always, dead and

became overgrown with filamentous algae, which killed off the tiny worms. Today, however, living corals possessing tubeworms are common and can easily be kept alive and grown, providing us with the opportunity of studying a remarkable relationship between two coral reef organisms at close quarters. Colonies imported for aquaria are usually the size of a fist and, if these are to survive, it is essential to place them in an well-illuminated spot, since shaded parts will bleach and eventually die. Christmas tree worms are filter feeders which can be fed with tiny food particles or "liquid food" suspended in the water. We have, however, experienced that the worms usually capture sufficient prey items from the aquarium water without having to be specially fed. Therefore, whether or not feeding is required, probably depends on the concentration of plankton produced within the system.

Genus *Goniopora*

The genus *Goniopora* is comprised of around 30 species (VERON, 1995), which are distributed in the Indo-Pacific. The genus has, however, not been revised since the early work of BERNARD (1903 and

1906), when 14 species were recognized; a revision is therefore absolutely necessary (VERON & PICHON, 1982). A differentiation of the separate species is best carried out by comparing skeletal structures with the structure of the living polyps seen under water. *Goniopora* spp. have been major reef-builders since ancient times and the present species still form mono- or multi-specific stands in inshore environments dominated by terrigenous sediments (VERON, 1995).

Colonies are usually columnar or massive, having corallites with thick, but porous, walls and calices that are filled with compacted septa and columella. However, a couple of species (*Goniopora somaliensis* and *G. stutchburyi*) develop flat or encrusting shapes. The polyps, which can be used to separate the different species when seen under water (VERON, 1986), are long and fleshy, each possessing 24 tentacles. Anyone interested in learning more about the skeletal details of the genus, should consult VERON & PICHON (1982).

One of the most common *Goniopora* species in the ocean, and probably also in trade, is *G. lobata*. It is distributed from the Red Sea and east Africa, eastwards to

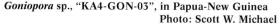

Goniopora sp., "KA4-GON-03", in Papua-New Guinea
Photo: Scott W. Michael

Large, pink-coloured *Goniopora* sp., "KA4-GON-04", photographed on a reef near Indonesia

the Fiji Islands and to Samoa. In the ocean, *G. lobata* creates large mono-specific stands, often in turbid water. The colonies are hemispherical or short, thick columns, and the polyps are very long, looking like those of *G. djiboutiensis*, but having smaller oral cones (the conical area surrounding the mouth found in the centre of each polyp). The calices are 3-5 mm in diameter.

This same habitat and way of life is also shared by *G. djiboutiensis*, whose skeleton resembles that of other *Goniopora* spp., but from which it can be separated by its large and prominent oral cones. It is found from the western Indian Ocean, to the Fiji and Marshall Islands.

Goniopora stokesii, whose colony shape varies greatly with habitat, can be found from the Red Sea and east Africa, to Vanuatu. It is distinguished from the other *Goniopora* species in that it often lives unattached, especially if found on soft-sediment bottoms. In such habitats, the colonies are normally small, with a diameter of less than 10 cm. Colonies that live on solid substrates can be attached and massive, or form short, thick columns (Veron & Pichon, 1982). A good way of identifying this species is that colonies are often hollow, with small daughter colonies often forming in the soft tissue of the parent colony (see chapter 2, page 62). Like the

other mentioned species of *Goniopora*, *G. stokesii* is also frequently found in the hobby.

The polyps of most *Goniopora* spp. are long and delicate, making the expanded colonies look extraordinarily beautiful and decorative. They are well loved by aquarists and are counted among the first stony corals to be imported. However, *Goniopora* species are not easily keep over a long period of time and seem to require specific aquarium conditions that we do not, as yet, know in detail. Over time, the polyps often tend to expand less and less fre-

quently until, after some months, the colony only expands very little, if at all. As far as we know, this is true for all species. There are, however, reports of *Goniopora* species that have lived for years in an aquarium without showing signs of closing. Dr. Bruce Carlson, the director of the Waikiki Aquarium, has been very successful with an "open aquarium system" (with constantly flowing fresh seawater), in which *Goniopora* have lived for more than 15 years.

The cause for the stunted growth observed in our closed aqua-

This close-up shows the typical structure of *Goniopora* species with 24 tentacles on each individual polyp. Photo: Scott W. Michael

Top left: *Alveopora catalai* in an aquarium
Bottom left: This close-up shows the typical structure of *Alveopora* species with 12 tentacles on each individual polyp.
Top right: Differently coloured *Alveopora catalai* in Papua-New Guinea

Photo: Scott W. Michael

rium systems is unknown to us. Perhaps one of the reasons may be found in the way that these corals ingest food. Various aquarists have reported differently about the food intake, many believing that the polyps do not catch plankton, but live entirely off dissolved substances found in the water, or on the products of their zooxanthellae. Indeed, it seems possible that *Goniopora* species may live mainly off essential substances in the water, which cannot be found in sufficient quantities in closed aquarium systems. Or, perhaps, they need nutritive substances that we cannot, at the moment, provide for in aquaria. It could also be that *Goniopora* are susceptible to parasite attack, but we are just speculating; we have not looked any further into this theory. Whatever the cause may be, we do not recommend importing *Goniopora* species, as long as the reasons for their stunted growth remains unexplained. We would also be thankful for reports on the conditions existing in aquaria where *Goniopora* spp.

have been kept successfully for a long period of time.

Genus *Alveopora*

The genus *Alveopora* is one of the larger genera of stony corals that has remained systematically unrevised since the beginning of the twentieth century. *Alveopora* species look very similar to *Goniopora* species, but have shorter polyps. Whereas the polyps of *Goniopora* always have 24 tentacles, *Alveopora* polyps only possess 12. The tips of the tentacles in *Alveopora* are usually swollen when fully expanded and, as in *Goniopora* they are usually extended, both during day and night. The skeleton of *Alveopora* species shows some similarities with that of *Goniopora* species, but there are differences as well. In general, the skeleton of *Alveopora* is simple and shows few distinctive features, making the members of the genus hard to describe.

Alveopora shows about the same distribution in the Indo-Pa-

cific as *Goniopora* and, although *Alveopora* contains, at least, 16 species, none are common. *Alveopora* species are seldom abundant on any reefs and, perhaps moreso than in other genera of stony corals, its occurrence is unpredictable (VERON & PICHON, 1982). Some *Alveopora* species, for example, the most common *A. catalai*, prefer turbid or deep water, while others, such as *A. verrilliana*, live on reef slopes with crystal-clear and nutrient-poor water.

A. catalai forms ramose colonies, composed of gnarled branches that divide irregularly. These branches have the same thickness within each colony: 12-55 mm in diameter on average (VERON & PICHON, 1982). The living coral is pale brownish-pink when the polyps are retracted, while expanded polyps are usually dull green, brown or yellow. *A. catalai* is one of the most common corals in turbid habitats and can form large mono-specific stands in such environments. This species is found in New Caledonia and Australia

Siderastrea radians: colony (left, photo: J. Sprung) and close-up of the corallites (right).

(VERON, 1986).

A more widely distributed species is *A. allingi* which is found from the Maldives in the west, to the Philippines and Samoa Islands in the east. The colonies are encrusting and submassive, or consist of short, irregular lobes with rounded even surfaces (VERON & PICHON, 1982). The tightly compacted polyps are usually green or brown in colour and can reach a length of as much as 10 cm. This species is, however, highly polymorphic. It occurs in deeper waters, on reef slopes and on reefs near the limit for reef appearance, and is represented by ecomorphs in these different habitats, see VERON & PICHON (1982) for details.

Alveopora gigas is found only around Australia, where it is common in the Houtman Abrolhos Islands in Western Australia, but is uncommon elsewhere. The colonies form blunt-ended, irregular columns and have corallites with a diameter of 4.3 - 7.6 mm. The polyps are very long and can reach 10 cm or more, with a diameter of more than 2 cm.

Alveopora verrilliana is found from Australia eastwards in the Pacific, to Hawaii, and has colonies that are composed of short, irregularly-dividing knob-like branches (VERON, 1986), a growth form which is not shared with other Australian species of the genus. This species prefers clear water on reef slopes.

Alveopora species are occasionally imported for aquaria, where they seem to prefer the bright light of HQI lamps and develop fluorescent pigments. They do not appear to capture plankton, but, according to our experience, are, like *Goniopora* spp., among the more difficult stony corals to keep alive over a long period of time.

Family Siderastreidae

This family of stony corals, Siderastreidae, incorporates six genera: *Anomastrea, Coscinaraea, Horastrea, Psammocora, Pseudosiderastrea* and *Siderastrea*.

Anomastrea, Horastrea and Pseudosiderastrea

All three genera are monotypic, which means that they contain only one species. The genera *Anomastrea* and *Horastrea* can only be found in the western Indian Ocean. *Anomastrea irregularis* is similar to the *Siderastrea* species, but its corallites are more elongated. *Horastrea indica* grows in placoid (plate-like) colonies and resembles the *Blastomussa* species from the family Mussidae, or the *Favia* species from the Faviidae. Its distribution is limited to Madagascar and the central coastal areas of east Africa. *Pseudosiderastrea tayamai* is a rare stony coral that is only known from the Indo-Malaysian archipelago. It is found exclusively on rock substrates in shallow waters where other corals are seldom found. It is one of the few corals that does not show any environmental or geographical growth variations (VERON, 1993).

Genus *Siderastrea*

There are differences of opinions about whether the genus *Siderastrea* contains two or three species. There is agreement among the experts, however, that there are two species in the Caribbean, *Siderastrea radians* and *S. siderea*. Some authors, namely VINE (1980), WOOD (1983) and DITLEV (1980), list a third species, *S. savignyana*, that was first described by MILNE-EDWARDS & HAIME in 1850, and can be found in the western Indian Ocean and the Red Sea. VERON (1993 and pers. com.) lists *S. savignyana* as a valid species from the Indo-Pacific. The type locality is the Red Sea, but *S. savignyana* is currently only known from a single specimen collected in the Philippines. *S. radians* is endemic to the west Atlantic and is probably not valid for the Indo-Pacific.

SHEPARD et al. (1992) have remarked on several occasions that *Siderastrea* species are very tolerant of extreme environmental conditions, such as temperature and salt content. The best features that help to recognize these species are the corallites, which are arranged in a star-shaped pattern.

Siderastrea radians and *S. siderea* can be found quite frequently in the Caribbean. *S. siderea* can create large massive colonies

Psammocora contigua

Distribution: Indo-Pacific; from the Red Sea and east Africa, to French Polynesia. Common in restricted shallow-water habitats in most central Indo-Pacific countries (VERON, 1993).

Size and growth form: The colonies are a mixture of flattened branches, columns or nodules. In deeper waters, all branches are flattened. The colonies are sometimes found in a free-living state (VERON, 1986 and 1993).

Food: Probably feeds primarily on products translocated from its zooxanthellae, but probably also utilizes minute plankton and, possibly, dissolved organic nutrients.

Description: The corallites are flat and shallow, giving the colony a smooth surface. The structure of the corallites varies greatly with environmental conditions, though. Colouring is usually pale brown to dark green-brown.

Aquarium maintenance:
– **General:** Very tenacious and among the easiest stony corals to keep. It is often brought into aquaria on pieces of live rock. Can grow into spectacular colonies.
– **Lighting:** Strong
– **Water circulation:** Moderate to strong.
– **Propagation possibilities:** Easy to propagate through fragmentation.

GA: + ; TO: + ; SE: +

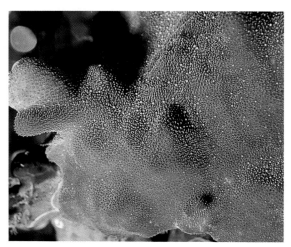

Photos:
– Top: This colony developed from live rock grown in an aquarium owned by Kenneth Olsen from Oslo, for more than 8 years.
– Bottom: Close-up of the corallites

and can be found down to depths of 40 m. It can be distinguished from *S. radians* because its corallites are larger and have a clearly recognizable dark spot in the centre. In addition, its often red-coloured colonies are larger than those of *S. radians*, which only attain a maximum diameter of 30 cm.

Siderastrea radians occupies most habitats in the Caribbean. It tolerates extreme environmental conditions, such as those encountered in tidal pools which can experience large fluctuations in temperature and salt content. Normally, *S. radians* is green in colour, although this can occasionally change into red, thus making it appear more like *S. siderea*. In some cases, *S. radians* can also exhibit an encrusted, creeping growth form.

We have little direct experience keeping *Siderastrea* species in aquaria. Based on the species' high tolerance for varying environmental conditions, these stony corals are likely to be suitable for coral reef aquaria.

Genus *Psammocora*

The genus *Psammocora* contains several species that are of interest for the coral reef aquarium. The corallites of *Psammocora* species are small, flat, and create patterns from which the species can be distinguished from one another. However, like most corals, *Psammocora* spp. exhibit geographical and environmental growth variations. The genus is found throughout the entire Indo-Pacific and east Pacific, from the Red Sea, to the west coast of Central America.

Psammocora contigua, which is often introduced with pieces of live rock, is the most common species seen in reef aquaria. It grows very rapidly and can develop into large colonies from the tiniest fragments. See fact page 386 for further information on this species.

Psammocora digitata is distributed from the Seychelles, to French Polynesia, where it most

Coscinaraea columna **is uncommon, but can be found in different habitats. This colony was photographed in the Coral Sea.**

often forms colonies in shallow-water biotopes. The form of the corallites is the same as in *P. contigua*. The colonies, however, are larger and stronger and composed of plates and columns.

Psammocora superficialis forms thick plates with irregular ridges and has small, shallow corallites which are irregularly distributed (VERON, 1986). Although it is well distributed in the Indo-Pacific and is found in a wide range of habitats, it is inconspicuous and often overlooked.

Genus *Coscinaraea*

The genus *Cosinaraea* contains eight species, most of which appear similar to *Psammocora* species. *Coscinaraea mcneilli* and *C. marshae* have never been found in tropical waters, but live exclusively in subtropical waters near southern Australia. This means that they tolerate substantially lower temperatures than all the other hermatypic stony corals; the reason for this remains unknown, however.

Coscinaraea exesa and *C. columna* are the only two species in the genus that are common in the Indo-Pacific. *C. exesa* can be found from the Philippines and Australia, to the Fiji Islands. Their colonies are columnar and can often be found in the shallow water of lagoons, where they rise to

a height of several metres. *C. columna* is not as common as *C. exesa*, but occurs in a wide range of shallow-water habitats and is found on most reefs. It develops encrusting or massive colonies and is grey or bright yellow in colour.

Another *Coscinaraea* species, *C. wellsi*, is widely distributed in the Indo-Pacific and can be found from Madagascar and east Africa, to the Marshall Islands, but is quite rare. It forms laminar colonies which can be abundant on vertical or overhanging rock faces where light is restricted (VERON, 1993).

Family Agariciidae

The family Agariciidae incorporates six genera: *Agaricia, Coeloseris, Gardineroseris, Leptoseris, Pachyseris* and *Pavona*. The genera *Coeloseris* and *Gardineroseris* will not be dealt with further in this volume.

Genus *Pavona*

The genus *Pavona* is the most interesting one in the Agariciidae from an aquatic hobby point of view, since some of the species grow very well in reef aquaria, for-

Pavona clavus in the shallow-water area of an Indonesian reef

ming delicate and most beautiful colonies. *Pavona* spp. are found in the Indo-Pacific and the eastern Pacific, from the Red Sea and east Africa, to the western coast of Central America. VERON (1986) lists eight species for Australia alone, while VERON (1993) gives a total of 15 species for the Indo-Pacific.

Most *Pavona* species are well defined, although the genus is not clearly delineated from *Leptoseris* (VERON, 1993). Usually, *Pavona* is divided into two groups:

❶ species that grow in foliaceous (leaf-like) forms;

❷ species that grow in non-foliaceous forms.

Pavona species can often be separated from the corresponding *Leptoseris* species by the fact that the former have corallites on both sides of the "leaf", whereas the latter develop corallites on one side of the "leaf" only. Most *Pavona* species are easy to maintain in an aquarium, but are difficult to identify. In many, including *P. cactus*, the corallites look like tiny stars, (see the close-up photograph on page 389). VERON (1986) gives the following description of the corallites in *Pavona*: "The corallites have poorly defined walls. They are small, shallow depressions, usually with a central columella, sometimes separated by ridges. Corallites are interconnected by prominent septocostae."

Without doubt, the best known species among aquarists is *Pavona cactus*. It has proved a very rapid grower and its foliaceous form is very decorative (see fact sheet on page 389).

Although the other species of *Pavona* can be identified and separated with few problems when seen in the wild, the identification of smaller colonies that develop in reef aquaria can be difficult. *P. decussata* has - unlike *P. cactus* - a thick skeleton and forms more massive colonies with strong, relatively short and upright branches. It can be found from the Red Sea, to Samoa, and often thrives in shallow-water habitats.

Pavona explanulata forms encrusting, or thin, unifacial colonies; sometimes, the colonies can even be submassive or columnar (VERON, 1986). This species is distributed from east Africa and Madagascar, to French-Polynesia. *P. clavus* forms columnar colonies and often occupies shallow habitats exposed to strong currents. It is commonly found in the Indo-Pacific, from the Red Sea and Madagascar in the west, to Central America in the east. *P. varians* grows submassive, laminar or encrusting colonies, or a combination of these three growth forms. This species is widely distributed in the Indo-pacific, from the Red Sea, to Tahiti and Hawaii.

Pavona maldivensis, which occurs in the Indo-Pacific from east Africa to the Pitcairn Islands and Panama, develops columnar colonies or thin, horizontal plates, or a combination of these structures,

Pavona venosa is often overlooked, but is very widespread in the Indo-Pacific.
Photo: Scott W. Michael

Pavona cactus

Distribution: Indo-Pacific; from the Red Sea, to the Marshall Islands and French Polynesia.

Size and growth form: This species exhibits a wide range of growth forms. The colonies are usually thin, contorted, bifacial, upright fronds, with or without thickened, branching bases. Can create colonies with a diameter of 10 m or more, especially in strong current areas which are protected from waves (VERON, 1986 and 1993).

Food: Probably feeds primarily on products translocated from its zooxanthellae, but probably also utilizes minute plankton and, possibly, dissolved organic nutrients.

Description: The foliaceous and twisted branches are thin and delicate and can break easily. Corallites are fine and shallow and aligned in irregular rows parallel to the margin, an arrangement that creates a characteristic pattern. Colouring is normally brown or green.

Aquarium maintenance:

– **General:** Must be handled with care, because the skeleton breaks easily. Otherwise grows very well and can occupy large areas of an aquarium. In general, an excellent species for the reef tank.

– **Lighting:** Strong.

– **Water circulation:** Moderate to strong.

– **Propagation possibilities:** Easy to propagate through fragmentation. However, the fragments are difficult to attach. They are light and thin, and can easily be swept away by currents.

GA: + ; TO: + ; SE: +

Photos:

– Top: Colony on the Great Barrier Reef

Photo: J. E. N. Veron

– Bottom right: A colony in a German reef aquarium

– Bottom left: Close-up of the corallites (magnified x 12)

Leptoseris species often grow in deeper regions of steep reef inclines; this one was found at a depth of 20 m in the Coral Sea.

the form probably being dependent on the strength of the currents and the waves to which the colony is exposed. *P. maldivensis* can be of intensive orange colour in areas with shallow water and can be recognized by its circular corallites. The beautiful *P. venosa* appears from the Red Sea to the Marshall Islands, but is rare.

Leptoseris cucullata, seen here in an aquarium, is common in the Caribbean.
Photo: J. Sprung

Genus *Leptoseris*

The genus *Leptoseris*is is closely related to the genus *Pavona*. It contains approximately 14 species, which are all quite similar to one another. In *Leptoseris* species, the skeleton is somewhat thick and not as brittle as in *Pavona*. The corallites have poorly defined walls; they are small shallow depressions with a central columella, usually separated by ridges and interconnected by fine septo-costae (VERON, 1986). *Leptoseris* colonies develop plate-shaped or spiral, foliaceous forms. Most species live in fairly deep water, where they can often be found around and over cave openings on reef inclines.

Leptoseris mycetoseroides is one of the more common species of the genus, but also one of the most variable ones. It is distributed from east Africa to the Marshall Islands and occurs in many habitats, from shallow reef flats, to deeper waters. *Leptoceris yabei*, which is found from the Maldives to Vanuatu, grow in creeping or foliaceous colonies that can be common on flat substrates (VERON, 1986). The relatively large corallites are found between the fold-shaped structures of the skeleton.

Leptoseris explanata is distributed from the Red Sea, to Australia and Vanuatu. Its skeleton and pattern of corallites, which are well separated from one another, appear similar to those found in *Pavona* spp. *Leptoseris papyracea*, distributed from Madagascar to middle America, and *Leptoseris gardineri*, only found between Malaysia and Samoa, both form delicate, unifacial, foliaceous colonies in which the fronds (or leaves) are irregularly divided and contain only a few corallites each. The fronds look almost contorted or spiral-shaped. Because of this characteristic, they are easy to separate from the other species. *L. gardineri* is, generally, uncommon, but can form large mono-specific stands in some lower reef slopes.

The genus *Leptoseris* is represented in the Caribbean exclusively by *Leptoseris cucullata*, which forms plate-shaped colonies with distinctive thin septa running towards the edges of the colonies. The colours are tan to yellow-brown, brown or grey, or may be fluorescent green (Hu-MANN, 1993).

Genus *Pachyseris*

According to VERON (1986), the genus *Pachyseris* contains 12 nominal species, of which the majority are probably synonyms of *Pachyseris rugosa* and *P. speciosa*, which exhibit a wide range of growth forms. The colonies grow as plates or ridges and have a strong skeletal structure, which allows them to be identified easily. No expanding polyps have been observed in *Pachyseris* species, either during the day, or night (VERON, 1986).

Pachyseris rugosa is widely distributed in the Indo-Pacific, occurring from the Red Sea, to Indonesia, Samoa, and the Marshall Islands. It can build large monospecific populations on some reefs, but is normally found as smaller colonies. We, ourselves, have seen *L. rugosa* in Indonesia, where the species was quite numerously represented in calm

Pachyseris rugosa photographed at Bunaken, Indonesia.

waters on a shallow reef flat, growing together with a variety of other stony corals.

Pachyseris speciosa seldom grows into colonies with a diameter exceeding 2 m. Colonies are usually unifacial and horizontal in growth. This species is found throughout most of the Indo-Pacific, from the Red Sea to French Polynesia. It is very abundant around Australia, especially in deeper water, but is more rarely seen towards higher latitudes (VERON,

1993). While *P. rugosa* shows a great deal of growth variation, the opposite is true for *P. speciosa*. The colonies of this species may develop upright ridges or columns, with more than one row of corallites sometimes occurring between the ridges.

We have not yet had any experience maintaining *Pachyseris* species in aquaria. Our observations carried out at some natural locations where *Pachyseris rugosa* is found lead us to assume,

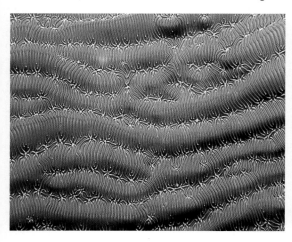
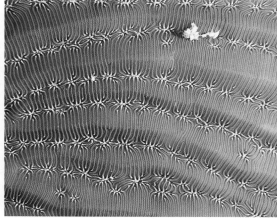

Of all the polyp and corallite structures found in stony corals, those of the genus *Agaricia* are, perhaps, the most beautiful. The picture on the left shows these structures in *A. grahamae*, while that on the right shows those of *A. lamarcki*. These species are difficult to separate, but the very thin septa that run between the polyps of *A. grahamae* are equal in size, in contrast to those in *Agaricia lamarcki*, where the septa alternate in height and thickness.

Photos: Scott W. Michael

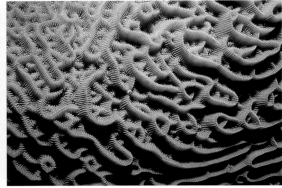

Agaricia agaricites is a beautifully formed stony coral (photo left: Dr. B. Carlson) which has a brittle corallite structure (photo right: J. Cairns-Michael).

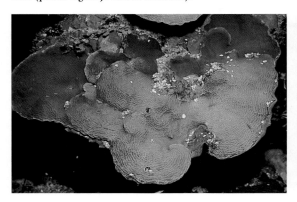

Agaricia grahamae (left) forms large, thin, laminar colonies that often grow on reefs, while *A. fragilis* (right) grows as small, free-living colonies.   Photos: Scott W. Michael

however, that *Pachyseris* species are suitable for coral reef aquaria.

Genus *Agaricia*

The genus *Agaricia* is endemic to the Caribbean and contains eight species. The majority grow in very beautiful colonies which are often plate-shaped, but can also exhibit varying forms, depending on habitat.

Agaricia agaricites is the most common species of its genus. It can even be found on mangrove roots. It is an indestructible stony coral which can regenerate itself quickly through fragmentation following damage (for example, by a hurricane). According to HUMANN (1993), this species occurs in four different growth forms.

Other *Agaricia* species are: *A. tenuifolia, A. undata, A. grahamae,* *A. lamarcki,* and *A. fragilis,* of which, *A. fragilis* is the only one which can also be found in the Bermudas. *Agaricia grahamae* forms large, thin plates that often overlap each other. The colonies have a dark colour and the shining white polyps contrast beautifully with this background. The very thin septa that run between the polyps are of equal size, in contrast to the same structure in *Agaricia lamarcki,* where the septa alternate in height and thickness (see figure on page 391). *A. lamarcki* exhibits the same growth forms and is as abundant in deeper reef areas as *A. grahamae* (HUMANN, 1993).

In general, the genus *Agaricia* has been little studied and few observations of captive specimens exist. We have, however, kept an *Agaricia* sp. in our aquarium. The colony in question grew solidly from the foot of a gorgonian. HQI-light appeared to be well tolerated.

Family Fungiidae

While the majority of stony corals live attached, the mushroom corals of the family Fungiidae are free-living, solitary species. It is only as very young corals that they live sedentary lives as anthocauli (singular: anthocaulus = small, attached polyp). Anthocauli detach themselves from the substratum to begin a life as free-living polyps which grow into circular, elongated or dome-shaped individuals. Mushroom corals have the largest single polyps of all the corals found in the family. Additionally, there are also colony-building species of Fungiidae, and one ahermatypic genus - *Fungiacyathus* - which lives at great depths. Generally, mushroom corals are seen in shallow water between sand and coral fragments.

The boundary between colonial and solitary corals is not as clearly defined as it may appear. Usually, a coral is defined as "colony-building" when it has more than one mouth opening, and as "solitary" when it has only one mouth opening. Among the Fungiidae, there are many species, for example, in the genera *Fungia* and *Diaseris*, which are solitary according to this definition. At the same time, there are atypical individuals of the same species which have several mouth openings (VERON, 1986). *Fungia simplex*, for instance, always has several mouth openings and, because of this, appears to be a colony. On the other hand, its other characteristics make it appear most similar to *Fungia echinata*, which is a solitary coral.

The family Fungiidae has been discovered among the oldest known stony coral fossil finds on numerous occasions. This leads to the conclusion that this is a very old family and, from this, it can be assumed that solitary corals were the ancestors of their colony-building counterparts - and not the other way around.

Another speciality of the species of this family is their substantial regenerative capability after damage. When corals live free, they can be easily thrown around by currents and waves and can, as a result, become damaged or covered in sand. In order to survive, they have to possess the ability to regenerate themselves. This regeneration can occur in the form of a "repair" to a polyp, or through the growth of a new generation of polyps after the mother polyp has divided. In other cases, the mother polyp can create a large number of daughter polyps as anthocauli, these daughter polyps growing quickly

A group of free-living polyps of a *Fungia* species photographed in a shallow lagoon in the Maldives.

Sessile anthocaulus of a *Fungia* species on a reef in the Maldives

Regeneration of a broken polyp of *Fungia granulosa* in the Red Sea
Photo: Dr. N. Furman

The corals of the family Fungiidae often propagate by forming daughter polyps called anthocauli. These can result through asexual propagation after damage to adult polyps, but can also be formed from a planula larva that has settled after sexual reproduction. Above left: two minute anthocauli have formed on the underside of a *Heliofungia actiniformis* polyp. Above right: several anthocauli have grown on the side of a giant clam shell. Håvard Nilsen is holding some daughter polyps just after they have become detached (below left). The largest polyp is about 3 cm in diameter. The photo below right shows how one of the stalks developed a new anthocaulus after the first one had freed itself.

and eventually detaching themselves.

The formation of anthocauli also occurs in aquaria. STÜBER (1990b and 1994) and NILSEN (1990) describe the process in detail (see also above). One peculiarity is that the stalk - after an anthocaulus has detached itself - regenerates to form new daughter polyps. To us, this appears to share many similarities with the strobilation of an Ephyra larva (page 36). It could also be thought of - very unscientifically - that, through anthocaulus formation, the Fungiidae exhibit a primitive level of development.

Owing to the generation of anthocauli, a continuous series of daughter polyps can be obtained in aquaria. It is therefore advisable to leave dying Fungiidae polyps in the aquarium, since, not infrequently, daughter polyps will be found after some time, either on the dying polyps themselves, or in the patches of dead skeleton. We have also observed a similar type of production of daughter polyps in *Cynarina lacrymalis* from the family Mussidae. In the ocean, sexual reproduction has also been observed, the result of which are stationary anthocauli.

In our opinion, mushroom corals are best suited to aquaria with a relatively large amount of sandy or rubble bottom, or containing shallow water over pieces of live rock; if possible, a combination of sand and live rock would be best. We would like to encourage aquarists to think up something new and to try to create coral reef aquaria in a different way to those dictated by "traditional" methods. One possibility could be a shallow sand- or rubble-zone aquarium with a flat decoration housing several corals from the family Fungiidae mixed in with other animals naturally found in such reef zones, for example, symbiotic shrimps and crabs. Setting up such a special system could prove an exciting experience and represent a most unusual interpretation of the term "reef aquarium".

Genus *Cycloseris*

The genus *Cycloseris* contains the smallest species in the family. VERON (1993) lists 11 species in the genus, of which only *Cycloseris cyclolites* can be said to be common. With a maximum diameter of 4 cm, it is small in comparison to *Fungia* species, but its construction is quite similar. *C. cyclolites* is distributed in the Indo-Pacific, from the Red Sea, to Australia, Belau (Palau) and Japan. It lives - sometimes in large numbers - on sandy ground and most often inhabits flat, sandy substrata between reefs. This species is recognized by its neat, fine symmetrical structure and concave lower surface (VERON, 1986). *Cycloseris patelliformis* is far more seldomly encountered than *C. cyclolites*, but can, nevertheless, be found in the same habitat. The remaining species of the genus must be regarded as very rare. We have, to date, only seen a *Cycloseris* species in an aquarium at Hagenbecks Tierpark in Hamburg, where a small group of polyps was growing on the sandy substratum and appeared to be doing very well. Because *Cycloseris* species are difficult to distinguish from young *Fungia* species, we do not rule out the possibility that one or other *Cycloseris* species may already exist in aquaria or may, at least, be available in shops.

Genus *Diaseris*

The genus *Diaseris*, which includes only two species: *Diaseris distorta* and *Diaseris fragilis*, is widely distributed throughout the Indo-Pacific. *D. distorta* can be found as far east as the west coast of Central America, while *D. fragilis* is only distributed westwards to the Marshall Islands. Both species are relatively uncommon, but can be found in large populations in certain locations where they occupy soft sediment bottoms. *Diaseris* species reproduce

Cycloseris species "KA4-FUN-01" in an aquarium at Hagenbecks Tierpark in Hamburg. This species is normally found in a free-living state on sandy reef areas. It is well suited to life in a coral reef aquarium that contains large sandy areas, or in a special sand-zone aquarium.

through natural autotomy, where a single polyp breaks up into several wedge-shaped daughter colonies that regenerate a mount and grow into healthy new polyps. The result is a population that consists of various stages of polyp regeneration and contains individual polyps of different shapes and ages. Autotomy can also be found in other Fungiidae. *Diaseris* species should be interesting subjects for reef aquaria, but they appear to be rare in the trade and we, ourselves, lack direct experience with them.

Genus *Heliofungia*

Heliofungia actiniformis is, from the aquaristic point of view, one of the oldest, most beautiful, most loved and most common mushroom corals. It is the only species in the genus and is easy to recognize because of its extremely long tentacles. Individuals with tentacles up to 50 cm long have been found - a record for stony corals.

Heliofungia actiniformis has a limited distribution in the central Indo-Pacific, with its central distribution in the Indo-Malaysian region, where it can be found in lagoons, often on sandy bottoms, or on ground covered with coral fragments. *H. actiniformis* is quite variable in its colouring, with green or green-brown specimens possessing brown or beige tentacles and a white "button" on the tips of the tentacles. More rarely, purple or pink individuals can be seen.

Heliofungia actiniformis requires a large amount of space in aquaria. According to our experience, a carefully acclimatized individual that has been imported without any damage, can live for years in an aquarium. However, we have discovered that *H. actiniformis* is very sensitive to increases in UV light. The polyp can die suddenly if the light from HQI lights becomes too strong, for example, when an old bulb is replaced with a new one, or when the coral is placed in a more intensely illuminated spot in the aquarium. We have also discovered that newly bought specimens can become the victims of bacterial infection shortly after they are introduced into a reef aquarium. In this respect, *H. actiniformis* seems to be more sensitive than many other corals. In our experience, it is most important to keep the polyp free from any form of damage. *H. actiniformis* should be treated very carefully by collectors and dealers, as well as by aquarists.

Heliofungia actiniformis
Anemone Mushroom Corals

Distribution: Indo-Pacific; from Singapore and Vietnam, east to Samoa and the Carolinas, south to New Caledonia and north to southern Japan. Usually found in protected areas, or in deeper fore reefs.

Size and growth form: Up to 50 cm in diameter, tentacles up to 25 cm, mouth opening up to 3 cm. Free-living, except for the juvenile stages, which live attached as anthocauli (see text page 394). Exhibit few geographical and envirnomental growth variations.

Food: Uncertain; definitely feeds in part from the products of its zooxanthellae, but also eats plankton and other organic material.

Description: Normally coloured green or brown, but occasionally also pink or red. Long tentacles with white, green, or red "buttons" at the end. The septa have long teeth (see drawing on page 398), but the skeleton is, essentially, similar to that of *Fungia* spp. The tentacles are extended day and night and are the longest found in stony corals.

Aquarium maintenance:

– **General:** Should be kept in a sand-zone or rubble-zone aquarium if possible. During purchase, be sure to look for injuries, because damaged polyps generally don't improve. Injured specimens are sensitive to bacterial infections. Therefore, care is necessary during transportation, acclimatization and placement in the aquarium. Acclimatized individuals are somewhat tenacious. Requires a large amount of space.

– **Lighting:** Medium to strong.

– **Water circulation:** Moderate.

– **Propagation possibilities:** We can confirm that anthocauli can develop on the underside of a polyp (see page 394). There is a least one report (from Germany; M. MEGERLE, pers. com.) that a polyp of *H. actiniformis* spawned in the reef aquarium and that the larvae developed into many sessile anthocauli that grew and developed succesfully in the aquarium.

GA: + ; TO: + ; SE: +/-

Photos:
– Top: Two different colour variations in an aquarium
– Centre: Pink colour variation in an aqaurium
– Bottom: Close-up of a polyp with symbiotic shrimp, *Periclimenes sp.*, photographed in Indonesia.

Photo: Scott W. Michael

Genus Fungia

With the about 33 species, the genus *Fungia* is the richest in the family. It occurs in most of the Indo-Pacific, from the Red Sea and east Africa in the west, to Hawaii and the Pitcairn Islands in the east. Characteristics of the genus include short, tapering tentacles packed with nematocysts and a very large mouth opening. The growth form is often round or convex, although some species, such as *Fungia simplex*, form elongated colonies. *Fungia* spp. are frequently hit and easily moved by waves. Therefore, on coral reefs, *Fungia* species often live in places where they are protected from strong wave action, as in lagoons or deep on reef inclines; they are seldom found on the reef edge.

The skeleton is built from many, very thin, septa which stretch from the mouth opening in the centre, to the sides of the polyp. These septa break very easily, so the polyps must be handled carefully. Individual species are distinguished from each other by the form of the serration of the polyp septa on the top and underside of the skeleton (see drawing on page 398); there is little geographical variation in the overall growth form of each species. In aquaria, *Fungia* species appear to be easy to keep, although we recommend that they be kept in a special sand-zone aquarium.

VERON (1986) divides the genus *Fungia* into five subgenera (see table below). The most common species is *Fungia (Fungia) fungites* which is very common throughout the range of the genus, except around the Cocos Keeling Atoll in the eastern Indian Ocean, where it is uncommon (VERON, 1993). The polyp reaches a maximum diameter of 28 cm.

Fungia (Danafungia) danai has very characteristic teeth on the septa on the underside of the skeletoon, although it appears similar in growth form to *F. fungites* and also reaches approximately the same size of a maximum of 30 cm. *F. danai* is distributed from Madagascar, to Tahiti and the Tuamotu Islands. *F. (Danafungia) horrida* is distributed from the Red Sea, to Tahiti, although it does not grow as large as the previous species; usually no more than 20 cm in diameter.

Fungia (Verrillofungia) repanda is very common and distributed in the Indo-Pacific from the Red Sea, to the Tuamotu Islands. It has fine teeth on the upper side and irregular spines on the underside of the septa. It attains a maximum diameter of 30 cm. *F. repanda* is very difficult to distinguish from *F. (Verillofungia) concinna*. The two species overlap in their distribution, although *F. concinna* attains a maximum diameter of 16 cm. Somewhat rarer is *F. (Verillofungia) granulosa*, which measures a maximum of 13.5 cm in diameter and is distributed from the Red Sea, to French Polynesia.

Fungia (Pleuractis) scutaria is easy to recognize, in that it has small bumps between the lime septa of the skeleton, where, normally, fine teeth are found. These bumps are often coloured a very decorative rich green. *F. scutaria*, which reaches a maximum 17 cm in diameter, is widely distributed in the Indo-Pacific: from the Red Sea and South Africa, to Hawaii and the Pitcairn Islands. *F. paumotensis* does also belong to subgenus *Pleuractis*. It is the first species of the family to be discussed here that exhibits a long, oval growth form, which can attain a maximum diameter of 25 cm. It is considered quite common and is distributed from the Red Sea and Madagascar, to Japan, Hawaii and the Tuamotu Islands.

Fungia (Ctenactis) echinata has a clearly elongated growth form. In contrast to the other elongated mushroom corals, it has only one mouth opening, which makes it immediately identifiable. It is commonly found from the Red Sea, to Japan and the Society Islands. *F. (Ctenactis) crassa* is similar to *F.*

Subgenera of the genus *Fungia*

(modified from VERON, 1986)

Subgenus	Number of Species	Polyp forms	Septal teeth	Costal spines	Species
Fungia	1	Circular	Triangular, pointed	Conical, smooth	*fungites*
Danafungia	6	Circular	Large, with a thickened rib	Elongated	*danai, corona, scruposa, horrida, valida, klunzingeri*
Verillofungia	4	Circular	Fine, usually with a series of ridges parallel to the margin	Blunt or granular	*repanda, concinna, scabra, granulosa*
Pleuractis	3	Elongated	Fine	Fine	*scutaria, paumontensis, moluccensis*
Ctenactis	2	Elongated	Fine	Fine	*echinata, crassa*

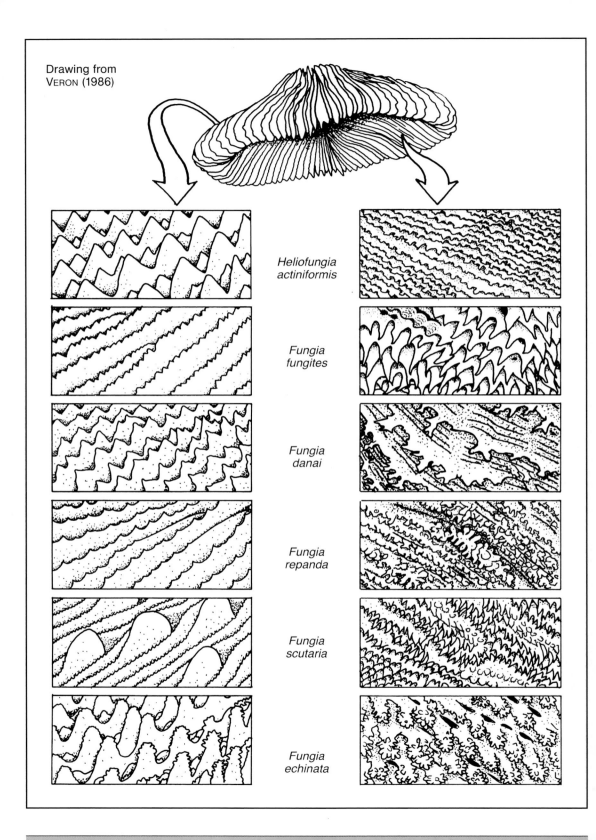

Drawing from
Veron (1986)

Heliofungia
actiniformis

Fungia
fungites

Fungia
danai

Fungia
repanda

Fungia
scutaria

Fungia
echinata

echinata, although it possesses more mouth openings along its long axis. Its distribution stretches from the Red Sea, to the Fiji Islands.

We have discussed this genus further on fact pages 400 - 401.

Genera *Herpolitha, Halomitra, Sandalolitha, Polyphyllia, Lithophyllon* and *Podabacia*

The genus *Herpolitha* contains two species that, like *Fungia*, show little geographical growth variation throughout their distribution range in the Indo-Pacific. *Herpolitha limax* (see fact page 402) is very commonly seen on the reefs and is very easy to maintain in aquaria. We have kept adult colonies for years, as well as grown smaller colonies from attached anthocauli. The other species, *Herpolitha weberi* is closely related to *H. limax*, but is, by comparison, relatively rare.

Halomitra pileus, probably the only species in its genus, has a characteristically strong convex growth form, which it why it is popularly called "Neptune's Hat". The colonies buckle so strongly as they grow upwards that a cavity is created underneath. This species lacks the axial furrow seen in *Herpolitha* and the tissue and skeleton are thin and delicate. It is distributed from east Africa, to Japan, New Caledonia and the Line Islands, but is absent from in the Red Sea.

Sandalolitha robusta has a similarly convex growth form to *Halomitra pileus*. Its distribution area stretches from the Andamanen Islands, to French Polynesia and it, too, is the only member of its genus. The colonies are large, freeliving, dome-shaped and lack an axial furrow. They look like *Halomitra pileus* colours, but the construction of *Sandalolitha robusta* is (as the species name indicates) much more solid and heavy. The corallites are placed further apart in *S. robusta* than in *H. pileus* (VERON, 1986).

While both *Halomitra* and *Sandalolitha* are rare in the trade, the opposite holds true for the genus

"Neptune's Hat", *Halomitra pileus*, in a lagoon in the Maldives

Polyphyllia talpina   Photo: Scott W. Michael

Podabacia crustacea in an aquarium at Hagenbecks Tierpark, Hamburg

Fungia spp.

Distribution: Widely distributed in the Indo-Pacific; from the Red Sea and East Africa, to southern Japan, Hawaii and Pitcairn. The most abundant and widespread of all fungiids. Normally found in deeper fore reefs, or in protected lagoons and seldom in habitats exposed to waves.

Size and growth form: Most species form circular, conical polyps with a diameter of 14-30 cm. Some species form elongated polyps or colonies (that have several mouths). Free-living, except for juvenile polyps, which live attached as anthocauli (see page 394). Exhibits little growth variation.

Food: Uncertain; definitely feeds in part from the products of its zooxanthellae, but also eats plankton and other organic material.

Description: According to Veron (1995), the genus contains about 33 species and is normally divided into subgenera (see table on page 397). Species differentiation is based on the teeth of the septa (see drawing on page 398). Normally, a large mouth opening. Colouring brown or green, occasionally pink or red.

Photos:
– Top left: *Fungia fungites*
– Centre left: *Fungia granulosa*   Photo: Dr. N. Furman
– Bottom left: *Fungia horrida*   Photo: Dr. N. Furman
– Bottom right: *Fungia scutaria*   Photo: Dr. N. Furman

Aquarium maintenance:

– **General:** Best kept in a sand-zone or rubble-zone aquarium, or on flat surfaces in front of aquarium decorations. Care is necessary during transportation, acclimatization and placement in the aquarium, because the polyps can easily develop bacterial infection if the skeleton is damaged; such infections are difficult or nearly impossible to heal. Acclimatized individuals of the majority of the species appear to be somewhat tenacious.

– **Lighting:** Medium to strong.

– **Water circulation:** Moderate.

– **Propagation possibilities:** The sexes are separate and we have observed *Fungia* spp. regulary spawning in aquaria (see also page 41, chapter 2). Many species produce anthocauli when they are damaged, an adaptation to their free-living life. Anthocauli can also be introduced into an aquarium on pieces of live rock.

GA: + ; TO: + ; SE: +

Photos:

– Top right: *Fungia* sp., "KA4-FUN-02", on coral debris in the Maldives

– Centre right: *Fungia* sp., "KA4-FUN-03" in an aquarium
Photo: Scott W. Michael

– Bottom right: *Fungia* sp. "KA4-FUN-04", in an aquarium
Photo: Scott W. Michael

– Bottom left: *Fungia simplex* photographed in Papua-New Guinea
Photo: Scott W. Michael

Herpolitha limax

Distribution: Indo-Pacific; from the Red Sea, to the Tuamotu Islands. Like *Fungia* spp., it is normally found in protected habitats.

Size and growth form: Forms elongated colonies that are normally up to 50 cm long (occasionally reaching 100 cm). Exhibits little geographical variation in growth form.

Food: Uncertain; definitely feeds in part from the products of its zooxanthellae, but also eats plankton and other organic material.

Description: The elongated colonies have convex top surfaces and concave undersides. Some individuals can have an "X"-, "Y"-, or "T"-shaped form. Several mouth openings. Colouring is normally green.

Aquarium maintenance:

– **General:** Requires a sand-zone aquarium or, at least, a flat surface of sand and/or coral debris in front of the aquarium decor. Very hardy and easy to keep, this species can live for decades in a reef aquarium.

– **Lighting:** Medium to strong.

– **Water circulation:** Moderate.

– **Propagation possibilities:** Damaged or dying colonies will normally produce large numbers of anthocauli that are easily grown into new colonies.

GA: + ; TO: + ; SE: +

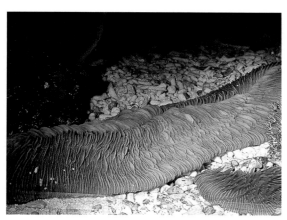

Photos:

– Top: A colony in a protected lagoon in the Maldives (night photograph)

– Centre: A colony in an aquarium

– Bottom: Sessile anthocaulus, which arrived in this aquarium on a piece of live rock. This photograph was taken in March 1993, when the diameter of the young colony was about 2 cm. By December 1997, the anthocaulus had since long detached itself and had grown to a diameter of more than 10 cm.

Polyphyllia which occurs regularly in shops. The colonies are regarded as colonial because they have many mouths evenly distributed over the upper surface, with the largest mouths aligned along the axial furrow. Most colonies are elongated, but some may be round and lack the furrow (VERON, 1986). The tentacles are long and almost always extended. *Polyphyllia* includes two species, of which only *Polyphyllia talpina* is common. It is very decorative and durable in reef aquaria. This species is found from Madagascar in the west, to Tonga in the east.

The other species in the genus is *Polyphyllia novaehiberniae*, which has an anomalous distribution, occurring from Papua-New Guinea, to Samoa. It does not occur in the central western Pacific or in the Indian Ocean, except for the coast of Kenya, where it is known from a single specimen (VERON, 1993).

Lithophyllon contains four species, of which *Lithophyllon edwardsi* is, by far, the most common, although all the species are, in general, regarded as being uncommon. Unlike other members of the family, these corals are attached to the substratum throughout their lives, forming unifacial, encrusting or laminar colonies that may attain several metres. The colours are dull green, gray or brown, sometimes with white margins or white centres around the mouth openings. *Lithophyllon* is distributed in the central Indo-Pacific, stretching as far eastwards as Samoa.

The distribution of the genus *Podabacia* stretches from the Red Sea and east Africa and Madagascar, to west Africa, the Great Barrier Reef and southern Japan, and east to the Tuamotu Islands. This genus occurs in most habitats, although it is not commonly found. There are two species, *Podabacia crustacea* and the rare *Podabacia motuporensis*. In *P. crustacea*, the base colour is somewhat dark, except for the septo-costae (radial elements of the corallites), which are cream-coloured. The colonies are attached and exhibit encrusting or laminar growth forms, which can reach a size of 1.5 metres across. *Podabacia crustacea* is certainly not common in the trade. We have, to date, seen only one colony in an aquarium, at Hagenbecks Tierpark in Hamburg.

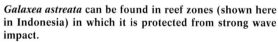

Galaxea astreata can be found in reef zones (shown here in Indonesia) in which it is protected from strong wave impact.

Acrhelia horrescens is a beautiful, but, unfortunately, very rare stony coral. We found this coral at a depth of 12 m near Bunaken, Indonesia.

Family Oculinidae

The members of genera and species of the family Oculinidae are relatively easy to identify. The five or six species of the two Indo-Pacific genera *Galaxea* and *Acrhelia* all have very beautiful corallites with a ring of pointed septa, which gives them a star-shaped appearance. Although the two genera are similar in anatomy, they each have very different environmental requirements. While *Galaxea* species often thrive in turbid water on coral reefs near the coast and can occasionally dominate the coral fauna, *Acrhelia horrescens* can be found where the water is clear and the light is good. In the Caribbean, the family is represented by the genus *Oculina*.

The majority of genera in the Oculinidae are, however, not tropical, but are found, instead, in sub-tropical and cold oceans, sometimes at very great depths, and include only ahermatypic, colony-building species. Examples of such genera are *Madrepora* and *Archohelia*.

Genus *Galaxea*

The total number of species in *Galaxea* is unknown. There are at least four species in the Indo-Pacific, of which only *Galaxea astreata* and *G. fascicularis* are common. *G. fascicularis* is very often found in the trade. It is distinguished by its extremely long "sweeper" tentacles, which contain powerful batteries of nematocysts; it is therefore essential to allow sufficient space between neighbouring corals in a reef aquarium. In

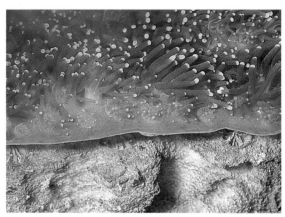

Galaxea fascicularis
Crystal Coral

Distribution: Indo-Pacific; from the Red Sea and east Africa, to the Fiji Islands and Samoa.

Size and growth form: Creates many different colony forms; from small encrusting types, to dome-shaped, creeping shapes which grow in arches, to large (several metres in diameter) columnar colonies with hollowed-out structures and small, short, irregular branches. Very common in a wide range of habitats; may be dominant on inshore reefs.

Food: Feeds on the translocated products of its zooxanthellae, but also captures plankton and possibly utilizes other food sources as well.

Description: The corallites are of mixed sizes, but polyps are usually about 6 mm in diameter with prominent sharp, septa, which reach into the centre of the corallites. Colouring is green or brown. Can often be found in polluted water of reefs near coasts, usually in places shaded by overhangs and with moderate light. Ejects long sweeper tentacles during the night; these may sting neighbouring corals.

Aquarium maintenance:
– **General:** Requires a large amount of free space so that other sessile animals are not stung. Sensitive to transportation and may get damaged and lose the tissue between individual polyps (coenosteum). Very durable and easy to maintain once established; it may thrive for many years. Can grow rapidly in a reef aquarium.
– **Lighting:** Medium to strong lighting intensity.
– **Water circulation:** Moderate to low.
– **Propagation possibilities:** Propagation in aquaria is possible by fragmentation.

GA: + ; TO: - ; SE: +

Photos:
– Top: Colony on the northern Great Barrier Reef
                                   Photo: Scott W. Michael
– Centre: Close-up of the polyps and marginal growth zones
– Bottom: Aquarium colony with extended sweeper tentacles

Nature, this species is highly variable in growth form. See fact page 404 for more details on *Galaxea fascicularis*.

Galaxea astreata is distributed from the Red Sea in the west, to Samoa in the east. It normally develops spreading colonies, but can also, on occasion, grow into columnar shapes. It is not as variable in growth form or in corallite structure as the previous species and its corallites have a maximum diameter of 4.5 mm. This distinguishes the species from *G. fascicularis*, whose corallites attain a diameter of up to 6 mm.

Genus *Acrhelia*

The genus *Acrhelia* is monotypic, with *Acrhelia horrescens* as its only species. According to VERON (1993), this is one of the most habitat-restricted of all coral species, occurring only in clear reef waters and almost never on fringing reefs. In contrast to *Galaxea*, the colonies are arborescent, either forming dense bushes, or growing as open branching structures. The colour is brown, yellow or green. We have only seen this species once, ourselves, off the island of Bunaken, in North Sulawesi, Indonesia, where we found a small colony on a reef slope at 12 m depth. *A. horrescens* is distributed from Taiwan, the Philippines and northern Australia, east to Samoa and south to New Caledonia. It is considered rare and we do not know if this coral has ever been kept in reef aquaria.

Genus *Oculina*

By far the most common species in the genus *Oculina* is *Oculina diffusa*. According to COLIN (1978), its presence has been ascertained in Florida, the Bermudas, the Bahamas, Cuba, Jamaica and Puerto Rico. It forms dense branches or thicket-like clumps and the branches, which are a maximum of 1 cm thick, bear many large, raised corallites. We found *O. diffusa* in Miami, Florida, in strongly polluted sewage water. This species can also be found

Meandrina meandrites

near reefs, in zones where the water has become cloudy due to sediment. We tried to keep *O. difusa* in a coral reef aquarium, but had little success with it. It is possible that this species may feel more comfortable in an aquarium without a skimmer, but with sediment build-up and algal growth.

Many authors mention *Oculina valenciennesi*, although the identity of this species appears to be unclear. *Oculina robusta* is a good species, with thicker branches than *O. diffusa*. The base of a branch can often be lumpy and thick. On the reef, *O. robusta* grows on hard substrata. It is especially numerous on the west coast of Florida (HUMANN, 1993). *Oculina tenella* is rare and creates small, lumpy or branched almost-white colonies. Without a doubt, the most beautiful species in the genus is *O. varicosa* which is glowing red to lavender in colour. Its branches are wound around one another, so that the colonies appear almost lumpy. They are most common near Florida, but are even rare here. In the remaining area of the Caribbean, they are considered very rare. This species normally grows at depths of more than 50 m.

Family Meandrinidae

The main distribution area of the family Meandrinidae is the Caribbean Sea. Only one species, *Ctenella chagius*, is known from the Indo-Pacific. This species can also be found in parts of the western Indian Ocean and, in structure, its anatomy and growth form, appear very similar to *Leptoria phrygia* from the family Faviidae.

In the Caribbean, the family contains many beautiful species which should be of interest to aquarists. They belong to the genera *Meandrina*, *Goreaugyra*, *Dichocoenia*, and *Dendrogyra*. However, like all stony corals, they are protected by law in the area, and cannot be collected.

Genus *Meandrina*

At first sight, *Meandrina meandrites* can appear somewhat similar to the well-known Indo-Pacific species *Trachyphyllia geoffroyi*. The colonies are hemispherical or flattened plates, occasionally encrusting in habit. *M.meandrites* is the most common species of its

Dichocoenia stokesii (above) can create flat or helmet-shaped colonies and has elongated corallite openings (below), which are characteristic of the species.   Photos: Scott W. Michael

Dendrogyra cylindricus (above) can create large, column-shaped colonies. Occasionally, these columns fall over and new colonies grow out of the horizontally-lying fragments.
Photo: J. Yaiullo

genus and can be found free-living, as well as attached. Free-living colonies are normally found on soft bottoms. They are smaller than attached colonies, which can attain a diameter of one metre or more.

Meandrina meandrites has unusually large septa, which stand far apart from one another: approximately seven septa per cm. Normally, this species is coloured light brown or yellow-white. It is found in most reef habitats, but according to HUMANN (1993), it is most common at depths from 6 to 25 metres on seaward slopes of 0.5 to 80 m (COLIN, 1978). This indicates that this coral could do well in an aquarium with moderate lighting.

Genera *Goreaugyra* and *Dendrogyra*

The genus *Goreaugyra* is monotypic, with the relatively recently described and very rare species, *Goreaugyra memorialis*, commonly called the "Maze Pillar Coral", being found only in the Bahamas. More common, and with the same growth form, is *Dendrogyra cylindricus*. It forms striking, columnar structures up to 3 m tall. The tips of the colony break easily and fall to the base of the mother colony, where they then begin to develop new growths. Occasionally, the entire mother colony tips over and, from this lying position, new vertical colonies are developed. *D. cylindricus* populations can be found in which several generations of columns lie on top of one another.

A speciality of *Dendrogyra cylindricus* is that it has polyps with numerous pale-brown, approximately 5 cm long tentacles, which are expanded throughout the entire day. This species is irregularly distributed throughout the Caribbean, being found most numerously along the coasts of Jamaica and the Bahamas at depths of 1 to 20 m (COLIN, 1978).

Genus *Dichocoenia*

The genus *Dichocoenia* was

thought to contain two species: *Dichocoenia stokesii* and *D. stellaris*. Colonies of *D. stokesi* are somewhat small and round or dome-shaped, with a maximum diameter of about 50 cm. Occasionally, pancake-flat colonies can also be found. This growth form was earlier recognised as a separate species (*D. stellaris*), but is now considered synonymous with *D. stokesii* (HUMANN, 1993). The corallites are round, long, or "Y"-shaped and measure up to 5 x 50 mm. The colouring varies from white, to light yellow and brown. *D. stokesii* is normally restricted to seaward and leeward reef slopes at depths between 3 to 30 m; it is absent from shallow reef flats. This coral is common in the Caribbean and the Bahamas, but is rarely seen in southern Florida (HUMANN, 1993).

Mycedium elephantotus in a shady spot on a reef wall in the Maldives

Family Pectiniidae

The family Pectiniidae includes the five genera: *Physophyllia*, *Echinophyllia*, *Oxypora*, *Mycedium* and *Pectinia*. All have unusually beautiful and colourful species, one of which, *Pectinia paeonia,* is well known in the aquatic hobby and is very easy to care for. Many of the remaining species are also well suited for aquarium life, but are, unfortunately, only sporadically imported.

Genus Physophyllia

The genus *Physophyllia* was earlier regarded as an ecotype of the genus *Pectinia*. Today, though, it is recognised as a valid genus with three species (*P. ayleni*, *P. wellsi*, and *P. patula*) by WOOD (1983), while VERON (1993) gives *P. ayleni* as the only species in the genus and states that *Physophyllia* is, in general, poorly defined. The various species or growth forms develop plate-shaped colonies, which occupy an intermediate position between the genera *Echinophyllia* and *Pectinia*. Pec-

tinia species do not build flat plates, and *Echinophyllia* species have more distinctive corallites than *Physophyllia*.

Genus Echinophyllia

The various species of the genus *Echinophyllia* form encrusting, laminar or foliaceous colonies

which are fragile and develop from paper-thin discs. Only the central parts of these discs are attached, the remaining part of the colonies often growing to form large and thin plates in free water. The majority of the species are coloured brown, although the corallites, which usually measure around 10 mm in diameter, can be

Pectinia lactuca on a reef flat in Indonesia.

Pectinia paeonia
Palm Lettuce Coral

Distribution: Indo-Pacific: from Sri Lanka and the Maldives, to New Caledonia and the Fiji Islands.

Size and growth form: Creates medium-sized colonies. Common in turbid water, especially on fringing reefs. Also found on reef flats with crystal-clear waters.

Food: Feeds on the translocated products of its zooxanthellae, but also captures plankton and possibly utilizes other food sources as well.

Description: The colonies consist of irregular, thin, upward-projecting plates or spires. Columellae are weakly developed. Septa are smooth or have small teeth. One of the most delicately coloured corals with nuances in brown, green or grey, occasionally also in fluorescent green or yellow. Usually lives in turbulent water.

Aquarium maintenance:
– **General:** Easy to care for and tenacious. Grows rapidly into beautiful colonies in reef aquariua.
– **Lighting:** Medium to high lighting intensity.
– **Water circulation:** Moderate to strong.
– **Propagation possibilities:** Nothing is currently known about its sexual reproduction in aquaria. Can be propagated by fragmentation.

GA: + ; TO: + ; SE: +

Photos:
– Top left: Colony on a reef flat in Indonesia
Photo: J. Olsen
– Centre left: Aquarium colony
– Bottom left: Close-up of a colony near Belau
Photo: Dr. D. Brockmann
– Bottom: Spawning colony on the Great Barrier Reef
Photo: B. Willis.

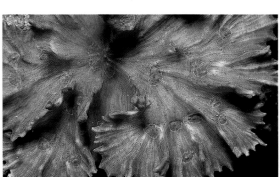

We were not able to identify this stony coral "KA4-MUS-01" from the family Mussidae. It shows similarities with *Cynarina lacrymalis*. For the present, we are referring to it as KA4-MUS-01. The picture on the left shows it when fully expanded, while that on the right shows what the polyps look like when it is completely retracted. The skeleton is clearly visible.

more boldly coloured.

Echinophyllia species are normally found on reef slopes or in somewhat shaded areas on the reef flat, for example, in the shadows of other large corals. The genus includes about eight species, of which *E. aspera* is, by far, the most common. Its distribution in the Indo-Pacific stretches from Madagascar, east Africa and the Red Sea, to Tahiti, and is especially abundant on high latitude reefs.

Genus *Oxypora*

The genus *Oxypora* contains at least three species with *Oxypora lacera* and *O. glabra*as the most common ones. They are very difficult to distinguish from the *Echinophyllia* species. The most common species is *O. lacera*, which is usually brownish grey or greenish, either uniformly coloured, or with bold green corallites, surrounded by brown ring discs. This species is widely distributed in the Indo-Pacific, from the Red Sea, to the Marshall Islands. It is commonly found in shallow, protected areas of reefs.

Oxypora glabra is similar to *O. lacera* and has thin, encrusting colonies of a uniformly pale brown colour. This species has only a limited distribution area in the central Indo-Pacific, being found from the Philippines, to New

Caledonia and Australia. In Australia, it is, according to VERON (1986), rare on the GBR, but is ommonly seen on the west coast.

Genus *Mycedium*

Mycedium contains just two species. The more common of these, *Mycedium elephantotus*, occupies a wide range of habitats, while the other species, *Mycedium robokaki* is rare and is only found in the central Indo-Pacific, extending from Indonesia to Vanuatu. *M. elephantotus* can be easily distinguished from *Echinophyllia* and *Oxypora* species by means of its large, conspicuous corallites, which are shaped like small noses facing towards the rim of the colonies. We found this species in shaded areas in several places on the reefs near the Maldives. One small colony, which was legally collected, and which we experimentally kept in an aquarium, did not flourish. This, however, could be traced to its long, rather rough, transportation from the Maldives.

Genus *Pectinia*

The genus *Pectinia* includes seven true species, some of which are most beautifully coloured in red, brown or green. DITLEV (1980) considersed all the species as ecotypes of one of the most com-

mon species in the genus, *Pectinia lactuca*, while VERON (1986), regarded them as good species. The growth form of *Pectinia* colonies is characteristic: sub-arborescent, covered with high, thin, acutely irregular walls that are usually arranged as wide valleys (VERON, 1986). When it occasionally grows encrusting, thick, leaf-shaped branches are developed, which create a shell or labyrinth shape. The polyps of *Pectinia* are extended only rarely, and always during the night.

Pectinia lactuca is distributed in the Indo-Pacific from Madagascar to the Fiji Islands. It can reach a diameter of over 1m and is normally coloured grey, brown or green. *P. alcicornis* appears similar to *P. paeonia*, although it grows taller and is more robustly built. It is distributed in the central Indo-Pacific, from the Maldives to Vanuatu. It grows especially well in somewhat turbid water. *P. teres*, which develops a more branched form than the other species, can only be found from Thailand to Papua-New Guinea and is rare.

Pectinia paeonia is the most common species in the genus and also the most common one in the hobby and trade. See fact page 408 for further information. It cannot be confused with any other species.

Pectina alcicornis is similar to *P. paeonia*, but its structures are

Cynarina lacrymalis
Button Coral

Distribution: Indo-Pacific: from the Red Sea and Madagascar, to southern Japan, Guam, and south east to the Kermadec Islands.

Size and growth form: Free-living or attached. Diameter of the individual polyp when fully contracted is 5 to 10 cm; can attain at least three to four times these sizes when fully expanded. Usually found on lower reef slopes where it is attached to walls and overhangs. Can tolerate various environmental conditions and is also found in turbid water on inshore reefs. It is seldom common, but easily recognised.

Food: Feeds on the products of its zooxanthellae, but also uses other food sources, such as plankton.

Description: The corals are oval or circular and each polyp has only one mouth. There is usually a base for attachment, but this is normally pointed if the coral lives unattached (VERON, 1986). The primary septa are very thick and conspicuous and have large teeth. The columellae are broad and compact. The balloon-shaped gills are well developed. Colouring is normally green or brownish. The skeleton and its large septa can be seen through the tissue when the polyps are expanded.

Aquarium maintenance:
- **General:** Very durable, beautiful and easily kept coral. Best placed in moderate light where it will expand beautifully. Can then become very large and will require partial shade. Can become somewhat large when pumped up to full size, and therefore needs adequate free space.
- **Lighting:** Weak to medium lighting intensity.
- **Water circulation:** Moderate.
- **Propagation possibilities:** Young daughter polyps (anthocauli) can develop from a dying mother colony (see photo on page 62, chapter 2).

GA: + ; TO: + ; SE: +

Photos:
- Top: Colony in an aquarium
- Centre: The skeleton is clearly visible through the tissue in this fully expanded colony.
  Photo: Scott W. Michael
- Bottom: Colony in the Truk Lagoon
  Photo: Dr. D. Brockmann

more solid. The upward-projecting spires can be very tall. The colours are, according to Veron (1986), a mixture of green, yellows and browns, with the central parts of the colony usually being darker than the marginal ones. This species is common in turbid waters in the central Indo-Pacific.

Family Mussidae

The species of Mussidae have sturdily constructed skeletons with large septal teeth and big, fleshy polyps with bright colours. Most of the genera are easily identified and most species are easily kept in reef aquaria. The family peaked in the Cenozoic era (ca. 67 - 1.6 my. ago) and most of its members are now extinct (Veron, 1995). The present fauna of Mussidae includes the genera *Cynarina*, *Blastomussa*, *Indophyllia*, *Scolymia*, *Australomussa*, *Acanthastrea*, *Mussimilla*, *Lobophyllia*, *Symphyllia*, *Mussa*, *Isophyllia*, *Isophyllastraea* and *Mycetophyllia*, with representatives in both the Indo-Pacific and Caribbean.

Genus *Cynarina*

One of our favourite stony corals, which is well suited to aquarium life, is *Cynarina lacrymalis*, whose distribution ranges from Madagascar and the southern Red Sea, eastwards to southern Japan, Guam and the Kermadec Islands. It is the only species in the genus and is normally found on lower reef slopes, where it lives a solitary existence, often under small overhangs where the light intensity is not particularly strong. See the fact sheet on page 410 for more details.

Genus *Blastomussa*

Aquarists count the genus *Blastomussa* among the best-loved and most beautiful and searched-for stony corals. There are three species, of which *Blastomussa mer-*

Blastomussa merleti colony in an aquarium owned by Jan Olsen from Aqua Design, Oldenburg, Germany.

leti and *Blastomussa wellsi* are well known among marine aquarists. Both are, nevertheless, relatively rare in the wild, though. When these two species first appeared in the trade in Germany in the early nineties, their colours stunned marine aquarists and they immediately became extremely popular. We introduce them in more detail in the fact sheet on page 412.

Blastomussa species can be found in two colour variations: deep red and a grey-green, both of which are different forms of the same species. This is a good example illustrating the fact that colouring is an unsuitable characteristic to choose for species identification. All the species exhibit a phaceloid growth form, with irregularly spaced, sprawling corallites. Additionally, they all share an unusual characteristic in that the corallites slowly lose their connection with one another, thus gradually giving rise to a collection of genetically identical, free-living coral polyps, which were once attached to each other as a colony. We present *Blastomussa* spp. in more detail on fact pages 412.

Genus *Scolymia*

The genus *Scolymia* is distributed in the Indo-Pacific, as well as the

Caribbean Sea. The species of the Caribbean are very close to those belonging to the genus *Mussa*, the only difference being whether or not they are free-living (Veron, 1995). The four known species are somewhat similar to *Cynarina lacrymalis*, although their septa are structured more finely and the septal teeth are smaller. The colonies are mostly round and monocentric, but can occasionally be polycentric (more than one columella centre in each polyp). Additionally, they are normally coloured green and have a more or less clear purple-coloured crown around the polyp edge.

Scolymia vitiensis and *S. australis* live in the Indo-Pacific. It is

In *Blastomussa* species (this is *Blastomussa merleti*), older colonies can lose contact with one another and begin to live as solitary polyps. The picture clearly shows that the polyps are only loosely connected.

Blastomussa spp.

Distribution: Indo-Pacific: from the Red Sea, to Ryukyu Island and Samoa. *B. merleti* is uncommon, while *B. wellsi* is generally rare throughout its range, but can be abundant in some lower reef slope habitats in Australia (VERON, 1986).

Size and growth form: Small colonies grow through budding of polyps from corallites on the edge of the colony. The colony, thus, appears lumpy or frayed. In the Pacific and in the Indian Ocean, the growth form of *B. wellsi* is phaceloid, while in high-latitude reefs, the western Indian Ocean and the Red Sea, it appears to be more cerioid-like (VERON, 1993).

Food: Feeds on the translocated products of its zooxanthellae, but also captures plankton and possibly utilizes other food sources as well.

Description: There are three species in the genus, of which *B. merleti* and *B. wellsi* can be found in trade. In *B. merleti*, the diameter of the tubular corallites, which create long tubes, is less than 7 mm. This species is uncommon in the wild. In *B. welsi*, the corallites are more robust, have a diameter of 9 to 14 mm and contain more septa. Colonies of both species are porous, and break apart very easily. With age, the polyps lose their contact with one another and become solitary. *Blastomussa* has two different colour morphs, one red and the other green or greenish brown (VERON, 1986).

Aquarium maintenance:

– **General:** Easy to keep. Requires various lighting strengths. Skeletons break easily, therefore handle with caution, especially when it comes to *B. merleti*. As older colonies form groups of solitary polyps, algae often appear in between the individual polyps and can sometimes cause problems by overgrowing the living tissue.

– **Lighting:** *B. merleti*: medium lighting intensity; *B. wellsi*: medium to high lighting intensity.

– **Water circulation:** Moderate to strong.

– **Propagation possibilities:** Colonies of both species can be carefully broken apart, divided into several small colonies and placed in separate areas of the aquarium. Polyp "expatriation" can then be observed.

GA: + ; TO: - ; SE: +

Photos:
– Top and centre: Two differently coloured colonies of *B. wellsi* in an aquarium (centre photo: Dr. D. Brockmann)
– Bottom: *B. merleti* on the Great Barrier Reef; the polyps are solitary, having lost contact with one another.

Photo: Prof. J. E. N. Veron

next to impossible for a non-expert to tell the adult polyps apart; in the case of young polyps, it is even difficult for experts to distinguish between the species. Both species are somewhat rare. The distribution of *S. vitiensis* stretches from east Africa and the Philippines, to the Fiji and Pitcairn Islands. *S. australis* is, to date, only known from Australia. Interestingly, it is also found along the southern coast of Australia, thus showing that it has a tropical, subtropical and near-cold-water distribution, a situation which is very unusual for stony corals.

In the Caribbean, three species can be found: *Scolymia cubensis*, *S. wellsi* and *S. lacera*. None is common, being found scattered in deeper reef areas throughout the Caribbean Sea, from the southern coast of Florida and the Bahamas. They prefer shaded spots and are suited for a life with weak light intensity; they should therefore also be suited to aquarium life, where they could be placed in cave openings or under overhanging rocks.

Genus *Mussa*

The genus *Mussa* is endemic to the Caribbean Sea and is, additionally, monotypic, with *Mussa angulosa* as its only representative. This species is very closely related to *Scolymia* and the

Mussa angulosa in the Cayman Islands   Photo: Scott W. Michael

two genera can easily be confused. *M. angulosa* forms massive, normally rounded (occasionally irregular or slightly elongated) colonies that consist of a clump of large corallites arising from a common base. The corallites are monocentric to tricentric and are separated by a gap of at least 5 mm. Polyp colours are usually combinations of pink, purple, red, green or brown, sometimes even fluorescent, while the polyps themselves are very fleshy (WOOD, 1983). Each polyp has many thin and strongly toothed septa. The completely opened polyps are very sturdy.

Mussa angulosa can most commonly be found at depths from 5 to 40 m. Although it is not numerous anywhere, it can be found in many habitats of southern Florida, near the Bahamas and further southwards in the Caribbean Sea.

Genus *Mycetophyllia*

The genus *Mycetophyllia* is endemic to the Caribbean and none of the five species are common (see HUMANN (1993) for an overview of

"KA4-MUS-02", a *Scolymia* species, in Papua-New Guinea   Photo: Scott W. Michael

"KA4-MUS-03", a *Scolymia* species from the Caribbean, photographed in an aquarium.

the *Mycetophyllia* species). All the species have a very peculiar, although decorative, appearance. The usually encrusting colonies form somewhat thick, flat discs that can attain one metre in diameter, although they can also sometimes be hemispherically shaped. The surface usually possesses ridges and valleys which gives the colony a coarse blue-green or grey-blue brain pattern. Occasionally, a combination of two colours can be found, usually a lighter and a darker one. *Mycetophyllia* species are normally found on outer reef slopes and are most common in deeper water.

Mycetophyllia ferox distinguishes itself somewhat from the other species in the genus in that its skeletal structure creates closed valleys; in the other species, the valleys run from the edge of the colony to the centre. *M. ferox* is also usually more lightly coloured than the other species.

In *Mycetophyllia reesi*, the valleys are completely absent. Instead, the colonies have many round, lumpy-shaped structures on the flat surface.

Genus *Isophyllia*

The genus *Isophyllia*, which, like the previous genus, is also endemic to the Caribbean, contains only two species: *Isophyllia sinuosa* and *I. rigida*. Both develop small, hemispherical colonies and can normally be found in shallow water, often in areas of agitated sediment. We do not know if they have ever been kept in aquaria.

Isophyllia sinuosa has a coarse, spiral-shaped brain structure and variable colouration in brown, green, or grey. It is distributed throughout the entire Caribbean, including Florida and the Bahamas.

Isophyllia rigida exhibits smaller valleys, which contain one or two polyps only. At first glance, it appears similar to a *Favia* species. Its distribution is limited to the Bahamas and Florida.

Genus *Acanthastrea*

With the genus *Acanthastrea*, we return once more to the Indo-Pacific. *Acanthastrea* species have a skeletal structure which is similar to that found in *Favites*, *Favia* and *Moseleya* species of the family Faviidae. The best way to separate *Acanthastrea* from members of the Faviidae is by examining the expanded polyps, which are large and fleshy in all members of the Mussidae. The completely expanded polyps distinguish themselves by the fact that they contain much more "robust" tissue,

Mycetophyllia danaana   Photo: Scott W. Michael

Mycetophyllia ferox   Photo: Scott W. Michael

which makes them appear larger and fleshier. This genus probably contains six species in total (VERON, 1986), although only *Acanthastrea echinata* is common on tropical reefs, the other species being more abundant in temperate areas.

Acanthastrea echinata normally grows in massive, flat colonies, which rarely attain a diameter over 1 m. This species is distributed from the Red Sea, to the Marshall and Tuamotu Islands, and can be found on the majority of reefs. Colonies are coloured grey, brown, or green, but can occasionally be purplish. The polyps have thick, concentric folds when retracted. We have no direct experience with *A. echinata* in reef aquaria, but see no reason why it should not be easy to keep.

Acanthastrea lordhowensis is distributed from Hongkong and the Philippines, to Australia (Lord Howe Island, as in the species name), i.e. from areas which are quite regularly involved in the export of aquarium animals. It is therefore conceivable that this species may have appeared in trade. The polyps are coloured shades of pink, purple and green. Like the majority of species in the genus, this species is also most commonly encountered in subtropical areas and is therefore most numerously found on the edge of coral reef distribution areas along the 20 °C - isotherm (see volume 1, map on page 58).

Genus *Lobophyllia*

Lobophyllia hemprichii is a stony coral which is very often imported and has been grown in European reef tanks since the beginning of the eighties. It is also the most commonly found species of the family Mussidae. *L. hemprichii* takes on many growth forms and often lives on reef slopes or at the reef edge, except in the most exposed areas. It is among the most resistant of all stony corals and one of the easiest to keep in the modern reef aquarium. A colony can be easily attached to a piece of living rock by boring a hole in

Acanthastrea echinata   Photo: B. Carlson, Waikiki Aquarium

the lower part of the colony (obviously, in such a manner that no living tissue is damaged). A plastic tube or a plastic screw should then be placed in this hole and the projecting end astened to a hole in the living rock. In this manner, colonies can be suspended in the aquarium, so that they create a natural looking group. Further information regarding *L. hemprichii* is included in the fact sheet on pages 416/417.

The genus *Lobophyllia* contains about nine known species, all of which are restricted to the Indo-Pacific. In contrast to *Lobo-*

phyllia hemprichii, the other species are not commonly found on reefs. *Lobophyllia corymbosa*, however, is relatively common, especially on upper reef slopes (VERON, 1986). This species has a hemispherical shape with one or two polyp centres per branch. The polyps have a greenish colour with pale centres. *L. corymbosa* is distributed from east Africa and the Red Sea, to Tahiti and the Tuamotu Islands and occurs through most of the genus' range.

The remaining *Lobophyllia* species are so rare that they do not

Large colony of *Lobophyllia hemprichii* on a reef edge in the Maldives

Lobophyllia hemprichii
Meat Coral

Distribution: Indo-Pacific: from the Red Sea and east Africa, to Tahiti, the Tuamotu Archipelago and the Pitcairn Islands.

Size and growth form: Very common and may be a dominant species of upper reef slopes where it can create large, mono-specific populations (see bottom picture on page 415). Generally found in all but the most exposed reef slopes.

Food: Feeds on the translocated products of its zooxanthellae, but also captures plankton and possibly utilizes other food sources as well.

Description: Very polymorphic. Colonies are flat or hemispherically-shaped and grow with a phaceloid or flabello-meandroid habit. Septa taper in thickness, becoming thinner from the corallite wall to the centre of the polyp, and have numerous sharp teeth. The shape of the individual polyps can vary within one and the same colony. Polyps are thick and fleshy when expanded. Exhibits a wide range of colour variations, from white and grey, to bright red. Stripes, patches and spots of contrasting colours are common.

Aquarium maintenance:
- **General:** Very durable and easy to keep, but requires a large amount of space. The skeleton is vulnerable to boring green algae. Be sure to look for undamaged colonies during purchase. Seems to do best when fed with *Mysis*, *Artemia* or other small, but fresh or frozen, food from time to time.
- **Lighting:** Medium to high lighting intensity.
- **Water circulation:** Moderate to strong.
- **Propagation possibilities:** Unknown.

GA: + ; TO: + ; SE: +

Photos:
Left:
- Top: Large, round colony on an outer reef of the Great Barrier Reef
- Centre: Colony in the Fiji Islands
  Photo: Scott W. Michael
- Bottom: Colony in the Waikiki Aquarium, Hawaii
  Photo: Scott W. Michael

Right:
- Top left: Close-up of polyps on a reef in Indonesia
- Centre left: Close-up of polyps, also on a reef in Indonesia Photo: Scott W. Michael
- Bottom left: Close-up of polyps on a reef in the Fiji Islands Photo: Scott W. Michael
- Top right: Two different colour morphs next to each other in the same aquarium
- Bottom right: Further colour variations in an aquarium

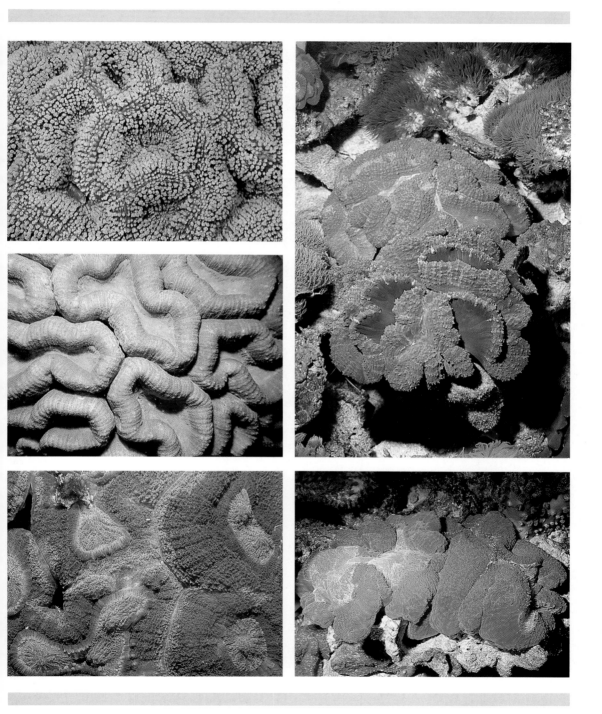

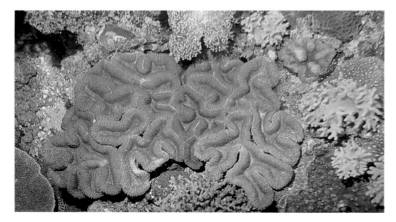

Lobophyllia hataii in Papua-New Guinea   Photo: Scott W. Michael

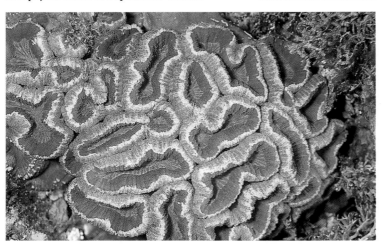

"KA4-MUS-04", a *Symphyllia* species in Indonesia

"KA4-MUS-05", a *Symphyllia* species photographed in an aquarium at the Löbbecke Museum, Düsseldorf.

warrant discussion here. We recommend VERON (1986) to those who would like more information on these species.

Genus *Symphyllia*

The genus *Symphyllia* contains perhaps the most beautiful species of the family Mussidae, two of which can be considered as being particularly beautiful. Of the approximately six good species, *Symphyllia recta*, *Symphyllia radians* and *Symphyllia agaricia* are the most common. They are all widely distributed in the Indo-Pacific and can, to some extent, be identified under water by the size of their valleys. *Symphyllia recta* has a hemispherical shape with a spiral polyp pattern form and sinuous valleys with a diameter of 12 to 15 mm. Normally, colonies are coloured brown, grey, or green, although, occasionally, red colonies can also be found. *S. recta* is distributed from the Maldives, east to the Marshall Islands and Samoa.

Symphyllia radians can have a hemispherical colony shape, although it can also grow as almost flat colonies. The spiral polyp pattern, which is so typical for many genera of the family Mussidae and especially the genus *Symphyllia*, also occurs in *Symphyllia radians*. This species resembles *S. recta*, but the valleys are wider and have a distance of up to 25 mm between the valley floors. At this size, it is larger than the previous species. The colour of *S. recta* is two-toned: grey and green, or brown and green. This species is very common and is often seen in the trade. In Nature, it can dominate on upper reef slopes. *S. radians* is distributed from the Lacadive and the Maldives in the west, to Fiji and New Caledonia in the east.

Symphyllia agaricia also forms hemispherical to flat colonies, but has valleys that are, on average, 35 mm in diameter and are usually separated by a narrow groove. The septa are thick, with very large teeth (VERON, 1986). As in the previous species, the walls and valleys usually have contrasting colours that can be brown, green or red. *S. agaricia* is distributed from eastern Africa and the Red Sea, to the Samoa Islands, but is not as common as the two previous species.

In aquaria, *Symphyllia* species require the same conditions as *Lobophyllia hemprichii*. The colonies can become relatively large and therefore require adequate space. Under high lighting intensity, they show their fluorescent colouring. *Symphyllia* species are magnificent eye-catchers in coral reef aquaria.

Symphyllia recta on the Great Barrier Reef and *Symphyllia radians* in the Coral Sea (photo left: J. E. N. Veron)

Family Merulinidae

The family Merulinidae is like the Mussidae, with whose species it shows morphological affinities. Like the Mussidae, it is a family that peaked in the Cenozoic era, but only has few representatives today. Although it is not the most species-rich family, it, nevertheless, contains many beautiful and interesting corals, which have proven themselves very durable in aquaria.

Genus *Hydnophora*

Hydnophora species are easy to recognize because of the small conical structures (called "hydnophores") which are evenly distributed over the entire skeleton. The genus contains about seven species distributed from the Red Sea, to the southern Pacific.

Hydnophora rigida is, by far, the most common species in the genus. It is distributed in the Indo-Pacific from east Africa, east to the Fiji Islands. It can sometimes be abundant in the Maledives, oc-casionally forming large monospecific stands on upper reef slopes and reef flats (VERON, 1995). *H. rigida* grows in a strongly branched manner and has, in contrast to other branched corals, no encrusting or creeping "adhesive" plate at the base of the colony. The colouring is usually beige, light yellow, or light brown. This species is sporadically imported and is very easy to keep, but does best under strong lighting and good water movement. It can easily be propagated through fragmentation.

Hydnophora exesa is also common in the Indo-Pacific, and can

The hydnophores of *Hydnophora* sp.   From VERON (1986)

Hydnophora spp.
Branch or Horn Corals

Distribution: Widely distributed in the Indo-Pacific: *H. rigida* from east Africa to the Fiji Islands, *H. exesa* from the Red Sea to Samoa.

Size and growth form: *H. rigida* can create large, branched colonies with a creeping base, and can cover wide areas of shallow reefs. *H. exesa* grows in somewhat massive, creeping, or only lightly branched, colonies.

Food: Feeds primarily on the products of its zooxanthellae, but also uses other food sources, such as plankton.

Description: There are about seven valid species in *Hydnophora* (VERON, 1995), of which *H. rigida* and *H. exesa* are, by far, the most common ones. *Hydnophora* species are easy to recognize owing to the beautifully sculptured conical protuberances or pimples (hydnophores see page 419, below) which cover the entire colony surface and are formed where sections of common wall between the corallites intersect. Short tentacles surround the base of each hydnophore, one tentacle between each pair of septa (VERON, 1986). The colonies are massive, encrusting or arborescent.

Aquarium maintenance:
- **General:** *H. exesa* is commonly pea-green and fluorescent, indicating a life underneath high lighting intensity. *H. rigida* is normally light green or brownish-green. Both species are easy to maintain once established, but can be difficult to adapt and acclimatize. These are not corals for beginners.
- **Lighting:** High light intensity.
- **Water circulation:** Moderate.
- **Propagation possibilities:** Can be easily propagated through fragmentation.

GA: + ; TO: + ; SE: +

Photos:
- Top: *H. exesa* colonies in an aquarium
- Centre: Close-up of the typical protuberances on the surface of a *H. exesa* colony
- Bottom: *H. rigida* colony in an aquarium

be found from the Red Sea, east to the Great Barrier Reef and to Samoa. It does not produce branched growth like *H. rigida*, but forms massive or encrusting, creeping colonies, instead, occasionally with short, stumpy lobes or branches. We describe both the species that are common in the trade, in more detail in the fact page 420.

Genus *Merulina*

The genus *Merulina* contains three species, the most decorative of which, *Merulina ampliata*, occurs in a wide range of reef habitats, where it creates artistic-looking, leaf-shaped or plate-shaped colonies. We found it to be numerous on protected reef flats in Indonesia, where it built terrace-shaped colonies. *M. ampliata* is widely distributed in the Indo-Pacific, from east Africa and the Red Sea, to southern Japan, the Great Barrier Reef and the Marshall and Line Islands. Our only experiences with this species concerns tiny colonies which did very well in reef aquaria, although we have not been able to find the species in trade up to now. According to our observations in Indonesia, *M. ampliata* appears to be solid and to grow very well. We therefore believe that this species is very well suited for life in an aquarium.

Merulina species, (this is "KA4-MER-01") photographed in Indonesia, exhibits variable growth form. It usually creates radial colonies (above), but can also grow in a laminar fashion when it occurs in shallow water that is exposed to strong sunlight (below).

Family Faviidae

The family Faviidae is, based on the number of genera, the most extensive genus of stony corals; it is also very rich in terms of species. Only the family Acroporidae contains more living representatives, but if we also count extinct species, the Faviidae is the most species-rich of all coral families. It is the only family that was a major reef builder during the Mesozoic and Cenozoic eras (VERON, 1995). In general, the present members have a very wide distribution, with faviid corals being abundant on most coral reefs. Two of the genera, *Montastrea* and *Favia*, are found, both in Indo-Pacific, and in the western Atlantic.

Many faviid corals have a corallite pattern which looks like the structure of a brain, as a result of which they are popularly known as brain corals. Some species, like *Diploastrea heliopora*, for example, can create giant colonies with diameters of several metres. The growth of brain corals is, usually, fairly slow, which means that such giant colonies are often several hundred – if not thousand – years old.

The identification of Faviidae species is, in general, very difficult, although it is not completely impossible for aquarists. We do need, however, to examine the skeleton and corallite structure, the latter of which varies a great deal. Faviid corals show, not only geographical variation, but also substantial variations within a single population found on the same reef. The structure of the corallites can vary even within one and the same colony (see photograph on page 319 and VERON, 1995). It is, however, a little easier to identify the different genera if the skeleton of the dead coral can be examined. Despite these difficulties, a few species are quite typical and are relatively easily identified. Often, a colony can be identified, at least, at generic level, since the majority of genera have particular characteristics, but even this can be difficult. See VERON & PICHON (1977) for a detailed review of the family. The family is distributed in all tropical oceans, with the genera *Favia* and *Montastrea* can be - as stated earlier - being found in the Indo-Pacific, as well as the Caribbean. *Diploria, Colpophyllia, Manicina, Solenastrea* and *Cladocora* are only found in the Caribbean and *Astreosmilia* and *Erthrastrea* are only distributed in the Red Sea and in the west Indian Ocean. The genera *Caulastrea, Barabattoia, Favites, Goniastrea, Platygyra, Australogyra, Leptast-*

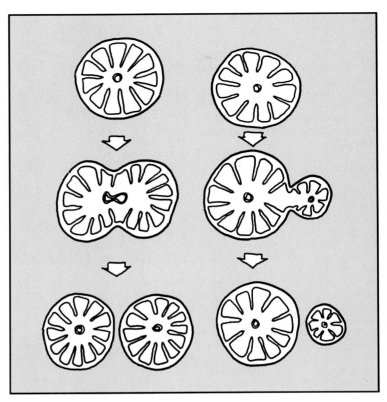

Intra-tentacular (left) and extra-tentacular (right) budding of daughter corallites in the family Faviidae   Drawing based on WOOD (1983)

rea, Cyphastrea, Echinopora and *Moseleya* are more or less widely distributed in the Indo-Pacific.

The genera *Favia, Favites, Goniastrea* and *Montastrea* are often confused with one another, although they are, in principle, not too difficult to separate, at least,

when the skeleton can be closely studied. Nevertheless, colony and corallite variations may make the situation somewhat problematic. In *Favia*, the colonies are massive, flat or hemispherically shaped and the corallite structure is plocoid, meaning that they are

Favia favus (?) in an aquarium

Favia pallida

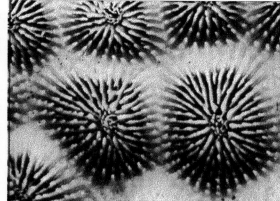

Favites abdita

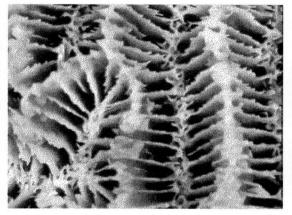

Platygyra daedalea

Goniastrea retiformis

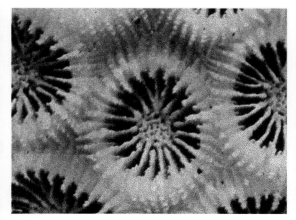

Montastrea curta

Cyphastrea serailia

Caulastrea furcata
Torch or Trumpet Coral

Distribution: Indo-Pacific: from east Africa, to the Fiji Islands and Tonga Islands

Size and growth form: Can create mono-specific populations with a diameter of more than 5 m, especially in sandy areas. Common in protected habitats with clear water.

Food: Feeds on the translocated products of its zooxanthellae, but also captures plankton and possibly utilizes other food sources as well.

Description: Colonies are phaceloid with diverging branches. The angles between the branches, their length before division and the distance between them, varies continuously. Corallites are oval or circular, normally with one mouth and numerous thin septa. When the corallites divide intra-tentacularily, they tend to become triangular with flattened sides (VERON & PICHON, 1977). Polyps are mostly brown, with bright greenish centres, occasionally, with white stripes on some or all polyps.

Aquarium maintenance:
– **General:** Beautiful and durable. Grows quickly, forming large colonies by constant division of the polyps. The branches die off in their lower parts and large colonies are fragile. Be careful not to move colonies around, as their structure will easily break up.
– **Lighting:** High to medium light intensity.
– **Water circulation:** Moderate to strong.
– **Propagation possibilities:** Propagates easily through fragmentation of the polyps taken from the colony edges. However, these shoots must not be placed under excessively strong lighting.
GA: + ; TO: + ; SE: +

Photos:
A colony in our aquarium photographed on December 10, 1991 (top), November 1, 1992 (centre) and March 15, 1994 (bottom). Dr. Bruce Carlson of the Waikiki Aquarium, gave us the offshoot in late 1991. This is a good example of how stony corals can be cultivated in captivity and spread among aquarists worldwide.

conical and have their own walls. Additionally, the corallites are slightly raised above the coenosteum. *Favia* species are more difficult to distinguish from *Montastrea* species than from the other three genera. While *Favia* species normally form new polyps through intra-tentacular budding (which means that a second mouth is built within the parent corallite, followed by a division of the mother polyp into two or more daughter polyps, see figure 422), producing daughter corallites of equal size, *Montastrea* polyps are normally formed through extra-tentacular budding (i.e. new polyps are created on the outside of the mother polyps). However, this rule is not without exceptions, as some species in both *Favia* and *Montastrea* exhibit both types of corallite formation, even within the same colony (VERON, 1986).

In *Favites* species, the colonies are also massive, flat or hemispherical, although the corallites are cerioid, which means that adjacent corallites share common walls. They grow by means of intra-tentacular budding only, and the daughter corallites are usually of unequal size. *Favites* species can be difficult to distinguish from *Goniastrea* species. However, *Goniastrea* have corallites with a neat, uniform appearance, which gives them a very regular skeleton structure and (often) one-level colony surface.

The brain corals of the family Faviidae are the best-loved stony corals among reef aquarium hobbyists. Many species can be considered easy to keep and most are durable in reef aquaria. Additionally, faviid corals have, both a growth rate and colony form, which are very different to the fast-growing branched stony corals, such as those from the family Acroporidae. The decorative effect of brain corals when placed in the company of other corals must be considered when one is planning a reef tank.

Genus *Caulastrea*

The genus *Caulastrea* includes four species, of which only *Caulastrea furcata* is common. It is one of our favourites and can be counted among the most beautiful coral species, owing to the attractive phaceloid colonies that it creates. Sometime ago, we received an off-shoot of this species from Dr. Bruce Carlson of the Waikiki Aquarium in Hawaii. We placed this in our test aquarium and it has since grown into a large, robust colony.

In Australia, along the Great Barrier Reef and in New Caledonia, *C. furcata* can often be found mixed with another similar-looking species, *Caulastrea curvata*. *C. curvata* is always pale brown and has more regular and larger corallites than *C. furcata*. We introduce *C. furcata* in more detail in the summary on page 424.

Caulastrea tumida is common on high-latitude reefs, where it is most abundant in turbid water. The other species of *Caulastrea* prefer clear water.

Genus *Favia*

Favia is a large genus with at least 30 living species, some of which are very common in shallow waters. Colonies are usually massive, either flat or dome-shaped and the corallites are monocentric and plocoid. All species of *Favia* are strict night-time feeders, a habit that can easily be observed in aquaria. During the night, the polyps are usually fully extended and the tiny tentacles surrounding each polyp are clearly visible.

Favia favus (see page 422) is a very common species, but is also the most variable of all *Favia* species. It is generally introduced into aquaria as small colonies or with pieces of living rock. It has large corallite openings with a diameter of 12 to 20 mm and its colouring is often one-toned brown, grey, or green, although the polyps, as in many other species of the genus, can also be two-toned. The colonies are massive, round or flattened. *F. favus* is distributed from the Red Sea, to Samoa, the Marshall Islands and French Polynesia.

Favia matthaii is another common species. It is distributed from the Red Sea to the Pitcairn Islands. The colonies are plocoid, with circular corallite opening measuring 9 to 12 mm in diameter. It is distinguished from the other species in that the septa are thickened, excert or ragged and have large teeth near the wall and well developed projecting, paliform (upright, stake-like) lobes (VERON, 1986) which are strongly notched. The colouring is often light, although dark brown or dark purple nearer the polyp centre.

Similarly notched and uneven septa are also characteristic of *Favia rotumana*, which has irregular and densely crowded corallites thay may be tri-centric. The septa are excert, thin and irregular. However, the structures of the corallites vary a great deal with the habitat in which the corals grow. The colonies of *F. rotumana* are usually flat and sub-plocoid and the colours spread over a wide range of patterns. Usually, though, the polyp centre and polyp rim have contrasting colours. This species is found in the south China Sea, south to Australia and eastwards to Samoa, where it is common on upper reef slopes (VERON, 1986).

The yellow or golden brown *Favia fragum* lives in the Caribbean Sea, where it is common at depths between 3 and 15 metres. It forms small, hemispherical, gold-brown colonies, normally at depths of 3 to 15 m. We do not know, however, if this species has been kept in aquaria.

Genus *Favites*

The genus *Favites* contains about 150 species and is especially abundant in high- and low-latitude reefs, such as in Japan and along the southeast coast of Australia (VERON, 1995). The most common species in the aquatic trade is, without doubt, *Favites flexuosa*, which grows in flat or hemispherical colonies, often coloured blue-grey to blue-green. This species - one of the most durable brain corals - has very large

Favites abdita

Distribution: Indo-Pacific: from the Red Sea to east Samoa and French Polynesia. Very widespread around Australia, where it occurs in almost all biotopes occupied by stony corals (VERON & PICHON, 1977).

Size and growth form: Small to medium-sized, massive colonies, either rounded, hillocky or flattened, only occasionally attaining a diameter of more than 1 m.

Food: Feeds on the translocated products of its zooxanthellae, but also captures plankton and possibly utilizes other food sources as well.

Description: Spectacular, massive colonies with cerioid corallite structure. Each corallite is, typically, 7-12 mm in diameter and has a round or triangular appearance. The colours are variable with habitat. Colonies from deep or turbid waters are usually dark, while those growing in clear water, or near high light intensities, usually exhibit shades of pale brown. The corallite centre is normally green.

Aquarium maintenance:
- **General:** Easy to keep. Should be placed some distance from other corals, as this species, like most faviid corals, can project long sweeper tentacles containing powerful nematocyst batteries that can harm neighbouring corals.
- **Lighting:** Medium to high light intensity, depending on the colour of the colony (see above).
- **Water circulation:** Moderate to strong.
- **Propagation possibilities:** Grows through extra-tentacular budding. We were able to observe the growth of daughter colonies in our aquarium.

GA: + ; TO: +/- ; SE: +

Photos:
- Top: Dark brown colony in an aquarium
- Bottom left: Brownish-green colony in an aquarium
- Bottom right: Spawning colony on the Great Barrier Reef
                                        Photo: Dr. P. Harrison

Favites flexuosa

Distribution: Widely distributed in the Indo-Pacific: at least from the Red Sea to French Polynesia.

Size and growth form: Small to medium-sized massive or encrusting colonies, usually flat or spherical in shape. The surface is normally even.

Food: Feeds on the translocated products of its zooxanthellae, but also captures plankton and possibly utilizes other food sources as well.

Description: Corallites are always completely cerioid and usually angular in outline. They have large openings (15 to 20 mm). Usually coloured green or brownish or blue-green.

Aquarium maintenance:
- **General:** Common in the trade and easy to keep. We have not yet observed sweeper tentacles in this species.
- **Lighting:** Medium to strong. Seems to tolerate variable light intensities well.
- **Water circulation:** Moderate to strong.
- **Propagation possibilities:** Unknown.

GA: + ; TO: + ; SE: +

Photos:
- Top: Close-up of the corallites
- Bottom: Round colony

Goniastrea favulus (?) in the muddy water of Alexandra Bay, in Queensland, Australia

Goniastrea retiformis can create micro-atolls, as seen here at Siladen, North Sulawesi, Indonesia

polyps. When its polyps are expanded, it can be easily confused with *Favia* species, but when the skeleton is examined, it can be seen that it is a *Favites*. We discuss this species in greater detail in the fact sheet on page 427.

Favites abdita is also very common and well known and loved by reef aquarium enthusiasts. It has a contrasting and very beautiful colour pattern, with brown-purple walls and green polyp centres (see fact page 426).

The massive colonies of *Favites complanata* have small (8 to 12 mm) corallite openings and exhibit a cerioid growth form. This species is widely distributed from the Red Sea to the Tuamotu Islands and Tahiti. It is usually brown with green polyp centres, although other colours can also be found.

Favites pentagona possibly has the smallest corallite openings of all species in the genus, measuring less than 6 mm in diameter. The colonies are sub-massive to encrusting in habit and can grow to diameters of more than one metre. The colours are bright and the species almost always has green polyp centres. *F. pentagona* is distributed from the Red Sea to New Caledonia.

Genus *Goniastrea*

The genus *Goniastrea* contains the most robust of all the brain corals. Its species are found on inshore reefs and on shallow reef flats where they can tolerate hours of exposure to the strongest sunlight, fluctuations in temperature and salinity and muddy conditions. These corals therefore occupy habitats that one would not normally associate with stony corals. Some of the 12 or so species grow on rocky coasts which are exposed to extreme wave action. The genus includes species which can handle unusual environmental conditions, as a result of which, the group is excellently suited for a special reef aquarium, such as a tidal aquarium designed for the flora and fauna found in muddy areas where sea grasses grow mixed with scattered boulders and corals. Unfortunately, *Goniastrea* species are not often imported.

The genus is distributed in the Indo-Pacific: from the Red Sea, east and south Africa in the west, plus the Persian Gulf, to southern Japan in the north, along the west, north and east coasts of Australia and throughout the Pacific, as far west as the Tuamotu Islands and Hawaii.

Goniastrea colonies are massive, with a regular corallite pattern. In some species, the corallites look like honeycombs, while other species have walls and valleys and form "brain corals". Others exhibit a spiral pattern, as found in other genera in this family. However, the skeletal structure is more even and uniform in *Goniastrea* species than in other brain corals (with the exception of *Leptoria* species). Approximately 10 species can be found in the Indo-Pacific.

Goniastrea retiformis (see fact-page 429) is commonly found on shallow reef flats and is often a dominant species of intertidal habitats of coastal reefs. We, ourselves, found it in one such habitat near North Sulawesi, Indonesia, where it grew together with several *Acropora* species, *Xenia* and *Sinularia* soft corals, the organ-pipe coral *Tubipora musica*, and the blue coral *Heliopora coerulea*. *G. retiformis* often creates micro-atolls as a result of the upper portion of the ball-shaped colonies dying off during low tide and growth occurring through horizontal expansion. Giant clams of the genus *Tridacna* can sometimes be found along the edges of the colony, where they have bored themselves deep into the coral.

Goniastrea edwardsi is similar to *G. retiformis*, although it has somewhat larger and more irregular corallite openings. It is distributed from east Africa, east to Samoa and often occurs in subtidal coral communities where it can grow to a colony size of more than 1 metre.

Goniastrea aspera lives in the same habitats as *G. retiformis* and colonies can occasionally be found growing close to one another along tropical coastlines. The corallite openings are almost tri-

Goniastrea retiformis

Distribution: Indo-Pacific: from the Red Sea to Samoa. May be a dominant species of intertidal habitats.

Size and growth form: Normally forms massive colonies, tending towards spherical or columnar growth forms and which can range in size from small, to nearly one metre across. Commonly found on shallow reef flats, where the tops of colonies often die and develop into small micro-atolls (see page 428). Deep-water colonies may exhibit an encrusting growth form.

Food: Feeds on the translocated products of its zooxan-thellae, but also captures plankton and possibly utilizes other food sources as well.

Description: The corallites are cerioid, with 4-6, angled straight side walls that give them a neat cellular apperance (VERON & PICHON, 1977). The openings of the corallites are, typically, 3-5 mm in diameter. Cream or pale brown, occasionally pink or green.

Aquarium maintenance:
– **General:** Hardy species that should be kept near the top of the aquarium. Try to experiment with a tidal rhythm set-up where the colony is exposed to open air for a short period every few hours.
– **Light:** Strong
– **Water circulation:** Strong to moderate. Tidal fluctuations preferable.
– **Propagation possibilities:** Not known

GA: + , TO: - , SE: +

Photos:
– Top: Habitat from Silanden, North Sulawesi, Indonesia
– Bottom: close-up of corallites

Two colonies of *Leptoria phrygia* (left, in the Maldives; right, in Indonesia)

angular and have a diameter of 7 to 10 mm.

Goniastrea pectinata and *Goniastrea favulus* have corallites which create a spiral pattern, although this is not as showy as in other such corals, e.g. *Platygyra*. *G. favulus* is most common in inshore and subtidal habitats and is distributed from the Laccadive Islands in the west, to New Caledonia in the east, while *G. pectinata* is widely distributed from the Red Sea to French Polynesia in most shallow-water reef areas.

Goniastrea australensis is probably the only species of the genus which is fully meandroid and is therefore easily distinguished from the other species. Its distribution stretches from the Red Sea and east Africa, to the Pitcairn Islands. With its brain spirals and contrasting two-colour pattern, it is almost impossible to distinguish it from *Platygyra* species, although it has more clearly defined polyp centres and paliform lobes. Its distribution stretches from the Red Sea and east Africa, to the Pitcairn Islands.

Genus *Platygyra*

The genus *Platygyra* fits the term "brain coral" perfectly. The colonies are massive, flat, or hemispherical, most often, with a typical meandroid spiral brain pattern. The genus is widely distributed in the entire Indo-Pacific. Living colonies of *Platygyra* species are very difficult to distinguish from

one another. As already stated, definite determination of *Platygyra* species is only possible by means of a microscopical examination of the skeleton. The most common and best known species is *Platygyra daedalea* (see also fact-page 432), which normally has a distinct contrasting colour pattern with brown walls and grey or green valleys. This species is found from the Red Sea to the Marshall Islands. *P. lamellina* has an overlapping distribution and is very similar to *P. daedalea*. However, the corallites create a brain pattern which is less spiraled than that of *P. daedalea* and, while the septa of *P. daedalea* appear ragged, those of *P. lamellina* are neat and rounded. *P. lamellina* is also much

rarer than *P. daedalea*. Both species have prominent septa.

This is not the case in *Platygyra pini*, where the septa are thin and widely spaced. Additionally, *P. pini* does not have as strong a meandroid corallite structure as the two previous species. It is a very decorative grey or brown, with yellow polyp centres, similar to *Favites abdita*. *P. pini* has a limited distribution from Malaysia and western Australia, to French Polynesia.

Platygyra sinensis can be found from the Red Sea to Samoa. It has long corallites with several mouth openings, or round or angular corallites with only one mouth opening. *P. sinensis* is normally lighter coloured than other *Platy-*

Oulophyllia bennattae (?), photographed in an aquarium at Hagenbecks Tierpark, in Hamburg, is rarely seen. It is, however (due to its large, angular corallites), relatively easy to identify.

gyra species, although, occasionally, it can also be boldly coloured.

Genus *Leptoria*

The genus *Leptoria* is monotypic, with *L. phrygia* as its only representative. This species is distributed from the Red Sea and east Africa, to southern Japan, New Caledonia and French Polynesia. It has a distinctive brain pattern which is created from many evenly formed and neatly arranged septa. The valleys are of indefinite length and always have the same width throughout. The skeleton is always very hard and dense (VERON & PICHON, 1977). It is often found on shallow reef flats exposed to strong light. We tried to maintain *L. phrygia* in a coral reef aquarium, but this turned out to be quite difficult. The colony that we acquired could have possibly been weakened before its arrival. *L. phrygia* is not commonly found in the hobby.

Genus *Oulophyllia*

Oulophyllia crispa is common in the hobby and is very easy to keep. The colonies, which are often green, have a massive hemispherical shape and can reach a diameter of 1 m in the ocean. See fact page 433 for details. Besides *O. crispa*, the genus also includes *O. bennettae*, which is similar to *O. crispa*, but has large, angular four-cornered corallites. It is distributed from Malaysia to Vanuatu and is, according to VERON (1986), seldom common, but very conspicuous. Both species are, however, very variable in appearance.

Genus *Montastrea*

The genus *Montastrea* includes several species which are easy to maintain in aquaria. About seven species are distributed from east Africa and the Red Sea, to the Line and Tuamotu Islands in the Indo-Pacific. The genus is also represented in the Gulf of Guinea (west Africa), in the Caribbean

Close-up of the corallite structure of *Montastrea annularis*
Photo: J. Cairns-Michael

and along the east coast of south America. There are about 13 *Montastrea* species, but the genus is, in general, poorly defined and includes several species that form distinctive geographical subspecies of doubtful taxonomic affinity (VERON, 1995).

Montastrea species are similar to *Favia* species, although, in *Montastrea*, new polyps are normally formed on the side of the mother polyp through extratentacular budding (see page 422). This is the most reliable characteristic for distinguishing between the two genera, even when there are exceptions, as there so often are, to this rule. Extra-tentacular budding is restricted to growing colonies; older colonies do not produce new corallites. It must be emphasized, though, that *Monastrea* species are fundamentally difficult to identify.

One of the most beautiful species in the genus is *Montastrea curta*. With its decorative hemis-

General view of a *Montastrea cavernosa* colony   Photo: J. Cairns-Michael

Platygyra spp.

Distribution: Widespread in the Indo-Pacific: from east Africa and the Red Sea and Gulf of Persia, to southern Japan, Line Islands and the Tuamotu Islands. In Australia, south to Lord Howe Island and Houtman Abrolhos Atoll.

Size and growth form: The colonies are massive, either flat or dome-shaped. Common on upper reef slopes.

Food: Feeds on the translocated products of its zooxanthellae, but also captures plankton and possibly utilizes other food sources as well.

Description: The colonies usually have a meandroid corallite structure, that creates the typical brain pattern. They are rarely cerioid and often grow on reef flats or reef rims. About 12 species are known. They usually have contrasting colours of brown or green. *Platygyra daedalea* is the most common one and is found in a wide range of habitats.

Aquarium maintenance:
– **General:** In our experience, *Platygyra* spp. are not as easy to keep as the members of the other faviid genera. Seem to require plenty of space and clear water that is low in nutrients and high in light intensity, at least, for those species that come from reef edges and outer reef slopes. Seem to be sensitive to shading, with the corallites easily dying off under such conditioins. Species from inshore habitats may be easier to keep. There are no reports on long term aquarium care.
– **Lighting:** High light intensity.
– **Water circulation:** Moderate to strong.
– **Propagation possibilities:** Unknown.
GA: +/- ; TO: + ; SE: +/-

Photos:
– Top: *Platygyra* sp. (possibly *P. daedalea*) on an outer reef slope in the Maldives
– Centre: *Platygyra sinesis* (?) in an aquarium
– Bottom: *Platygyra pini* in an aquarium

Oulophyllia crispa

Distribution: Widespread in the Indo-Pacific: from the Red Sea and east Africa, eastwards to the Phoenix Islands and Samoa, northwards to southern Japan and southwards to Lord Howe Island.

Size and growth form: The colonies are usually large and massive and tend to be hemispherical. Their size can be more than one metre.

Food: Feeds on the products of its zooxanthellae, but seems to use other food sources as well.

Description: Colonies are hemispherical or flat, with wide, "V"-shaped valleys that, in huge colonies in the wild, can measure as much as 2 cm across, the average being 9-20 mm. The average depths of the valleys are 4-14 mm. The valley walls have acute upper margins. The large and fleshy polyps are extended only during the night and have conspicuous white tentacle tips. The septa are thin and usually compact. The colours are pale greenish, or contrasting brown walls and greyish or greenish valleys.

Aquarium maintenance:
– **General:** The colonies that are imported are usually small, compared to older colonies in the wild. They are durable and easy to keep, growing very rapidly into large colonies. Develops sweeper tentacles, and has therefore to be placed some distance away from other corals.
– **Lighting:** Medium to high light intensity.
– **Water circulation:** Modereate to strong.
– **Propagation possibilities:** Unknown.
GA: + ; TO: +/- ; SE: +

Photos:
– Top: Flat-growing colony in an aquarium
– Bottom right: Hemispherical colony in an aquarium
– Bottom left: Close-up of the corallites with retracted polyps

Montastrea valenciennesi

Distribution: Indo-Pacific: from Madagascar to the Marshall Islands.

Size and growth form: The colonies are normally medium-sized, massive, rounded or flattened, or sometimes encrusting. Occurs in a wide range of habitats.

Food: Feeds on the translocated products of its zooxanthellae, but also captures plankton and possibly utilizes other food sources as well.

Description: The corallites are polygonal or hexagonal, 8-15 mm in diameter. Some colonies have an even surface, while others are more convoluted. A "groove and tubular" system between the corallites is characteristic for this species. This system consists of very thin-walled tubes (maximum 0.5 mm in diameter) which have circular or elongated openings at irregular intervals on their upper surfaces. See VERON & PICHON (1977), ROSEN (1968) and CHEVALIER (1971) for more details on these structures. The pore system (small openings between the polyps) is well developed. Colouring of *M. valenciennesi* is usually greenish to blue-green or yellow.

Aquarium maintenance:
– **General:** Commonly found in trade. Durable and easy to keep. Sweeper tentacles have not yet been observed.
– **Lighting:** Medium to high light intensities.
– **Water circulation:** Moderate.
– **Propagation possibilities:** Unknown. New polyps are created through extra-tentacular budding.

GA: + ; TO: + ; SE: +

Photos:
– Top: Colony in an aquarium
– Bottom left: Close-up of polyps
– Bottom right: Corallite structure showing the tubercular tube openings between the corallites.

From VERON & PICHON (1997)

Montastrea curta

Distribution: Indo-Pacific: from the Red Sea and Madagascar, to the Pitcairn Islands. Common on reef flats.

Size and growth Form: Medium-sized massive colonies, spherical or flattened, but, occasionally, encrusting.

Food: Feeds on the translocated products of its zooxanthellae, but also captures plankton and possibly utilizes other food sources as well.

Description: The corallites are moderately excert, usually circular, but can sometimes be squeezed into an irregular shape, with an opening of 2.5 - 7.5 mm. The septa are of three sizes and regularly arranged. Colonies growing in weak light have widely spaced corallites and are generally dark-coloured, while those growing in strong light are cream or orange and have tighter-placed corallites (VERON & PICHON, 1977; VERON, 1986). Often grows on reef flats.

Aquarium maintenance:

– **General:** Occasionally imported, but very durable and easily kept. Grows steadily. Needs to be evenly illuminated, as shaded parts will bleach and die. The colonies usually imported into Europe are, mostly, uniformly light green or yellow-green. We have not observed this species extending long sweeper tentacles, although it possesses short ones. Grows steadily and quickly through extra-tentacular division.

– **Lighting:** High light intensities.
– **Water circulation:** Moderate to strong.
– **Propagation possibilities:** Unknown.
GA: + ; TO: + ; SE: +

Photos:
– Top: Close-up of the polyps
– Bottom: Colony in an aquarium

Close-up of the corallites of *Cyphastrea serailia*

Photo: E. Lovell; from VERON, 1986

pherical shape and (often) light green base colour with green polyp centres, it is an eye-catcher in any aquarium. Unfortunately, this durable and easy-to-grow brain coral is only sporadically available in trade.

In our experience, *Montastrea valenciennesi* is very commonly imported. It has smaller corallites than *M. curta* and often produces unevenly shaped, moderately sized, creeping/spreading colonies; alternatively, it can develop irregular, almost columnar or hemispherical growth forms. *M. valenciennesi* is discussed in the fact sheet on page 434.

Montastrea annularis and *Montastrea cavernosa* live in the Caribbean. Both species can form massive colonies, which look similar to pyramids or uneven lumps. Sometimes, encrusting flat forms can also be created. Both species are easy to distinguish by means of their corallite structure. In *Montastrea annularis*, the corallites are small, clearly conical and placed very close to one another. *Montastrea cavernosa* has larger corallites which are not as conically formed as those of *M. annularis*. In addition, there is a much wider space between the individual polyps.

Genera *Cyphastrea*, *Diploastrea* and *Leptastrea*

The genus *Cyphastrea* probably contains no more than eight or nine species (VERON, 1995), although, at least, 26 nominal species have been mentioned in the literature over the years (VERON & PICHON, 1977). The members of the genus are relatively easy to identify because of their very small, plocoid corallite openings (maximum 3 mm in diameter) and gnarled colony surface between the conical corallites (coenosteum). *Cyphastrea serailia* is the most common species, with a distribution from the Red Sea to the Marshall Islands. This species exhibits a great degree of variability in growth form and colouring from population to population. Usually, the colours are grey, brown or cream. *C. microphthalma* is similar, but the two species can be separated by the number of polyp septa they possess (VERON, 1986).

The genus *Diploastrea* is monotypic, with *D. heliopora* as its only species. It is easy to recognize because it possesses typical, strongly conical corallites with small openings. In the ocean, this species can grow into huge hemispherical colonies which can attain up to 7 m in diameter and can be hundreds, if not thousands, of years old. *Diploastrea heliopora* is distributed from the Red Sea and east Africa, to the Marshall Islands and Samoa.

The genus *Leptastrea* includes six to eight Indo-Pacific species which all produce massive, often flat or hemispherical colonies. *Leptastrea inaequalis* and *Leptastrea purpurea* are the most common species and are distributed from the Red Sea to Hawaii. They should be easy to keep in reef aquaria, but there are few reports specifically dealing with their maintenance in captivity.

Genus *Echinopora*

Echinopora species grow to form highly variable colonies. These can start off by producing encru-

Close-up of the corallites of *Diploastrea*

Photo: Scott W. Michael

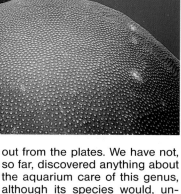

Top: A *Leptastrea* species, photographed in the Maldives, in which a scale-eating blenny of the genus *Plagiotremus* has hidden itself.
Right: *Diploastrea heliopora*, seen here in the Coral Sea, creates hemispherical colonies which are several metres in diameter and are hundreds of years old.

Photo: E. Svensen

sting shapes, which can then develop branches and, at a later stage, can again form plates. Such growth variations are not found among other species of Faviidae and are rare among stony corals in general. The only growth form that is lacking is the typical hemispherical "brain coral shape" which is so characteristic of the rest of the family. There are five to seven Indo-Pacific species (VERON, 1986), of which *Echinopora lamellosa* is, by far, the most common. This species is distributed from east Africa and the Red Sea, to Samoa and the Marshall Islands. It is usually amber, brow-

nish or greenish, with darker brown or green oral discs and with lighter colony margins. *E. mammiformis* is common in the Indo-Australian archipelago, from the Philippines, to Australia and New Caledonia. It has a very smooth coenosteum and is creamy-coloured with purple or violet coloured corallites (without the small points which we find in the other species of the genus). Overall, *E. mammiformis* presents a combination of shape and form which cannot be found in other corals of the family. The colonies form flat plates, sometimes with oddly twisted branches which jut

out from the plates. We have not, so far, discovered anything about the aquarium care of this genus, although its species would, undoubtedly, be quite interesting.

Genus *Moseleya*

The only species in *Moseleya*, *Moseleya latistellata*, is generally uncommon, but very conspicuous. It occurs in turbid waters on muddy bottoms and is known from a restricted area of the central Indo-Pacific, stretching from the Philippines, to northern Australia and along the Great Barrier Reef. The colonies are flat, sub-

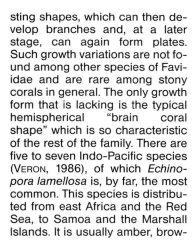

Echinopora lamellosa: the picture on the left shows a colony on a shallow reef flat at the Maldives Island of Kurumba; the right photograph shows a colony from the Great Barrier Reef.

Moseleya latistellata. The polyps become progressively smaller away from the central polyp. Photo: J. E. N. Veron; from VERON, 1986

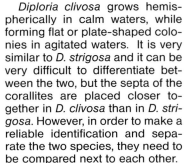

Diploria clivosa grows hemispherically in calm waters, while forming flat or plate-shaped colonies in agitated waters. It is very similar to *D. strigosa* and it can be very difficult to differentiate between the two, but the septa of the corallites are placed closer together in *D. clivosa* than in *D. strigosa*. However, in order to make a reliable identification and separate the two species, they need to be compared next to each other.

Diploria labyrinthiformis is easy to recognize. It has a coarse spiralled corallite structure and has deep canals in the walls which separate the corallites from one another. In our opinion, *D. labyrinthiformis* is one of the the most beautiful of all brain corals. As far as we know, there are few, if any, reports of its durability in the modern reef aquarium.

massive or disc-like and sometimes unattached. The corallites are cerioid and there is a large central corallite that can be up to 35mm across. This central corallite is surrounded by angular daughter corallites that are 4-, 5- or 6-sided and are produced by extra-tentacular budding. The polyps are very light-sensitive and are extended only on dark nights (VERON, 1986; VERON & PICHON, 1977).

We have not yet seen this rare coral in trade, but bearing in mind its habitat preferences, we believe it should be an interesting species for the reef aquarium, especially for inshore sand-zone or sea grass displays.

Genus *Diploria*

There are several Caribbean brain corals of the family Faviidae which are just as beautiful as their Indo-Pacific relatives. We are thinking here of a few *Diploria* species. *Diploria strigosa* often forms flat or hemispherical colonies with a typical spiral brain pattern corallite structure. It can grow into colonies with a diameter of up to 2 m. The genus is common in the Caribbean, including Florida and the Bahamas.

Genus *Manicina*

Manicina areolata has two differing growth forms, the most common one consisting of small elliptical colonies with a conical underside. This is a colony form which appears similar to that of *Trachyphyllia geoffroyi* and is most often seen in colonies occupying sea grass beds, sandy zones or areas of coral rubble. The other growth form, with small, round, or hemispherical colonies and flat undersides, can be found on the same reef between other corals

Top: Close-up of the corallite structure of *Diploria strigosa*
Photo: J. Cairns-Michael

Left: General view of a *Diploria strigosa* colony
Photo: Scott W. Michael

Top: Close-up of the corallite structure of *Diploria labyrinthiformis*
Photo: J. Cairns-Michael

Top right: General view of a *Diploria
labyrinthiformis* colony
Photo: Dr. B. Carlson

To the right: *Manicina areolata* in the
Cayman Islands, Caribbean
Photo: Scott W. Michael

(HUMANN, 1993). *M. areolata* is
white, has a meandroid corallite
structure and lives unattached,
although young colonies are anchored.

Genus *Colpophyllia*

The largest brain coral of the Caribbean is *Colpophyllia natans*,
which creates huge, hemispherical colonies that can attain a diameter of several metres (see below to the right). The spiralled
polyp pattern is constructed from
an endless convoluted system of
ridges and valleys and has a contrasting colour pattern, usually
brown or green. *C. natans* is common in Florida, near the Bahamas
and in the entire Caribbean. Earlier, *C. breviserialis* was also listed
as a species of this genus, but it
is now regarded as a synonym of
C. natans (HUMANN, 1993).

To the right: *Colpophyllia natans*,
shown here near the Cayman Islands, Caribbean, creates huge hemispherical colonies.
Photo: Scott W. Michael

Night-time view of a grey colony of *Trachyphyllia geoffroyi* in an aquarium. The polyps are fully expanded ready to trap plankton.

fluorescent colonies are collected in habitats exposed to strong light and can, therefore, tolerate such conditions in captivity. *T. geoffroyi* can be fed with relatively coarse plankton at night, when its many small tentacles unfold, allowing it to search for food. A limited evening feeding with brine shrimp is an excellent method of providing it with suitable prey. We, ourselves, never feed it according to any plan.

Family Trachyphylliidae

The Trachyphylliidae includes an old acquaintance of the early marine aquarists: *Trachyphyllia geoffroyi*, which is closely related to the family Faviidae and, in particular, to the genus *Moseleya* (VERON, 1995). This beautiful coral was frequently imported from Indonesia and Singapore into Scandinavia and the rest of Europe in the very early days, long before we knew how to keep stony corals alive in captivity. It is still common and among the best loved of all stony corals.

This species is distributed in the Indo-Pacific, from east Africa and the Red Sea, to Papua-New Guinea, southern Japan and New Caledonia. *T. geoffroyi* is especially numerous in coastal areas or on sandy substrata, where it lives together with other unattached corals, such as *Cycloseris* spp. We found the species ourselves at Magnetic Island, near Townsville, Australia, in shallow and rather muddy water. Some colonies live attached, but the majority are free-living and lie loose on soft ground.

Trachyphyllia geoffroyi forms small, flabello-meandroid colonies with a maximum skeleton diameter of 8 cm. With completely expanded polyps, a colony can reach about 20 cm in diameter and contain one to three separate mouths. The polyps are very large and occasionally show fluorescent colouring in green or red, although they are usually light green, grey, or pink. *T. geoffroyi* lives mainly from the products of its zooxanthellae, but also uses other food sources, such as plankton and organic compounds.

During purchase, it is important to check specimens for damage; the living tissue should cover the entire skeleton, including the external and internal surfaces. After proper acclimatization, a healthy colony will last a very long time in an aquarium. A damaged one, on the other hand, will quickly become infected with boring green algae. When this happens, one can easily see the skeleton becoming light green. In most cases, this results in the damaged colony dying after just a few months.

Trachyphyllia geoffroyi requires (depending on its colouring), a medium to strong light intensity. Grey colonies do well under medium intensity, while bright green,

Family Caryophylliidae

The Caryophylliidae contains a number of stony corals that are of great interest to marine aquarists. Most are also easily identifiable and easy to keep in captivity. Genera, such as *Euphyllia, Catalaphyllia* and *Plerogyra* are well-known to coral reef aquarium enthusiasts, as their members have been around in the trade for many years. The family also contains coldwater, non-photosynthezing corals like the cosmopolitan, beautiful and slow-growing *Lophelia pertusa* among others found in deeper waters in the fjords and off the coasts of Norway. Recently a group of up to 400 metres long, 150 metres wide and 30 metres high "cold water reefs" (biotherms) were discovered at depths from 250 to 350 metres on the continental shelf off Mid-Norway (Mortensen et al., 1995; Hovland et al., 1997). The fauna associated with these deep water reefs is highly interesting and diverse (Jensen & Fredriksen, 1992). Other non-photosynthetic members of the Caryophylliidae exist in the genera *Phacelocyathus* and *Coenocyathus*. These species are solitary and widely distributed in tropical oceans. The small *Caryophyllia smithi* is the only solitary coral found along the coasts of Norway as far north as Trondheim.

It has often been asserted that it is not possible to maintain large-polyp corals of the Caryo-

Red-green colony in an aquarium
Photo: Scott W. Michael

Green colony in an aquarium   Photo: T. Luther

Colony on the Great Barrier Reef   Photo: E. Lovell

Grey colony in an aquarium

Differently-coloured colonies in an aquarium

Besides *Plerogyra sinuosa*, the genus *Plerogyra* also contains other species of Bubble Corals: left "KA4-PLE-01", right "KA4-PLE-02".

phylliidae together with small polyp stony corals in the same aquarium and, in principle, we agree with this statement. These large stony corals with big polyps and the ability to grow and expand to huge sizes are best kept in a special aquarium where they can dominate. Such an aquarium can look very decorative; additionally, these corals are easy to care for and can grow magnificently. On the other hand, we have kept this coral in our test aquarium with numerous *Acropora* species for many years without experiencing any association problems. However, the colonies must be given sufficient space to expand their long, strongly-stinging tentacles, and grow (under favourable conditions, they grow very quickly).

Genus *Euphyllia*

Euphyllia includes nine extant species (VERON, 1995). Six of these are combined in two groups and cannot be separated by skeletal characters alone. The first of these groups contains *Euphyllia ancora* and *Euphyllia divisa*, both common in Nature, as well as in aquaria. The two species were originally described as one: *Euphyllia fimbriata*. The second group contains, at least, four species: *Euphyllia. glabrescens*, which is common in the wild and regulary found in the trade, plus *Euphyllia paradivisa*, *Euphyllia pa-*

raancora and *Euphyllia paraglabrescens*, which are all rare.

The polyps of *Euphyllia* are large and their tentacles distinct, a feature that might be linked to their feeding habits. *Euphyllia* is one of the few genera (if not the only one) in which the species can be identified by the shape of the tentacles and polyps, at least, as far as the most common species are concerned. We introduce three of these on pages 443 to 445.

Euphyllia cristata is rare, both in the ocean, as well as in trade. The skeleton form is similar to that of *E. glabrescens*, while the shape of the tentacles are like those of *E. glabrescens*, but distinct excert septa project between them when they are expanded. The skeleton of small colonies of *Plerogyra sinuosa* (see page 447) look like those of *E. cristata*, but the living polyp is very different. This species is distributed in the central Indo-Pacific and is among others recorded from Indonesia, Vietnam, Taiwan, southern Papua-New Guinea, the Philippines and eastern and western Australia.

Euphyllia yaeyamaensis is uncommon and was originally described from the Ryukyu Islands. It is known from the Philippines to Vanuatu.

All *Euphyllia* species have a strong stinging cells and possess long sweeper tentacles with which they can damage neighbouring corals if these are too

close. The stinging cells are not like those of other stony corals which are arranged in groups, but are, instead, evenly distributed along the entire tentacle surface. This can be an adaptation that allows these species to take in small food organisms which float in the water.

Euphyllia species have separate sexes and normally shed gametes, thus exhibiting external fertilisation, although the brooding of larvae can occur in equatorial locations (VERON, 1986).

Genus *Cataluphyllia*

The genus *Cataluphyllia* is monotypic, with *C. jardinei* as its only species. *C. jardinei* is a fantastic stony coral which has been commonly offered in trade during the last several years, although at a high price. As we mentioned in volume one (page 141) *C. jardinei* is found among sea grass beds on muddy bottoms and is perfect for a special aquarium displaying such a habitat. A completely expanded *C. jardinei* is very similar in appearance to a symbiotic anemone and can be mistaken for such by the inexperienced aquarist. See fact page 446 for more information.

Genera *Plerogyra*, *Physogyra* and *Nemenzophyllia*

The genus *Plerogyra* includes, according to VERON (1993), at

Euphyllia ancora
Hammer or Anchor Coral

Distribution: Indo-Pacific: Philippines, Indonesia and southern Japan. The distribution cannot be reported with certainty because the skeleton is very difficult to distinguish from that of *E. divisa*.

Size and growth form: Medium-sized to large colonies with phacelo-meandroid corallite structure with excert septa.

Food: Feeds mainly on the products of its zooxanthellae, but probably also uses other food sources as well.

Description: The polyps have hammer or "T"-shaped tentacles. The colours are blue-grey to light green, or almost fluorescent greenish. Possesses unusually strong poison. Can be a dominant species when it grows on flat substrata in deep areas, although it can also be found in the shallow water of reef flats.

Aquarium maintenance:
– **General:** Commonly found in trade. Durable and easy to maintain; can grow into large colonies. Must be handled with care. The nematocysts are very powerful and we have observed and experienced ourselves that aquarists have reacted allergically to this coral. Be careful not to touch your eyes just after handling *P. ancora*. Some of the imported colonies are clearly pieces of large colonies that have been broken. These pieces are sensitive to damage. In general, the skeleton is susceptible to infestation with boring green algae.
– **Lighting:** Medium to high light intensities.
– **Water circulation:** Moderate.
– **Propagation possibilities:** Daughter colonies can be created along the base of the parent colonies (see photo on page 62, chapter 2). Like all *Euphyllia*, *E. ancora* has separate sexes.

GA: + ; TO: - ; SE: +

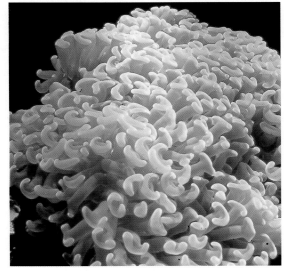

Photos:
– Top: Colony near Indonesia
– Bottom: Colony in an aquarium

Euphyllia divisa
Frogspawn or Fine Grape Coral

Distribution: Indo-Pacific: Philippines, Indonesia and southern Japan. The distribution cannot be reported with certainty because it is very difficult to distinguish this species from *E. ancora*. Common in Houtman Abrolhos Islands, Western Australia.

Size and growth form: Forms large colonies that in the wild exceed 1 metre across. Imported colonies are much smaller, but grow very fast.

Food: Feeds on the translocated products of its zooxanthellae, but also captures plankton and possibly utilizes other food sources as well.

Description: Phacelo-meandroid corallite structure with excert septa. The skeleton is very much like that of other *Euphyllia* spp. Tentacles with small side branches. Colouring is light green or yellow-green.

Aquarium maintenance:
– **General:** Commonly found in trade. Durable and very easy to keep. Grows rapidly and produces new corallites by intra-tentacular budding. It can, in this way, form huge colonies in the aquarium and therefore requires ample free space into which it can grow. Must be treated with care as the tentacles have powerful nematocysts. Susceptible to boring green algae.
– **Lighting:** Medium to strong light intensities.
– **Water circulation:** Moderate.
– **Propagation possibilities:** Separate sexes. Male colonies have often been observed to spawn in reef aquaria. Can bud new colonies along the base of the mother colonies.

GA: + ; TO: +/- ; SE: +

Photos:
– Top: Colony in an aquarium
– Bottom: Close-up of the tentacles

Photo: Scott W. Michael

Euphyllia glabrescens
Torch Coral

Distribution: Indo-Pacific: from the Red Sea, to the Marshall Islands and Samoa. Is not very common, but is found in many different habitats.

Size and growth form: Medium-sized colonies in which the individual corallites are usually separated by 50-100 % of the corallite diameters.

Food: Feeds mainly on the products of its zooxanthellae, but probably also uses other food sources as well.

Description: Corallite structure is phaceloid; the corallite openings are 3 to 5 cm in diameter. Large dark brown or green tentacles with white buttons on the tips.

Aquarium maintenance:

– **General:** Belongs to the group of *Euphyllia* coral species which are, in our experience, a bit more difficult to keep than the two previously mentioned ones, but they can, nevertheless, be kept and grown. Must, however, be carefully acclimatised. Has powerful nematocyst batteries that secrete a strong poison and must therefore be kept at a safe distance from neighbouring colonies. Susceptible to boring algae. Requires good water quality. Reported on several occasions to have grown from living rock.

– **Lighting:** High lighting intensity.

– **Water circulation:** Moderate to strong.

– **Propagation possibilities:** Separate sexes. Can bud new colonies along the base of the mother colonies.

GA: + ; TO: +/- ; SE: +/–

Photos:
– Top: Colony on a reef flat near Bunaken, Indonesia
– Bottom: Colony with expanded polyps in the Maldives
– Left: Colony in an aquarium

Catalaphyllia jardinei
Elegance Coral
Introduced as *Catalaphyllia plicata* by WILKENS (1987), as *Euphyllia* spec. by GROSSKOPF (1987) and as *Euphyllia picteti* by HAYWOOD & WELLS (1989).

Distribution: Indo-Pacific: from Aldabra, the Seychelles (it is not found in the Maldives) and the Andamans, eastwards to the Salomons, northwards to southern Japan and southwards to New Caledonia. Occurs only in turbid waters, commonly among sea grasses on muddy bottoms in areas with high concentrations of organic and other types of suspended particles.

Size and growth form: Medium-sized free-living colonies, which can attain a diameter of 50 cm when fully expanded.

Food: Feeds on the products of its zooxanthellae and on dissolved organic compounds in the water.

Description: Closely related to *Euphyllia* spp. Corallite structure is flabello-meandroid with straight-edged septa forming "V"-shaped valleys (VERON, 1986). Has large, striped greenish or brownish oral disc base with several mouth openings and long, tube-shaped tentacles that are brownish with pink or white tips. The basic colouring is greenish or brown.

Aquarium maintenance:
– **General:** Easy to keep and common in the trade. Best kept in a special aquarium with a flat, soft bottom among sea grasses or *Caulerpa*. See volume 1, page 141. The aquarium water should be more nutrient-rich than that of a normal coral reef aquarium, as this species utilizes dissolved organic nutrient for food. Do not place among other corals that are mounted on living rock to form a reef slope. The Elegance Coral comes fully into its own only in an aquarium simulating its natural habitat.
– **Lighting:** Medium to high light intensities.
– **Water circulation:** Moderate to low.
– **Propagation possibilities:** Unknown.
GA: + ; TO: + ; SE: +

Photos:
– Top: Brown colony in an aquarium
– Centre: Green colony in an aquarium

Photo: T. Luther.
– Bottom: The mouth openings are easy to see in this aquarium colony.

Plerogyra sinuosa
Bubble, Pearl or Grape Coral

Distribution: Indo-Pacific: from the Red Sea, east Africa and Madagascar, to the Marshall Islands and Samoa.
Size and growth form: Normally found as medium-sized colonies, but can, occasionally, create colonies with a diameter over 1 m.
Food: Feeds on the products of its zooxanthellae, but also consumes plankton.
Description: The colonies are phaceloid to flabello-meandroid, with the valleys more or less connected by a lightly blistered coenosteum (VERON, 1986). Can be easily recognized by the clusters of bubble-shaped grey vesicles which develop from the tentacles, although it can sometimes be confused with *Physogyra* spp. Normally grows in caves on vertical substrata; occasionally, larger colonies can be found on flat substrata.
Aquarium maintenance:
– **General:** Has powerful nematocyst batteries and requires a large amount of space. Easy to keep. In our experience, the skeleton is susceptible to infestation with boring green algae. Should be fed with living plankton and organic compounds in the water when it is grown under weak lighting conditions.
– **Lighting:** Weak to medium lighting.
– **Water circulation:** Moderate.
– **Propagation possibilities:** We have observed this coral budding off daughter colonies in aquaria.
GA: + ; TO: - ; SE: +

Photos:
– Top: Small colony on a cave wall in the Maldives; a typical habitat
– Centre: Large colony photographed with a daughter colony in an aquarium
– Bottom: Close-up of tentacles and clusters of vesicles

"KA4-PLE-03", also a *Plerogyra* species (?)

least three species. *Plerogyra* usually lives on muddy bottoms, but can also be found in other habitats and the occurrence of the genus is unpredictable. By far the most common species is *Plerogyra sinuosa*, commonly known by its popular name of bubble coral or "grape coral", which refers to the odd grape-shaped tentacle vesicles or "bubbles". The bubbles, themselves, lack nematocysts, these being found in large numbers on the tentacles. *P. sinuosa* has been kept in aquaria for years and, like *Trachyphyllia geoffroyi*, was among the very first stony corals to be imported. If

algal growth - which *P. sinuosa* is very susceptible to - can be avoided, this coral can be maintained for years in an aquarium. We present "the bubble coral" in detail in the fact sheet on page 447.

WOOD (1983), as well as VERON (1993), also include *Plerogyra simplex*, which is very similar to *P. sinuosa*. The corallites are, however, more rounded on the edges than those of *P. sinuosa*. *P. simplex* has been little studied, but is found from Malaysia to Samoa. *Plerogyra eurysepta* is also a poorly known species occurring from the Philippines to Japan.

Nemenzophyllia turbida was

described by HODGSON & ROSS (1981). Although VERON (1986) regarded the genus as doubtful, it is now clear that *Nemenzophyllia* is a valid genus. *N. turbida* does, however, have almost identical skeletal features as a species of *Euphyllia*, and this was the reason for doubting the validity of the genus (J.E.N. VERON, pers. com.). Its distribution is currently known to stretch from the tip of the Sinai Peninsula, along the east African coast, to southern Madagascar. Although it is not known in the eastern Indian Ocean, it appears again in Indonesia and in a restricted area in the Philippines. *Nemenzophyllia turbida* normally creates fairly small colonies with a flabello-meandroid corallite structure. It has a small, spiralled skeleton and large foliaceous polyps. In Nature, it is known only from habitats with partially muddy substrates (VERON, 1993).

N. turbida is, however, not among the easiest stony corals to keep in captivity. Its skeleton is often infected with boring green algae and collected specimens are easily damaged. Most imported colonies seem to be broken off from larger colonies and this could very well be the reason for the damage. Sometimes, or even often, such colony fragments heal, recover and even start to grow under healthy captive conditions, but beginners should avoid this species; neither should it be introduced into fresh set-ups. Once established, though, it is hardy.

We would recommend trying this species in sea grass set-ups, where it could be displayed together with species like *Catalaphyllia jardinei* and *Montipora digitata*.

The genus *Physogyra* is often confused with the genus *Plerogyra*. In truth, the two can only be distinguished by their skeleton structure. Normally, *Physogyra* species have smaller and more elongated tentacle vesicles than *Plerogyra* species. The genus *Physogyra* includes, according to VERON (1986), three species, of which *P. lichtensteini* (see to the left) is, undoubtedly, the most common.

Physogyra lichtensteini on a reef flat at Bunaken, Indonesia

Two colonies of *Nemenzophyllia turbida*, photographed in an aquarium.

Genera *Thalamophyllia* and *Eusmilia*

Two beautiful corals from the Caryophylliidae family can be found in the Caribbean Sea. *Thalamophyllia riisei* is a small solitary coral with conical corallites and often grows in groups under cliff overhangs. This light red coral is of no significance for aquarists.

Eusmilia fastigiata creates hemispherical colonies in which the corallites are tubular and oval, and have coarse septa. These are characteristics which give the species an unmistakable appearance. The colouring is often light beige, brown or blue. *E. fastigiata* is widely distributed in the entire Caribbean Sea, including Florida and the Bahamas.

Genera *Phacelocyathus* and *Coenocyathus*

The Caryophylliidae also contains ahermatypic solitary corals, such as the genera *Phacelocyathus* and *Coenocyathus*, which are widely distributed in tropical oceans. We will not introduce these in further detail, though, as they are of no significance for the reef aquarium hobby. For those interested, we recommend VERON (1986) and HUMANN (1993).

Family Dendrophylliidae

The Dendrophylliidae, with which we will end this chapter on stony corals, is known, above all, for the genera *Tubastraea* and *Dendrophyllia*. Both genera consist exclusively of ahermatypic species which lack zooxanthellae. Many of the ahermatypic dendrophylliid corals are found in deeper waters, where they generally have large yellow or orange polyps surrounded by stout, pointed tentacles which trap plankton

Eusmilia fastigiata in the Cayman Islands, Caribbean
Photo: Scott W. Michael

Tubastraea diaphana in the Maldives

very effectively. These corals are often traded under the name *Tubastraea aurea*, but this is only one of the many species. Classification and nomenclature are so confusing in these corals that it is very difficult to distinguish the *Dendrophyllia* and *Tubastraea* species from one another. A determination is only possible if based on the form and position of the mesenterial filaments, characteristics which are impossible to recognize in living animals.

Genera *Dendrophyllia*, *Tubastraea* and *Balanophyllia*

Of the ahermatypic genera commonly found on corals reefs, the above three are the most common. Of these, at least *Tubastraea* is well known to aquarists.

The genus *Dendrophyllia* includes, at least, six species while *Tubastraea* includes at least 4 species from Australian waters (VERON, 1986), while WOOD (1983) mentions 4-5 species from the Indo-Pacific. All species are found from shallow water, down to 1500 metres. They prefer to grow on overhanging rocks and vertical substrata, or in caves, in shaded localities. The colonies are dendroid and, with the exception of the strongly branched *Tubastraea micrantha*, which is easily recognisable, all species are very similar and can hardly be distinguished from one another without a close inspection of the skeleton.

Tubastraea spp. occur frequently in the trade. We are, however, of the opinion that they are very difficult to keep for any length of time in aquaria. In principle, we would therefore advise against importing these species. Although there are reports that some colonies do well for some time and, although the genus is known to multiply in captivity by producing asexual planula larvae that settle and develop into tiny polyps (see volume 1, page 178), *Tubastraea* spp. are definitely species for the advanced and very experienced aquarist. If kept at all, they should be given a special tank - an aquarium where their requirements for light, current and amount of food, as well as their apparent need for a vertical substratum, can be taken into account.

Tubastraea micrantha was originally described by J. DANA in his Atlas of Zoophytes in 1849. He named the species "*Dendrophyllia nigrescens*", a name which is still commonly used. This species occurs on the reef where the current is strong, usually at depths greater than 10 m. It develops fantastic branched colonies with a beautiful brown-black colouring, often with dark green fluorescent polyps. Colonies can grow to more than 1 metre across. We are of the opinion that it is not possible to maintain this species successfully in reef aquaria.

Tubastraea diaphana usually has darker polyps than the other species of the genus, although we are not sure if this is a usable species characteristic. In *T. faulkneri*, the polyps sit close to one another in a compact coenosteum, although the colonies are

Tubastraea micrantha in the Maldives   Photo: I. Erga

Population photographed in Papua-New Guinea.
Photo: Scott W. Michael

Population photographed in the Gulf of California.
Photo: Scott W. Michael

Population photographed in the Galapagos Islands.
Photo: Dr. D. Brockmann

A fully expanded colony photographed during a night dive off Bunaken, Indonesia.

Fully expanded colonies in a reef aquarium

Tubastraea (above) and Dendrophyllia (below) can only be separated by looking at the arrangement of the septa. In Dendrophyllia the septa are fused according to Pourtalés Plan. Such an arrangement is only found in immature polyps of Tubastraea (Veron, 1986).

Photos from Veron, 1986

not branched, as, for example, in T. coccinea. T. coccinea is the only species which, according to Wood (1983), is distributed in the Indo-Pacific, as well as in the Caribbean. According to Veron (1986), however, T. faulkneri is the only species with a circumtropical distribution. A Tubastraea species which cannot be further identified is commonly imported.

Dendrophyllia spp. are very similar to Tubastraea and can only be separated from them by looking at their septal arrangements (see figures to the left). According to Wood (1983), there are about 3-4 species occuring in shallow reef waters, where they prefer the same type of substratum as Tubastraea spp.

All Dendrophyllia and Tubastraea species require strong currents and large amounts of food (plankton) in aquaria. In the ocean, they often grow under cliff overhangs and this should be taken into consideration when placing them in an aquarium. If, for example, the colonies are laid on the base of the aquarium, so that the polyps face towards the top, they can easily collect debris between the polyps, causing the tissues to die off. However, the underside of the colony can be bored and suspended on a cliff overhang in its natural growth position using a plastic screw.

Feeding requirements are so large, that they can only be met in a special aquarium; frugal feeding will quickly kill off the colonies. All species are, with our current knowledge and maintenance techniques, difficult to keep alive over long periods of time. We would therefore, as stressed earlier, advise against importing these corals.

Balanophyllia is the third ahermatypic genus of the family. It is often overlooked, as the polyps are small and solitary. The species are, however, cosmopolitan and grow in shady places, often on caves ceilings or underneath rocks and cliff overhangs.

Balanophyllia spp. have beautiful red colouring and robust tentacles, which are quite similar to those of *Tubastraea*. The polyps are oval, tapering towards the base, and the septa are fused, as in *Dendrophyllia*.

Genus *Turbinaria*

In contrast to the ahermatypic species of the family, the hermatypic members are easily kept in reef aquaria. The genus *Turbinaria* is the exact opposite, in aquarium terms, to the above-named genera, the various species being easy to care for in aquaria and, in good conditions, developing into large colonies.

The genus *Turbinaria* includes, at least, ten true species and as many as 80 nominal ones. The species are some of the most variable of all stony corals, these variations arising as responses to different light intensities. The genus is distributed throughout the entire Indo-Pacific and is especially common in high-latitude locations. This can perhaps be linked to the fact that these corals spawn in the autumn, when the temperature falls (in contrast to the vast majority of other hermatypic corals that spawn in the summer, see chapter 2; VERON, 1986). *Turbinaria bifrons*, *Turbinaria radicalis* and *Turbinaria heronensis* are three species that are all rare in tropical locations, but common in temperate waters. Most common in tropical waters is *Turbinaria peltata*, which is also regularly imported. The robust yellow *T. reniformis* and the strongly pleated *T. mesenterina* are two further species of the tropics, which also occur sporadically in the trade. We introduce all three species in more detail in the factpages 454 to 456.

Genus *Duncanopsammia*

Very rare and rather special corals, such as *Duncanopsammia axifuga*, the only species of the genus, are occasionally seen in reef tanks. This species, more than any other coral, combines many of the characters of both hermatypic and ahermatypic dendrophylliid corals. Based on

Duncanopsammia axifuga **is an extremely rare stony coral. The upper picture shows colonies in an aquarium owned by Kjell Nagy, Flekkefjord, Norway, just after they had been placed there; the lower picture shows their growth after eight months.**

its corallite structure alone, *D. axifuga* would easily fit into the ahermatypic genus *Balanophyllia* (VERON, 1993 and 1995). Its distribution is limited to the waters of northern tropical Australia, to south Papua-New Guinea and further southwards to the central Great Barrier Reef. It is normally found in habitats deeper than 20 metres, where it is attached to a solid substratum in habitats dominated by soft bottoms (VERON, 1986). This species has, however, also been observed in caves in shallow, turbid water in the central GBR (DELBEEK & SPRUNG, 1994). We received a small colony from Julian Sprung, Miami, and

this thrived for us. The colonies are dendroid and have long, tubular corallites, 10-14 mm in diameter, all facing upwards. The polyps are very large and green to blue-green in colour. In captivity, *D. axifuga* grows rapidly and must be regarded as very easy to keep. It builds a hard skeleton and continually buds off new polyps. It can be fragmented by splitting a colony into a number of pieces, or by breaking off a few polyps, although the skeleton is difficult to break. It can be inferred that, in the ocean, *D. axifuga*, in addition to feeding off the products of its zooxanthellae, also feeds on plankton and other organic food.

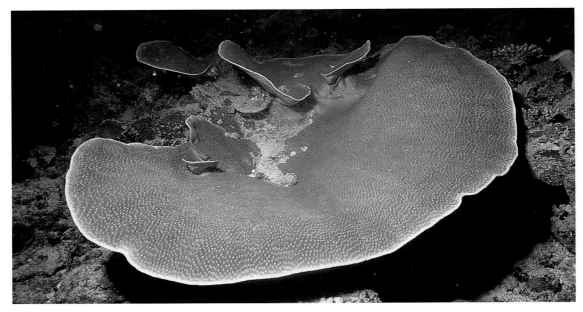

Turbinaria mesenterina

Distribution: Indo-Pacific: from the Red Sea, east Africa and Madagascar, to the Marshall Islands and French Polynesia.

Size and growth form: Can create large colonies with diameters of up to several metres. The shape of the colonies varies with habitat (see photographs).

Food: Feeds on the products of its zooxanthellae, but also uses other food sources.

Description: The colonies are composed of unifacial laminae. In shallow water, they are usually strongly convoluted; in deeper or turbulent water, they are usually more plate-shaped. The polyps are smaller than those of *T. peltata* and are crowded and slightly excert with a corallite opening of 1 to 2 mm in diameter. Colouring is normally light brown or grey. Very common and may occupy a wide range of habitats. Found in shallow turbid water, on clear reef flats and on deeper reep slopes.

Aquarium maintenance:

– **General:** Rarely found in trade. Very durable and easy to keep, where shallow-water colonies are concerned. Should be given plenty of space in order to create the characteristic convoluted growth form. Can be occasionally fed with plankton or organic compounds.

– **Lighting:** Dependant on natural habitat (see above). Medium to high lighting intensity.

– **Water circulation:** Moderate to strong.

– **Propagation possibilities:** Unknown.

GA: + ; TO: + ; SE: +

Photos:

– Top: Colony at 25 m depth on a reef slope in the Maldives

– Left: Convoluted-growing colony in shallow water of a reef flat on the Suva Reef, Fiji

Turbinaria peltata

Distribution: Indo-Pacific: from east Africa, to Samoa and the Marshall Islands. Common in a wide range of habitats.

Size and growth form: Can create large colonies with diameters of up to several metres.

Food: Feeds on the products of its zooxanthellae, but also uses other food sources.

Description: The colonies are flat or plate-shaped, often growing in overlaying layers. There can also be cup-shaped colonies with several columns or, alternatively, it can develop as a single large column. Corallites are embedded within the skeleton, or in tubes. Openings in the corallites are 3 to 5 mm in diameter. Colouring is normally light brown to grey.

Aquarium maintenance:

– **General:** Very common in the trade and easy to keep. Grows rapidly. When a colony becomes cup-shaped, it can collect a fairly large amount of debris inside. This must be removed to prevent the tissue on the base of cup from dying. Should receive a supplement of tiny plankton.

– **Lighting:** Medium to high light intensities.

– **Water circulation:** Moderate to strong.

– **Propagation possibilities:** Unknown.

GA: + ; TO: + ; SE: +

Photos:

– Top: Column-shaped colony   Photo: Scott W. Michael

– Bottom right: A somewhat atypical cup- or saucer-shaped colony growing in an aquarium

– Bottom left: Colony in an aquarium exhibiting the typical growth form

Turbinaria reniformis

Distribution: Indo-Pacific: from Saudi Arabia and the Persian Gulf, to Tonga and the Cook Islands. Can sometimes form large stands in turbid waters (VERON, 1986).

Size and growth form: Can create large colonies with diameters of up to several metres.

Food: Feeds on the translocated products of its zooxanthellae, but also captures plankton and possibly utilizes other food sources as well.

Description: Plate-shaped horizontal-growing colonies. Corallites are widely separated, thick-walled and immersed to conical VERON (1986). The openings of the corallites are 1.5 to 2 mm in diameter. Polyps are smaller than those of *T. peltata*. Colouring is garish yellow or green.

Aquarium maintenance:

– **General:** Rarely found in the trade. Durable and easy to keep. Should be given a large amount of space to allow it to develop the typical plate-shaped growth form. Can occasionally be given a supplement of organic compounds, but this is not essential.

– **Lighting:** Medium to high light intensities.

– **Water circulation:** Moderate to strong.

– **Propagation possibilities:** Unknown.

GA: + ; TO: + ; SE: +

Photos:

– Top: Colony in the Coral Sea   Photo: E. Svensen

– Bottom left: Colony on the Great Barrier Reef. Note the widely spaced corallites.   Photo: Scott W. Michael

– Bottom right: Close-up of a large colony

Photo: T. Luther

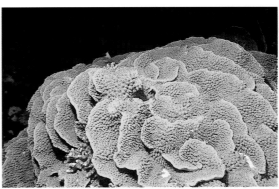

Hermatypic stony corals form massive underwater frameworks, such as steep reef slopes like this. They are the builders of the world's richest underwater ecosystem - "the coral reef" - and offer living space and protection to an unlimited number of organisms.
Photo: T. Luther

A biocoenosis at Vanuatu: host anemone, anemonefishes and shrimps.   Photo: P. Lange

List of References
and
Index

Underwater scenery of a fringing reef at Sinai at a depth of 5 metres.   Photo: Dr. W. Loch

List of References

ACHITUV, Y & Z. DUBINSKY(1990): Evolution and Zoogeography of Coral Reefs. In: DUBINSKY, Z. (edt.): *Ecosystems of the world, vol 25 Coral Reefs.* Elsevier, Amsterdam: 1-9.

ACHTERKAMP, A. (1991): Studeriotes sp.: een moeilijke kostganger ? *Het Zee Aquarium* **41** (10): 176.

ALDERSLADE, P. (1983): Dampia pocilloporaeformis, a new genus and a new species of octocorallia (Coelenterata) from Australia. *The Beagle* (Occasional Papers of the Nothern Territory Museum of Arts and Science) **1** (4): 33-40.

ALDERSLADE, P. (1986): An unusual leaf-like Gorgonian (Coelenterata: Octocorallia) from the great Barrier Reef, Australia. *The Beagle* (Occational Papers of the Northern Territory Museum of Arts and Science) **3** (1): 81-93.

ALLEN, G. R. (1975): *The Anemonefishes: their Classification and Biology.* 2nd. edition TFH Publ. Inc. USA.

ANON. (1985). *The Marine Stinger Book.* The Surf Life Saving Association of Australia. 3 ed.

ATKINSON, S. & M. J. ATKINSON (1992): Detection of estradiol 17β during a mass coral spawn. *Coral Reefs* **11** (1): 33-36.

AYRE, D. J. & J. M. RESING (1986): Sexual and asexual production of planual in reef corals. *Mar. Biol.* (90): 187-190.

BABCOCK, R. C. (1984): Reproduction and distribution of two species of Goniastrea (Scleractinia) from the Great Barrier Reef Province. *Coral Reefs* **2** (4): 187-195.

BABCOCK, R. C., (1985) Growth and mortality on juvenils corals (Goniastrea, Platygyra and Acropora): the first year. *Proc. 5th. Int Coral Reef Symp, Tahiti, 1985* (4): 355-360.

BABCOCK, R. C., G. D. BULL, P. L. HARRISON, A. J. HEYWARD, J. K. OLIVER, C. C. WALLACE & B. L. WILLIS (1986): Synchrounous spawnings of 105 scleractinian coral species on the Great Barrier Reef. *Mar. Biol.* (90): 379-394.

BABCOCK, R. C. & J. S. RYLAND (1990): Larval development of a tropical zoanthid (Protopalythoa sp.). *Invert. Reprod. Develop.* **17**: 229-236.

BARNES, R. D. (1980): *Invertebrate zoology.* Saunders College, Philadelphia.

BARNES, D. J. & B. E. CHALKER (1990): Calcification and Photosynthesis in Reef-building Corals and Algae. In: DUBINSKY, Z. (edt.) *Ecosystems of the World, vol. 25 Coral Reefs.* Elsevier, Amsterdam, pp 109-131.

BATES, J. (1997): Growth Rate Study of Acropora cervicornis at the Smithsonian's Exploring Marine Ecosystems Microcosm. *Aquarium Frontiers On-Line* (http://www.aquariumfrontiers.com), July 1997 issue.

BAUMEISTER, W. (1990): *Meeresaquaristik.* Eugen Ulmer Verlag, Stuttgart.

BAYER, F. M. (1956): Octocorallia. In MOORE, R. C. (ed.): *Treatise on Invertebrate Paleontology. Part F. Coelenterata*: 166-231, figs. 134-162. Geological Society of American University of Kansas Press.

BAYER, F. M. (1961): The shallow-water Octocorallia of the West Indian region. *Stud. Fauna Curacao* (2): 1-373, figs. 1-101, pls. 1-27.

BAYER, F. M. (1973): Colonial Organization in Octocorals. In BOARDMAN R. S, A. H. CHEETHAM & W. A. OLIVER (edts.): *Animal Colonies: Development and Function Through Time*: 69-93. Dowden, Hutchinson & Ross, Inc., Stroudsburg, Pa., USA.

BAYER, F. M. (1981): Key to the genera of octocorallia exclusive Pennatulacea (Coelenterata: Anthozoa) with diagnoses of new taxa. *Proc. Biol. Soc. Wash.* **94** (3): 902-947.

BAYER, F. M. (1992): The Helioporacean Octocoral Epiphaxum. Recent and Fossile. *Studies in Tropical Ocenography, Miami.* (15): VII + 76 pp.

BAYER, F. M. (1993): A New Scleraxonian Octocoral (Coelenterata: Anthozoa) from Antarctic Waters. *Precious Corals & Octocora Research* (2): 11-18.

BAYER, F. M. & M. GRASSHOFF (1994): The genus group taxa of the family Ellisellidae, with clarification of the genera established by Gray (Cnidaria: Octocorallia). *Senckenbergiana biologica*, **74**: 21-45.

BAYER, F.M., M. GRASSHOFF & J. VERSEVELDT (edts.) (1983): *Illustrated Trillingual Glossary of Morphological Terma applied to Octocorallia.* E. J.Brill/Dr. W. Blackhuys, Leiden, Holland.

BENEDEN, E. VAN (1897): *Les Anthozonaries de lan Plankton-Expedition. Resultat de la Plankton-Exp. Der Humboldt-Stiftung*, vol II K. E.: 1-222, pls. 1-16.

BENNETT, I. (1986): *The Great Barrier Reef.* Lansdowne Press, Dee Why West, NSW., Australia.

BERMERT, G. & R. ORMOND (1981). *Red Sea coral reefs.* Paul Kegan International Ltd., London.

BERNARD, H. M. (1896): The genus Turbinaria. The genus Astraeopora. *Cat. Madreporarian Corals Br. Mus. (Nat. Hist.)* 2: 1-166, pl. 1-33.

BERNARD, H. M. (1903): The family Poritidae. I. The genus Goniopora, Pt. I. Porites of the Indo-Pacific region. *Cat. Madreporarian Corals Br. Mus. (Nat. Hist.)* 2: 1-166, pl. 1-33.

BERNARD, H. M. (1905): The family Poritidae. II. The genus Porites, Pt. I. Porites of the Indo-Pacific region. *Cat. Madreporarian Corals Br. Mus. (Nat. Hist.)* 5: 1-303, pl. 1-35.

BERNARD, H. M. (1906): The family Poritidae. II. The genus Porites, Pt. II. Porites of the Atlandic and the West indies with European fossil forms. Thew genus Goniopora, a supplement to vol. IV. *Cat. Madreporarian Corals Br. Mus. (Nat. Hist.)* 6: 1-173, pl. 1-17.

BEUL, H. R. (1987): Parasieten op lagere dieren. *Het Zee Aquarium* **37** (1): 13-15.

BIRKHOLZ, J. (1982a): 4400 Liter Seewasser und gute Erfolge bei Pflege von Steinkorallen. *das Aquarium* **16** (8): 425-429.

BIRKHOLZ, J. (1982b): Eine parasitische Schnecke an Anthelia (Weichkorallen). *das Aquarium* **16** (11): 599-600.

BIRKHOLZ, J. (1983a): Wie ein Wolf im Schafspelz. *das Aquarium* **17** (8): 425-426.

BIRKHOLZ, J. (1983b): Gelungene Vermehrung von Xenia im Aquarium. *das Aquarium* **17** (12): 649-651.

BIRKHOLZ, J. (1986): Blaue Koralle Heliopora coerulea. *das Aquarium* **20** (6): 318-320.

BIRKHOLZ, J. (1987): Palythoa tuberculata. *das Aquarium* **21** (12): 641-643.

BIRKHOLZ, J. (1988a): Stylophora pistillata. *das Aquarium* **22** (10): 603-604.

BIRKHOLZ, J. (1988b): Ein Riffbaumeister aus der Karibik, Montastrea cavernosa (LINNAEUS). *das Aquarium* **22** (1): 29-30.

BIRKHOLZ, J. (1989): Prosit Neujahr oder die Besetzung einer ökologischen Nische, Acropora humilis am natürlichen Standort und im Aquarium. *das Aquarium* **23** (1): 27-30.

BLAINVILLE, H. M. (1830): *Dictionaire des Sciences naturelles (1816-1830)*, Pt. 60: 1-546. Levrault, Paris & Strasbourg.

BLANQUET, R. S., J. C. NEVENZEL & A. A. BENSON (1979): Acetate incorporation into the lipids of the anemone Anthopleura elegantissima and its associated zooxanthellae. *Mar. Biol.* (54): 185-194.

BOULLON, J. & N. HOUVENHAGHEL-CREVECOEUR (1970): Etude monographique du Heliopora de Blainville (Coenothecalia - Alcyonaria - Coelenterata). *Musee Royal De L'Afrique Central. Tervuren. Annales Sciences Zoologiques* 178: i-viii + 1-83, pls. 1-12.

BOURNE, G. C. (1914): On Acrossota liposclera, a New Genus and Species of Alcyonarian with Simple Tentacles. *Quarterly Journal of Microscopical Science n.s.* (60): 261-272, pl. 22.

BRIGGS, D. E. G., D. H. ERWIN & F. J. COLLIER (1994): *The Fossils of the Burgess Shale*. Smithsonian Institution Press, Washington and London.

BROCKMANN, D. (1982a): Scheibeanemone Ricordia florida aus der Karibischen See. *das Aquarium* 16 (5): 253-254.

BROCKMANN, D. (1982b): Haltbare Hornkoralle, Psammogorgia arbuscula. *das Aquarium* 16 (9): 481-483.

BROCKMANN, D. (1984): Elefantenohren. *das Aquarium* 18 (10): 531-535.

BROCKMANN, D. (1985a): Ein Parasit, Baumchenschnecke, Dendronotus sp. *das Aquarium* 19 (7): 361-362.

BROCKMANN, D. (1985b): Eine haltbare Steinkoralle aus dem Indopazifik. *das Aquarium* 19 (9): 473-474.

BROCKMANN, D. (1985c): Dörnchenkorallen, Cirrhipates anguina von den Malediven. *das Aquarium* 19 (12): 641-643.

BROCKMANN, D. (1989): Ecksternkoralle Favites abdita (Ellis & Solander, 1786). *das Aquarium* 23 (2): 95-97.

BROCKMANN, D. (1990): Hydroidpolypen. *das Aquarium* 24 (10): 40-46.

BROCKMANN, D. (1991): Zwei Hornkorallen aus der Karibik, Pseudopterogoria und Plexaura. *das Aquarium* 25 (1): 38-40.

BROCKMANN D. (1994) Vermehrung einer Porites-Art im Korallenriff-Aquarium. *das Aquarium* 28 (10): 25-29 and (11): 25-29

BROCKMANN, D. & P. RÜGGEBERG (1994): Pickelkorallen - Zur Pflege von Hydnophora-Arten im Korallenriff-Aquarium. *das Aquarium* 28 (5): 25-29

BRONS, R. (1982): Kwallen in het zee aquarium. *Het Zee Aquarium* 32 (7/8): 197-203.

BRONS, R. (1989): Eine Polypenkolonie in Dauerkultur. *Mikrokosmos* 78 (7): 193-198.

BRONS, R. (1992): Quallen - selten gepflegte Tiere im Seewasseraquarium. *DATZ* 45 (1): 28-33.

BROWN, B. E. (1990). Coral bleaching. *Coral Reefs* 8 (4) 153- 232.

BROWN, B. E. & SUHARSONO (1990): Damage and recovery of coral reefs affected by El Ni(o related seawater warming in the Thousand Islands, Indonesia. *Coral Reefs* 8 (4): 163-170.

BRUCE, A. J. (1973): Shrimps and Prawns of Coral Reefs, with special reference to commensalism. In: *Biology and Geology of Coral Reefs*, Vol. III. Academic Press, New York.

BRUCE, A. J. (1976): Shrimps and Prawns of Coral Reefs, with special reference to commensalism. In: *Biology and Geology of Coral Reefs*, Vol. III. Academic Press, New York.

BULL, G. (1986) Distribution and abundance of coral plankton. *Coral Reefs* (4): 197-200.

BULLOUGH, W. S. (1981): *Practical Invertebrate Anatomy* 2. Edition. The Macmillan Press Ltd., London.

BURNETT, W. J., J. A. H. BENZIE, J. A. BEARDMORE & J. S. RYLAND (1997): Zoanthids (Anthozoa, Hexacorallia) from the Great Barrier Reef and Torres Street, Australia: systematics, evolution and a key to species. *Coral Reefs* 16: 55-68.

BURNS, T. P. (1985): Hard coral distribution and cold-water disturbance in South Florida: Variation with depth and location. *Coral Reefs* (4): 117-124.

CARLGREN, O. (1900): Zur Kenntnis der Stichodactylinen Actiniarien. *Ofvers. K. Vetensk. Akad. Förh. Stockh.* (57): 277-287, figs. 1-2.

CARLGREN, O. (1943): East-Asiatic Corallimorpharia and Actiniaria. *Kungl. svenska Vetenskapsakademiens Handlinger* 3. ser. 20 (6): 1-43.

CARLGREN, O. (1949): A surwey of the Ptychodactiaria, Corallimorpharia and Actiniaria. *Kungl. Svenska Vetenskapsakademiens Handlinger* 4. ser. 1 (1).

CARROLL, D. J. & S. C. KEMPF (1990): Laboratory Culture of the Aeolid Nudibranch Berghia verrucicornis (Mollusca, Ophistobranchia): Some Aspects of Its Development and Life History. *Biol. Bull.* 179: 243-253.

CARROLL, D.J. & S. KEMPF (1994): Changes occur in the general nervous system of the nudibranch Berghia verrucicornis (Mollusca, Ophistobranchia) during development. *Biol. Bull.* 186 (2): 243-253.

CHAPMAN, G. (1966): The structure and functions of the mesogloea. In: *The Cnidaria and their Evolution* W. J. REES (edt.) Academic Press, London.

CHEN, C. A. (1993): Taxonomic Survey of the Tropical Corallimorpharians (Anthozoa: Corallimorpharia) in the Great Barrier Reef. *Final Report, Great Barrier Reef Marine Park Authority*.

CHEN, C. A., C. CHEN & I. CHEN (1995a): Sexual and asexual reproduction of the tropical corallimorpharian Rhodactis (=Discosoma) indosinensis (Cnidaria:Corallimorpharia) in Taiwan. *Zool. Studies* 34: 29-40.

CHEN, C. A., C. CHEN & I. CHEN (1995b): Spatial variability of size and sex in the tropical corallimorpharian Rhodactis (=Discosoma) indosinensis (Cnidaria:Corallimorpharia) in Taiwan. *Zool. Studies*, 34 (2): 82-87.

CHEN, C. A., D. M. ODORICO, L.M. TEN, J. E. N. VERON & D. J. MILLER (1995): Systematic relationship within the anthozoa (Cnidaria:Anthozoa) using 5'-end of the 28SrRNA. *Mol. Phyl. Evol.* 4 (2):175-183.

CHEN, C. A. & D. J. MILLER (1996): Analysis of ribosomal ITS1 sequences indicates a dee divergence between Rhodactis (Cnidaria:Anthozoa:Corallimorpharia) species from the Caribbean and the Indo-Pacific/Red Sea. *Mar. Biol.* 126: 423-432.

CHEN, C. A., B. L. WILLIS & D. J. MILLER (1996): Systematic relationship between tropical corallimorpharians (Cnidaria:Anthozoa:Corallimorpharia): Utility of the 5.8S and internal transcribed spacer (ITS) regions of the SrRNA transcription unit. *Bull. Mar. Sci.* 59 (1): 196-208.

CHORNESKY, E. A. & E. C. PETERS (1987): Sexual reproduction and colony growth in the scleractinian coral Porites asteroides. *Biol. Bull.* (172): 161-177.

COLES, S. L. & P. L. JOKIEL (1977a): Effects of temperature on the mortality and growth of Hawaiian reef corals. *Marine Biology (Hawaii)* (43): 201-208.

COLES, S. L. & P. L. JOKIEL (1977b): Effects of temperature on photosynthesis and respiration in hermatypic corals. *Marine Biology (Hawaii)* (43): 209-216.

COLGAN, M. W. (1984): The Cretaceous coral Heliopora (Octocorallia, Coenothecalia) - a common Indo-Pacific reef builder. In: ELDRIDGE, N. & S. M. STANLEY: *Living Fossils*. New York, Berlin etc. Springer Verlag. i-xi + 1-291 pp.

COLIN, P. I. (1978): *Caribbean reef invertebrates and plants*. TFH Publications, N. J. USA.

COLIN, P. & C. ARNESON (1995): *Tropical Pacific Invertebrates*. Coral Reef Press, California, USA.

COLL, J. C., S. BARRE, P. W. SAMMARCO, W. T. WILLIAMS & G. J. BAKUS (1982): Chemical defences in soft corals (Coelenterata: Octocorallia) of the Great Barrier Reef: a study of comparative toxicities. *Mar. Ecol. Prog. Ser.* 8: 271-278.

COLL, J. C., S. BARRE, P. W. SAMMARCO, W. T. WILLIAMS & G. J. BAKUS (1982): Chemical defences in soft corals (Coelenterata: Octocorallia) of the Great Barrier Reef: a study of comparative toxicities. *Mar. Ecol. Prog. Ser.* 8: 271-278.

COLL C. & P. W. SAMMARCO (1983): Terpenoid toxins of soft corals (Cnidaria, Octocorallia): their nature, toxicity, and ecological significance. *Toxicon*, suppl. (3): 69.

COLL C. & P. W. SAMMARCO (1986): Soft Corals: Chemistry and Ecology. *Oceanus* 29 (2): 33-37.

COLLINGWOOD, C. (1868): Note on the excistance of gigantic seaanemones in the China Sea, containing within them quasiparasitic fish. *Ann. Mag. Nat. Hist.* ser. 4, 1 (1): 31-33.

COOKE, W. J. (1976): Reproduction, growt and some tolerances of Zoanthus pacificus and Palythoa vestitus in Kaneohe Bay, Hawaii. In G. O. MACKKIE (Red.): *Coelenterate ecology and behavior*. Plenum Press, N. Y., USA: 281-288.

CROCKER, L. A. & H. M. REISWIG (1981): Host specificity in sponge-encrusting Zoanthidea (Anthozoa: Zoantharia) of Barbados, West-Indies. *Mar. Biol.* 65: 231-236.

CROSSLAND, C. J. & M.A. BOROWITZKA (1980): Diurnal lipid and mucus production in the staghorn coral Acropora acuminata. *Mar. Biol.* **60**: 81-90.

CROSSLAND, C. J., D. J. BARNES, T. COX & M. DEVERAUX (1980): Compartmentation and turnover of organic carbon in the staghorn coral Acropora formosa. *Mar. Biol.* **59**: 181-187.

CUTRESS, C. E. (1977): Order Corallimorpharia. In: DEVANEY & ELDREDGE (edts): *Reef and Shore Fauna of Hawaii*, section 1: Protozoa through Ctenophora. B.P. Bishop Museum Special Publication 64 (1): I-XII, p. 130.

D'ELIA C. F. (1977): The uptake and release of dissolved phosphorous by reef corals. *Limnl. Oceanogr.* **22** (2): 301-315.

DANA, J. D. (1846): Zoophytes. *U.S. Exploring during the years 1838-42* (7): I-X, 1-740, txt-figs. 1-45, pls. 1-61.

DAVIS, P. S. (1984): The role of zooxanthellae in the nutritinal energy requirements of Pocillopora eydouxi. *Coral Reefs* **2** (4): 181-186.

DEBELIUS, H. (1990): Da kenne sich einer aus: Meeresanemonen. *DATZ* **43** (12): 728-731.

DEKKER, L. N. (1984): Xenia elongata. *Het Zee Aquarium* **34** (6): 132-133.

DELBEEK, J. C. & J. SRUNG (1994): *The Reef Aquarium*, vol. 1. Ricordea Publishing, Miami, USA.

DEVANEY, D. M. & L. G. ELDREDGE (edts.) 1977. Reef and Shore Fauna of Hawaii. *Bernice P. Bishop Museum Special Publication* **64** (1).

DINESSEN, Z. D. (1983): Patterns in the distribution of soft corals across the Central Great Barrier Reef. *Coral Reefs* **1** (4): 229-236.

DISALVO, L. H. (1971): Regenerative functions and microbial ecology of coral reefs: Labelled bacteria in coral reef microcosm. *J. Exp. Mar. Ecol.* **7**: 123-136.

DISALVO, L. H. (1974): Soluble phosphorus and amino nitrogen released to seawater during recoveries of coral reef regenerative sediments. *Proc. 2nd Int. Coral Reef Symp.* (1): 11-19

DITLEV, H. (1980): *Reef-building corals of the Indo-Pacific*. Scandinavian Science Press, Ltd., Klampenborg.

DONE, T. J. (1982): Patterns in the distribution of coral communities across the Central Great Barrier Reef. *Coral Reefs* **1** (2): 95-107.

DONE, T. J., J. C. OGDEN, W. J. WIEBE & B. R. ROSEN (1996): Biodiversity and Ecosystem Function of Coral Reefs. In: MOONEY, H. A. J. H. CUSHMAN, E. MEDINA, O. E. SALA & E.-D. SCHULZE (edts.): *Functional Roles of Biodiversity: A Global Perspective.* John Wiley and Sons Ltd., N.Y., USA, pp 393-429.

DUBINSKY, Z. (ed.) (1990) *Ecosystems of the World, vol. 25: Coral Reefs.* Elsevier, N.Y.

DUNLAP, W. C. & B. E. CHALKER (1986): Identification and quantitation of near UV-absorbing compounds (S-320) in a hermatypic scleractinian. *Coral Reefs* **5** (3): 155-160.

DUNN, D. F. (1981): The Clownfish Sea Anemones: Stichodactylidae (Colenterata: Actinaria) and Other Sea Anemones Symbiotic with Pomacentrid Fishes. *Trans. Amer. Phil. Soc.* **71** (1): 1-113.

DUNN, D. (1982): Cnidaria. In: PARKER, S. P.: *Synopsis and Classifications of living organisms* (1): i-xvii, 1-1166, pls. 1-87.

DUNN, D. F. & W. H. HAMNER (1980): Amplexidiscus fenestrafer n.gen., n. sp. (Coelenterata: Anthozoa), a Tropical Indo-Pacific Corallimorpharian. *Micronesia* **16** (1): 29-36.

DUCHASSAING, P. & J. MICHELOTTI (1864): Supplement au mémoire sur les Coralliaires des Antilles. *Ibidem* **2** (23): 97-206 (reprint paged 1-112), pls. I-II.

EHRENBERG, C. G. (1834): *Die Corallenthiere des rothen Meeres.* Königl. Akad. Wiss. Berlin.

ELLIS, J. (1755): *An essay towards a natural history of the corallines, and other marine productions of the kind, commonly found on the coast of Great Britain and Ireland.* London.

EREZ, J. (1990): On the importance of food sources in coral-reef ecosystems. In Z. DUBINSKY (edt):*Ecosystems of the World, vol. 25 Coral Reefs.* Elsevier, N.Y.

FADLALLAH, Y. H. (1983): Sexual Reproduction, development and larval biology in scleractinian corals. A review. *Coral Reefs* **2** (3):129-150.

FADLALLAH, Y. H., R. H. KARLSON & K. P. SEBENS (1984): A comparative study of sexual reproduction in three species of Panamanian zoanthids (Coelenterata: Anthozoa). *Bull. mar. Sci.* (35): 80-89.

FAULKNER, D. & R. CHESHER (1979): *Living Corals.* Clarksom N. Potter, Inc., New York.

FAUTIN, D.G. (1990): Sexual differation and behaviour in phylum Cnidaria. In: K. G. ADIYODI & R. G. ADIYODI (Edts.): *Reproductive Biology of Invertebrates*, 4. John Wiley and Sons, London, UK.

FAUTIN, D. G. & G. R. ALLEN (1992): *Field Guide to Anemonefishes and their Host Sea Anemones.* Western Australian Museum, Perth.

FAUTIN, D. G. & J. M. LOWENSTEIN (1992): Phylogenetic relationships among scleractinians, actinians, and corallimorpharians (Coelenterata:Anthozoa). *7th Int. Coral Reefs Symposium, Guam.*

FISHELSON, L. (1970): Littoral fauna of the Red Sea: the population of non scleractinian anthozoans of shallow waters of the Red Sea (Eilat). *Mar. Biol.* **6** (2): 106-116.

FISHELSON, L. (1971): Ecology and distribution of the bentic fauna in the shallow waters of the Red Sea. *Mar. Biol.* **10** (2): 113-133.

FORSKÅL, P. (1775): Descriptiones animalium avium, amphibiorum, piscium, insectorum, vermium; quae in itinere orientali observavit Petrus Forskal, Prof. Havn. Post mortem auctoris edidit Carsten Niebuhr. *Havniae, ex Officina Molleri, aulae Typographi*: 1-64.

FOSSÀ, S. A. & A. J. NILSEN (1992a): *Korallenriff-Aquarium* Band 1, Birgit Schmettkamp Verlag, Bornheim

FOSSÀ, S. A. & A. J. NILSEN (1992b): *Korallenriff-Aquarium* Band 2, Birgit Schmettkamp Verlag, Bornheim

FOSSÀ, S. A. & A. J. NILSEN (1994): Können Steinkorallen in Aquariensystemen wachsen? *das Aquarium* part 1 **28** (2): 23-28; part 2 **28** (4): 26-30; part 3 **28** (6):23-28.

FOSSÀ, S. A. & A. J. NILSEN (1995): *Korallenriff-Aquarium* Band 4, Birgit Schmettkamp Verlag, Bornheim

FOSSÀ, S. A. & A. J. NILSEN (1996): *The Modern Coral Reef Aquarium*, vol. 1. Birgit Schmettkamp Verlag, Bornheim, Germany.

FOSSÀ, S. A. & A. J. NILSEN (1998): *Korallenriff-Aquarium* Band 6, Birgit Schmettkamp Verlag, Bornheim

FRANZISKET, L. (1969): Riffkorallen können autotroph leben. *Naturwissenschaften* **56**: 144.

FRANZISKET, L. (1973): Uptake and accumulation of nitrate and nitrite by reef corals. *Naturwissenschaften* **60**: 552.

FRIESE, U. E. (1972): *Sea Anemones.* TFH Publications, N. J., USA.

FURNAS, M. J, A. W. MITCHEL, M. GILMARTIN & N. REVELANTE (1990): Phytoplankton biomass and primary production in semi-enclosed reef lagoons of the central Great Barrier Reef, Australia. *Coral Reefs* **9** (1): 1-10.

GAWEL, M. J. (1976): Asterospicularia randalli: A NewSpecies of Asterospiculariidae (Octocorallia: Alcyonacea) from Guam. *Micronesia* **12** (2): 303-307.

GEORGE, D. & J. GEORGE (1979): *Marine Life.* Harrap, London. UK.

GLADFELTER, W. B. (1975): Sea anemones with zooxanthellae: Simultanious contraction and expansion in response to changing in light intensity. *Science* (189): 570-571.

GLEIBS, S., D. MEBS & B. WERDING (1995): Studies on the origin and distribution of palytoxin in a Caribbean coral reef. *Toxicon* **33**: 1531-1537

GOLDBERG, W. M. (1973): The ecology of the coral-octocoral communities off the soutest Florida coast: geomorphology, species composition and zonation. *Bull. Mar. Sci.* **23** (3): 465-488.

GOHAR, H. A. F. (1940): Studies on the Xeniidae of the Red Sea. *Publ. Mar. biol. Sta. Ghardaqa*, no. 2: 25-118.

GOHAR, H. A. F. (1948): A description and some biological studies of a new alcyonarian species „Clavularia hamra Gohar". *Publ. Mar. biol. Sta. Ghardaqa*, no. 6: 3-33.

GOREAU, T. F., N. I. GOREAU & C. M. YONG (1971): Reef corals; Autotrophs or heterotrophs ?. *Biol. Bull.* (141): 247-260.

GOREAU, T. F. & A. H. MACFARLANE (1990): Reduced growth rate of Montastrea annularis following the 1987-1988 coral-bleaching event. *Coral Reefs* **8** (4): 211-215.

GOSLINER, T. M., D. W. BEHRENS & G. C. WILLIAMS (1996): *Coral Reef Animals of the Indo-Pacific.* Sea Challengers, Monterey, California, USA.

Gosse, P. H. (1860): *Actinologica Brittannica.* A History of British Sea-Anemones and Corals: i-xl, 1-362, text-figs., pls. 1-12, Van Voorst, London.

Gotshall, D. W. (1994): *Guide to Marine Invertebrates. Alaska to Baja California.* Sea Challengers, Monterer, California, USA.

Graaf, F. de (1980): *Alt om saltvattensakvariet.* ICA Bokforlag, Vesteras.

Grasshoff, M. (1981): Polypen und Kolonien der Blumentiere (Anthozoa), II: Die achstrahligen Korallen (Octocorallia). *Natur und Museum* **3** (2): 29-45.

Grasshoff, M. (1992): Die Flachwasser-Gorgonarien von Europa und Westafrika (Cnidaria, Anthozoa). *Courier Forschunginstitut Senckenberg* 149: 1-35

Gravier, C. (1918): Note préliminaire sur les Hexatinaires recueillis au cours des croissères de la Princesse-Alice et de l'Hirondelle de 1888 à 1913 inclusivement. *Bull. Inst. Oceanogr. Monaco* **346**: 1-24, figs. 1-9.

Grosskopf, J. (1985): Blumentiere - Fauna wie aus dem Garten Eden. Serie in *DATZ* **38** (2) bis **38** (8).

Haywood, M. & S. Wells (1989): *The Interpet Manual of Marine Invertebrates.* Salamander Books, London.

Habermann, E., G. Ahnert-Hilger, G. S. Chatwal & L. Beress (1981): Delayed haemolytic action of palytoxin. General characteristics. *Biochim. biophys. acta.* (649): 481.

Hamner, W. M. & D. F. Dunn (1980): Tropical Corallimorpharia (Coelenterate: Anthozoa): Feeding by Envelopment. *Micronesia* **16** (1): 37-41.

Hansen, P. A. & B. W. Halstead (1971): The Venomous Sea Anemone Actinodendron plumosum Haddon of South Vietnam. *Micronesica* **7**: 122-136.

Harriott, V. J. (1983): Reproductive ecology of four scleractinian species at Lizard Island, Great Barrier Reef. *Coral Reefs* **2** (1) :9-18.

Harrison, P. L. (1980): *The fine structure of Acropora formosa (Dana, 1846) (Scleractinia: Anthozoa).* B. Sc. (Hons) thesis, James Cook University, Townsville.

Harrison, P. L. (1985): Sexual characteristic of scleractinian corals; systematic and evolutionary implications. *Proc. 5th Int. Coral Reef Congress, Tahiti, 1985.* (4): 337-342.

Harrison, P. L. (1988a): Pseudo-gynodioecy: an unusual breeding system in the scleractinian coral Galaxea fascicularis. *Proc. 6th. Int. Coral Reef. Symp., Townsville, 1988* (2): 699-705.

Harrison, P. L. (1988b): *Comparative ultrastructure of scleractinian spermatozoa and its evolutionary implications.* Ph. D. Thesis, James Cook University, Townsville.

Harrison, P. L., R. C. Babcock, G. D. Bull, A. J. Heyward, J.K. Oliver, C. C. Wallace & B. L. Willis (1984): Mass spawning in tropical reef corals. *Science* (223): 1186-1189.

Harrison, P. L. & C. C. Wallace (1990): Reproduction, dispersal and Recruitment of Scleractinian Corals. In: Dubinsky, Z. (ed.) *Ecosystems of the World, vol. 25 Coral Reefs.* Elsevier, N.Y. pp 133-208.

Hartog, J. C. den (1980): Caribbean Shallow Water Corallimorpharia. *Zoologische Verhandlingen.* (176): 1-83 + 14 plates.

Hartog, J. C. den (1990): Associated occurrence of Cyclocoeloma tuberculata Miers, 1880 (Decapoda: Majidae) and species of Discosomatidae (Anthozoa: Corallimorpharia). *Zool. Mededelingen* (64): 161-168.

Hartog, J. C. den (1977): Descriptions of two new Ceriantharia from the Caribbean region, Pachycerianthus curacaoensis N.sp. and Arachnanthus nocturnus N.sp., with a discussion of the cnidom and of the clasification of the Ceriantharia. *Zoologische Mededelingen* **51** (14): 211-242, pls. 1-6.

Hartog, J. C. den (1997): The sea anemone fauna of Indonesian coral reefs. In: *The Ecology of the Indonesian Seas,* part 1. *The Ecology of Indonesia Series,* vol. VII. T., pp 350-370. Tomascik, A. J. Mah, A. Nontji & M. K. Moosa (edts.), Periplus Editions.

Hartog J.C. den, O. Ocana & A. Brito (1993): Corallimorpharia coillected during the CANCAP expeditions (1976-1986) in the south-eastern part of the North Atlantic. *Zool. Verhandlingen* (282): 1-76.

Haywood, M. & S. Wells (1989): *The Interpet Manual of Marine Invertebrates.* Salamander books Ltd., London, UK.

Hebbinghaus, R. (1984): Eine Anthelia aus Kenia. *DATZ* **37** (2): 68-71.

Herberts, C. (1972a): Étude Systematique de Quelques Zoanthaires Tempé et Tropicaux. *Tethys,* Suppl. 3: 69-156.

Herberts, C. (1972b): Contribution a l'Étude Biologique de Quelques Zoanthaires Tempé et Tropicaux, 1. -Reproduction, Croissance Somatique, Bourgeonnement. *Tethys* **4** (3): 711-728.

Herberts, C. (1987): Ordre des Zoanthaires. In: P.-P. Grasse & D. Doumenc (Red.): *Traité de Zoologie, anatomie, systematique, biologie.* Tome 3: 783-810.

Heyward, A. J. (1986): Sexual reproduction in five species of the coral Montipora. In: P. L. Jokiel, R. H. Richmond & R. A. Rogers (Edts.) *Coral Reef Population Biology.* Hawaii Inst. Mar. Biol. Tech. Rep. No. 37: 170-178.

Heyward, A. J. & R. C. Babcock (1986): Self- and crossfertilasation in scleractinian corals. *Mar. Biol.* (90): 191-195.

Hickson, S. J. (1895): The anatomy of Alcyonium digitatum. *Quarterly Journal of Microscopical Science* (new Ser.) **37** (4): 343-388.

Hickson, S. J. (1916): The Pennatulacea of the Siboga Expedition, with a general survey of the order. *Siboga Expeditie Monogr.* **14** (Livr. 77): 1-265.

Hodgeson, G. & M. A. Ross (1986): Unreported Scleractinian Corals from the Philippines. *Proc. 4th Int. Coral reef Symposium,* Manilla, Philippines: Marine Science Center, University of the Philippines. 2: 171-175.

Holliday, L. (1989): *Coral Reefs.* Salamander Books, London.

Hoppe, W. F. (1988): Reproductions patterns in three species of large coral reef sponges. *Coral Reefs* **7** (1): 45-50.

Hovland, M., P. Buhl-Mortensen, E. Thomsen & T. Brattegard (1997): Substratum-related ahermatypic coral banks on the Norwegian Continental Shelf. *Proc. 8th Int. Coral Reef Symp.* **2**: 1203-1206.

Humann, P. (1992): *Reef Creature Identification.* 1. Edition (3. Edition; 1994). New World Publications, Inc., Florida, USA.

Humann, P. (1993): *Reef Coral Identification.* New World Publ., Inc., Florida, USA.

Hunter, C. L. (1985): Assessment of clonal diversity and population structure of Porites compressa (Cnidaria; Scleractinia). *Proc. 5th. Int. Coral Reef Congress, Tahiti, 1985.* (6): 69-74.

Jansen, K. (1991): Zur Beleuchtung von Riffaquarien. *das Aquarium* **25** (12): 24-27.

Jensen. A & R. Fredriksen (1992): The Fauna associqted with the bank-forming deepwater coral Lophelia petrusa (Scleractinia) on the Faroe Shelf. *Sarsia* **77**: 53-69.

Johannes, R. E. (1974): Sources of nutritional energy for reef corals. *Proc. 2nd. Int Coral Reef Symp.* (1): 133-137.

Johannes, R. E. & L. Tepley (1974): Examination of feeding of the reef coral Porites lobata in situ using time lapse photography. *Proc. Second 2nd. Coral Reef Symp.* (1): 127-131.

Johannes, R.E., S. L. Coles & N. T. Kuenzel (1970): The role of zooplankton in the nutrition of some corals. *Limnol. Oceanogr.* (15): 579-586.

Jokiel, P. L. (1984): Long Distance Dispersal of Reef Corals by Rafting. *Coral Reefs* **3** (2): 113-116.

Jokiel, P. L. (1985): Lunar periodicity of planula release in the reef coral Pocillopora damicornis in relation to various enviromental factors. *Proc. 5th. Int. Coral Reef Congress, Tahiti, 1985.* (4): 307-312.

Jokiel, P. L. & S. L. Coles (1990): Response of Hawaiian and other Indo-Pacific reef corals to elevated temperature. *Coral Reefs* **8** (4): 155-162.

Jokiel, P. L. & R. H. York Jr. (1982): Solar ultraviolet photobiology of the reef coral Pocillopora damicornis and symbiotic zooxanthellae. *Bull. Mar. Sci.* **32**: 301-315.

Jokiel, P. L., R.Y. Ito & P. U. Liu (1985): Night irradiance and synchronization of lunar release of planula larvae in the reef coral Pocillopora damicornis. *Mar. Biol.* (88): 167-174.

Jussieu, B. de (1742): Examen des quelques productions marins qui ont ete mises au nombre des plantes, et qui sont l'ouvrage d'une sorte d'Insectes de Mer. *Mem. l'Acad. Royal Sciences.*

KAESTNER, A. (1984): *Lehrbuch der Speziellen Zoologie*, Band 1. Gustav Fischer Verlag, Stuttgart, Germany.

KAWAGUTI, S. (1953): Ammonium metabolism of the coral reef. *Biol. Jour. Okayama Univ.* (1): 171-176.

KEMPF, S. C. (1991): A „Primitive" Symbiosis between the Aeolid Nudibranch Berghia verrucicornis (A. Costa, 1867) and a Zooxanthella. *J. Moll. Stud.* **57**: 75-85.

KEMPF, S. C. & M. BRITTSAN (1996): Berghia verrucicornis, a nudibranch predator of the aquarium „weed" anemone Aiptasia. *Regional Conference Proceedings, American Zoo and Aquarium Association.* Audubon Park and Zoological Garden, New Orleans, Louisiana. pp. 95-99.

KELLOG, R. B. & J. S. PATTON (1983): Lipid droplets, medium of energy exchange in the symbiotic anemone Condylactis gigantea: a model coral polyp. *Mar. Biol.* (75): 137-149.

KERSTITCH, A. (1989): *Sea of cortez Marine Invertebrates - A Guide for the Pacific Coast, Mexico to Equador*. Sea Challengers, Monterey, California, USA.

KIMURA, S., Y. HASHIMOTO & K. YAMAZATO (1972): Toxity of the Zoanthid Palythoa tuberculosa. *Toxicon* (10): 611.

KINSEY, D. (1990): Global Warming - Sea levle rise. *Reef Encounter* (8): 11-12.

KINSEY, D. W. (1983): Standards of performance in coral reef production and carbon turnover. In: *Perspectives of Coral Reefs*: 209-218. Australian Inst. Mar. Science.

KINSMAN, D. J. J. (1969): Interpretation of Sr^{2+} concentrations in carbonate minerals and rocks. *J. Sediment Petrol.* (39): 486-508.

KINSMAN, D. J. J. & H. D. HOLLAND (1969): The copresepitation of cations with $CaCO_3$ IV. The copresipitation of Sr^{2+} with argonite between 16° and 96° C. *Geochim. Cosmochim. Acta* (33): 1-17.

KOJIS, B. L. (1986a): Sexual reproduction in Acropora (Isopora) species (Coelenterata: Scleractinia). I: A. cuenata and A. palifera on Heron Island reef, Great Barrier Reef. *Mar. Biol.* (91): 291-309.

KOJIS, B. L. (1986b): Sexual reproduction in Acropora (Isopora) species (Coelenterata: Scleractinia). II: Latitude variation in A. palifera from the Great Barrier Reef and Papua New Guinea. *Mar. Biol.* (91): 311-318.

KOJIS, B. L. & N. J. QUINN (1981): Aspects of sexual reproduction and larval development in the shallow water hermatypic coral, Goniastrea australiensis (Edwards and Haime, 1857). *Bull. Mar. Sci.* (31): 558-573.

KOJIS, B. L. & N. J. QUINN (1982): Reproductive strategies in four species of Porites (Scleractinia). *Proc. 4th. Int. Coral Reef Symp., Manila, 1981* (2): 145-151.

KOJIS, B. L. & N. J. QUINN (1984): Seasonal and depth variation in fecundity of Acropora palifera at two reefs in Papua New Guinea. *Coral Reefs* **3** (3): 165-172.

KOJIS, B. L. & N. J. QUINN (1985): Puberty in Goniastrea favulus. Age or size limited ? *Proc. 5th. Int. Coral Reef Congress, Tahiti, 1985* (4): 289-293.

KÖLLIKER, R.A. (1865): Die Bindesubstanz der Coelenteraten. *Icones histiologicae oder Atlas der vergleichenden Gewebelehre* **2** (1): 87-818, figs. 16-28, A and B, pls. 10-19.

KOLONKO, K. (1926): Beiträge zu einer Revision der Alcyonarien. Die Gattung Sinularia. *Mittl. zool. Mus. Berlin* **12** (2): 291-334, pls. 1-4.

KREMPF. A. (1904): Sur l'hétérogénété du groupe des Stichodactylines. *C.R. Soc. Biol. Paris* **139**: 816-819.

KÜHLMANN, D. (1984): *Das Lebende Riff*. Landbuch Verlag, Hannover, Germany.

KÜKENTHAL, W. (1910): Alcyonaria. *Die Fauna Südwest-Australiens; Ergebn. Hamburger Südwest-Austr. Forschungsr. 1905* **3** (1): 1-108, pls. 1-4.

KÜKENTHAL, W. & H. BROCH (1911): Wissenschaftliche Ergebnisse der Deutschen Tiefsee-Expedition auf dem Dampfer „Valdivia" 1898-199. **13** (1) Lieferung 2: 113-576.

KÜKENTHAL, W. (1915): Pennatularia. *Das Tierreich* (47): I-VX + 1-132.

KWIETNIEWSKI, C. R. (1897): Actiniaria von Ambon und Thursday Islands. In: SEMON, R (ed.) *Zoologische Forschungsreisen in Australien und in dem malaiischen Archipel ausgeführt in den Jahren 1891-1893*. 5. Denkschr. Naturw. Ges. Jena. **8**: 385-430. Gustav Fischer, Jena, Germany.

LANGE, J. & R. KAISER (1991): *Niedere Tiere tropischer und kalter Meere im Aquarium*. Verlag Eugen Ulmer, Stuttgart, Germany.

LANGE, J. & R. KAISER (1992): Ungewöhnliche, aber interessante Aquarientiere: Mangroven- und Hydroquallen. *DATZ* **45** (5): 298-300.

LANGE, J. & R. KAISER (1994): Haltung von frei schwimmenden Quallen im Zoo-Aquarium Berlin. *DATZ* **47** (1): 35-37.

LARSON, K. S. & R. J. LARSON (1982): On the ecology of Isaurus duchassaingi (Andres) (Cnidaria: Zoanthidea) from South Water Cay, Belize. *Smiths. Contr. Mar. Sci.* (12): 475-488.

LATKA, R. (1993): Zooxanthellen, Treibhäuser des Lebens. *das Aquarium* part 1 **27** (3); part 29-31, part 2 **27** (5): 40-43; part 3 **27** (7): 27-29.

LESSER, M. P., W. R. STOCHAJ, D. W. TAPLEY & J. M. SHICK (1990): Bleaching in coral reef anthozoans: efects of irradiance, ultraviolet radiation, and temperature on the activities of protective enzymes against active oxygen. *Coral Reefs* **8** (4): 225-232.

LEWIS D. H. & D. C. SMITH (1971): The autotrophic nutrition of symbiotic marine coelenterates with special reference to hermatypic corals. I. Movement of photosyntetic products between the symbionts. *Proc. Roy. Soc. London* (178): 111-129.

LEWIS, J. B. (1989): The ecology of Millepora. *Coral Reefs* **8** (3): 99-107.

LEWIS, J. B. (1991): Banding, age and growth in the calcareous hydrozoan Millepora complanata Lamark. *Coral reefs* **9** (4): 209-214.

LINNAEUS, C. (1758): *Systema naturae per regne tria naturae*. Edito deciema, reformata.

LIVINGSTON, H. D. & G. THOMSON (1971): Trace element consentrations in some modern corals. *Limnol. Oceanogr.* (16): 786-796.

MARENZELLER, E. VON (1886): Ueber die Sarcophytum benannten Alcyoniiden. *Zool. Jahrb. (Syst.)* (I): 341-368, pl. 9.

MARISCAL, R. N. (1970): The nature of the symbiosis between Indo-Pacific anemone fishes and sea anemones. *Mar. Biol.* (6): 58-65.

MARISCAL, R. N. (1971a): Experimental studies on the protection of anemone fishes from sea anemones. In T. C. CENG (ed.): *Aspects of the Biology of Symbiosis*. University Park Press, Baltimore, USA, pp. 283-315.

MARISCAL, R. N. (1971b): Effect of a Disulfid Reducing Agent on the Nematocyst Capsules from Some Coelenterates, with an illustrated Key to Nematocyst Classification. In: LENNHOFF, H. M. (ed.): *Experimental Coelenterat Biol. Univ. of Hawaii*. pp 157-168.

MARISCAL, R. N., E. J. CONKLIN & C. H. BIGGER (1977): The Ptychocyst, a major new category of cnida used in tube construction by a Cerianthid anemone. *Biol. Bull.* **152**: 392-405.

MARSHALL, J. F. (1996): Calcification in Hermatypic and Ahermatypic Corals. *Science* **271**: 637-639.

MATHER, P. & I. BENNETT (edt.). (1993): *A Coral Reef Handbook* 3rd ed. Surrey Beatty & Sons PTY Limited, Chipping Norton, NSW, Australia.

MAY, W. (1898): Die von Dr. Stuhlmann in Jahre 1889 gesammelten ostafrikanischen Alcyonaceen des Hamburgs Museums. *Mitt. naturhist. Mus. Hamburg* **15** (2): 1-38.

MAYR, E. & P. D. ASHLOCK (1991): *Principles of Systematic Zoology*, 2. Ed. McGraw, Hill.

McCLANAHAN, T. R. (1990): Kenyan coral reef-associated gastropod assemblages: distribution and diversity patterns. *Coral Reefs* **9** (2): 63.

McCLOSKEY, L. R. & L. MUSCATINE (1984): Production and respiration in the Red Sea coral Stylophora pistillata as a function of depth. *Proc. R. Soc. London* (222): 215-230.

McCONNAUGHEY, B. H. & E. McCONNAUGHEY (1994): *Pacific Coast*. Alfrea A. Knopf, Inc., N.Y., USA.

MEBS, D. (1989): *Gifte im Riff*. Wissenschaftliche Verlagsgesellschaft mbH, Stuttgart, Germany.

MEBS, D. (1992): *Gifttiere*. Wissenschaftliche Verlagsgesellschaft mbH, Stuttgart, Germany.

MERGNER, H. (1979): Quantitative ökologische Analyse eines Rifflaguneareals bei Aqaba, (Golf von Aqaba, Rotes Meer). *Helgol. Wiss. Meeresunter.* (32): 476-507.

MERGNER, H. & A. SVOBODA (1977): Productivity and seasonal changes in selected reef areas in the Gulf of Aquaba (Red Sea). *Helg. Wiss. Meeresunt.* (30): 383-399.

MERGNER, H. & H. SCHUHMACHER (1974): Morphologie, Ökologie und Zonierung von Korallenriffe bei Aqaba, (Golf von Aqaba, Rotes Meer). Helgol. Wiss. Meeresunter. (26): 238-358.

MERGNER, H. & E. WEDLER (1977): Über die Hydroidpolypenfauna des Roten Meeres und seiner Ausgange. Meteor Forsch. Ergebn. (24): 1-32.

MEYER, J. L. & E. G. SCHULTZ (1985): Migrating haemulid fishes as a source of nutrients and organic matter on coral reefs. Limnl. Oceanogr. (30): 146-156.

MEYER, J. L., E. G. SCHULTZ & G. S. HELFMAN (1983): Fish schools: An asset to corals. Science (220): 1047-1049.

MIGOT, A. (1922): Sur les rapports entre la formation de squelette et le mode de fixation chex les coelentérés. Bull. Soc. Zool. Fr. 47: 269-278, figs. 1-5.

MILNE-EDWARDS, H. & J. HAIME (1851): Monographie des Polypiers fossiles des terrains Palaeozoiques, pré d'un tableau général de la classification des Polypes. Archs. Mus. Hist. nat. Paris (5): 1-502, pls.1-20.

MOHAN, P. J. (1990): Ultraviolet ligth in the marine reef aquarium. FAMA 13 (1): 4-6, 156, 158, 160.

MOORE, R. E. & G. BARTOLINI (1981): Structure of palytoxin. J. Am. Chem. Soc. (103): 2491.

MOORE, R. E., P. HELFRICH & G. M. L. PATTERSON (1982): The deadly seaweed of Hana. Oceanus (25): 54.

MORTENSEN, P. B., M. HOVLAND, T. BRATTEGARD & R. FARESTVEIT (1995): Deep water biotherms of the Scleractinian Coral Lophelia pertusa (L.) at 64° N on the Norwegian Shelf: Structure and associated megafauna. Sarsia 80: 145-158.

MOSELEY, H. N. (1877): On new forms of Actiniaria dredged in the Deep Sea, with a description of certain pelagic surface-swimming species. Trans. Linn. Soc. London, (2) Zoology I: 205-305, pl. 45.

MUIR, P. R. (1984): Periodicy and asexual planula production in Pocillopora damicornis (Linnaeus) at Magnetic Island. Thesis, James Cook University of North Queensland, Townsville, Australia.

MUIRHEAD, A. & J. S. RYLAND (1985): A review of the genus Isaurus Gray, 1828 (Zoanthidea), including new records from Fiji. Jour. Nat. Hist. (19): 323-335.

MUSCATINE, L. (1973): Nutrition of corals. In: O. A. JONES & R. ENDEAN (edt.): Biology and Geology of Coral Reefs (2): 77-115.

MUSCATINE, L. (1990): The role of Symbiotic Algae in Carbon and Energy Flux in Reef Corals. In: DUBINSKY, Z. (ed.): Ecosystems of the World, vol. 25: Coral Reefs. Elsevier, N.Y., pp. 75-87

MUSCATINE L. & E. CERNICHIARI (1969): Assimilation of photosyntetic products of zooxanthellae by reef coral. Biol. Bull. (137): 506-523.

MUSCATINE, L. & C. F. ELIA (1978): The uptake, retention and release of ammonium by reef corals. Limnol. Oceanogr. 23 (4): 725-734.

MUSCATINE, L. & C. HAND (1958): Direct evidence for the transfer of materials from symbiotic algae to the tissue of coelenterate. Proc. Nat. Am. Soc. Zool. 44: 1259-1263.

MUSCATINE, L. & J. W. PORTER (1977): Reef corals: mutalistic symbiosis adapted to nutrient-poor enviroments. Bioscience (27): 454-459.

MUSCATINE, L., L. R. McCLOSKEY & R. E. MARIAN (1981): Estimating the daily contribution of carbon from zooxanthellae to coral animale respiration. Limnol. Oceanogr. 26: 601-611.

MUSCATINE, L., R. R. POOL & E. CERNICHIARI (1972): Some factors influating selective release of souble organic material by zooxanthellae from reef corals. Mar. Biol. (13): 298-308.

NEWELL, N. D. (1959): Question of coral reefs, part I. Nat. Hist. Mag. (68): 118-131.

NILSEN, A. J. (1990): Pilzkorallen. das Aquarium 24 (11): 37-43.

NILSEN, A. J. (1991a): Ein Riffaquarium in Oslo mit ungewöhnlichen Dimensionen. das Aquarium 25 (9): 27-32.

NILSEN, A. J. (1991b): The Successful Coral Reef Aquarium. Part 5, A large Reef Aquarium in Oslo. FAMA 14 (3): 114-115, 119-122, 190.

NILSEN, A. J. (1998): Mass Coral Spawning in a Captive Reef Tank. Aquarium Frontiers On-Line (http://www.aquariumfrontiers.com) January 1998 issue. 5 pages.

NUTTING, C. C. (1910): The Gorgonacea of the Siboga Expedition IV. The Plexauridae. Siboga Expeditie 13b.

OAKLEY, S. G. (1988): Settlement and growth of Antipathes pennacea on a shipwreck. Coral Reefs 7 (2): 77-79.

OMMEN, J. H. VAN (1989): Een uitstekend houdbare gorgoon. Het Zee-Aquarium 39 (2): 29-30.

OPRESKO, D. M. (1973): Abundance and distribution of shallow-water gorgonians in the area of Miami, Florida. Bull. Mar. Sci. 22 (4): 535-558.

PATTON, J. S. & J. S. BURRIS (1983): Lipid syntesis and extrusion by fleshy isolated zooxanthellae (symbiotic algae). Mar. Biol. (75): 131-136.

PAUL, J. H., M. F. DeFLAUN & W. H. JEFFERY (1986): Elevated levels of microbial activity in the coral surface microlayer. Mar. Ecol. Prog. (33): 29-40.

PAX, F. (1940): Anthozoa. Klassen und Ordnungen des Tierreichs 2 3:177-336.

PINGITORE, N.E. Jr., Y. RANGEL & A. KWARTENG (1989): Barium variation in Acropora palmata and Montastrea annularis. Coral Reefs 8 (1): 31-36.

POLICANSKY, D. (1982): Sex change in plants and animals. Ann. Rev. Ecol. Syst. 13: 471-495.

POLOVINA, J. J. et al. (1984): Model of a coral reef ecosystem, I-III. Coral Reefs 3 (1): 1-12, 13-22, 23-28.

POMEROY, L. R. & E. J. KUENZLER (1969): In: D. J. NELSON & C. F. EVANS (edts.) Proceedings of The Second National Symposium on Radioecology, pp. 474-482.

PRATT, E. M. (1903): The Alcyonaria of the Maldives. II. The genera Sarcophytum, Lobophytum, Sclerophytum and Alcyonium. Fauna Geogr. Mald. Laccad. Arcip. 2 (1): 503-539, pls. 28-31.

QUOY, J. R. & J. P. GAIMARD (1833): Zoophytes. Voyage de découvertes de l'Astrolabe. Zool. (4): 1-390, pls. 1-26.

RANDALL, J. E. & W. D. HARTMANN (1968): Spongefeeding fishes of the Westindies. Mar. Biol. (1): 216.

RANDALL, R. H. & R. F. MYERS (1983): Guide to the Coastal Resources of Guam, Vol 2: The Corals. University of Guam Press.

READER, J. (1988): Livets opprinnelse. J. W. Cappelens Forlag, Norway.

REIMER, A. A. (1971a): Feeding Behavior in the Hawaiian Zoanthids Palythoa and Zoanthus. Pacific Science 25 (4): 512-520.

REIMER, A. A. (1971b): Observations on the relationships between several species of tropical zoanthids (Zoanthidea, Coelenterata) and their zooxanthellae. J. exp. mar. Biol. Ecol. (7): 207-214.

RESING, J. M. & D. J. AYRE (1985): The usefulness of the tissue grafting bioassay as an indicator of clonal identity in scleractinian corals (Great Barrier Reef-Australia). Proc. 5th. Int. Coral Reef Congress, Tahiti, 1985 (6): 75-81.

RHODES, F. H. T. (1976): The Evolution of Life, 2nd. edition. Penguin Books, England.

RISK, M. J & H. R MÜLLER (1983): Porewater in coral heads: Evidence for nutrient regeneration. Limnol. Oceanogr. 28 (5): 1004-1008.

RICHMOND, R. H. (1985): Variation in the population biology of Pocillopora damicornis across the Pacific. Proc. 5th. Int. Coral Reef Congress, Tahiti, 1985 (6): 101-106.

RICHMOND, R. H. & C. L. HUNTER (1990): Review - Reproduction and recruitment of corals: comparison amonng the Caribbean, the Tropical Pacific, and the Red Sea. Mar. Ecol. Prog. Ser. 1: 145-152.

RINKEVICH, B. & Y. LOYA (1979): The reproduction of the Red Sea coral Stylophora pistillata. II. Synchronisation in the breeding and seasonality of planula shedding. Mar. Ecol. Progr. Ser. 1: 145-152.

ROUGERIE, F. & B. WAUTHY (1993): The endo-upwelling consept: from geothermal convection to reef construction. Coral Reefs 12 (1): 19-30.

ROSEN, B. R. (1981): The tropical high diversity enigma - the corals' eye view. In: GREENWOOD P. H. & P. L. FOREY: The evolving Biosfere (Chance, change and challenge). British Museum Nat. Hist & Cambridge Univ. Press. pp 103-129.

ROXAS, H. (1933): Philippine Alcyonaria, part II. The families Alcyoniidae and Nephthyidae. The Philippine Journal of Science 50 (4): 345-470, pls. 1-5.

RÜPPELL, E. & F. S. LEUKART (1828): Neue Wirbellose Thiere des Rothen Meeres. In: E. RÜPPELL: Atlas zu der Reise im nördlichen Afrika Pt. 5 (Heft 9): 1-50, pls. 1-12.

RYAN, P. R. (edt). (1986). *Oceanus* **29** (2): 1-124.

RYLAND, J. S. (1997): Budding in Acrozoanthus Saville-Kent, 1893 (Anthozoa: Zoanthidea). In *Proceedings of the 6th International Conference on Coelenterate Biology (1995)* : J. C. DEN HARTOG (ed.), Leiden, 423-428.

RYLAND, J. S. & R. C. BABCOCK (1991): Annual cycle of gametogenesis and spawning in a tropical zoanthid, Protopalythoa sp. *Hydrobiologia* (216/217): 117-123.

SAMMARCO, P. W. (1981): A new mode of reproduction in corals under stress: is there a life after death in Seriatopora ? *Aust. Mar. Sci. Biol. Ecol.* (75): 20 (Abstract).

SAMMARCO, P.W. (1982): Polyp bail-out: An escape response to enviromental stress and a new means of reproduction in corals. *Mar. Ecol. Progr. Ser.* 10: 57-65.

SAMMARCO, P. W. (1986): Coral Reproduction, Dispersal, and Survival. *Oceanus* **29** (2): 28-19.

SAMMARCO, P. W., J. C. COLL, S. LaBARRE & B. WILLIS (1982): Competetive strategies of soft corals (Coelenterata: Octocorallia): alleopathic effects on selected scleractinian corals. *Coral Reefs* **1** (3): 173-178.

SATO, M. (1985): Mortality and growth of juvenil coral Pocillopora damicornis (Linnaeus). *Coral Reefs* **4** (1): 27-33.

SCHEER, G. & K. OBRIST (1986): Distichopora nitida Verrill (Cnidaria, Hydrozoa) from the Maldives, a new record from the Indian Ocean. *Coral Reefs* **5**: 151-154.

SCHENK, A. (1895): Clavulariiden, Xeniiden und Alcyoniiden von Ternate. *Abhandl. Senkenb. naturf. Ges. Frankfurt* **23** (I): 41-80, pls. 2-4.

SCHILLER, C. & G. J. HERNDL (1989): Evidence of enchanced microbial activity in the intertital spce of branched corals:possible implications for coral metabolism. *Coral Reefs* **7** (4): 179-184.

SCHLAIS, J. (1979): Aiptasia: Nature's filter. *FAMA* **2** (5): 51-53, 69-70.

SCHMID, P. & D. PASCHKE (1990): *Underwaterguide Red Sea, Invertebrates*. Verlag Stephanie Nagelschmidt, Stuttgart, Germany.

SCHMIDT, H. (1972): Die Nesselkapseln der Anthozoen und ihre Bedeutung für die phylogenetische Systematik. *Helgoland wiss. Meererunetrs.* **23**: 422-458.

SCHMIDT, H. (1974): On the Evolution in Anthozoa. *Proceedings of the second international Coral Reef Symposium* 1: 533-560.

SCHMIDT, H & D. ZISSLER (1979): Die Spermien der Anthozoen und ihre phylogenetische Bedeutung. *Zoologica Stuttgart* **129**: i-viii, 1-79, pls. 1-25

SCHUHMACHER, H. (1982): *Korallenriffe*. BLV Verlaggesellschaft, München, Germany.

SCHUHMACHER, H. & H. MERGNER (1985a): Quantitative Analyse von Korallengemeinschaften des Sanganeb-Atolls (mittleres Rotes Meer). I. Die Besedelungsstruktur hydrodynamisch unterschiedlich exponierter Aussen- und Innenriffe. *Helg. Wiss. Meeresunt.* (39): 375-417.

SCHUHMACHER, H. & H. MERGNER (1985b): Quantitative Analyse von Korallengemeinschaften des Sanganeb-Atolls (mittleres Rotes Meer). II. Vergleich mit einem Riffareal bei Aquana (Nördliches Rotes Meer) am Nordrande des indopazifischen Riffgürtels. *Helgol. Wiss. Meersunt.* (39): 419-440.

SCHUHMACHER, H. & H. ZIBROWIUS (1985): What is hermatypic? *Coral Reefs* **4** (1): 1-9.

SEMB-JOHANNSSON (Edt.) (1988): *Verdens Dyr, Virvelløse Dyr II.* (Bind 13) Cappelens Forlag, Norway.

SHEPPARD, C., A. PRICE & C. ROBERTS (1992): *Marine Ecology of the Arabian Region*. Academic Press, London, UK.

SHIBATA, K. (1969): Pigments and UV-absorbing substance in corals and blue-green algae living in the Great Barrier Reef. *Plant and Cell Physiol*. (10): 325-335.

SIMKISS, K. (1964a): The Inhibitory Effects of some Metabolites on the Precipitation of Calcium Carbonate from Artificial and Natural Sea Water. *J. Cons. Cons. Perm. Int. Explor. Mer.* (29): 6.

SIMKISS, K. (1964b): Possible effects of Zooxanthellae on Coral Growth. *Experientia* (2): 140.

SIMPSON, C. J. (1985): Mass spawning of scleractinian corals in the Dampier Archipelago and the implications for management of corals reefs in Western Australia. *West. Aust. Dep. Conserv. Environ. Bull*. (244): 1-35.

SIMPSON, G. G. (1990): *Principles of Animal Taxonomy*. Columbia University Press.

SMITH, S. V. (1978): Coral reef area and the contribution of reefs to processes and resources of the world's oceans. *Nature* (273): 225-226.

SOONG, K. & J. C. LANG (1992): Reproductive intergation in reef corals. *Biol. Bull.* (183): 418-431.

SOROKIN, Y. I. (1990): Aspects of Trophic Relations, Productivity and Energy Balance in Coral-Reef Ecosystems. In: DUBINSKY, Z. (edt.): *Ecosystems of the world 15 Coral Reefs*. Elsevier, N.Y. pp. 1-9.

SOROKIN, Y. I. (1973): On the feeding of some scleractinian corals with bacteria and dissolved organic matter. *Limnol. Ocenogr.* (18): 380-385.

SOROKIN, Y. I. (1995): *Coral Reef Ecology*, 2nd. edition. Springer Verlag, New York, USA.

SPIES, G. (1984): Wirbellose des Meeres. *das Aquarium* **18** (12): 643-648.

SPIES, G. (1985): Anemonen und ihre Partner. *DATZ* **38** (12): 554-558.

SPRUNG. J. & J. C. DELBEEK (1997): *The Reef Aquarium*, vol. 2. Ricordea Publishing, Miami, USA.

STEPANOV, D. (1994): Coral feeding in nature and in the aquarium. *FAMA* **17** (1): 43-53.

STEPHENS, G. C. (1960): Uptake of Glucose from Solution by the solitary Coral, Fungia. *Science* (131): 1532 ff.

STEPHENS, G. C. (1962): Uptake of organic material by aquatic invertebrates. I Uptake of glucose by the solitary coral, Fungia scutaria. *Biol. Bull.* (123): 648-659.

STEPHENS, G. C. (1968): Dissolved organic matter as a potential source of nutrition for marine animals. *Am. Zool.* (8): 95-106.

STEPHENSON, T. A. (1921): On the classification of Actiniaria, Pt. 2. Consideration of the whole group and its relationships with special reference to forms not treated in part I. *Q. Jl. Microsc., Sci.* **65**: 493-576, figs. 1-20.

STEPHENSON, T. A. (1922): On the classification of Actiniaria, Pt. 3. Definitions connected with the forms dealt with in part 2. *Q. Jl. Microsc., Sci.* **66**: 247-319.

STERRER, W. (edt.) (1986): *Marine Fauna and Flora of Bermuda*. John Wiley & sons, Inc. USA.

STIMSON, J. S. (1978): Mood and timing of Reproduction in Some Common Hermatypic Corals of Hawaii and Enewetak. *Marine Biol.* (48): 173-184.

STODDART, J. A. (1986): Coral Genetics: New Directions. *Oceanus* **29** (2): 41.

STÜBER, D. (1987): Mein Aquarium wie es mir gefällt. Langsam wächst ein echtes Riff heran. *das Aquarium* **21** (5): 249-250.

STÜBER, D. (1988): Riffbildende Steinkorallen. Grundlagen für die Aquarienhaltung. *das Aquarium* **22** (2): 95-99.

STÜBER, D. (1989a): Die Vermehrung einer Seriatophora-Art im Aquarium. *das Aquarium* **23** (1): 31-38.

STÜBER, D. (1989b): Niedere Tiere für ein Riffaquarium unter dem Aspekt der Raumkonkurrenz. *das Aquarium* **23** (6): 357-362.

STÜBER, D. (1990a): Aus Resten zu neuem Leben erwacht. *das Aquarium* **24** (5): 38-40.

STÜBER, D. (1990b): Ein kleines Juwel. Oder: Wie groß muß ein Meerwasser-Aquarium sein ? *das Aquarium* **24** (8): 27-29.

STÜBER, D. (1994): Fungia-Korallen, scheibenweise. *das Aquarium* **28** (1): 31-34.

SZMANT, A. M. (1986): Reproductine ecology of Caribbean reef corals. *Coral Reefs* **5** (1): 43-53.

SZMANT, A. M. & N. J. GASSMAN (1990): The effects of prolonged „bleaching" on the tissue biomass and reproduction of the reef coral Montastrea annularis. *Coral Reefs* **8** (4): 217-224.

SZMANT-FROELICH, A. M. (1985): The effect of colony size on the reproductive ability of the Caribbean coral Montastrea annularis (Ellis and Solander). *Proc. 5th. Int. Coral Reef Congress, Tahiti, 1985* (4): 295-300.

SZMANT-FROELICH, A. M. (1981): Coral Nutrition: Comparison of the fate of EP14C from ingested labelled brine shrimp and from the uptake of NaH₁₄CO₃ by its zooxanthellae. *J. Exp. Mar. Biol. Ecool.* (55): 133-144.

SZMANT-FROELICH, A. M., P. YEVICH & M. E. Q. PILSON (1980): Gametogenesis and early development of the temperate coral Astrangia danae (Anthozoa: Scleractinia). *Biol. Bull.* (158): 257-269.

TALBOT, F. (ed.) (1984): *Reader's Digest book of the Great Barrier Reef.* Readers Digest Services Pty. Ltd.

TAPLEY, D. W., J. M. SHICK & J. P. S.(III) SMITH (1988): Defenses against oxidative stress in the sea anemones Aiptasia pallida and Aiptasia pulchella. *Amer. Zool.* 28, 105A (abstract).

TAPLEY, D. W. (1989): Photoinactivation of catalase but not superoxide dismutase in the symbiotic sea anemone Aiptasia pallida. *Amer. Zool.* 29, 53A (abstract).

THOMSON, J. A. & L. M. I. DEAN (1931): The Alcyonacea of the Siboga Expedition with an addendum to the Gorgonacea. *Siboga-Exp. Monogr.* 13 (d): 1-227, pls. 1-28.

THOMSON, J. A. & W. D. HENDERSON (1906): Alcyonaria from Zanzibar. *Proc. Zool. Soc.*, Vol. I, No. XXIX (2): 90-196.

THORSON, G. (1964): Light as an ecological factor in the dispersal and settlement of larvae of marine bottom invertebrates. *Ophelia* 1 (1): 167-208.

TIXIER-DURIVAULT, A. (1966): Octocoralliaires de Madagascar et des iles avoisinantes. *Fauna de Madagascar* (21): 1-456, figs. 1-399.

TRUSCH, B. & A. TRUSCH (1982): The soft coral community on a sheltered reef quadrat at Laing Island (Papua New Guinea). *Mar. Biol.* (65): 321-332.

TYREE, S. (1993): Tropical Coral Reef Environment Rhytmicity and Techniques for Including Captive Corals Spawning. *The Breeders Registry newsletter* 1 (3, summer 1993).

TYREE, S. (1994): Sexual Reproduction and Recruitment of the Stony Coral Pocillopora verrucosa (Ellis and Solander, 1786) with discussion of Spawning Induction Techniques. *Aquarium Frontiers* (Spring 1994): 13-26.

UEMURA, D., Y. HIRATA, T. IWASHITA & H. NAOKI (1985): Studies on palytoxins. *Tetrahedron* (41): 1007.

UTINOMI, H. (1951) Asterospicularia laurae, n. gen. et n. sp., the type of a New Family of Alcyonarians with Stellate Spicules. *Pacific Science* vol. V (2): 190-196.

VENCE-PEYRÉ, M.-T. (1991): Distribution of living benthic Foraminifera on the back-reef and outer slopes of a high island (Moorea, French Polynesia. *Coral Reefs* 9 (4): 193-204.

VERON, J. E. N. (1992): *Hermatypic Corals of Japan.* AIMS Monograph Series, Volume 9, Australian Institute of Marine Science (AIMS), Townsville, Australia.

VERON, J. E. N. (1993a): *Corals of Australia and the Indo-Pacific,* 2nd. edition. Angus & Robertson Publishers, North Ryde NSW, Australia & London.

VERON, J. E. N. (1993b): *A Biogeographic Database of Hermatypic Corals. Species of the Central Indo-Pacific. Genera of the World.* AIMS Monograph Series Volume 10, Australian Institute of Marine Science (AIMS), Townsville, Australia.

VERON, J. E. N. (1995): *Coral in Space and Time. The Biogeography Evolution of the Scleractinia.* Comstock/Cornell, Itacha and London.

VERON, J. E. N. & G. HODGSON (1989): Annonated checklist of the hermatypic corals of the Philippines. *Pac. Sci.* 43: 234-287.

VERON, J. E. N. & M. PICHON (1976): Scleractinia of Eastern Australia. Part I: Thamnasteridae, Astrocoeniidae, Pocilloporidae. *Australian Institute of Marine Science Monographs series, vol. 1.*

VERON, J. E. N. & M. PICHON (1977): Scleractinia of Eastern Australia. Part II: Faviidae and Trachyphyllidae. *Australian Institute of Marine Science Monographs series, vol. 3.*

VERON, J. E. N. & M. PICHON (1982): Scleractinia of Eastern Australia. Part IV: Poritidae. *Australian Institute of Marine Science Monographs series, vol. 5.*

VERON, J. E. N. & C. WALLACE (1984): *Scleractinia of Eastern Australia. Part V: Acroporidae.* Australian Institute of Marine Science Monograph Series, Vol. 6. ANU Press.

VERSEVELDT, J. (1966): Biological Results of the Snellius Expedition XXII. Octocorallia from the Malaya Archipelago (Part III). *Zool. Verhandlingen, Leiden* (80): 1-109, figs. 1-59, pls. 1-16.

VERSEVELDT, J. (1976): Alcyonacea from the Seychelles (Coelenterata, Octocorallia). *Rev. Zool. Africaine, Bruxelles* (90): 497-513, figs. 1-5, pl. 1.

VERSEVELDT, J. (1980): A revision of the genus Sinularia May (Octocorallia, Alcyonacea). *Zool. Verhandlingen, Leiden* (179): 1-128, figs. 1-68, pls. 1-38.

VERSEVELDT, J. (1982): A revision of he genus Sarcophyton Lesson (Octocorallia, Alcyonacea). *Zool. Verhandelingen, Leiden* (192): 1-91, 21 plates.

VERSEVELDT, J. and F. M. BAYER (1988): Revision of the genera Bellonella, Eleutherobia, Nidalia and Nidaliopsis (Octocorallia: Alcyoniidae and Nidaliidae), with descriptions of two new genera. *Zool. Verhandlingen Leiden* (245): 1-131.

VERSEVELDT, J. & Y. BENAYAHU (1983): On two old and fourteen new species of Alcyonariacae (Coelenterata: Alcyonaria) from the Red Sea. *Zool. Verhandlingen, Leiden* (208): 3-34.

VERWEY, J. (1930): Coral reef Studies. I. The symbiosis between damselfishes and sea anemones in Bitavia Bay. *Treubia* 12 (3-4): 305-366.

VINE, P. (1972): Spirobinae (Polychaeta: Serpulidae) from the Red Sea including description of a new genus and four new species. *Zool. J. Linn. Soc.* 51 (2): 177-201

VINE, P. (1986): *Red Sea Invertebrates.* Immel Publ., London, UK.

WAINWRIGHT, S. A. (1967): Diurnal activity of a hermatypic gorgonian. *Nature* (216): 1041.

WALLACE, C. C. (1978): The coral genus Acropora (Scleractinia: Astrocoeniina: Acroporidae) in the central and southern Great Barrier Reef Province. *Memoirs of the Queensland Museum* 18: 273-319, pls 43-103.

WALLACE, C. C. (1994): New Species and a New Species-group of the Coral Genus Acropora (Scleractinia: Astrocoeniina: Acroporidae) from Indo-Pacific Locations. *Invertebr. Taxon.* 8: 961-988

WALLACE, C. C. (1997): New species and new records of recently described species of the coral genus Acropora (Scleractinia: Astrocoeniina: Acroporidae) from Indonesia. *Zoological journal of the Linnean Society* 120: 27-50.

WALLACE, C. C, R. C. BABCOCK, P. L. HARRISON, J. K. OLIVER & B. L. WILLIS (1986): Sex on the Reef: Mass Spawning of Corals. *Oceanus* 29 (2): 38-42.

WALLACE, R. A., J. L. KING & G. P. SANDERS (1986): *Biology the Science of Life.* 2nd. ed. Scott, Foresman & Co., USA.

WEBB, K. L., C. D. D'ELIA & W. D. DUPAUL (1977): Biomass and nutrient flux measurements on Holothuria atra populations on winward reef flats at Enewetak, Marshall Islands. *Proc. 3rd. Int. Coral Reef Symp.* (1): 409-414.

WEBB, L. & J. C. COLL (1983): Effects on alcyonarian coral terpenes on scleractinian coral photosynthesis and respiration. *Toxicon* suppl. 3: 69.

WEBER, J. N. (1973): Incorporation of strontium into reef coral scletal carbonate. *Geochim. Cosmochim, Acta.* (37): 2173-2190.

WEINGARTEN, R. A. (1992): Notes on the Reproduction and development of the Heliopora coerulea the blue coral. *FAMA* 15 (1): 160, 164, 167, 170

WEILL, R. (1934): Contributions à l'étude des cnidaries et de leurs nématocystes. I. Recherches sur les nématocystes. 2. Valeur taxonomique du cnidom. *Trav. Stn. Zool. Wimereux* 10 11: 1-101.

WELLS, J. (1955): *A Survey of the Distribution of Reef Coral Genera in the Great Barrier Reef Region.* Cornell University.

WELLS, S., M. JENKINS & C. SHEPARD (edts). (1988): *Coral Reefs of the World.* vol. 3. Belhaven Press, USA.

WERNER, B. (1965): Die Nesselkapseln der Cnidaria, mit besonderer Berücksichtigung der Hydroidea. *Helgoländer Wiss. Meeresunt.* (12): 1-39.

WILEY, E. O. (1981): *Phylogenetics: The Theroy and Practice of Phylogenetic Systematics.* John Wiley & Sons.

WILKENS, P. (1973): *The saltwater aquarium for tropical marine invertebrates* vol 1. Engelbert Pfriem Verlag, Wuppertal, Germany.

WILKENS, P. (1980): *Niedere Tiere im tropischen Seewasser-Aquarium.* vol 2. Engelbert Pfriem Verlag, Wuppertal, Germany

WILKENS, P. (1983): Beobachtungen an der Scheibeanemone Actiniodiscus nummiformis. *das Aquarium* **17** (9): 483-486.

WILKENS, P. (1984a): Ein gefräßige Scheibenanemone. *das Aquarium* **18** (7): 367-368.

WILKENS, P. (1984b): Blumenwunder des Meeres - Zylinderrosen. *Aquarien Magazin* **18** (8): 369-373.

WILKENS, P. (1985): Die rote Orgelkoralle, Tubipora musica. *das Aquarium* **19** (10): 531-534.

WILKENS, P. (1990): *Invertebrates: Stone and False Corals, Colonial Anemones.* Engelbert Pfrien Verlag, Wuppertal, Germany.

WILKENS, P. & J. BIRKHOLZ (1986): *Invertebrates: Tube-, Soft- and Branching Corals.* Engelbert Pfriem Verlag, Wuppertal, Germany.

WILKINSON, C. R. (1984): Immunological evidence for precambrian orgin of bacterial symbiosis in marine sponges. *Proc. R. Soc. London.* (B 220): 509.

WILKINSON, C. R. (1987): Productivity and abundance of large sponge poppulations on Flinders Reef flats, Coral Sea. *Coral Reefs* **5** (4): 183-188.

WILKINSON, C. R. & A. C. CESHIRE (1989): Patterns in the distribution of sponge poppulations across the central Great Barrier Reef. *Coral Reefs* **8** (3): 127-134.

WILKINSON, C. R. & E. EVANS (1989): Sponge distribution across Davis Reef, Great Barrier Reef, relative to location, depth and water movement. *Coral Reefs* **8** (1): 1-7.

WILLIAMS, G. C. (1989): The Pennatula genus Cavernularia Valenciennes (Octocorallia: Veretillidae). *Zoological Journal of the Linnean Society* **95**: 285-310.

WILLIAMS, G. C. (1993): Biotoc diversity, biogeography, and phylogeny of pennatulacean octocorals associated with corals reefs in the Indo-Pacific. *Proceedings of the Seventh International Coral Reef Symposium* 2: 729-735

WILLIAMS, G. C. (1995): Living genera of sea pens (Coelenterata: Ocotcorallia. Pennatulacea): illustrated key and synopses. *Zoological Journal of the Linnean Society* **113**: 93-140.

WILLIS, B. L. & D. J. AYRE (1985): Asexual reproduction and genetic determination of growth form in the coral Pavona cactus: biochemical genetic and immunogenetic evidence. *Oecologia* (65): 516-525.

WOOD, E. M. (1983): *Corals of the world.* TFH Publications Inc., N. J., USA.

WRIGHT, E. P. & T. STUDER (1899): Report on the Alcyonaria collected by H.M.S. Challenger during the years 1873-1876. *Voyage of the Challenger, Zoology* 31:i-1xxii + 1-314, 43 pls.

YAMAZATO, K. (1970): Calcification in a solitary coral, Fungia scutularia Lamarck, in relation to environmental factors. *Bull. Sci. Engag. Div. Univ. Ryukyus (Hawaii)* (13): 1-122.

YAMAZATO, K., F. YOSHIMOTO & N. YOSHIHARA (1973): Reproductive cycle in a zoanthid Palythoa tuberculosa Esper. *Publs. Seto mar. biol. Lab.* (20): 275-283.

YONGE, C. M. (1930a): Studies on the physiology of corals. I. Feeding mechanisms and food. *Sci. Rep. Great Barrier Reef Exped.* (1): 13-57.

YONGE, C. M. (1930b): Studies on the physiology of corals. III. Assimilation and excreation. *Sci. Rep. Great Barrier Reef Exped.* (1): 83-91.

YONGE, C. M. (1968): Living corals. *Proc. Royal Soc.* (169): 329-344.

YONGE, C. M. & A. G. NICHOLS (1931): Studies of the physiology of corals IV: The structure, distribution and physiology of zooxanthellae. *Sci. Rep. Great Barrier Reef Exped.* (1): 135-212.

ZAHN, M. (1980): Strobilation, Aufzucht und Haltung der Medusen der Ohrenqualle (Aurelia aurita, Scyphozoa, Cnidaria) und ihre Darstellung im Schauaquarium. *Zeitschr. Kölner Zoo* 23 (2): 71-75.

ZAHN, M. (1990): Nun auch im Aquarium: Geschlechtliche Fortpflanzung der Saugschirmqualle Cassiopeia. *DATZ* **43** (2): 87-88.

ZAHN, L. P. & L. BOLTON (1985): The distribution, abundance and ecology of the blue coral Heliopora coerulea (Pallas) in the Pacific. *Coral Reefs* **4** (2): 125-134.

ZANN, L. P. (1980): *Living together in the Sea.* TFH Publications Inc. Ltd., Neptune, N.J., USA.

The modern coral reef aquarium of Mr. A. Hochmuth, Berlin, Germany.

Photo: T. Luther

Index